ENGINEERING
MATERIALS
SCIENCE

Wadsworth Engineering Science Series
E. A. Trabant, Editor

CEDRIC W. RICHARDS

Stanford University

ENGINEERING MATERIALS SCIENCE

CHAPMAN & HALL LTD

11 New Fetter Lane · London EC4

L.C. Cat. Card No.: 61–5917

Printed in the United States of America

First printing, March 1961
Second printing, August 1961

To Mary Helen

PREFACE

This book is intended to prepare the engineering student to make the most effective use of the materials at his disposal. He is given a basic understanding of the makeup of real materials and the underlying theory that accounts for their behavior. The various areas of engineering application of materials are explored systematically at the same time that their behavior is shown to be a logical manifestation of theory. This approach has long been put to excellent use in the other engineering sciences. In using theory to tie the whole subject together coherently it has been possible to replace memorization of fact with application of logic—a real boon to the student, to whom the field of materials must often have seemed to be a great mass of unrelated facts.

The pattern followed throughout this book is first to discuss the general, then the specialized, aspects of materials and their applications. Part One introduces the concepts and problems involved in the use of materials and discusses the structure of solids. Principles of physics and chemistry are reviewed from a specialized and unified viewpoint, and essential new principles from solid state physics are introduced as needed. These principles are used simply to explain the *why* of the behavior of solids, and are therefore treated less rigorously than in physics textbooks. For example, the discussion of crystallography and molecular structure is limited to how crystalline and amorphous solids are formed.

The behavior of materials under the various conditions encountered in engineering is analyzed with emphasis on what happens within the material

vii

itself and how its structure affects the way it reacts.   Mechanical behavior is treated in Part Two.   The discussion begins with uniaxial static stresses (tension, compression, bending) and continues with complex static stresses (combined stresses such as torsion, hydrostatic compression and tension, biaxial plane stresses, effects of stress concentrations and notches).   The effects of rate of loading and temperature on the mechanical behavior of materials leads up to a study of the ductile-brittle transition and notch effect.   The fundamentals of creep and fatigue are treated with special consideration for methods of predicting failure.   Hardness is related to structure, and hardness measurements are examined as a useful research tool.

It is desirable that the student have some familiarity with the concepts of stress and strain, preferably from a first course in mechanics of materials. As an aid to review, the fundamental theorems are developed from elementary principles as the need arises.

Lack of quantitative theory in such areas as creep, fatigue, ductile-brittle behavior—even, to some extent, in simple static stress—means that predicting such behavior depends ultimately on experiment.   Consequently appropriate experimental methods are interspersed throughout for use as a guide to laboratory study as well as to introduce concepts important to the student's understanding of the mechanical behavior of materials.

Physical behavior, treated in Part Three, includes electrical, magnetic, and thermal behavior, the principles of corrosion, and the effects of radiation.   The treatment is intended for general use in engineering.   In some more specialized areas, such as transistors, fine-particle permanent magnets, dielectrics, and specific heat, only a brief introduction is given.   More extensive works are available for advanced study.

Purposely omitted is descriptive matter on such topics as the manufacture and fabrication of materials and mining of ores.   Processing of materials is taken up only as it affects their properties.   Discussion of metal alloys and special heat treatments is left for the most part to books on metallurgy.

I am grateful for the encouragement given me by Professor S. P. Timoshenko in my studies in the materials field, which led me to undertake writing this book.   I wish to thank Professors Harry Williams, James M. Gere, William M. Fairbank, and Glen Wade of Stanford University for their helpful suggestions, and T. J. Dolan of the University of Illinois, Joseph Pistrang of the City College of New York, Dan H. Pletta of Virginia Polytechnic Institute, and E. A. Trabant of the University of Buffalo for their valuable and detailed criticisms.

C. W. R.

CONTENTS

ix

PART TWO.   MECHANICAL BEHAVIOR

ELASTICITY

BEYOND THE ELASTIC RANGE

EXPERIMENTAL METHODS

ELASTICITY

BEYOND THE ELASTIC RANGE

EXPERIMENTAL METHODS

PURE BENDING

PART ONE

GENERAL
PRINCIPLES

CHAPTER 1

INTRODUCTION

You are working on a design of a new rocket. One of the parts is a shell that must combine high stiffness with compressive strength. Furthermore, it must retain these characteristics at an operating temperature of 2500°F for a short time. Is there a material readily available that will do this? What advantages are offered by new materials or special combinations such as a ceramic coating on a metal base, or sandwich construction?

A bridge is to be built, and the choice of materials is up to you, as chief engineer. Shall steel or concrete be selected, or are there newer materials that might prove superior? The choice must be based on several factors: availability of materials, economy, ease of handling and fabrication, strength, and durability.

To reduce dielectric losses in an electronic device you need a material having a low dielectric constant and loss factor. How do various materials compare in this respect? Perhaps the choice is between a plastic and a ceramic. Which would you choose?

A part in a nuclear reactor has unexpectedly become embrittled from exposure to radiation. What material can you suggest for a replacement? Can the resistance of the material to radiation be improved by proper treatment?

A routine manufacturing process has suddenly broken down and you trace the trouble to a slight change in the material used. Ordinary ac-

3

ceptance tests have not revealed the change. New controls are clearly needed. What should they include?

Decisions having to do with materials are an essential part of all branches of engineering practice. Every engineering design must finally be expressed in a material structure or device. Every technological advance must eventually be embodied in a material form. The choice of the right materials for given engineering requirements, the proper use of those materials, including the development of new ways of using them for greater effectiveness, even the production of new materials—all are the direct responsibility of the engineer.

To fulfill his responsibility the engineer must have a thorough understanding of the *nature* and *behavior* of materials. The study of the *nature* of materials has its foundation in chemistry and physics, where the student is introduced to the elements of matter, their chemical combinations, the physical structure of the atom, radiation, and other basic concepts. The study of the *behavior* of materials involves the application, so far as they will go, of the principles of the nature of materials, under the varied conditions found in engineering practice. Because conditions of use profoundly affect the behavior of materials, the study of behavior is tied closely to the engineering sciences—mechanics of solids, fluid mechanics, thermodynamics and heat flow, and electrical theory. Moreover, many aspects of the behavior of materials are still beyond the realm of theory, and can be studied fruitfully only by experimental means. Any study of the behavior of materials is therefore incomplete without a certain amount of experimental research, from which a familiarity with experimental methods and experience in their proper interpretation can be obtained.

In modern technology the engineer finds himself dealing with nearly all materials known to science, and in all states of aggregation: solid, liquid, and gaseous. In this text only materials in the *solid* state will be considered. The nature of these materials involves their atomic and molecular structure, which, in turn, depends on the bonding forces and energies associated with the solid state. The response of the material to imposed conditions can often be traced directly to its basic structure and its internal forces and energies. But there is an equally important factor to be considered: the presence of imperfections in all solid structures. This characteristic opens up an entire field for investigation and some of the most important developments have come from it, as will be seen in the chapters that follow.

The behavior of solid materials involves their response to all sorts of conditions: mechanical, electrical, thermal, chemical, and radiological. Because mechanical conditions—externally applied loads, the weight of the material itself, and interactions between mechanical and other effects—are always present, they are of primary importance to the engineer and are treated extensively in later chapters. Other conditions are covered to the extent considered essential for all engineers.

Each condition of use is covered by a section or chapter in which the response of solid materials in general is first discussed, after which special characteristics of various materials are considered. Closing each section is a discussion of appropriate experimental methods.

1.1 PROPERTIES OF MATERIALS

A quantity that defines a specific characteristic of a material is a *property*. The properties of a material provide a basis for predicting its behavior under various conditions. They are the tools the engineer uses to solve his materials problems. Some of the most important properties of materials are:

Mechanical: strength, stiffness, ductility, notch sensitivity, hardness.
Electrical: conductivity, dielectric permittivity, dielectric strength.
Magnetic: permeability, coercive force, hysteresis.
Thermal: specific heat, thermal expansion, conductivity.
Chemical: corrosion resistance, acidity or alkalinity, chemical composition.
Physical: dimensions (size and shape), density, porosity, structure.

Fundamentally the properties of a material depend on the nature of that particular material alone. Nearly all those properties listed, however, are also inseparably tied in with conditions of use, environment, and the state of the material. The actual evaluation of a property depends on all these factors. Mechanical strength, for example, differs for various forms of loading, and is commonly expressed by such terms as *tensile* strength, *compressive* strength, or *fatigue* strength. Dielectric permittivity varies with the frequency of the alternating field, so that different values must be listed for different frequencies. Materials that are ordinarily brittle are transformed to a ductile state during application of high hydrostatic pressures. Many properties vary with the temperature.

Most properties must be evaluated entirely by experiment: certain specific conditions are applied, and the corresponding properties are measured. Even when properties can be derived theoretically, experiment must provide the necessary confirmation.

Experiments for determining properties are usually called *tests*. Tests may provide properties for use in design or information on the quality of a material (control testing). The procedures are usually standardized, because if identical procedures are always followed, the results of a number of tests may be compared with some assurance. Much of the standardization of tests is done by the American Society for Testing Materials (ASTM), a national organization set up to improve the use of materials in industry and engineering. The ASTM *Standards*, one of its publications, gives standard test methods of all kinds, in addition to standard specifications for materials and standard definitions of terms.

Experiments used in research and development often follow standardized test procedures to assure the reliability of comparisons. Experiments of this kind are involved in developing new materials or new uses for old materials and in the search for better information on the behavior of materials. This kind of research is actively promoted by such groups as the American Society for Metals (ASM), American Society for Testing Materials, and American Society of Mechanical Engineers (ASME). Numerous technical papers are published every year in the proceedings and other publications of these societies.

Whether standard or special experimental procedures are used, results must always be interpreted with care. All the conditions under which the experiment is carried out can influence the observed results. Furthermore laboratory conditions often differ from service conditions. It is therefore essential that the experimenter have a thorough understanding of the behavior of materials and develop a sound judgment for interpreting experimental results.

1.2 SELECTION OF MATERIALS

Selection of materials for engineering applications depends first upon their properties in relation to intended use: mechanical strength, if significant loads are to be supported; thermal conductivity, if high temperatures are to be encountered; magnetic permeability, if magnetic fields are involved. The engineer should keep on the alert for new materials that may be developed, but he should also keep his mind receptive to possible new ways of using existing materials.

The next important considerations are economy and availability. Sometimes a material must be selected, even though it has inferior properties, because the "right" material is too expensive or not available. If the properties involved are strength and durability, any inferiority may sometimes be offset by using more material. If the choice is simply between roughly equivalent materials, it can be based entirely on economy.

The engineer should remember that many factors enter into economic considerations. A high materials cost may be accompanied by easier fabrication, with a significant saving in labor. Or it may be accompanied by long life owing to a property such as corrosion resistance so that annual cost of replacement would be considerably lower.

Ease of handling and fabrication are usually the result of certain properties such as ductility, machinability, and light weight. Durability involves resistance to wear and corrosion or resistance to freezing and thawing.

Appearance is sometimes a factor in deciding between otherwise similar materials. Properties such as metallic sheen in metals, color in plastics, transparency in plastics and glass, or texture in concretes can add greatly to the aesthetic appearance of a structure or device in which the material is used.

CHAPTER 2

STRUCTURE
OF
SOLID
MATERIALS

In all branches of engineering an understanding of the fundamental nature of solid materials is becoming increasingly vital. Not only are requirements for materials for engineering applications growing more complex, but there are more materials to choose from every day. The engineer can no longer be satisfied with a superficial knowledge of a few standard properties of a few commonly used materials. So many new and unusual conditions are met with and so many variations in properties are available that he must have a more basic understanding of the behavior of materials. This understanding can be developed only through a knowledge of the structure of solids.

The conventional picture of solid materials as homogeneous or continuous media, while satisfactory for deriving many of the formulas for mechanics of materials, does not provide the necessary insight into their behavior under engineering conditions. Solid materials are made up of many particles of many sizes, held together by internal cohesive forces. These particles or "building blocks" of matter may be fibers, crystals, chunks of stone, molecules, or atoms, to name a few. It is the *cohesive forces* between these particles and the *energies* associated with them that determine the reaction of a given material to external influences, such as those imposed by mechanical, electrical, chemical, or thermal action.

In some materials the largest building blocks are *macroscopic*, or visible to the unaided eye. Wood and concrete are common examples. In others even the largest building blocks can be seen only through a microscope; metals, for example, have a *microscopic* grain structure, in which the grains are individual metal crystals. Plastics often contain fillers made up of microscopic particles such as glass fibers, wood flour, or clay particles. Whether the building block is macroscopic or microscopic, it imparts certain typical properties to the material of which it is a structural unit.

When we go still farther down the size scale, we find that all structural units, large or small, are made up of *submicroscopic* particles: molecules, submicroscopic crystals, atoms, electrons, and the particles of the atomic nucleus. Since it is the atom and its internal structure that ultimately determines the nature of each element, we shall concern ourselves first with this basic particle.

ATOMS AND BONDS

2.1 THE ATOM

Constituent Parts

The atom is commonly visualized as a nucleus surrounded by electrons in a sort of planetary system (Fig. 2.1). The nucleus is made up of heavy

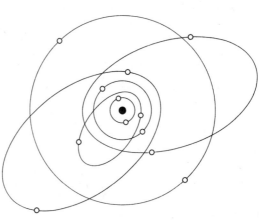

Fig. 2.1 Schematic representation of atomic planetary system.

particles that account for almost all the mass of the atom and determine its atomic weight. The two basic nuclear particles (*nucleons*) are the *proton*, which carries a fixed positive electrical charge, and the *neutron*, which carries no charge. Both have approximately the same mass, and their total number indicates the atomic weight. For example, iron, whose nucleus contains 26 protons and 30 neutrons, has an atomic weight very close to 56. Other nuclear particles have been discovered, but they are not important for this discussion.

The *electron* is a very light particle,* only about $\frac{1}{2000}$ the mass of a proton, but it carries an electrical charge of equal magnitude and opposite sign. The charge on a proton is denoted by $+e$ and that on an electron by $-e$, where

$$e = 1.602 \times 10^{-19} \text{ coulomb.}$$

In a stable atom the net charge is zero, since there are just as many electrons as protons. The number of either electrons or protons is the *atomic number, Z*. Thus iron, whose atomic number is 26, has 26 electrons balancing its 26 protons.

Whereas the number of electrons or protons in a stable atom is a fixed characteristic of each element, the number of neutrons varies somewhat among the atoms of a given element. The resulting variation of atomic weight accounts for the *isotopes* found in most elements. Isotopes of iron have been isolated, for example, that contain 28, 31, and 32 neutrons instead of the usual 30. The atomic weights of these isotopes are 54, 57, and 58, respectively. Natural iron contains a mixture of isotopes that produces a net atomic weight of 55.85.

Electron Structure

The arrangement of the electrons around the nucleus determines the manner in which atoms interact to form a solid. Although there are similarities between electrons and the planets of a solar system, there are also fundamental differences. All matter has certain wavelike characteristics, and in particles as small as electrons these characteristics assume considerable importance. For example, a stream of electrons produces a diffraction pattern when it passes through a crystalline film, and it is reflected from the surface of a single crystal like a ray of light from a diffraction grating.

One effect of the wave properties of electrons is to limit the number of orbits that they can occupy. This effect can be illustrated by analogy with a vibrating string. If a violin string is plucked, it vibrates in a series of distinct modes, each consisting of a system of standing waves whose wave length is a simple fraction of the length of the string. The wave length of the first harmonic, or fundamental, equals the length of the string; that of the second, one-half the length of the string, and so forth. No other wave lengths are possible in a string of given length, and its

---

* The mass of an electron is denoted by m, where $m = 9.11 \times 10^{-28}$ g.

vibrations might be said to be quantized.   Similarly the motion of an electron around the nucleus is limited to discrete orbits, or *quantum states*, each corresponding to a *normal mode* of harmonic vibration of the electron wave. Each quantum state of the electron represents a discrete level of energy, an integral multiple of fundamental energy units or *quanta*.

Another effect of the wave properties of electrons is that even within the framework of discrete energy levels the exact state of an electron cannot be specified.   Rather, we must think in terms of the probability of finding an electron in any given position at any given time.   The states of the electrons in atoms are given by the Schrödinger wave equation, which is founded on advanced mathematical concepts that cannot be treated here.

It is sufficient for our purposes to imagine the atom as a planetary system whose makeup is governed by certain apparently arbitrary rules; this visual model is designed only to help us remember some of the rules we will need later.

In our model we imagine the electrons in orbits confined to specific regions or shells of different diameters, surrounding the nucleus as shown in Fig. 2.2.   Each shell represents an energy level: the smallest shell repre-

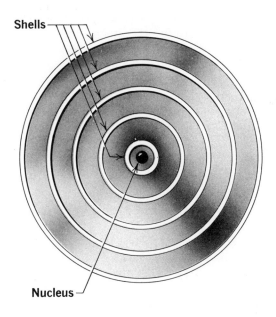

Shells

Fig. 2.2   Schematic representation   of   electron shell structure.

Nucleus

sents the lowest level and so on as we proceed outward to higher energy levels.   Radiation or absorption of energy by an atom involves shifts of electrons between energy levels.

Each shell or energy level has a fixed electron capacity, or can accommodate only a certain number of electrons.   This rule is part of a general law known as *Pauli's exclusion principle*, which governs the states of the electrons in the atomic structure.   For example, the innermost shell can contain only two electrons; hence the three electrons in the element lithium must be divided between the first two shells (two in the first, one in the second).   The second shell, however, has room for eight electrons, and the electrons of any of the elements from lithium (3 electrons) to neon (10 electrons) can occupy the first two shells.

If the elements are listed in order of increasing atomic number, it is found that their properties vary in a periodic manner.   Each period contains a sequence of elements, and for each element in any one period there are elements in corresponding positions in the other periods that have similar properties.   Groups of elements whose properties are similar are referred to as families.   This is the basis of the periodic table (Table 2.1).

It is helpful in studying the structure of the atom to imagine the elements as being built up in order of ascending atomic number.   We may start with the simplest, hydrogen, and add electrons one at a time, together with the necessary nuclear particles, until the entire list of known elements has been covered.   As electrons are added, they have a natural preference for the lowest energy levels, and the shells therefore fill successively, starting with the innermost and progressing outward as each reaches its capacity.

Not only are the electrons in the atomic planetary systems confined to shells, each of which can accommodate only a given number of electrons, but these shells are divided into *subshells*.   Each subshell, too, can hold only a specified number of electrons.

The main electron shells are designated by letter—K, L, M, N, O, P, and Q—and by the corresponding principal quantum numbers, $n = 1, 2, 3$, 4, 5, 6, and 7.   The K shell, for example, has the principal quantum number $n = 1$.   The subshells in each main shell are designated by small letters, s, p, d, and f, with quantum numbers $l = 0, 1, 2$, and 3, respectively. The number of subshells in a given main shell is the same as its principal quantum number, n (although in none of the known elements do any of the last three shells—O, P, Q—contain more than three subshells).

Thus the number of electrons that can occupy a given main shell can be found by adding the electron capacities of the subshells: $s = 2$; $p = 6$; $d = 10$; $f = 14$.   (Note that each subshell can hold just 4 more than the preceding one.)   The final capacities of the first four closed shells are:

	SUBSHELL				TOTAL CAPACITY
MAIN SHELL	s	p	d	f	
K ($n = 1$)	2				2
L ($n = 2$)	2	6			8
M ($n = 3$)	2	6	10		18
N ($n = 4$)	2	6	10	14	32

Table 2.1 Periodic Table of the Elements[a]

							VIII	VIII	VIII								
IA	**IIA**	**IIIB**	**IVB**	**VB**	**VIB**	**VIIB**				**IB**	**IIB**	**IIIA**	**IVA**	**VA**	**VIA**	**VIIA**	**Rare Gases**
1 H 1.0080																	2 He 4.003
3 Li 6.940	4 Be 9.013											5 B 10.82	6 C 12.010	7 N 14.008	8 O 16.0000	9 F 19.00	10 Ne 20.183
11 Na 22.997	12 Mg 24.32											13 Al 26.98	14 Si 28.09	15 P 30.975	16 S 32.066	17 Cl 35.457	18 A 39.944
19 K 39.100	20 Ca 40.08	21 Sc 44.96	22 Ti 47.90	23 V 50.95	24 Cr 52.01	25 Mn 54.93	26 Fe 55.85	27 Co 58.94	28 Ni 58.69	29 Cu 63.54	30 Zn 65.38	31 Ga 69.72	32 Ge 72.60	33 As 74.91	34 Se 78.96	35 Br 79.916	36 Kr 83.8
37 Rb 85.48	38 Sr 87.63	39 Y 88.92	40 Zr 91.22	41 Nb 92.91	42 Mo 95.95	43 Tc (99)	44 Ru 101.7	45 Rh 102.91	46 Pd 106.7	47 Ag 107.880	48 Cd 112.41	49 In 114.76	50 Sn 118.70	51 Sb 121.76	52 Te 127.61	53 I 126.91	54 Xe 131.3
55 Cs 132.91	56 Ba 137.36	57–71 Rare Earths	72 Hf 178.6	73 Ta 180.88	74 W 183.92	75 Re 186.31	76 Os 190.2	77 Ir 193.1	78 Pt 195.23	79 Au 197.2	80 Hg 200.61	81 Tl 204.39	82 Pb 207.21	83 Bi 209.00	84 Po (210)	85 At (211)	86 Rn 222
87 Fr (223)	88 Ra 226.05	89– Actinides															
Alkali Metals (BCC)	Alkali Earths (HCP)			(BCC)[b]	(BCC)		(FCC)	(FCC)	(FCC)	(FCC)	(HCP)				Chalcogens	Halogens	Rare Gases

Rare Earths (Lanthanide series)

57 La 138.92	58 Ce 140.13	59 Pr 140.92	60 Nd 144.27	61 Pm (145)	62 Sm 150.43	63 Eu 152.0	64 Gd 156.9	65 Tb 159.2	66 Dy 162.46	67 Ho 164.94	68 Er 167.2	69 Tm 169.4	70 Yb 173.04	71 Lu 174.99

Actinide series

89 Ac (227)	90 Th 232.12	91 Pa 231	92 U 238.07	93 Np (237)	94 Pu (242)	95 Am (243)	96 Cm (245)	97 Bk (249)	98 Cf (249)	99 E (253)	100 Fm (254)	101 Mv (256)

[a] Reproduced by permission from Sinnott, *The Solid State for Engineers*, John Wiley & Sons, Inc., New York, 1958.
[b] Crystal structure commonly found in metals of this group.

13

It should be pointed out that capacities thus found apply only to the inner, completed main shells.   The outermost main shell never has more than 8 electrons.   As soon as this number is reached, the shell becomes stable even though the sum of its subshell capacities may be more than 8. The next electrons to be added start to fill the next main shell, taking positions in its s subshell.   Only after both spaces in this s subshell have been filled does the inner incomplete main shell go on filling up.   This process produces the transition elements.

It is interesting to note that the letters used to designate electron shells had their origin in spectroscopic studies leading to our present knowledge of the atom.   The letters K through Q were the letters assigned to certain spectral lines observed in X-ray emissions.   The letters s, p, d, and f also referred originally to spectral lines and stand for sharp, principal, diffuse, and fundamental.

Another property of electrons is their angular momentum, or *electron spin*, which produces a magnetic moment in each electron.   The spin of an electron can be represented by a spin vector, whose sense is determined by the direction of spin.   In most atoms the electrons arrange themselves in pairs with spin vectors parallel but in opposite directions.   The net magnetic moment of each pair is therefore zero and contributes nothing to the overall magnetism of the material.   In a few elements a small number of unpaired electrons produces a certain amount of magnetism in the bulk material (compare Art. 11.3).

We are now in a position to examine the development of the periodic system.   (The process can be followed in Table 2.2, which shows the electron structure of all the known elements.)   The first element, hydrogen ($Z = 1$), has only one electron, and it is in the K shell.   This element is designated by the notation $1s^1$.   The $1s$ refers to the principal quantum number, $n = 1$, and to the s subshell (the only subshell present); the superscript 1 is the number of electrons in this subshell.   Addition of one electron (plus a proton and two neutrons in the nucleus) gives us helium, $1s^2$. The first subshell (also the main shell in this instance) is now closed.   As we would expect, helium is a stable element.

A third electron must now settle in the L shell ($n = 2$) and in its first, or s, subshell to produce lithium, $1s^2; 2s^1$.   Because there is only one electron in the L shell, which has room for eight, we find that lithium, unlike helium, is not stable but chemically active.   Addition of more electrons gradually fills the L shell through its s and p subshells until in the element neon ($1s^2; 2s^2, 2p^6$) it, too, is closed.   All the intermediate elements are chemically active, but neon is again a stable or inert element like helium.

The next element to be formed is sodium ($Z = 11$), and here again we have one extra electron which must settle in the next or M shell ($n = 3$) and in its first or s subshell.   Its designation is $1s^2; 2s^2, 2p^6; 3s^1$.   The properties of sodium are quite similar to those of lithium because each has one extra electron outside its closed shells. Magnesium ($1s^2$; $2s^2$, $2p^6$; $3s^2$), with two electrons outside its closed shells, has properties analogous to those of beryllium ($1s^2$; $2s^2$). Similar comparisons can be made for all the elements, which can be arranged in groups or families having like numbers of extra electrons and consequently similar properties.

These extra electrons, representing all the electrons in the outermost *incomplete main shell*, are the *valence electrons*. As indicated in Table 2.2, all the alkali metals have 1 valence electron, the alkali earths 2, the carbon family 4, and the halogens 7. Because the outermost main shell can never have more than 8 electrons, the number of valence electrons is always *less than* 8. If electrons are added to the valence shell to bring the total to 8, the atom becomes stable, like the corresponding inert gas. It is the valence electrons that account for most of the properties of the elements, and that enter into the various bonds that hold materials together. They are relatively loosely bound to the rest of the atom and may be removed by various means.* Similarly valence electrons from other atoms may be added.

Removal of an electron from an atom leaves the atom in an unstable state. The atom acquires a net positive charge and is then referred to as an *ion*. Ions may also be formed by addition of an electron, producing a net negative charge. Additional electrons may be added or subtracted, increasing the charge on the ion. Since unlike charges attract each other and like charges repel, the charged ions attract or repel one another accordingly. Electrostatic action accounts for a large part of the force between atoms in a solid.

2.2 INTERATOMIC BONDS

The bonds between atoms make it possible for them to combine in large masses to form a solid. These bonds are made up of attractive and repulsive forces that tend to hold adjacent atoms at a certain spacing such that the opposing forces just balance. Any deviation from this equilibrium spacing results in an unbalance that tends to pull the atoms back to equilibrium spacing.

Interatomic bonds are of three principal types: *covalent, ionic,* and *metallic*. The attractive forces in all three are directly associated with the valence electrons. The outer shell, which contains the valence electrons, is in a high energy state and is relatively unstable. If it can acquire more electrons to bring the total up to eight, or lose all its electrons to another atom, it can become stable. This is how atomic bonds are formed.

A *covalent bond* results from the sharing of pairs of valence electrons by

---

* Electrons are removed from atoms in a solid (ionization) by applying an electrical voltage to the solid, by irradiating it with gamma rays, or by bombarding it with charged particles.

Table 2.2 Electron Structure of the Elements

SHELL / SUBSHELL	K(n=1)	L(n=2)		M(n=3)			N(n=4)				O(n=5)				P(n=6)			Q(n=7)
	s	s	p	s	p	d	s	p	d	f	s	p	d	f	s	p	d	s
CAPACITY	2	2	6	2	6	10	2	6	10	14	2	6	10	14	2	6	10	2
1 H	1																	
2 He	2																	
3 Li	2	1																
4 Be	2	2																
5 B	2	2	1															
6 C	2	2	2															
7 N	2	2	3															
8 O	2	2	4															
9 F	2	2	5															
10 Ne	2	2	6															
11 Na	Filled (2; 2 − 6)			1														
12 Mg				2														
13 Al				2	1													
14 Si				2	2													
15 P				2	3													
16 S				2	4													
17 Cl				2	5													
18 A				2	6													
19 K	Filled (2; 2 − 6; 2 − 6)						1											
20 Ca							2											
21 Sc						1	2											
22 Ti						2	2											
23 V						3	2											
24 Cr						5	1											
25 Mn						5	2											
26 Fe						6	2											
27 Co						7	2											
28 Ni						8	2											

Transition elements (Manganides)

SHELL / SUBSHELL	K(n=1)	L(n=2)		M(n=3)			N(n=4)				O(n=5)				P(n=6)			Q(n=7)
	s	s	p	s	p	d	s	p	d	f	s	p	d	f	s	p	d	s
29 Cu	Filled (2; 2 − 6; 2 − 6 − 10)						1											
30 Zn							2											
31 Ga							2	1										
32 Ge							2	2										
33 As							2	3										
34 Se							2	4										
35 Br							2	5										
36 Kr							2	6										
37 Rb	Filled (2; 2 − 6; 2 − 6 − 10; 2 − 6)										1							
38 Sr											2							
39 T									1		2							
40 Zr									2		2							
41 Nb									4		1							
42 Mo									5		1							
43 Tc									6		1							
44 Ru									7		1							
45 Rh									8		1							
46 Pd									10									

Transition elements (Technetides)

SHELL / SUBSHELL	K(n=1)	L(n=2)		M(n=3)			N(n=4)				O(n=5)				P(n=6)			Q(n=7)
	s	s	p	s	p	d	s	p	d	f	s	p	d	f	s	p	d	s
47 Ag	Filled (2; 2 − 6; 2 − 6 − 10; 2 − 6 − 10)									Empty	1							
48 Cd											2							
49 In											2	1						
50 Sn											2	2						
51 Sb											2	3						
52 Te											2	4						
53 I											2	5						
54 Xe											2	6						

Table 2.2   *Continued*

SHELL SUBSHELL		K(n = 1) s	L(n = 2) s	p	M(n = 3) s	p	d	N(n = 4) s	p	d	f	O(n = 5) s	p	d	f	P(n = 6) s	p	d	Q(n = 7) s
CAPACITY		2	2	6	2	6	10	2	6	10	14	2	6	10	14	2	6	10	2
55	Cs											2	6			1			
56	Ba											2	6			2			
57	La											2	6	1		2			
58	Ce										2	2	6			2			
59	Pr				Filled						3	2	6			2			
60	Nd				(same as above)						4	2	6			2			
61	Pm										5	2	6			2			
62	Sm										6	2	6			2			
63	Eu										7	2	6			2			
64	Gd										7	2	6	1		2			
65	Tb										9	2	6			2			
66	Dy										10	2	6			2			
67	Ho										11	2	6			2			
68	Er										12	2	6			2			
69	Tm										13	2	6			2			
70	Yb										14	2	6			2			
71	Lu										14	2	6	1		2			
72	Hf													2		2			
73	Ta													3		2			
74	W				Filled									4		2		Transition	
75	Re				(2; 2 − 6; 2 − 6 − 10; 2 − 6 − 10 − 14; 2 − 6)									5		2		elements	
76	Os													6		2		(Rhenides)	
77	Ir													7		2			
78	Pt													8		2			
79	Au															1			
80	Hg															2			
81	Tl															2	1		
82	Pb				Filled											2	2		
83	Bi				(2; 2 − 6; 2 − 6 − 10; 2 − 6 − 10 − 14; 2 − 6 − 10)										Empty	2	3		
84	Po															2	4		
85	At															2	5		
86	Rn															2	6		
87	Fr				Filled											2	6		1
88	Ra				(same as above)											2	6		2
89	Ac															2	6	1	2
90	Th															2	6	2	2
91	Pa														2	2	6	1	2
92	U														3	2	6	1	2
93	Np				Filled										5	2	6		2
94	Pu				(same as above)										6	2	6		2
95	Am														7	2	6		2
96	Cm														8	2	6	1	2
97	Bk														9	2	6		2
98	Cf														10	2	6		2

two or more atoms.   A halogen atom, for example, has 7 valence electrons, and two atoms are held together in a molecule by sharing one pair of electrons.   As the electrons circulate around the two atoms, each atom has alternately 6 and 8 electrons, instead of 7, in its outermost shell; therefore it is charged alternately positive and negative.   Because they are always of unlike sign, the two atoms attract each other with an electrostatic force. Since the number of electrons in the outermost shell can never exceed 8, even momentarily, neither atom can take on more than one additional electron in the sharing process.   Therefore only *one* electron pair can be shared, and only a single bond can be formed.   Elements that form molecules with covalent bonding include those with four or more valence electrons: i.e., the carbon, phosphorus, sulfur, and chlorine families (columns IVA, VA, VIA, and VIIA in the periodic table).   Hydrogen is the one exception; it also enters into covalent bonds with these elements. Generally speaking, then, the number of covalent bonds that can be formed by an element is determined by the number of electrons that can be added to the valence shell without exceeding 8.   According to this rule the maximum number of covalent bonds is $(8 - N)$, where N is the number of valence electrons.*

The covalent bond is found in a wide variety of materials since it can be formed between atoms of the *same or different* elements.   It characterizes many molecules like hydrogen (H_2), nitrogen (N_2), silicon carbide (SiC), and the organic molecules.   It is also responsible for the hard diamond structure.   A characteristic property is low electrical conductivity (see Chapter 11).

In the *ionic bond* atoms of different elements transfer electrons one to the other so that both have stable outer shells and at the same time become ions, one positively and the other negatively charged.   The attractive force is strictly electrostatic.   A typical example of an ionic bond is that between the positive sodium ion and the negative chlorine ion in sodium chloride (Na^+Cl^-).   Here the sodium atom gives up its one valence electron and takes on the stable electron structure of neon.   The chlorine atom takes over the extra electron to complete its outer shell so that, like argon, it is stable.   The ionic bond is most easily formed when one of the atoms has a small number of valence electrons, such as the alkali metals and alkali earths.   Other solids having ionic bonding are potassium oxide (K_2O) and lithium hydride (LiH).   High hardness and low conductivity are typical properties of these solids (see Chapters 10 and 11).

---

* Occasionally one atom will provide both electrons needed to form a bond.   In such instances the maximum number of bonds can exceed $8-N$.   Sulfur trioxide is an example: since $N = 6$ for both sulfur and oxygen, the rule would limit the number of possible bonds to two.   However, the sulfur atom furnishes both bonding electrons for one of the bonds and can thus form bonds with two additional oxygen atoms.

In the *metallic bond* atoms of the same or different elements give up their valence electrons to form an electron cloud (frequently referred to as an "electron gas") throughout the space occupied by the atoms. Having given up their valence electrons, the atoms are, in reality, positive ions. They are held together by forces that are similar to those of the ionic bond in that they are primarily electrostatic, this time between the ions and the electrons. This type of bond is characteristic of the elements having small numbers of valence electrons, which are loosely held, so that they can easily be released to the common pool. Solids held together by this type of bond have such properties as ductility and good electrical conductivity and are classed as metals. Some of these elements may be combined with other elements using one of the other types of bond and hence are not always in the metallic state.

The repulsive forces between atoms are caused by the interaction of their electron shells. When two atoms of any kind approach closely, the negatively charged electron shell of one comes much closer to the negatively charged shell of the other than to its positive nucleus. At larger distances the repulsion between electron shells and the repulsion between nuclei are just balanced by the attractions between one electron shell and the other nucleus. At close spacing the repulsion between electron shells predominates, and the atoms appear to each other to be negatively charged. Thus the repulsive force rises rapidly as the shells begin to overlap. Additional repulsive forces exist between the positively charged ions in metals.

The bonding force, F, between atoms may be represented approximately by the general equation

$$F(r) = \frac{A}{r^M} - \frac{B}{r^N} \quad (N > M), \tag{2.1}$$

where r is the center-to-center spacing between atoms and A, B, M, and N are constants that depend on the form of bond. The first term represents the attractive force and the second the repulsive force. As two atoms approach, they are drawn together by the attractive force until they reach equilibrium spacing, after which, if they continue to approach, the repulsive force predominates, tending to push them back to their equilibrium spacing. Near the equilibrium position the two particles act as though connected by a spring whose neutral length is the same as the equilibrium spacing. Hence the second term must increase more rapidly for diminishing values of r than does the first, and N is necessarily always greater than M.

Because the attractive forces in interatomic bonds are largely electrostatic, the form of the first term is usually taken to be the same as that for the force between electric charges. According to Coulomb's law this force is inversely proportional to the square of the spacing; M is therefore usually 2. The value of N is not so easy to approximate, but it usually takes on values from 7 to 12 (7 to 10 for metallic bonds and 10 to 12 for ionic and covalent bonds).   Figure 2.3 shows the variation of the net attractive force between atoms according to Eq. 2.1, with $M = 2$ and $N = 7$.   The equilibrium spacing is r_0, where the net force is zero and r_0 is of the order of 10^{-8} cm or 1 Å.   It commonly varies with the different bonds between 1

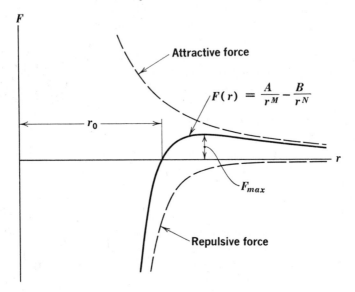

Fig. 2.3   *Interatomic force*, F, *vs atomic spacing*, r.

and 4 Å.   If the atoms are pulled apart from this spacing, an attractive force is built up that just balances the applied force, and when the applied force is released, they will return to equilibrium at r_0.   To separate the atoms completely a force equal to the maximum ordinate of the curve, F_{max}, must be applied.   This force, then, corresponds to the cohesive strength of the material.

EXAMPLE 2.1

Determine the equilibrium spacing, r_0, of two atoms in terms of the constants in Eq. 2.1.

Solution:
$$F = \frac{A}{r^M} - \frac{B}{r^N}.$$

At $r = r_0$, $F = 0$.   Therefore
$$\frac{A}{r_0^M} = \frac{B}{r_0^N},$$

$$r_0^{N-M} = \frac{B}{A},$$

and
$$r_0 = \left(\frac{B}{A}\right)^{\frac{1}{N-M}}.$$

2.3   BOND ENERGY

The potential energy between two atoms is defined as the capacity of the acting forces to do work when the system returns to some arbitrarily chosen datum or reference configuration. If one of the forces acting on a system is X_1, its contribution to the potential energy is equal to the work that it will do; since it may be a variable force, its work must be expressed in general terms as an integral

$$U_1 = \int X_1 dx.$$

Consider the Coulomb attraction, for example. This force has the form $X_1 = A/r^2$ and will provide a potential

$$U_1 = \int \frac{A}{r^2} dr = -\frac{A}{r} + C.$$

The reference configuration may be chosen at will, but here, to simplify the expression it is commonly taken as infinite spacing. If we set $U_1 = 0$ when $r = \infty$, we find $C = 0$. The expression for U_1 is then

$$U_1 = -\frac{A}{r}$$

in terms of atomic spacing r, and can be represented graphically as in Fig. 2.4.

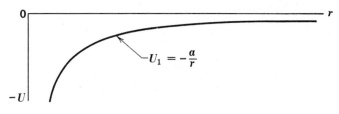

Fig. 2.4   *Potential energy of Coulomb attraction.*

In general terms the potential energy between two atoms is found by integrating Eq. 2.1 as follows:

$$U(r) = \int F(r)dr = \int \left(\frac{A}{r^M} - \frac{B}{r^N}\right) dr$$

$$= -\frac{A}{M-1}\frac{1}{r^{M-1}} + \frac{B}{N-1}\frac{1}{r^{N-1}} + C_1$$

$$= -\frac{a}{r^{M-1}} + \frac{b}{r^{N-1}} + C_1.$$

Again setting $U = 0$ when $r = \infty$ we find $C_1 = 0$, and

$$U(r) = -\frac{a}{r^m} + \frac{b}{r^n} \quad (n > m), \tag{2.2}$$

where a and b are new constants that are related to A and B, $m = M - 1$, and $n = N - 1$. This equation is represented as the solid curve in Fig. 2.5.

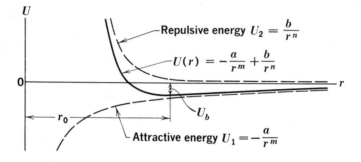

Fig. 2.5   Potential   energy   vs   atomic spacing.

Equilibrium spacing for the two atoms is also a configuration of lowest potential energy, as we may show by taking the derivative of the general potential energy expression

$$U(r) = \int F(r)dr$$

$$\frac{dU(r)}{dr} = F(r). \tag{2.3a}$$

It is seen that when $F(r) = 0$, as it does at equilibrium, the energy curve is horizontal.   Furthermore

$$\frac{d^2U(r)}{dr^2} = \frac{dF(r)}{dr} \tag{2.3b}$$

can be measured from the slope of the force displacement curve.   Since this slope is positive at r_0, the curve of $U(r)$ has a minimum at equilibrium. This minimum acts as a sort of potential trough, and energy is required to displace the atom from equilibrium at the bottom of the trough.   The bonding energy is defined as the energy necessary to separate the atoms completely and is equal in magnitude to the potential energy at the bottom of the trough, U_B (Fig. 2.5).

Since the potential energy with respect to a datum at ∞ is given by

$$U(r) = \int_r^\infty F(r)dr, \tag{2.3c}$$

the bonding energy is also equal to the area under the curve for $F(r)$ from the equilibrium spacing r_0 to infinity. All stable arrangements of atoms in solids are such that the potential energy is a minimum. This is one way of explaining the cohesion of atoms in solid aggregates.

STRUCTURE

In the formation of solids certain basic groupings of atoms into structural units can be identified. These units are of great importance in determining the behavior of the material, mechanically and otherwise. In most materials the atoms combine to form either *crystals* or *molecules*, and solid bodies can be considered as aggregates of these structural units.

2.4 CRYSTALS

A crystal is formed whenever atoms arrange themselves in an orderly three-dimensional pattern, in which rows can be identified running in various directions, along which the atoms are regularly spaced. The locations of the atoms and their particular arrangement in a given crystal are described by means of a *space lattice*, which is a three-dimensional network of straight lines that acts as a coordinate system in space. A simple cubic space lattice is illustrated in Fig. 2.6. The axes of this lattice are those

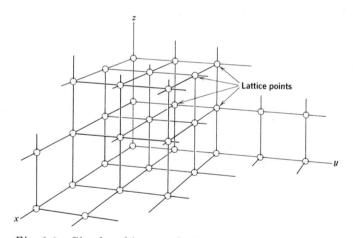

Fig. 2.6   Simple cubic space lattice.

commonly used in space geometry: three lines at right angles to one another. The lines that make up the lattice are parallel to the axes and equally spaced along them. The atoms of a simple cubic crystal structure occupy the lattice points, which are the intersections of the lines. Other space lattices include those in which the axes are still at right angles but the spacing of lines differs along different axes, and those in which the axes are inclined to each other at different angles.

In each type of crystal structure a certain fundamental grouping of atoms is repeated indefinitely in all three dimensions. This fundamental grouping is called a *unit cell*, and it is convenient to describe the whole crystal in terms of a single unit cell. The crystal can then be thought of as being built up of a series of parallel repetitions of the unit cell. Some examples are shown in Fig. 2.7.

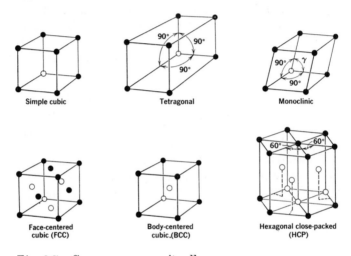

Fig. 2.7   Some common unit cells.

Materials whose basic structural units are crystals include the metals, salts like NaCl, many oxides, and certain plastics. Crystals are usually thought of as being composed of atoms, although in metallic and ionic crystals the atoms have actually been transformed into ions through giving up or acquiring electrons in the process of forming bonds. Sometimes groups of atoms (molecules) are involved in the makeup of the crystals, which are then referred to as *molecular crystals*.

2.5 MOLECULES

The molecule is basically a chemical entity; it is the smallest particle that retains the chemical properties of the original material. In many materials, moreover, molecules also play the role of basic structural unit. Molecules range from diatomic molecules to long-chain types and even two- and three-dimensional types of many atoms each. Diatomic molecules often form permanent electric dipoles, one end charged positively and the other negatively. The characteristics of these dipoles have an important bearing on electrical and mechanical properties (see Chapter 11). Some atoms tend to form large sheet molecules (e.g., graphite and antimony, Art. 2.9). Chain molecules may intertwine, with a marked effect on the mechanical behavior of the material.

2.6 INTERMOLECULAR BONDS

The forces that hold molecules together to form a solid are considerably weaker than atomic bonds and are often referred to as *secondary bonds*. They are also known as *van der Waals bonds*, after J. D. van der Waals, who in 1873 proposed a new thermodynamic equation of state for a real gas which took into account these weak attractive forces between gas molecules. Three types of intermolecular bonds are known: dispersion bonds; dipole bonds; and hydrogen bonds.

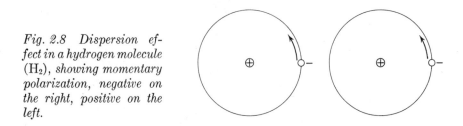

Fig. 2.8 Dispersion effect in a hydrogen molecule (H₂), showing momentary polarization, negative on the right, positive on the left.

Bonds of the first type are made possible largely because the electrons of adjacent atoms in a molecule tend to repel each other. As the electrons rotate around their nuclei, they tend to keep in phase, as illustrated in Fig. 2.8 for a hydrogen molecule. The result is that the molecule has a small fluctuating net charge on each end and acts as an oscillating dipole. The hydrogen molecule in Fig. 2.8 is instantaneously charged negatively on the right end and positively on the left. This fluctuating charge on one molecule tends to interact with the fluctuating charge on a neighboring molecule, resulting in a net attraction. The strength of the bond depends on the ease with which one atom can influence the other. Molecules of the inert gases, which consist of single atoms, are held together by dispersion forces when the gases are solidified. In many organic solids the most important bonding forces between molecules are of this type.

Dipole bonds are caused by permanent electric charges on some molecules. For example, in the covalent-bonded hydrogen chloride (HCl) molecule the net effect of the electron-sharing process is to give the chlorine atom a slightly negative charge while the hydrogen atom has a corresponding positive charge. The charges are actually quite small, being

0.816 × 10⁻¹⁰ esu* compared with 4.8 × 10⁻¹⁰ esu for a single electron. The spacing of the atoms is 1.28 × 10⁻⁸ cm, resulting in a net dipole moment of 1.04 × 10⁻¹⁸ cm × esu. Adjacent HCl molecules therefore attract each other by means of the electrostatic attraction between their oppositely charged ends. The attraction is small compared with that between ions because the charge on an ion is at least equal to that of one electron, 4.8 × 10⁻¹⁰ esu. Dipole bonds are consequently much weaker than ionic bonds, but at the same time they are considerably stronger than dispersion bonds. Some other materials subject to dipolar bonding, and their dipole moments in cm × esu are: sulfur dioxide (SO₂) 1.60 × 10⁻¹⁸; hydrogen bromide (HBr) 0.78 × 10⁻¹⁸; and hydrogen cyanide (HCN) 2.93 × 10⁻¹⁸.

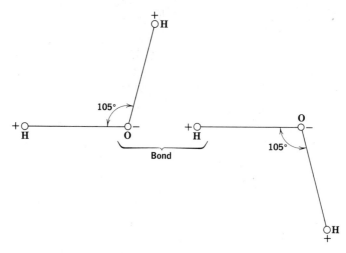

Fig. 2.9   Hydrogen bond between two water molecules.

The hydrogen bond might be considered as a special type of dipole bond, but one that is considerably stronger. It occurs between molecules in which one end is a hydrogen atom. The one electron belonging to the hydrogen atom is fairly loosely held, and if the adjacent atom in the molecule is strongly electronegative, it may keep all the electrons around itself, leaving the hydrogen atom in effect a positive ion. A strong permanent dipole is created that can bond to other similar dipoles with a force near that involved in the ionic bond. A good example of hydrogen bonding is water or ice. In water the hydrogen and oxygen atoms are held by covalent bonds in a configuration as shown in Fig. 2.9. It is seen that this

* Electrostatic units.

special form of dipole bond is connected with the dipole moment of the
H—O bond rather than that of the molecule as a whole.

Like interatomic bonds, intermolecular bonds involve forces of the form

$$F(r) = \frac{A}{r^M} - \frac{B}{r^N} \quad (N > M).$$

Since the attractive forces in intermolecular bonds are smaller and of
shorter range than the Coulomb attractive forces in interatomic bonds, the
values of M are higher. Whereas $M = 2$ for the interatomic bond, it may

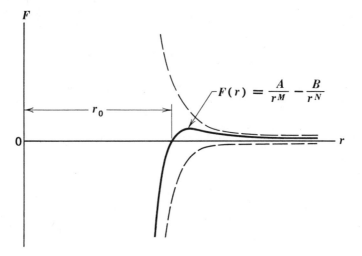

*Fig. 2.10   Intermolecular force vs. molecu-
lar spacing.*

be as high as 7 for the van der Waals bond. Figure 2.10 shows the corresponding variation of $F(r)$ with $M = 7$ and $N = 12$.

2.7   THERMAL ENERGY

The existence of equilibrium spacings between atoms and molecules in
a solid does not imply that these particles are stationary. Actually there
is constant motion—even violent motion—among the atoms and molecules
of all solids at ordinary temperatures. This motion is the thermal agitation caused by heat. Atoms and molecules oscillate continuously about
their equilibrium positions. The amplitude of the oscillations is small, of
the order of 10^{-9} cm or 0.1 Å, whereas the equilibrium spacings are of the
order of 1 Å. The frequencies, however, are very high, possibly 10^{15} cps.
The result is that atoms in solids attain enormous velocities in their oscilla-

tions, of the order of 10^7 cm/sec or 63 mi/sec.   Even at absolute zero some of this motion persists.

The kinetic energy possessed by the atoms and molecules in a substance is its thermal energy.   This energy is in addition to the potential energy owing to structure or order, which is present only in solids and liquids, not in gases.   According to the classical kinetic theory of heat, each atom of a crystalline solid has, on the average, a total energy kT for each degree of freedom, where k is Boltzmann's constant,

$$k = 3.30 \times 10^{-24} \text{ (cal/°K)/atom,}$$

and T is the absolute temperature in °K.*   Of this amount about half is kinetic (thermal) and half potential (structure).   If each atom behaves as a point mass, it has *3* degrees of freedom in translation and none in rotation. Thus the *total energy of an individual atom averages 3 kT*.

If we now choose as a unit of mass one containing a fixed number of atoms, then by classical theory the total energy in such a unit will be the same for all crystalline materials.   A *mole* of a crystalline substance is a quantity which contains N atoms, where N is Avogadro's number

$$N = 6.02 \times 10^{23}.$$

The mass of one mole is the atomic weight expressed in grams† (also re-ferred to as a *gram-atom*).   Thus the energy in a mole of any crystalline material is given by $3 NkT$, regardless of the material.

The product Nk is known as the *universal gas constant* and is denoted by R, where

$$R = 1.987 \text{ (cal/ °K)/mole}$$

(usually approximated by 2).   Thus the total energy, E, for one mole of a crystalline solid is $E = 3\,RT \approx 6\,T$.   This equation is approximately cor-rect for many materials at ordinary temperatures.   At low temperatures it is considerably in error, as explained in Chapter 12.

Activation

The thermal energy of a solid is available for the activation of various processes, such as chemical reactions and certain types of mechanical deformations.

The concept of *activation* of a process can be illustrated in many ways,

---

* For many purposes the absolute temperature scale is essential.   The following conversions are useful:

°K (Kelvin) = °C + 273; °R (Rankine) = °F + 460.

† A mole of atoms.   A mole of molecules is that quantity of a molecular substance containing N molecules; similarly a mole of electrons contains N electrons.

mechanically.   For example, consider the rectangular prism shown in Fig. 2.11 in a position of stable equilibrium (position A).   The process to be studied is that of tipping the prism over onto its side (position C).   To do

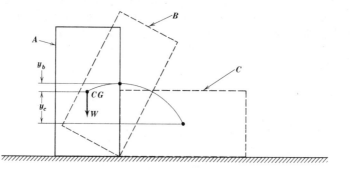

Fig. 2.11   *Tilting prism, illustrating metastable (A), unstable (B), and stable (C) positions.*

this a force must be applied to bring the prism to the unstable position, B, balanced on its edge, after which it will continue the process of its own accord.   The energy that must be put into the prism to activate the process

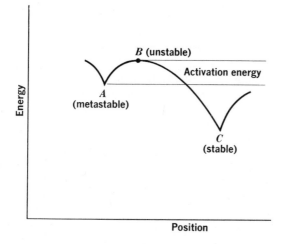

Fig. 2.12   *Energy of tilting prism.*

is equal to its weight multiplied by the rise of the center of gravity during the first stage.   Thus $E_a = Wy_b$, where E_a is the *activation energy* required, W is the weight of the block, and y_b is illustrated in Fig. 2.11.   Observe that both positions A and C are stable, but that the potential energy of C is lower than that of A. Consequently the net energy change associated with the process is negative, and energy is released during it. The net change is $\Delta E = -Wy_c$, which is considerably larger than E_a. Position A is referred to as *metastable*. Figure 2.12 shows the variation of energy in going from position A to position C. The hump in the curve represents a potential barrier which must be overcome through the aid of the activation energy.

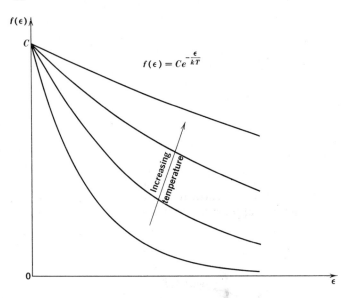

Fig. 2.13   Distribution of relative frequencies, f(ϵ), with which an atom is found to
have a given energy, ϵ. Family of curves
represents distributions at different temperatures.

Many physical processes not only involve shifts of atoms from metastable to stable configurations of lower energy but also require a small activation energy to get the process started. The rapid fluctuations of thermal energy can provide the necessary impulses to activate such processes. These energy impulses vary in a statistical, or random, manner. The rate at which the process proceeds depends on the frequency with which the impulses give the atoms the necessary energy to overcome their potential barriers and thus be activated. This frequency, in turn, depends on the distribution of thermal energy among the atoms in the solid, a problem in statistical mechanics. The actual calculation of the distribution is beyond the scope of this text, but for a given temperature it turns out to be an exponential one. The distribution is illustrated in Fig. 2.13, which shows the relative frequency (or probability) with which an atom is found to have a given energy ϵ. The equation is of the form

$$f(\epsilon) = Ce^{-\beta\epsilon},$$

where C and β are constants for a given temperature and e is the base of natural logarithms. Note that low energy impulses occur more frequently than those of higher energy.

The effect of increasing temperature is to increase the frequency of higher energies. When we introduce the absolute temperature into the calculation, the Maxwell-Boltzmann distribution is obtained:

$$f(\epsilon) = Ce^{-\frac{\epsilon}{kT}},$$

where kT, as noted before, is the classical thermal energy of an atom per degree of freedom. Thus an increase in temperature results in higher curves, all passing through the point C on the vertical axis (Fig. 2.13).

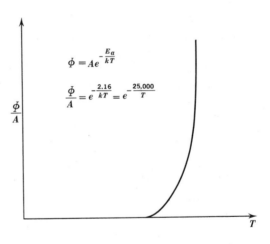

Fig. 2.14 Variation of Φ with temperature according to the Arrhenius equation, for $E_a = 2.16$ ev.

If we replace ϵ by E_a, the activation energy per atom of the substance, the rate at which the process proceeds is proportional to the above frequency, $f(\epsilon)$, and the following equation for the rate of a process is obtained:

$$\Phi = Ae^{-\frac{E_a}{kT}} \tag{2.4}$$

in which A is a constant and the other factors are as defined above. This is known as the *Arrhenius equation*, after the chemist S. Arrhenius, who first proposed a rate equation of this form in 1893. It should be remembered that in the above equation kT is an energy term. If k is expressed in terms of cal/°K, and T in °K, then at room temperature (70°F = 21°C = 294°K) $kT = 0.97 \times 10^{-21}$ cal. The activation energy, E_a, is frequently expressed in terms of electron volts (ev), which are much smaller units of energy. One *electron volt* is defined as *the work done in moving an electron through a potential difference of one volt in an electric field*, and is given by

$$1 \text{ ev} = 3.83 \times 10^{-20} \text{ cal.}$$

If kT is expressed in the same units, we find that at room temperature $kT = 0.0253$ ev $\approx \frac{1}{40}$ ev.

The variation of Φ with temperature is illustrated in Fig. 2.14. Note the steepness of the variation.

Diffusion

An important physical process involving shifts of atoms and molecules to new positions is that of diffusion. Molecules in gases diffuse rapidly and quickly bring about a uniform concentration in a container. This shift takes place because the passage of molecules is not interfered with appreciably by other molecules.

Molecules in liquids are much closer together and are actually connected by bonds. To diffuse they must move through holes between other molecules, a much slower process than in gases.

In solids atoms or molecules are even more closely spaced and occupy definite equilibrium positions. The migration of an atom through a crystal, for example, involves displacements of other atoms that would be almost impossible in a perfect crystal. However, the imperfections normally present in all solids (see p. 47) make diffusion possible, and since their numbers increase with thermal agitation diffusion becomes more and more important as the temperature rises.

Diffusion takes place in solids when the existing configuration is metastable with respect to some other configuration, which is stable. If the concentration of atoms of one element is higher at one point than at another, the atoms will diffuse from the region of higher concentration to that of lower concentration. Such a condition exists in a soldered joint in copper wire, for instance, or a cemented joint between two plastics. Other conditions leading to solid-state diffusion include internal stresses and nonuniform structure.

Under any given condition, such as a certain concentration gradient or a certain internal stress, the rate at which diffusion takes place is governed by the temperature, as expressed by the Arrhenius equation. Thus the rate of diffusion increases very rapidly with temperature and is always significant at high temperatures.

At some high temperature thermal agitation becomes violent enough to pull the atoms and molecules apart bodily, and either melting or disintegration takes place.

SOLID BODIES

We have seen how the elementary particles like electrons and protons are put together to make the atom, and how atoms may combine in either of two basic structural units, crystals or molecules. We are now ready to study the construction of a solid body using these building blocks.

2.8   CLASSIFICATION OF SOLIDS

Solids may be classified as crystalline or amorphous, or a combination of the two. Crystalline solids are usually built up of a number of crystals, in which the crystals may be of similar or widely varying sizes. Sometimes a crystal becomes large enough to form a complete body, which is then referred to as a *single crystal.* Amorphous materials usually have molecules as their basic structural units, but their principal characteristic is their more-or-less disordered state—one with little regularity of arrangement—which results in a lower density than for crystalline materials, which are highly regular.

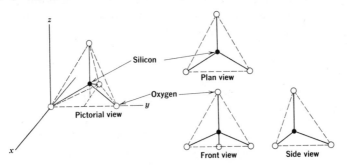

Fig. 2.15   Crystalline quartz, showing tetrahedron formed by silicon and oxygen atoms.

An interesting material that can exist in either form is silica (SiO_2). As quartz, silica is a crystalline solid in which each silicon atom is surrounded by a tetrahedron of oxygen atoms (Fig. 2.15). Bonds are covalent, in which electrons are shared by neighboring atoms. As indicated in Table 2.2, oxygen has 2 empty spaces in its $2p$ valence shell and can form 2 covalent bonds; silicon, on the other hand, has 4 empty spaces in its $3p$

shell and can thus form 4 covalent bonds.   As a result each silicon atom
bonds with 4 oxygen atoms while each oxygen atom bonds with only 2
silicon atoms, thus forming the structure shown in Fig. 2.15.   While it is

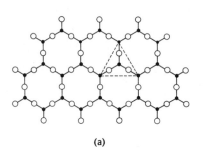

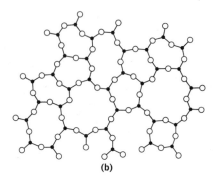

(a)   (b)

*Fig. 2.16   Structure of crystalline quartz
compared with that of amorphous silica.
(Part (b) reprinted by permission from
Zachariasen,* J. Am. Chem. Soc. *54, 3846
(1932))*

somewhat difficult to picture this structure in two dimensions, the regularity of the atomic configuration can be illustrated by the plan view in
Fig. 2.15.   Figure 2.16a is a corresponding plan view of a crystal containing

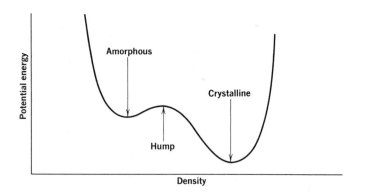

Fig. 2.17   Potential energy vs density.

a number of unit cells.   The noncrystalline form, amorphous silica, is
illustrated by a similar view in Fig. 2.16b, which shows the irregularity of
the network.   A network is still formed because the bonds between the

atoms are the same as before, but the structure is disordered, and no regular lattice is evident.

The structure of amorphous silica is metastable. Its potential energy is at a minimum point, but since the crystalline form is more dense, the potential energy of the latter is at a still lower minimum. The situation may be illustrated by an energy curve (Fig. 2.17) wherein two minima, one somewhat lower than the other, are separated by a hump as in Fig. 2.12. If activation energy is provided sufficient to overcome the potential barrier between them, the metastable, amorphous type can be changed to the stable, crystalline type. This transition has been made experimentally: prolonged heating at high temperatures, accompanied by mechanical stress, supplies the necessary activation energy to crystallize amorphous silica.

2.9 CRYSTALLINE SOLIDS

Atomic crystals are formed having all three types of bonding: covalent, ionic, and metallic. The characteristics associated with each type, however, are decidedly different.

Metallic Crystals

Metallic crystals have wide use in engineering owing to their favorable properties of strength, ductility, conductivity, and reflection. In the formation of a metal crystal the ions are connected only indirectly, through the free electrons surrounding them. There are therefore no directional properties involved in the metallic bond, and each atom attracts as many neighboring atoms as it can. The result is a closely packed structure having short, strong bonds and a high density.

For crystals in which all atoms are identical there are two forms of closest packing: hexagonal close-packed (HCP), and face-centered cubic (FCC). These are basically similar, with only one point of difference. To illustrate the two forms it is convenient to represent each atom by a solid sphere having a diameter that can be adjusted to equal the equilibrium spacing of the atoms as they exist in the crystal structure. These spheres may then be packed together like ping-pong balls in a variety of arrangements.

First consider a single layer of these spheres; it is clear that only one closely packed pattern is possible, a hexagonal one, as shown in Fig. 2.18. A three-dimensional array, or crystal, can then be built up by stacking layers of this type, one on top of another. The second layer can be placed in any position over the first, or lower, one. Again it is clear that there is only one position for closest packing, the lowest possible position of the second layer, in which each sphere rests in a cup formed by a hole between the spheres in the first layer. Any such position will do, as all possibilities are identical (Fig. 2.19). In putting on the third layer, however, we find *two possible locations* that give *equally close packing* but otherwise are not quite the same. Using the same procedure as for the second layer, we place each sphere of the third layer in a cup formed by a hole in the second layer, but now we find two sets of these holes, depending on position relative to the first layer: one lies directly over the spheres in the first layer and the other over the holes in the first layer. Hence there are two pos-

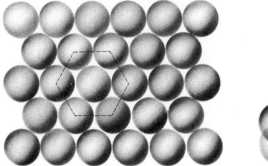

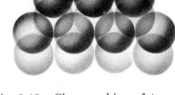

Fig. 2.18   Single layer of spheres, showing close packing.

Fig. 2.19   Close packing of two layers of spheres.

sible positions of the third layer relative to the first two. The first position gives a hexagonal close-packed (HCP) structure, the second a face-centered cubic (FCC) structure. The two arrangements are shown in Figs. 2.20 and 2.21. In Fig. 2.20 the typical hexagonal grouping of a hexagonal close-packed structure is shown. Figure 2.21 shows the typical triangular grouping of a face-centered cubic structure (a), together with the more familiar view in which the cubic structure is emphasized (b); in (b) only the centers of the spheres are shown—the spheres themselves are omitted to reduce confusion.

That the arrangements in Fig. 2.21a and b are identical can be seen if one imagines that he is looking along the diagonal of the cube toward the origin and identifies the atoms having the same letters in both views. Note that the plane ACE is the octahedral plane of the cube (i.e., the plane that intersects the three rectangular axes at equal distances from the origin); the plane GHJ is formed by the three atoms at the centers of the near faces of the cube; and K is the nearest corner atom.

Although the crystal structures just described represent equally close packing, and apparently identical potential energies, only one is found in a given metal under given conditions. For example, magnesium always crystallizes in the HCP structure while aluminum is always in the FCC form.   Other metals may assume one form at room temperature and the other at a different temperature or pressure.   This behavior is known as *polymorphism* or *allotropy*.   For example, cobalt changes from HCP to FCC as the temperature increases through 477°C; iron changes from BCC (α-iron, or ferrite) at room temperature to FCC (γ-iron, or austenite) at 906°C.   Many factors in addition to closeness of packing enter into the choice of crystal structures.   The atoms are, after all, not actually hard

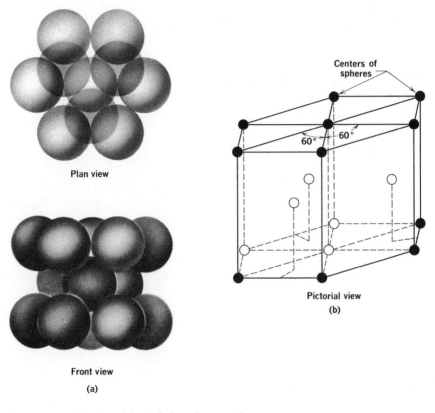

Plan view

Centers of spheres

60°   60°

Pictorial view

(b)

Front view

(a)

Fig. 2.20   Close packing of three layers of spheres in hexagonal (HCP) structure.

spheres.   One of the most important considerations is the electron shell structure of the atoms.   The bonding energy, U_b, of the solid crystal involves not only the potential energy of the lattice, which depends on the density of packing, but also the energy associated with the free electrons.[*]

---

[*] Boas, W., *An Introduction to the Physics of Metals and Alloys*, John Wiley & Sons, Inc., New York, 1947, p. 54.

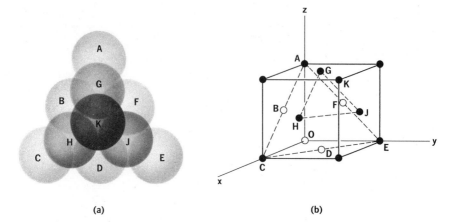

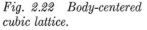

Fig. 2.21 *Close packing of spheres in face-centered cubic (FCC) structure. (Corresponding atoms are lettered the same in both views.)*

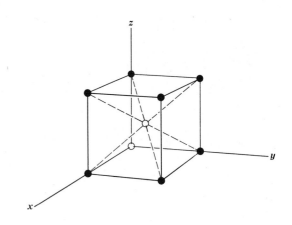

Fig. 2.22 *Body-centered cubic lattice.*

For a given metal this energy variation from one crystal type to another accounts for the preference for one or the other of the two close-packed structures.

The same considerations can be used to explain why a number of metals prefer a slightly less closely packed structure—the body-centered cubic (BCC). This structure is illustrated in Fig. 2.22, and is typical of iron at room temperature and the alkali metals. The crystal structures commonly found in many metals are indicated in Table 2.1.

Density of packing can be expressed in terms of the number of nearest neighbors surrounding an atom in a crystal. If we refer to Fig. 2.18, it is clear that each sphere is surrounded by six others in that plane. Regardless of which method of close packing is used, there can be just three spheres in each of the planes above and below that will touch the original sphere (Figs. 2.20 and 2.21). Thus the total number of nearest equidistant neighbors is 12 in the closest-packed structures. This number is called the *coordination number*. In the BCC structure each central atom is sur-

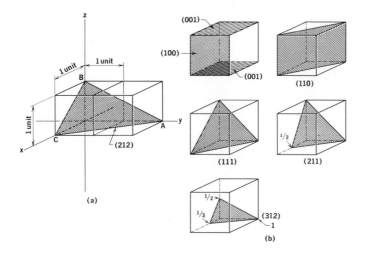

Fig. 2.23 Miller indices for various planes. Plane ABC intersects the x-, y-, and z-axes at distances of 1, 2, and 1 unit(s), respectively, from the origin. The reciprocals of these distances are 1, $\frac{1}{2}$, and 1, and the smallest integers having the same ratio are 2, 1, and 2, the Miller indices of ABC and any parallel plane.

rounded by 8 nearest equidistant neighbors, the corner atoms. Likewise each corner atom can be visualized as the central atom of a new cube, the corners of which are the central atoms of the original cubes. Hence all atoms are surrounded by 8 nearest equidistant neighbors, and the coordination number is 8. Generally speaking the lower the coordination number, the less dense the packing.

A standard system is used to designate the various crystallographic planes. Any plane, together with all planes parallel to it, is defined by a set of numbers called *Miller indices*. For a cubic crystal the indices are

found as follows.   Write down the three numbers representing the intercepts of the plane on the three cubic axes (for example, axes x, y, and z
in Fig. 2.21b).   Numbers representing multiples or fractions of the dimen-

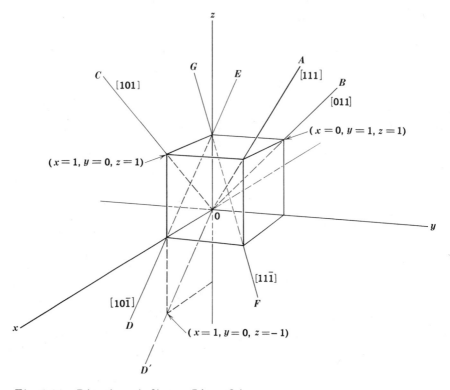

*Fig. 2.24   Direction   indices.   Line   OA
passes through the origin and the point
having coordinates x = 1, y = 1, z = 1.
Its indices are therefore [111].   Line DE
does not pass through the origin.   Line
D′O, parallel to DE, is therefore drawn
through the origin; D′O passes through the
point having coordinates x = 1, y = 0,
z = −1, and its indices are [10\overline{1}].   Line
DE, parallel to D′O, has the same indices,
[10\overline{1}].   Note that negative coordinates are
indicated by a line above the number.*

sions of the unit cell (cube) may be used.   The reciprocals of these numbers, reduced to the three smallest integers having the same ratio, determine
the Miller indices of the plane.   They are conventionally enclosed in

parentheses. Figure 2.23 illustrates the indices for some common planes: for example, the octahedral plane ABC in Fig. 2.21 is designated by (111) and the base plane of the cube by (010). When one of the indices is negative, its sign is indicated by a dash above the number.

The direction of a line is specified by indices representing the coordinates of a point on a vector in that direction, through the origin. The smallest integers that will define the point are chosen and placed in *brackets*. Figure 2.24 illustrates the indices for a few directions.

Figure 2.25 shows a system of indices used in connection with hexagonal crystals. Since there are four axes, a_1, a_2, a_3, and c, four indices are used. They are determined in the same way as Miller indices.

If all the atoms in a metallic solid are not identical, as in an alloy, a variety of crystal forms is possible. A controlling factor is the relation between the sizes of the atoms involved. This relation can be expressed as the ratio of the radii of the solid spheres used to represent the atoms. If, for example, two kinds of atoms are involved, and the ratio of their radii is $r_1/r_2 = 0.414$, it is possible for the larger atoms to form a close-packed structure (FCC or HCP) in which the smaller atoms just fit into the interstices. Each interstitial atom is surrounded by four nearest neighbors (coordination number 4). The resulting combination is called an *interstitial alloy*.

Actually, although 0.414 is the largest ratio for which solid spheres can be packed in the above manner, real atoms can form interstitial alloys having somewhat larger ratios because they can be distorted and the crystal lattice expanded. In the important alloy, carbon steel, the carbon atoms, having a radius of 0.77 Å, are squeezed into interstitial positions between the iron atoms, which have a radius of 1.24 Å. The ratio is 0.62. A ratio of approximately 0.6 is the limit for formation of interstitial alloys, so that steel is a borderline case. It is worth mentioning that carbon, although a nonmetal, enters into a metallic compound with the iron in steel. For this reason it is sometimes called a *metalloid*. Other metalloids are hydrogen, nitrogen, and boron, all elements having small atoms.

An important classification of metals is into simple metals and transition metals (Table 2.2). The former have all electron shells inside their valence shells completely filled. In the transition metals one of the d subshells is at a slightly higher energy level than the following s subshell, and the latter therefore fills first. For example, in the group from scandium (21) to nickel (28) the $3d$ subshell is incomplete while the $4s$ shell may be filled. The one or two electrons in the $4s$ subshell in the N shell are the valence electrons, even though the 3 or M shell is not completely filled. This condition leads to a number of interesting properties such as ferromagnetism (see Chapter 11).

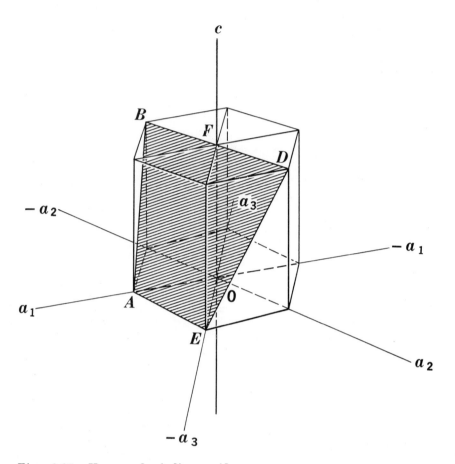

Fig. 2.25 Hexagonal indices. Along each axis the unit length is the distance from the origin to the extremity of the unit cell (OA along axis a, OF along axis c). The upper base plane, being parallel to axes a_1, a_2, and a_3, has infinite intercepts on these axes and intersects the c-axis at 1 unit distance from O. The reciprocals are 0, 0, 0, and 1, and the indices are therefore (0001). Plane ABDE, being parallel to axis a_2, has an infinite intercept on that axis. It intersects axes a_1, a_3, and c at 1, −1, and 1, respectively; its indices are therefore (10$\bar{1}$1).

Nonmetallic Crystals

Nonmetallic crystals may have covalent or ionic bonding, or any of a great variety of mixed bonds. Atoms of two or more kinds are frequently involved. Hence the radii of the individual atoms are important. These radii, however, vary considerably, depending on the type of bond, the temperature, pressure, and other factors. Table 2.3 shows the approximate atomic radii of a number of elements, for the three primary types of bond. The previously introduced concept of adjustable solid spheres may be used to approximate the spacing between any two atoms by adding the appropriate radii. This calculation facilitates qualitative analyses of crystal structures.

Table 2.3   Approximate Atomic Radii[a]

	ATOMIC RADIUS, Å			
			IONIC BOND	
ELEMENT	METALLIC BOND	COVALENT BOND	NEGATIVE	POSITIVE
H		0.37	(1−)2.08	
O		0.74	(2−)1.35	(6+)0.09
N		0.74	(3−)1.71	(5+)0.11
C		0.77	(4−)2.60	(4+)0.15
B		0.88		(3+)0.20
Cl		0.99	(1−)1.81	(7+)0.26
Si		1.17	(4−)1.98	(4+)0.40
Sb		1.41	(3−)2.08	(5+)0.62
Sn		1.41	(4−)2.94	(4+)0.74
Fe	1.24	1.16		(2+)0.83
Al	1.43	1.25		(3+)0.55
Ti	1.45	1.32		(2+)0.76
Hf	1.59	1.44		(4+)0.86
Na	1.90	1.57		(1+)0.98
Cs	2.67	2.35		(1+)1.70

[a] From Pauling, Linus, *The Nature of the Chemical Bond,* 3rd ed., Cornell University Press, Ithaca, N. Y., 1960, and other sources. It should be noted that all radii may vary considerably, depending on the actual structure of the solid in question.

In covalent crystals the most important factor is the number of bonds that can be formed by each atom. When all possible bonds are formed, the number of nearest neighbors surrounding each atom is given by $8 - N$, where N is the number of valence electrons. Thus the coordination number of each atom is also $8 - N$. Since this number also indicates the valence of the atom, these crystals are sometimes called valence crystals.

A simple example of a covalent crystal is crystalline carbon. Here $8 - N = 4$, and each carbon atom is surrounded by four other carbon atoms (coordination number 4). Although all carbon atoms are alike (radius ratio = 1), the limitation on the number of bonds prevents the formation of one of the close-packed structures. The four nearest neighbors tend to space themselves equally around the central atom to form a tetrahedron (Fig. 2.26). The angles made by the lines joining the central

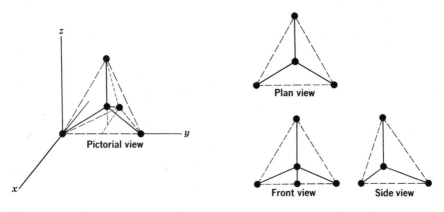

Fig. 2.26   Crystalline   carbon: diamond structure.

atom with the corner atoms are 109.5°. The complete crystal is formed by joining many of these tetrahedra. Each atom can be considered as a central atom surrounded by four nearest neighbors in identical arrangements. This is the *diamond structure*, noted for its strength and rigidity. Other elements in the carbon family (silicon, germanium, and tin) form similar crystals since all have four valence electrons. Another crystalline material of this same type is crystalline quartz, in which silicon and oxygen atoms combine to form a diamond-like structure. This crystal, too, has a high hardness.

Other important crystals having covalent bonding are the crystallized polymers or plastics.

Like the metals, some nonmetallic crystals change form at different temperatures or pressures (polymorphism). Tin, for example, crystallizes in a nonmetallic diamond structure (gray tin) at low temperatures, while at room temperature it forms a metallic structure (white tin).

A number of elements are on the borderline between metals and nonmetals and tend to form combination structures having both metallic and covalent bonding. Carbon and antimony are two examples. Graphite is formed when carbon atoms use only three of their possible covalent bonds, leaving one valence electron free to enter into a metallic-type bond. The three covalent bonds attract three nearest neighbors, which arrange themselves in a plane triangle around the central atom. This structure is repeated to form a plane of atoms or "sheet molecule" in which the atoms are about 1.42 Å apart (Fig. 2.27). The metallic bond involving the fourth

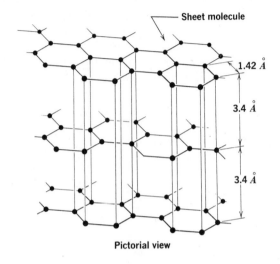

Sheet molecule

1.42 Å

3.4 Å

3.4 Å

Fig. 2.27 Structure of graphite, illustrating sheet molecules connected by metallic bonds.

Pictorial view

electron of each atom acts to hold these sheets together with a spacing of about 3.4 Å. A similar lattice is formed by antimony, mica, and talc. In antimony, the sheet molecules are "puckered," the atoms being alternately slightly above and below a common plane; the bonds holding the molecules together are either metallic or molecular. In mica the sheets are built of silicon and oxygen atoms having covalent bonding, while the sheets themselves are held together by ionic bonds. In talc the sheets are held together by weak molecular bonds.

In ionic crystals positive and negative ions must be so combined as to keep the net charge zero. In sodium chloride (NaCl), for example, the ions are arranged alternately, and each ion is surrounded by an equal number of ions of the opposite sign. The exact number of these surrounding ions (the coordination number) is determined by the relative sizes of the ions. From Table 2.3 the ionic radius of Cl^- is found to be 1.81 Å, while that of Na^+ is 0.98 Å, only about half as large. When the radius ratio is in this range (0.54), only 6 large spheres can be packed around one small sphere. Only 6 Cl^- ions can surround one Na^+ ion, and since there must be equal numbers of both, they must assume a cubic structure (Fig. 2.28). The central Cl^- ion is surrounded by 6 Na^+ ions at the centers of the cube faces. A close inspection will reveal that two FCC structures are superimposed: the entire cube is an FCC unit cell of sodium, while the central plane, *ABCD*, is the face plane of an overlapping FCC unit cell of chlorine.

Cesium chloride (CsCl) is similar to NaCl except that the ions are more nearly the same size (radius ratio 0.94). Hence 8 Cl^- ions can be packed around each Cs^+ ion to give a body-centered cubic structure (Fig. 2.22).

Two characteristics that distinguish metallic from nonmetallic crystals are ductility and conductivity. Nonmetallic crystals are less ductile (more brittle) than metallic crystals because of the importance of the relative locations of atoms when covalent or ionic bonds are involved. If one layer of atoms in a nonmetallic crystal is shifted with respect to the adjacent

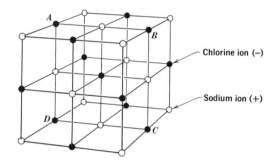

Chlorine ion (−)

Sodium ion (+)

Fig. 2.28   Sodium chloride lattice.

layer, there is a permanent disruption of many bonds. For example, if a positive ion is shifted next to another positive ion, no ionic bond can exist between them. In metals, on the other hand, all atoms look alike to each other, and layers may occupy any position relative to one another with no reduction in bond strength. This factor accounts for the high ductility of the metals.

The electrical conductivity of nonmetallic crystals is low because the valence electrons are tightly bound to the atoms when bonds are formed between them (Art. 11.2). In metallic crystals the free electron cloud provides ample electrons for conducting electricity through the solid. Intermediate materials like graphite allow some conductivity because of the free electrons associated with their metallic bonds.

Properties of crystals can best be observed in single crystals. Crystals of many materials, e.g., metals, quartz, and rochelle salt, can be grown under carefully controlled conditions. Single crystals of some materials, such as sodium chloride and diamond, are formed naturally. The study of single crystals has yielded an enormous amount of information on all forms of crystalline solids. It is important in interpreting such studies, however, to remember that single crystals reflect the inherent directionality of the crystal structure. There are marked differences in properties for different crystal directions. For example, when a single crystal is heated it expands by different amounts in different directions. Similar differences are noted for such properties as optical refraction, mechanical stiffness, resistance to chemical attack, electrical conductivity, and many others. This characteristic is called *anisotropy*. It does not detract from the usefulness of single crystals for scientific study, and has actually been used to advantage in many engineering applications. On the other hand, if overlooked it can have unexpected effects on the behavior of materials.

Imperfections

A characteristic of crystals that stands out most prominently is the presence of imperfections. Many important engineering properties are affected by imperfections or defects and by changes in their number or configuration, far out of proportion to the space they occupy in the crystal. Although we speak of an ideal crystal as a perfectly regular solid, such perfection is never found in real materials. There are always some defects, and their effects on material properties is often critical.

Imperfections in crystals are of several forms:

Vacancies: lattice sites from which atoms are missing.

Interstitials: atoms occupying positions between the atoms of the ideal crystal.

Impurities: foreign atoms occupying positions between the atoms of the ideal crystal, or occupying lattice sites from which the regular atoms are missing (substitutional atoms).

Dislocations: local discontinuities along surfaces where two parts of the crystal having slightly different spacings or lattice orientations come together.

Mosaic structure or lineage structure: a crystal substructure consisting of slightly disoriented blocks caused by unequal growth of parts of the crystal.

Excess electrons and holes: in nonmetallic crystals, extra valence electrons not needed to form covalent bonds; or electrons missing from such bonds (holes).

Excitons and phonons: energy quanta associated with excitation and vibrations of crystals.

2.10 AMORPHOUS SOLIDS

Materials in which the molecule is the basic structural unit, and which have no regular structure that can be called crystalline, are classified as *amorphous*. Glass is a common amorphous material. Most glasses are essentially oxides of various elements. A good example is amorphous silica (SiO_2), which was discussed earlier.

Among the most important amorphous materials are the polymers. These molecular materials include what are commonly known as *plastics*

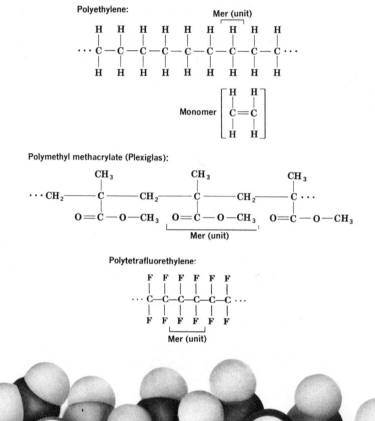

Polyethylene:

Mer (unit)

$$\cdots \overset{\overset{\displaystyle H}{|}}{\underset{\underset{\displaystyle H}{|}}{C}} - \overset{\overset{\displaystyle H}{|}}{\underset{\underset{\displaystyle H}{|}}{C}} - \overset{\overset{\displaystyle H}{|}}{\underset{\underset{\displaystyle H}{|}}{C}} - \overset{\overset{\displaystyle H}{|}}{\underset{\underset{\displaystyle H}{|}}{C}} - \overset{\overset{\displaystyle H}{|}}{\underset{\underset{\displaystyle H}{|}}{C}} - \overset{\overset{\displaystyle H}{|}}{\underset{\underset{\displaystyle H}{|}}{C}} - \overset{\overset{\displaystyle H}{|}}{\underset{\underset{\displaystyle H}{|}}{C}} - \overset{\overset{\displaystyle H}{|}}{\underset{\underset{\displaystyle H}{|}}{C}} - \overset{\overset{\displaystyle H}{|}}{\underset{\underset{\displaystyle H}{|}}{C}} \cdots$$

Monomer
$$\begin{bmatrix} \overset{\displaystyle H}{|} & \overset{\displaystyle H}{|} \\ C{=}C \\ \underset{\displaystyle H}{|} & \underset{\displaystyle H}{|} \end{bmatrix}$$

Polymethyl methacrylate (Plexiglas):

$$\cdots CH_2 - \underset{\underset{\displaystyle O{=}C-O-CH_3}{|}}{\overset{\overset{\displaystyle CH_3}{|}}{C}} - CH_2 - \underset{\underset{\displaystyle O{=}C-O-CH_3}{|}}{\overset{\overset{\displaystyle CH_3}{|}}{C}} - CH_2 - \underset{\underset{\displaystyle O{=}C-O-CH_3}{|}}{\overset{\overset{\displaystyle CH_3}{|}}{C}} \cdots$$

Mer (unit)

Polytetrafluorethylene:

$$\cdots \overset{\overset{\displaystyle F}{|}}{\underset{\underset{\displaystyle F}{|}}{C}} - \overset{\overset{\displaystyle F}{|}}{\underset{\underset{\displaystyle F}{|}}{C}} - \overset{\overset{\displaystyle F}{|}}{\underset{\underset{\displaystyle F}{|}}{C}} - \overset{\overset{\displaystyle F}{|}}{\underset{\underset{\displaystyle F}{|}}{C}} - \overset{\overset{\displaystyle F}{|}}{\underset{\underset{\displaystyle F}{|}}{C}} - \overset{\overset{\displaystyle F}{|}}{\underset{\underset{\displaystyle F}{|}}{C}} \cdots$$

Mer (unit)

Fig. 2.29 Chain molecules. Structural formulas for polyethylene, Plexiglas, and polytetrafluoroethylene (in which single dashes are electron-pair (covalent) bonds and double dashes are double bonds) are shown; restricted to the plane of the paper, these formulas can give only a partial picture of the actual spatial relations between atoms. Below is a pictorial representation of a part of the polyethylene molecule, illustrating actual spatial relations between carbon atoms (shaded) and hydrogen atoms. (The representation adapted from Hopkins, Bell Laboratories Record, Vol. XXXVI, No. 1, January 1958, p. 6 published by Bell Telephone Laboratories)

and *rubbers (elastomers)*. The relative weakness of the bonds between molecules is largely compensated for by increasing the size of the molecules so that they can be linked together in additional ways. In polymer formation molecules of ordinary size are combined into long chains and networks in which thousands of the original molecules may be involved. This process is called *polymerization,* and the original molecules are referred to as *monomers.*   Figures 2.29 and 2.30 illustrate the molecular structure of some typical polymers. Some natural polymers used by engineers are wood and textiles. The fibrous structure of wood is attributed to long molecules of cellulose.

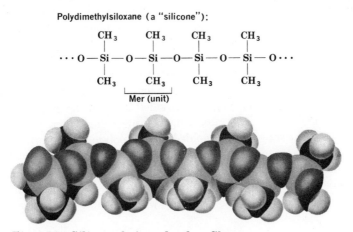

Fig. 2.30 *Silicone chain molecule. Shown are the structural formula for polydimethyl-siloxane, and the corresponding pictorial representation (courtesy Arthur S. LaPine and Company, Chicago, Ill.).*

The bonds formed within the macromolecules are interatomic covalent bonds, and the molecules are therefore strong within themselves.   If they are in the form of long chains, they may be linked together by becoming entangled, or by forming cross-links between atoms of adjacent chains. Cross-links, being interatomic bonds, are strong and give the entire structure a higher strength.   Additional strengthening results from increasing the surface areas of the molecules to provide correspondingly larger intermolecular bonds.   For example, if a long-chain molecule is held in place by many small secondary bonds, the force necessary to displace it may exceed the strength of the primary bonds within the molecule.   The strengthening of occasional molecules that results will cause a small overall increase in strength.

One important classification of polymers is that of *thermoplastic* and *thermosetting* types. Thermoplastic polymers are composed of linear or long-chain molecules. Application of heat weakens the intermolecular bonds by increasing thermal agitation of the molecules, and the material softens.   The atomic bonds within the molecules are not affected until much higher temperatures are reached.   These materials are therefore actually plastic at high temperatures and can be molded and remolded without damage.   They are variously called *thermoplasts, thermoplastic resins,* or simply plastics.

Thermosetting polymers are those in which a three-dimensional network has been built up through extensive cross-linking between the macromolecules.   The weak intermolecular bonds are replaced by stronger interatomic bonds, largely covalent in character.   This process is an irreversible chemical reaction, and the entire structure becomes essentially a single molecule.   After polymerization is complete, the material cannot be softened by heat.   Instead, at sufficiently high temperatures it will begin to disintegrate as activation energy is provided to break the interatomic bonds within the molecule.   Thermosetting polymers are therefore plastic only in the sense that they can be molded during polymerization.

The reason that some polymers form long-chain molecules only, without cross-linking, is that their covalent bonds are all used up, or saturated, as monomers are added to the end of each molecule.   If side bonds are left open (unsaturated), growth can take place in all directions to form a network.

2.11   AGGREGATES

Few engineering materials are purely crystalline or amorphous in character.   The vast majority are built up of aggregates of particles that may be either amorphous or crystalline in themselves.   Plastics, for example, are made with fillers of all kinds: carbon black, asbestos, mica, chopped cotton fibers, glass fibers.   The particles of filler are embedded in a matrix of polymer.   The characteristics of the *polymer* are referred to in describing the plastic as amorphous or crystalline although the filler particles may also be of either type.

If a solid is built up of an aggregate of small crystals, it is called a *polycrystalline* material.   Metals are usually of this form, as are crystallized polymers and many minerals.   The properties of polycrystalline materials depend upon the individual properties of the crystals, which in turn depend on their structures, and upon how they are put together—the state of aggregation.

Polycrystalline materials are often considered, for the sake of simplicity, as *isotropic*, or having the same properties in all directions.   This is true only if the individual crystals are oriented completely at random—and even then it is true only on a macroscopic scale.   Complete randomness is seldom, if ever, possible.   There are many conditions that influence crystals to assume certain "preferred" orientations.   Isotropy is an idealized condition that is only *approached*. It is approached quite closely, however, in many instances; consequently the assumption of isotropy is useful when used discriminately.

Concrete may be described as an aggregate of particles of sand and gravel embedded in an amorphous matrix of hardened Portland cement paste, which may also contain silicate and aluminate crystals. Ceramics may be partly amorphous and partly crystalline, with an amorphous framework consisting of silicates. Some ceramics are wholly crystalline and can be made in the form of single crystals (magnesium oxide (MgO), potassium chloride (KCl), and lithium fluoride (LiF)).* Wood is composed of long tubular cells that grow in the direction of the axis of the tree and form the grain. Here the aggregate is formed into a solid mass by the lignin cement. Wood is, of course, a definitely anisotropic material having radically different properties in the two principal directions—parallel to and across the grain.

When an aggregate of particles is formed, certain inherent imperfections are to be expected in actual materials: grain boundaries in polycrystalline materials such as metals; weak particles; voids formed during such operations as sintering of ceramics and plastics; cracks; inclusions of nonmetallic particles in metals; and knots or checks in wood.

The role of imperfections in the behavior of engineering materials is vital. Many of the most important material properties depend largely on the distribution of different types of imperfections. These are called *structure-sensitive* properties, although sometimes the term *defect-sensitive* is used. They include such properties as mechanical strength, crystal growth, magnetic hysteresis, dielectric strength, and conduction in semiconductors. The effect of imperfections on the structure-sensitive properties may be beneficial or detrimental, depending on the circumstances. An analogous situation is that of friction, which can be very damaging to bearings and other rubbing surfaces in machines, but is absolutely necessary between wheels and roadways if any traction is to be obtained. Carbon steel is an example of a material whose properties are improved by imperfections. The interstitial carbon atoms, which may be thought of as imperfections in the cubic crystal structure of iron, add tremendously to its strength. On the other hand, minute holes left in a sheet of plastic film by a sintering process will greatly decrease the dielectric strength of the film. In both examples the effect is far out of proportion to the space occupied by the imperfections.

Some properties of materials, such as stiffness, density, and electrical conductivity, depend on the defects present only in proportion to their

---

* Parker, Earl R., "Modern Concepts of Flow and Fracture" (1957 Edward de Mille Campbell Memorial Lecture) *Transactions* Am. Soc. Metals **50**, 100 (1958).

numbers.   The stiffness of a piece of steel, for example, is not appreciably affected by small numbers of imperfections.   Even the addition of alloying elements to a metal changes its stiffness only in proportion to the amounts added.   Structure-insensitive properties are therefore more easily controlled than those that are structure-sensitive.

BIBLIOGRAPHY

Steiner, L. E., and Campbell, J. A., *General Chemistry*, The Macmillan Company, New York, 1955.
  Chapters 12 through 15 discuss the periodic classification of the elements, the structure of the atom, and bonding.   General college chemistry for additional review.

Freudenthal, Alfred M., *The Inelastic Behavior of Engineering Materials and Structures*, John Wiley & Sons, Inc., New York, 1950.
  Chapters 1 and 2 present a somewhat more elaborate discussion of the area covered in Chapter 2 of this text.

Sinnott, Maurice J., *The Solid State for Engineers*, John Wiley & Sons, Inc., New York, 1958; Zwikker, C., *Physical Properties of Solid Materials*, Interscience Publishers, Inc., New York, 1954.
  For the student who wishes to continue his study of the structure of solids.

PROBLEMS

2.1   Without referring to the text tell how many protons, neutrons, and planetary electrons you would expect to find in neutral atoms of boron ($Z = 5$, atomic wt = 10.82); carbon ($Z = 6$, atomic wt = 12.010); titanium ($Z = 22$, atomic wt = 47.9); germanium ($Z = 32$, atomic wt = 72.60).

2.2   What is the maximum number of electrons that can occupy the M shell (a) if the N shell is the valence shell, (b) if the M shell is the valence shell?

2.3   Write the electron shell structure designations (e.g., sodium: $1\ s^2; 2\ s^2, 2\ p^6; 3\ s^1$) for the following elements: nitrogen, sulfur, scandium, arsenic, silver.

2.4   How many valence electrons does each of the following designated elements have?

$1\ s^2; 2\ s^2, 2\ p^4$
$1\ s^2; 2\ s^2, 2\ p^6; 3\ s^2, 3\ p^5$
$1\ s^2; 2\ s^2, 2\ p^6; 3\ s^2, 3\ p^6, 3\ d^3; 4\ s^2$
$1\ s^2; 2\ s^2, 2\ p^6; 3\ s^2, 3\ p^6, 3\ d^{10}; 4\ s^2, 4\ p^6$
$1\ s^2; 2\ s^2, 2\ p^6; 3\ s^2, 3\ p^6, 3\ d^{10}; 4\ s^2, 4\ p^6, 4\ d^{10}; 5\ s^2, 5\ p^2.$

2.5 Indicate which of the following designated elements should have similar physical and chemical properties:

$1\ s^2$

$1\ s^2;\ 2\ s^2$

$1\ s^2;\ 2\ s^2,\ 2\ p^2$

$1\ s^2;\ 2\ s^2,\ 2\ p^5$

$1\ s^2;\ 2\ s^2,\ 2\ p^6;\ 3\ s^2$

$1\ s^2;\ 2\ s^2,\ 2\ p^6;\ 3\ s^2,\ 3\ p^3$

$1\ s^2;\ 2\ s^2,\ 2\ p^6;\ 3\ s^2,\ 3\ p^6;\ 4\ s^2$

$1\ s^2;\ 2\ s^2,\ 2\ p^6;\ 3\ s^2,\ 3\ p^6,\ 3\ d^5;\ 4\ s^1$

2.6 An atom of a certain element has 3 electrons in the p subshell of its outermost main shell, which is the N shell. How many valence electrons does this element have?

2.7 Compute in coulombs the maximum negative charge on a chlorine ion, a bismuth ion, and a silicon ion.

2.8 How many covalent bonds can normally be formed between atoms of germanium? Between atoms of iodine? Between atoms of sulfur?

2.9 Develop a new form of the equation for the force between two atoms or molecules (Eq. 2.1), in which the constants are r_0, A, M, and N. Determine from this equation expressions for the following properties of the force curve: (a) its slope at $r = r_0$ (the equilibrium point); (b) the spacing, r_1, for which the force is maximum (F_{max}); (c) the value of F_{max}.

2.10 Evaluate the expressions derived in Problem 2.9 for the following cases: (a) $M = 2$, $N = 6$, $r_0 = 4$ Å, $A = 1$ unit. (b) $M = 2$, $N = 11$, $r_0 = 1$ Å, $A = 1$ unit.

2.11 Develop a new form of the equation for the potential energy of a pair of atoms or molecules (Eq. 2.2), in which the constants are r_0, a, m, and n. Determine from this equation expressions for the following properties of the energy curve: (a) the potential energy at $r = r_0(U_b)$; (b) the spacing, r_1, at the point of inflection.

2.12 Evaluate the expressions described in Problem 2.11 for the following cases: (a) $m = 1$, $n = 5$, $r_0 = 4$ Å, $a = 1$ unit; (b) $m = 1$, $n = 10$, $r_0 = 1$ Å, $a = 1$ unit.

2.13 Plot interatomic force and energy curves for cases (a) and (b) of Problems 2.10 and 2.12.

2.14 How might the energy required to separate two atoms to an infinite spacing be determined graphically from the force curve (F vs r)?

2.15 Calculate the value of Boltzmann's constant, k, in electron volts per °K. Using this value, verify the value of $kT \approx \frac{1}{40}$ ev at room temperature.

2.16 The activation energy for a process is 1.8 ev per atom. Plot the variation of Φ/A with temperature, T, in the neighborhood of 1000°F. (Use the value of k determined in Problem 2.15.)

2.17 Show that in Eq. 2.4 if E_a is in cal/mole of substance, Boltzmann's constant must be replaced by R, the universal gas constant.

2.18 The activation energy for a process is 55,000 cal/mole. If the rate is known at 400°C, how much should the temperature be raised to double this rate?

2.19 Construct a graph showing $\log(\Phi/A)$ vs $1/T$ for the Arrhenius equation, assuming $E_a = 2$ ev per atom, and including the range of temperatures from 500 to 1000°K. (Use the value of k determined in Problem 2.15.)

2.20 Make careful sketches showing planes represented by the following indices:
(a) (010), (101), (011), (1$\bar{1}$0), ($\bar{1}$10), ($\bar{1}$01), (01$\bar{1}$)
(b) (111), (1$\bar{1}$1), (11$\bar{1}$), (1$\bar{1}\bar{1}$)
(c) (221), (123), (124)
(d) (10$\bar{1}$0), (01$\bar{1}$0), ($\bar{1}$100) (hexagonal indices)
(e) (10$\bar{1}$2), (11$\bar{2}$1) (hexagonal indices).

2.21 Find the Miller indices of all the diagonal planes of a cubic crystal (i.e., planes containing diagonally opposite edges of the cube).

2.22 Find the Miller indices of all octahedral planes in a cubic crystal.

2.23 Find the indices of the vertical planes forming the sides of the unit cell in the hexagonal close-packed structure.

2.24 Make careful sketches showing lines represented by the following indices: [1$\bar{1}$1], [$\bar{1}$10], [121], [11$\bar{2}$].

2.25 Find the direction indices of the following lines in a cubic crystal:
(a) All edges of the cube
(b) The diagonals of all faces of the cube
(c) The body diagonals of the cube.

2.26 Three spheres of diameter d are arranged in a triangle, touching each other. Show that the diameter of the largest sphere that will fit into the space between the three given spheres is 0.155 d.

2.27 Four spheres of diameter d are arranged in square, touching each other. Show that the diameter of the largest sphere that will fit into the space between them is 0.414 d.

2.28 Determine which of the metalloids have radius ratios less than 0.414 when compared with (a) iron, (b) titanium, (c) hafnium, (d) cesium.

2.29 Without referring to the text, name some of the imperfections found in crystals.

2.30 Without referring to the text, distinguish between thermoplastic and thermosetting polymers.

PART TWO

MECHANICAL
BEHAVIOR

CHAPTER 3

STATIC
TENSION

Mechanical strength is a basic property of all solid materials. Every engineering structure or device imposes certain requirements of mechanical strength on the material to be used: structures designed to sustain loads must have the necessary mechanical strength before they can serve any other function; in devices whose primary purpose is nonmechanical, the members are always subjected to loads, which are often a critical factor in design. Members must always support their own weights, for example, and if accelerations are involved, there will be inertia forces. Sufficient strength can sometimes be assumed if a member is large enough to satisfy the requirements of its primary purpose, or if it is made according to past experience without any careful consideration of its strength. Situations in which this assumption is safe become rarer as service requirements become more and more exacting. High accelerations, violent vibrations and shock, or extremes of heat and cold all emphasize the importance of mechanical strength. The electronic equipment in a rocket is a prime example; while its primary purpose may be far from mechanical, the loads imposed by its conditions of use make the mechanical properties of the material of basic concern.

In its broadest sense mechanical strength may be defined as the ability to sustain loads without undue distortion or failure. Applied to a member of a structure, it depends on two major factors: *the strength inherent in the material itself*, and *the way in which this strength is utilized*, through the size and shape of the member and the manner in which it is loaded. We are mainly concerned with the strength inherent in materials, as measured by their *mechanical properties*. How these properties are utilized is the subject of *mechanics of materials*. The two subjects are, however, inseparably tied together in that mechanical properties are often affected by such factors as manner of loading, sizes and shapes of members, and previous treatment.

Mechanical properties are usually expressed in terms of *unit* values, such as load per unit area or energy per unit volume, so that they may be applied directly to design problems. Some, however, are given in terms of the value for a standard specimen, or in numbers on an arbitrary scale. These properties cannot be applied directly to design but are used in other ways, such as comparison of materials.

There are good reasons for beginning our study of fundamental mechanical properties of materials with their behavior under simple static tension. Members of engineering structures and devices are often subjected to steady axial loads in tension. Moreover, the response of materials to other types of loading can sometimes be explained or predicted on the basis of their behavior in simple tension. And this behavior is among the easiest to study experimentally.

ELASTICITY

3.1 MECHANISMS OF ELASTIC ACTION

When a solid bar is loaded axially in tension, it elongates as the load increases. The mechanism by which elongation takes place in the solid material can usually be pictured as a simple separation of its atoms in the direction of loading. The atoms are displaced from their normal equilibrium positions just enough to develop attractive forces between them which will balance the applied load (compare Fig. 2.3). This simplified picture can be applied to the initial deformation of many materials, such as crystalline materials or glasses. In materials having more complex atomic arrangements, other mechanisms are involved (for example, the relative displacements of molecules in plastics).

So long as the only mechanism involved is simple separation of the atoms by relatively small amounts, release of the applied force will allow the atoms to return to their normal equilibrium positions. The axially-loaded bar will return to its original size and shape, and the deformation is said to be *elastic*. Elastic action is any action under which no part of the deformation remains after removal of the load, i.e., elastic deformation is reversible.

Stress and Strain

Two related phenomena are involved in elastic action in simple tension. The first is an internal distributed force, or *stress*, made up of the sum total of all the elementary interatomic forces.   On any plane at right angles to the axis of the bar the stress is uniformly distributed and normal to the plane—from a macroscopic point of view.   Since this stress must balance the applied load, we have $\sigma A = P$, or

$$\sigma = \frac{P}{A},\tag{3.1}$$

where σ is the *normal stress*, P the load, and A the area of the right section. The units of stress are usually pounds per square inch (psi), or *kips* per square inch (1 kip = 1000 lb).   In technical publications metric units are becoming more common, and it is therefore well to remember the conversion factors from metric to English units.   For stress, we have

$$\sigma(\text{psi}) = 14.22 \times \sigma(\text{kg/cm}^2)*$$
$$= 14.50 \times 10^{-6} \times \sigma(\text{dynes/cm}^2).$$

The second phenomenon involved in elastic action is a deformation of all parts of the bar.   If the bar is prismatic, it will elongate uniformly along its length.   The elongation per unit length is called the *strain*. Since the total elongation is the sum of the elongations of the parts, we have $\delta = \epsilon l$, or

$$\epsilon = \frac{\delta}{l},\tag{3.2}$$

in which ϵ is the strain, δ the total elongation, and l the original length of the bar.   Since strain is the ratio of the two lengths, it is dimensionless and is the same whether expressed as in./in. or cm/cm.

As the atoms are pulled farther apart in the direction of the applied force, they are simultaneously pulled in laterally.   Figure 3.1 illustrates schematically the cause of this lateral contraction.   The close-packed crystal structure (a) has rows in three directions containing atoms at their normal equilibrium spacing.   These are the three directions in which the atomic bonds are the strongest, and for simplicity the load is assumed to be applied along one of them.   Consider a group of four atoms m, n, p, q,

---

* As an aid to remembering that the conversion factor is approximately 14, note that 1 atmosphere (standard atmospheric pressure), which is about 14 psi, is also about 1 kg/cm².

shown isolated at (b): if the distance *mn* were lengthened by external tension while *pq* remained the same, bonds *mp*, *mq*, *np*, and *nq* would all be lengthened as shown.   Since these bonds were originally at their normal length, the result would be to set up attractive forces between *p* and *q*

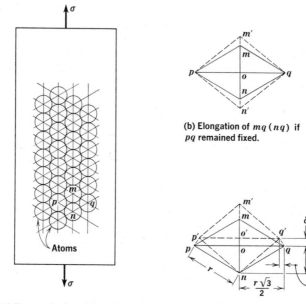

(b) Elongation of *mq* (*nq*) if *pq* remained fixed.

(a) Close-packed crystal structure in material subject to tensile stress.

(c) Contraction of *pq* when diagonal bond length, *r*, remains fixed.

Fig. 3.1   Schematic demonstration of lateral contraction accompanying longitudinal elongation of a crystal.

that would tend to pull them closer together.   Hence, if the bar is free to contract laterally, it will do so, allowing the four diagonal distances to remain the same.   This is what actually happens.   The figure *mnpq* is simply distorted, with *mn* elongating and *pq* contracting correspondingly.

The ratio between unit lateral contraction, or lateral strain, and longitudinal strain is called *Poisson's ratio*.   It varies with different materials, and for nonporous solids is usually between $\frac{1}{4}$ and $\frac{1}{2}$.   For the foregoing illustration it is $\frac{1}{3}$, computed geometrically as follows, using Fig. 3.1c. Holding atom *n* fixed, as a reference, we distort *mnpq* as shown.   If we consider the triangle *noq* and let δ_x be the longitudinal displacement of *q*, the longitudinal strain is

$$\epsilon_x = \frac{\delta_x}{on}.$$

Since nq remains constant, point q moves, for small displacements, in a direction perpendicular to nq, and the lateral component of this displacement is δ_y. The small triangle whose legs are δ_x and δ_y is a 30-60 right triangle, so that $\delta_y = \dfrac{\delta_x}{\sqrt{3}}$. Now the lateral strain is

$$|\epsilon_y| = \frac{\delta_y}{oq} = \frac{\delta_x/\sqrt{3}}{on\sqrt{3}} = \frac{1}{3}\frac{\delta_x}{on} = \frac{1}{3}\epsilon_x.$$

Hence Poisson's ratio for this idealized case is $\frac{1}{3}$. In general the relation between lateral and longitudinal strain can be written

$$\epsilon_y = -\mu\epsilon_x. \tag{3.3}$$

The minus sign indicates that ϵ_y is a contraction where ϵ_x is an elongation, and vice versa. Most metals are found to have values of μ close to $\frac{1}{3}$, an indication that the idealized case illustrated above represents the true situation closely.

The effect of tensile force on the volume of the material can now be investigated. Consider an element of volume whose length in the direction of the load is l, and whose lateral dimensions are a and b. After loading the length is increased by an amount $\delta = \epsilon_x l$, and the lateral dimensions are shortened by the amounts $-\mu\epsilon_x a$ and $-\mu\epsilon_x b$. The new volume is then

$$
\begin{aligned}
V_1 &= (l + \epsilon_x l)(a - \mu\epsilon_x a)(b - \mu\epsilon_x b) \\
&= lab(1 + \epsilon_x)(1 - \mu\epsilon_x)^2 \\
&= V[1 + \epsilon_x(1 - 2\mu) + \epsilon_x^2(\mu^2 - 2\mu) + \mu^2\epsilon_x^3],
\end{aligned}
$$

in which V is the original volume (lab). If ϵ_x is small, say 0.01 or less, as is usually true, we can neglect ϵ_x^2 and ϵ_x^3 in comparison with ϵ_x. The unit change in volume is then

$$\frac{\Delta V}{V} = \frac{V_1 - V}{V} = \epsilon_x(1 - 2\mu), \tag{3.4}$$

which is always positive so long as $\mu < \frac{1}{2}$, an indication that an increase in volume or *dilatation* accompanies elongation. For the usual case where $\mu \approx \frac{1}{3}$, $\Delta V/V = \epsilon_x/3$. If for any reason μ approaches $\frac{1}{2}$, the lateral contraction will approach half the axial elongation and no volume change will accompany tensile loading.

Relations between Stress and Strain

To study the elastic behavior of a material in static tension, a bar of the material is loaded slowly and simultaneous readings of load and elongation taken at regular intervals. These readings are converted to stress and strain and plotted as shown in Fig. 3.2. The resulting curve, called a *stress-strain diagram,* is usually linear (a), although it may sometimes be nonlinear (b).   The essential feature is that the curve return to the origin upon unloading.

Many engineering materials do exhibit a linear relation between elastic stress and strain, expressed by Hooke's law

$$\sigma = E\epsilon, \tag{3.5}$$

in which E is the *modulus of elasticity,* a measure of the stiffness of the material.   From Fig. 3.2a, in which OA represents Hooke's law graphically,

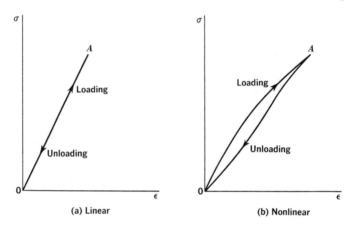

Fig. 3.2   Elastic stress-strain diagrams.

it is seen that E is the slope of this line.   For most engineering materials E is a very large number (e.g., 10,000,000 psi for aluminum).

EXAMPLE 3.1

A solid cylindrical steel bar is 48 in. long, and the diameter of its circular cross-section is 2 in.   If an axial tensile load of 75,000 lb is applied, determine the total change in length, diameter, and volume.   Assume elastic behavior.

Solution: Given $d = 2$ in., $l = 48$ in., $P = 75,000$ lb,

$$A = \frac{\pi d^2}{4} = 3.14 \text{ in.}^2,$$

whence

$$\sigma = P/A = 23,900 \text{ psi.}$$

From Table A.1 (Appendix A), $E = 30 \times 10^6$ psi.   Substituting in Eq. 3.5, we get

$$\epsilon_x = \sigma/E = 0.000797.$$

The change in length,

$$\delta = \epsilon_x l = +0.0382 \text{ in. (increase).}$$

Substituting in Eq. 3.3, using $\mu = 0.3$, we get

$$\epsilon_y = -\mu\epsilon_x = -(0.3)(0.000797)$$
$$= -0.000239.$$

The change in diameter, $\Delta d = \epsilon_y d = -0.000478$ in. (decrease). Substituting in Eq. 3.4, we get

$$\Delta V/V = \epsilon_x(1 - 2\ \mu) = (0.000797)(0.4)$$
$$= 0.000319.$$

But

$$V = Al = 150.8 \text{ in.}^3$$

Therefore

$$\Delta V = (0.000319)(150.8)$$
$$= +0.0480 \text{ in.}^3 \text{ (increase).}$$

To illustrate the extent of ordinary elastic action we shall use the curve of Fig. 3.3, which is similar to that of Fig. 2.3, in which interatomic force

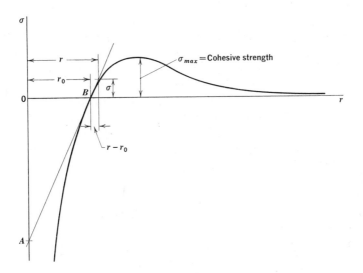

Fig. 3.3   Variation of bond stress with atomic spacing.

is plotted against atomic spacing. Instead of representing the *force* between two atoms, however, the vertical scale represents the *intensity* of that force in pounds per square inch, or *stress*. The horizontal scale still represents atomic spacing, r. On this diagram the value of E can be represented graphically. Line BA is tangent to the curve at B, the equilibrium (zero stress) point. For small atomic displacements we may assume that this line practically coincides with the curve and its slope can be expressed approximately by $\sigma/(r - r_0)$, where σ and r are corresponding values of stress and atomic spacing.

The distance OA is equal to r_0 multiplied by this slope:

$$OA = r_0 \left(\frac{\sigma}{r - r_0} \right) = \frac{\sigma}{\left(\dfrac{r - r_0}{r_0} \right)}.$$

Since $(r - r_0)/r_0$ represents the strain corresponding to stress σ, we see that

$$OA = \frac{\sigma}{\epsilon} = E$$

or that *distance OA is equal in magnitude to the modulus of elasticity.* This fact serves to establish a scale for the vertical stress axis so that the following comparisons can be made.

First we notice that the stress corresponding to the cohesive force between atoms, σ_{max}, is of nearly the same order of magnitude as E. In contrast, *elastic action* in most materials terminates by yielding or rupture at stresses as low as one-thousandth of the modulus of elasticity of the material. As an example, low-carbon steel has an elastic strength of roughly 30,000 psi, while E is 30,000,000 psi. Thus the theoretical cohesive strength is probably 100 to 1000 times as great as the maximum elastic stress. The elastic range is clearly limited to a very minute part of the curve of Fig. 3.3. The assumption that the curve coincides with its tangent in this range is therefore accurate well within normal requirements.

The fact that the elastic strength of a material is seldom if ever anywhere near its theoretical cohesive strength is attributable to the imperfections present. Because of the highly localized effects of the imperfections, the simultaneous rupture of all the bonds between two planes of atoms is never encountered. The overall average stress nearly always remains relatively low in the elastic range. Because it depends on the structure of the material—particularly its imperfections—elastic strength is said to be *structure-sensitive.*

Complex Mechanisms

This basic mechanism of elastic action applies to a large group of engineering materials, of which crystalline materials are typical. In some materials, however, the mechanism is much more complex than a simple separation of the atoms. Polymers provide examples of other mechanisms. Thermoplastic polymers, being composed of long-chain molecules, deform elastically by a combination of displacements of atoms and molecules. Intertwining of the chains causes some of the intermolecular bonds to be shortened and others to be lengthened, and brings into play the interatomic bonds within the chains.

Rubber molecules are especially interesting. They are produced by combining isoprene units (monomers) into chains containing large numbers of such units (usually several thousand). Each chain has the chemical composition and structure shown in Fig. 3.4. The single dashes represent

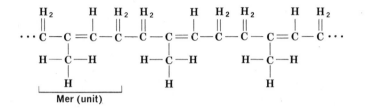

Fig. 3.4 Structural formula of a rubber molecule, illustrating chemical composition and structure. Because representation is restricted to a plane, only a partial picture of actual spatial relations is possible.

covalent bonds formed by two atoms sharing one pair of electrons. The groups of atoms can rotate freely around such a bond, e.g., any of the C—C bonds between monomers. As a result the molecules always tend to form more-or-less coiled configurations. In relaxed rubber thermal agitation of the molecules produces an infinite variety of these configurations throughout the material. In this random distribution the most probable shapes are those in which the molecules are coiled to a certain extent. A straight configuration is the least probable, and hence very few molecules are straight. When the material is stretched, the first effect is to straighten the coils. This process does not appreciably change the energy of the molecules since the energies of all configurations are about the same. However, because straight configurations are less probable, the process does require work. Thermodynamically, producing preferential orientations of the molecules involves a decrease in the entropy of the system.*

As the rubber is stretched more and more, the effect of uncoiling becomes less important as the molecules become straight. Entangling of the molecules begins to bring into play other forces, which increase as stretching continues. An elastic stress-strain curve of the type shown in Fig. 3.5 results, a striking example of elastic behavior that does not follow Hooke's law—a nonlinear elasticity. Other materials exhibiting this characteristic

---

* Entropy is a thermodynamic property which is related to the statistical distribution of energies in a system. The greater the disorder in a system, the higher its entropy.

relation between stress and strain include fibers like wool, in which the chain molecules have a crumpled form in the relaxed state.

3.2   LINEAR ELASTIC PROPERTIES

The elastic properties of a material in static tension include *stiffness*, *elastic strength*, and *resilience*.   If the material follows Hooke's law, i.e., has a linear stress-strain relation (Fig. 3.6), its stiffness is measured by E,

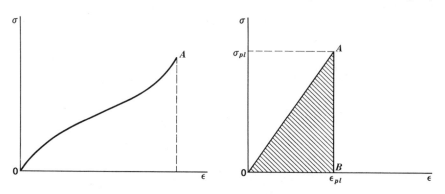

Fig.   3.5   Elastic stress-strain curve for rubber.

Fig.   3.6   Linear elastic stress-strain relation.

found geometrically from the stress-strain diagram by measuring the slope of the straight line, since $E = \sigma/\epsilon$. (The related property, *Poisson's ratio*, μ, is measured by observing the lateral contraction in tension.)   Table 3.1 compares stiffnesses of several important engineering materials.

Table 3.1   Comparative Stiffnesses of Several Engineering Materials

MATERIAL	MODULUS OF ELASTICITY, E, psi
Osmium and tungsten carbide	80,000,000
Molybdenum	42,000,000
Steel	30,000,000
Aluminum	10,000,000
Lead and carbon	2,000,000
Acrylics[a]	400,000

[a] Plexiglas and Lucite, for example.

Elastic strength is determined from the highest stress at which the behavior of the material remains elastic.   In most materials the proportionality between stress and strain holds throughout almost the entire range of elastic action.   Elastic strength can therefore usually be measured as the stress marking the end of this proportionality, the *proportional limit*, σ_{pl}.   The proportional limit is found by plotting a stress-strain diagram and determining the point at which the first deviation from linearity is noticeable.   This deviation is more-or-less gradual (Art. 3.7), and the point at which it is first noticeable depends to some extent on the accuracy of observation and the care with which the diagram is plotted (Art. 3.17).

Another common measure of elastic strength is yield strength, which will be discussed later (Art. 3.12) since its determination depends on the beginning of *inelastic* action.

Elastic resilience is the capacity of a material to absorb energy elastically. When a bar is elongated by a tensile force, the energy it absorbs comes directly from the work done by the applied forces.   So long as the deformation is both elastic and linear this energy is stored in the material in a recoverable form as *strain energy*.   The strain energy may therefore be determined from the work done by the applied force,

$$U = \int_0^\delta P(x)\, dx, \tag{3.6}$$

where $P(x)$ is the force as a function of elongation x.   Figure 3.7 illustrates the linear case.

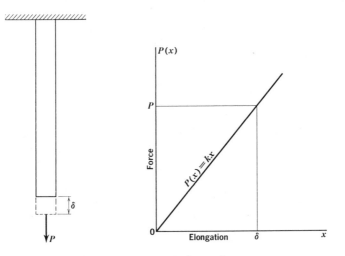

Fig. 3.7   *Variation of force with elongation for a linear elastic bar.*

To find the strain energy per unit volume we note that $P(x) = \sigma A$, and $x = \epsilon l$.   Equation 3.6 then becomes

$$U = Al \int_0^{\epsilon_1} \sigma\, d\epsilon,$$

where $\epsilon_1 = \delta/l$, and we can divide by the volume Al to obtain

$$u = \int_0^{\epsilon_1} \sigma d\epsilon. \tag{3.7}$$

Thus the strain energy per unit volume, u, is equal to the area under the stress-strain diagram, from zero strain to strain ϵ_1. For the linear case $\sigma = E\epsilon$ (Eq. 3.5), and

$$u = E \int_0^{\epsilon_1} \epsilon d\epsilon = \frac{E\epsilon_1^2}{2}. \tag{3.7a}$$

Alternative expressions which can be derived are

$$u = \frac{\sigma\epsilon}{2} \text{ and } u = \frac{\sigma^2}{2E}. \tag{3.7b}$$

The *modulus of resilience* is defined as the strain energy absorbed per unit volume when the material is stressed to its proportional limit, and is denoted by u_r. Substituting σ_{pl} and ϵ_{pl} in Eq. 3.7b we have

$$u_r = \frac{\sigma_{pl}\epsilon_{pl}}{2} = \frac{\sigma_{pl}^2}{2E}. \tag{3.8}$$

Both are useful forms. The shaded area OAB in Fig. 3.6 is numerically equal to u_r. For a given value of E the modulus of resilience increases with the square of the proportional limit stress. On the other hand, for a given σ_{pl}, u_r decreases with increasing stiffness.

Typical values of σ_{pl} and u_r are shown in Table 3.2 for some important engineering materials.

Table 3.2   Typical Elastic Properties of Engineering Materials

MATERIAL	PROPORTIONAL LIMIT,[a] σ_{pl}, psi	MODULUS OF RESILIENCE, u_r, in.-lb/in.^{3}
Alloy steel[b]	210,000	735
Aluminum alloy[c]	60,000	180
Structural steel[d]	35,000	20
Acrylics[e]	2,000	4

[a] Determined by conventional testing methods.
[b] Manganese-silicon steel.
[c] Alloy 7075-T6 (heat-treated).
[d] C1020 hot-rolled.
[e] Plexiglas, Lucite.

3.3   NONLINEAR ELASTIC PROPERTIES

The stiffness of a material that does not follow Hooke's law is clearly not constant, but varies with stress. Sometimes the average stiffness is

the best measure of this quantity at a given stress. It is given by the
secant modulus,

$$E_{sec} = \left[\frac{\sigma}{\epsilon}\right]_{\sigma=\sigma_A}, \qquad (3.9)$$

and represents the average slope of the curve or the slope of the secant,
illustrated by line OA in Fig. 3.8. Obviously the value obtained for the

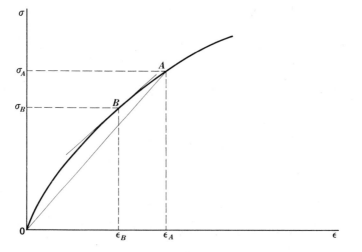

Fig. 3.8   Nonlinear elastic curve, illustrating secant modulus and tangent modulus.

secant modulus depends on the location of A, which is usually specified in
terms of the stress at A.

If the stiffness associated with a small increase in load is wanted, the
instantaneous stiffness can be found from the slope of the tangent to the
curve at that point. This slope is called the *tangent modulus*

$$E_t = \left[\frac{d\sigma}{d\epsilon}\right]_{\sigma=\sigma_B} \qquad (3.10)$$

and is illustrated at point B in Fig. 3.8. As for the secant modulus, the
stress at point B must be specified.

The strain energy per unit volume stored in a nonlinear elastic material is
given by Eq. 3.7, which is not restricted to the linear case; it is therefore
equal to the area under the stress-strain diagram. The modulus of resilience, however, is no longer applicable because a proportional limit does
not exist in the nonlinear case.

Even though the material is elastic, the strain energy stored is not always
fully recoverable. Figure 3.9 is a typical stress-strain diagram for rubber,

a nonlinear elastic material. Curve 1 represents loading from O to A. The area between it and the strain axis gives the strain energy stored per unit volume when the rubber is stretched. When the rubber is unloaded, the resulting curve is usually somewhat lower than the loading curve (curve 2, Fig. 3.9), and the area under it is smaller than for loading. The

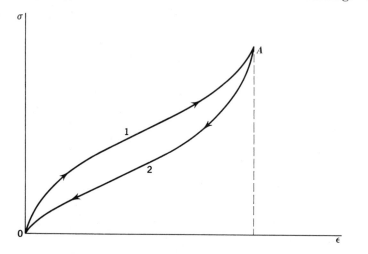

Fig. 3.9 Stress-strain diagram for rubber, showing loading and unloading curves.

strain energy recovered is therefore less than that put into the material originally. Some energy has been lost in the form of internal friction in the rubber and is represented by the area between the two curves. This is a good example of mechanical hysteresis and accounts for the high damping capacity of rubber when used as supports for vibrating machinery.

The term *resilience* denotes the ratio between the recoverable energy and the energy put into the material during the deformation. It is measured by the ratio between the area under curve 2 to that under curve 1, expressed as a per cent. A low resilience is desirable for good damping, and a high resilience for low internal heat generation (see Chapter 7). Resilience must not be confused with *modulus of resilience*.

BEYOND THE ELASTIC RANGE

3.4 INELASTIC ACTION

As the tension on a solid bar increases and the atoms are pulled farther apart, a point is reached at which other things begin to happen within the material, marking the end of the elastic range. Elongation is no longer a simple separation of atoms; irrecoverable structural changes take place, and the behavior is said to be *inelastic*.   There are two possible ways for the elastic range to end: by *fracture* or by *yielding*.

Fracture

Fracture is initiated by some imperfection, such as a microscopic crack, which, like a notch, causes the stress at that point to rise to a high value.* If this high local value equals the cohesive strength of the material (Fig. 3.3), the atomic bonds in that region will be broken.   As they are broken the imperfection, originally localized at a point, spreads across the bar, causing complete fracture almost instantaneously.   If this should happen while the overall deformation is still elastic, the material would be called *perfectly brittle*.   Glass, some ionic crystals, oxides, and cast iron approach this condition.   All are brittle, although there is always some small but finite yielding just before fracture.

The observed fracture strength of a brittle material depends largely on the magnitudes of the stress concentrations at imperfections.   These in turn depend on the size and orientation of the imperfections and are consequently distributed at random through the material.   The imperfection that causes fracture in one member, therefore, will in general differ from that in another member, and the two members will have different observed strengths.   Thus there actually is no single value of fracture strength for a brittle material.   Instead fracture strength must be conceived of as a statistical distribution of values for individual specimens.

Because they are so strongly influenced by imperfections, the distributions of fracture strengths show considerable scatter.   The best single value is an average, such as the arithmetic mean or the median of a set of observed values.   Even so it should be remembered that approximately half the observed strengths are *less* than this average.   A more complete specification is sometimes desirable, in terms of the statistical properties of the distribution.   This is treated in more detail in Art. 9.4 in connection with fatigue, which also involves statistical distributions.

A further consequence of dependence of fracture strength on random distribution of imperfections in the material is the variation of strength with size in members made of brittle materials.   If we compare a large and a small member of the same material, the large one, having a larger distribution of imperfections, may be expected to have more extreme values in its distribution.   Therefore there is a higher probability of the large member containing large flaws.   Consequently large members, on the

---

* For a discussion of stress concentrations, see any elementary text on mechanics of materials.

average, have lower strengths than small ones. In many brittle materials the variation of strength with size is large. This fact should always be kept in mind when the results of laboratory tests on small specimens are used to predict strengths of full-sized members.

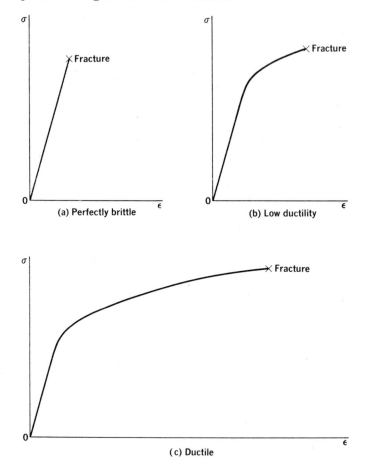

Fig. 3.10   Typical stress-strain diagrams for three classes of materials. A material such as (b) is frequently classed as brittle, since its ductility is so much less than that of material (c).

Yielding

Yielding involves the possibility that some of the atoms or molecules in the material will, under the distortion produced by tension, slip to new equilibrium positions at which they can form new bonds, thus permitting an elongation in excess of that produced by the simple elastic separation of atoms.   If the atoms form new bonds in their new positions, the material is not weakened, but there is no tendency for the atoms to return to their original positions.   Thus elongation is inelastic or irrecoverable.   Such behavior is also called *plastic deformation,* and the material is said to be *ductile.*

If tension is increased slowly and simultaneous readings of load and elongation are continued, a stress-strain diagram may be plotted showing both elastic and inelastic ranges.   Figure 3.10a shows a typical diagram for a perfectly brittle material, which, according to the above definition, contains only an elastic range.   The material in Fig. 3.10c is ductile, while that in (b) is intermediate and may be classed as either brittle or of low ductility.

3.5 YIELDING IN CRYSTALS

The most common mechanism of yielding in crystalline materials is *slip,* in which two planes of atoms slip past each other, causing one whole section of the crystal to shift relative to another (Fig. 3.11).   Slip occurs most

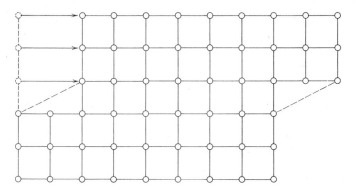

Fig. 3.11   Slip of one section past another in a crystal.   Total slip = 2 atomic distances.

easily on certain crystallographic planes, depending on the crystal structure.   Generally speaking the planes of easy slip are those in which the atoms are most closely spaced—those having the largest number of atoms per unit area.   That these planes are also the most widely separated accounts for the comparative ease of slip.   In face-centered cubic crystals, for example, the slip plane is the (111) or octahedral plane (*ACE* in Fig.

2.21b).   The *direction* of easy slip also depends on the crystal structure. It is usually along a line in the slip plane on which the atoms are most closely spaced.   If we again use the face-centered cubic crystals as an example, the direction of easy slip is [110] (the diagonals of the cube faces in Fig. 2.21b).

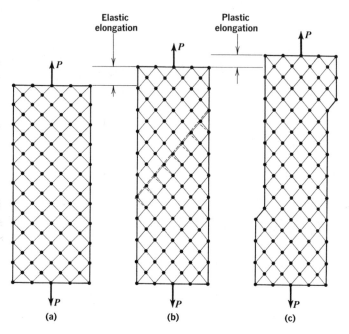

Fig. 3.12   Schematic representation of slip in a single crystal.

To illustrate the basic principles of slip in tension Fig. 3.12 shows a bar made from a single crystal; a simple cubic structure is chosen for simplicity.   The crystal is so oriented that the cubic planes, which are the closest-packed planes, make an angle of 45° with the axis of the bar.   With this orientation, because of the distribution of stress in the bar under simple tension, slip will take place along these atomic planes when the tension in the bar becomes great enough.

When an axial load, P, is applied, a normal stress, σ_x (Eq. 3.1) acts on any plane at right angles to the axis,

$$\sigma_x = \frac{P}{A},$$

where A is the area of the right section.   If another plane, whose normal is inclined by an angle ϕ to the axis, is considered, the stress will be smaller because the area of this plane is larger than A. If we call the area of the inclined plane A', it can be shown geometrically that for a prismatic bar $A' = A/\cos \phi$ (Fig. 3.13). Hence the stress on A' is equal to

$$\frac{P}{A'} = \frac{P}{A} \cos \phi = \sigma_x \cos \phi.$$

This stress, however, being parallel to P, is inclined to the plane of A' by the angle ϕ, and can be resolved into components perpendicular and parallel

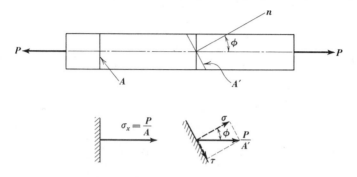

Fig. 3.13   Stresses in a bar in tension.

to the plane. The component perpendicular to the inclined plane, called the *normal stress*, is

$$\sigma = \frac{P}{A'} \cos \phi = \sigma_x \cos^2 \phi, \qquad (3.11)$$

while that parallel to it, called the *shearing stress*, is

$$\tau = \frac{P}{A'} \sin \phi = \sigma_x \sin \phi \cos \phi = \frac{\sigma_x}{2} \sin 2\phi. \qquad (3.12)$$

It is this shearing stress component that is responsible for slip between atomic planes. It can be seen that τ reaches its maximum value of $\frac{\sigma_x}{2}$ when $\sin 2\phi = 1$ or $\phi = 45°$. *In simple tension a maximum shearing stress equal to one-half the tensile stress always acts on any plane making 45° with the axis of applied stress.*

When the single crystal of Fig. 3.12 is placed in tension, the maximum shearing stress acts along the cubic planes of atoms. The effect of the shearing stress is to shift these planes of atoms relative to each other, as shown in Fig. 3.12b. When the applied stress reaches the value at which yielding begins, one of the planes of atoms slips past the adjacent plane, as shown in Fig. 3.12c, and the entire bar becomes slightly longer. As yielding progresses more layers of atoms slip past each other and the crystal gradually elongates.

Resolved Shear Stress

In general, none of the slip planes in a crystal coincides with the plane of maximum shear. It is then necessary to determine the shearing stress

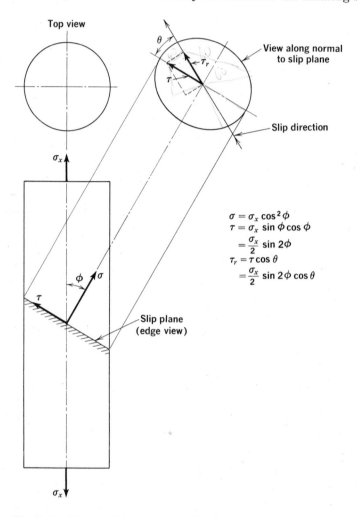

$$\sigma = \sigma_x \cos^2 \phi$$
$$\tau = \sigma_x \sin \phi \cos \phi$$
$$= \frac{\sigma_x}{2} \sin 2\phi$$
$$\tau_r = \tau \cos \theta$$
$$= \frac{\sigma_x}{2} \sin 2\phi \cos \theta$$

Fig. 3.14 Derivation of resolved shear stress.

on a given potential slip plane, and from that, its component in the direction of easy slip. This *resolved shear stress* can be found by using Eq. 3.12 and resolving the resulting τ into components in the slip plane (Fig. 3.14). Thus the resolved shear stress is

$$\tau_r = \frac{\sigma_x}{2}\sin 2\phi \cos \theta. \tag{3.13}$$

The stress at which slip begins on this particular plane is the *critical resolved shear stress*, τ_{cr}. In Fig. 3.12, $\phi = 45°$, $\theta = 0$, and $\tau_r = \sigma_x/2$. For other orientations the resolved shear stress on any slip plane will always be less than the maximum shear stress, $\sigma_x/2$, and to bring it up to the critical value will require a larger tensile stress, σ_x. The plane on which slip will first take place will be that having the highest resolved shear stress.

The stress required to separate two planes of atoms, breaking all the bonds simultaneously, is much larger than the maximum elastic stress (Art. 3.1). Similarly it can be shown that the shearing stress necessary to shift one layer of atoms past another all at the same time is much larger than the actual critical resolved shearing stress for a single crystal. The reason is that slip is progressive rather than simultaneous; it starts at one point in the glide plane where the presence of an imperfection makes it possible and moves through the crystal by a progressive shifting of atoms along the plane.

Yielding may also involve other mechanisms. At ordinary temperatures, a crystal may deform through the formation of *twins*.* Twinning usually accounts for a much smaller part of the total deformation than slip, and in some crystals it has never been observed. It seems to be governed by laws similar to those of slip, and sometimes the two mechanisms are closely interrelated.

3.6   DISLOCATIONS

The imperfections usually responsible for slip are called *dislocations*. These are small groups of atoms in the crystal lattice that are displaced from their regular positions, distorting the lattice slightly. Dislocations are present in great numbers in all crystals, having been formed during growth and by previous plastic deformation. The concept of dislocations was introduced in 1934 by Taylor, Orowan, and Polanyi, each working independently. Figure 3.15 is an example of a dislocation. At (a) the crystal is shown in its original state. A dislocation is indicated, in which a few atoms are squeezed out of place by the presence of an extra row of atoms in the upper half of the crystal. The application of a shear stress, τ, causes a general distortion of the crystal so that atom A moves closer to C while atom B moves farther away. At a relatively small distortion the bond between B and C is broken, and a new bond is formed between A and C. Thus the dislocation is shifted through one atomic distance to the

---

* Keyser, Carl A., *Basic Engineering Metallurgy*, Prentice-Hall, Inc., Englewood Cliffs, N. J., 1952, p. 33.

right.   If the stress, with its accompanying distortion, is maintained, the dislocation will continue to move to the right until it reaches the edge of the crystal, resulting in a general slip of one atomic distance along glide plane *aa*, as shown at (b).

Since Fig. 3.15 shows only a cross-section of the crystal, it is clear that each row of atoms represents the edge view of a plane of atoms perpendicular to the plane of the paper.   The extra row of atoms above *A* in Fig. 3.15a is therefore really an extra plane of atoms in the crystal, and the

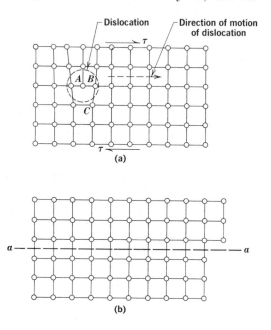

Fig. 3.15   Slip caused by motion of a dislocation through a crystal.

dislocation localized about atom *A* is really a *line imperfection* extending indefinitely into the crystal structure.   Such a dislocation is known as an *edge dislocation*.   It may extend in a straight line all the way through the crystal, but usually, for various reasons, it follows an irregular path.   It may also be very short, the extra plane of atoms being only a small patch inserted in the crystal structure; if so, the other edges of the patch would also be edge dislocations.   All edge dislocations have the characteristic cross-section shown in Fig. 3.15.

Passage of a single dislocation along a slip plane through a crystal causes slip of one atomic distance.   The amount of slip that can be measured by ordinary means requires the passage of many thousands of such dislocations.   When a crystal yields, the slip on any one active slip plane is ordinarily of the order of 1000 atomic distances, and slip on many such planes is required to produce significant yielding.

The multitudes of dislocations needed for yielding originate in two principal ways. During crystal formation many dislocations appear as a natural consequence of crystal growth. Even in a nearly perfect crystal there is an equilibrium concentration of imperfections, including dislocations; it provides the basic supply but is a minor source of the dislocations actually needed for yielding. The other source is found in the yielding process itself. It is referred to as the Frank-Read source, after F. C. Frank and

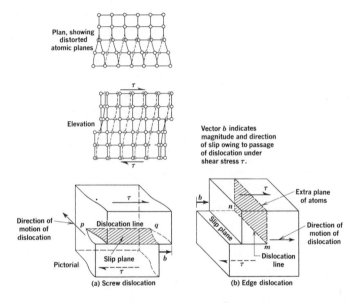

Fig. 3.16   Screw dislocation, with edge dislocation for comparison.

W. T. Read, who first conceived of the mechanism in 1950. Operational details of the mechanism are beyond the scope of this text.* In principle, however, the source is an edge dislocation that has become anchored by an obstacle and thereafter rotates around it as long as slip takes place. Each rotation generates a new edge dislocation, which moves on through the crystal to produce another unit of slip. By this mechanism the dislocations originally in the crystal are multiplied many fold during the process of yielding.

A second type of dislocation should be mentioned—the *screw dislocation*,

---

* See Parker, Earl R., "Modern Concepts of Flow and Fracture" (1957 Edward de Mille Campbell Memorial Lecture) *Transactions* Am. Soc. Metals **50**, 56 (1958) for a description of the Frank-Read mechanism.

in which the atoms are displaced *along* the line of the dislocation instead of *at right angles* to it. Figure 3.16a shows three views of a screw dislocation: a plan and elevation showing the planes of atoms distorted by the presence of the dislocation, and a pictorial view in which the crystal is represented by a solid block. The shear stress, τ, displaces the upper and lower parts of the crystal only at the near side, while the portion beyond the dislocation line pq is only slightly distorted. Continued application of the shear stress, however, causes the dislocation line pq to move in the direction indicated, and the slip is propagated through the crystal at right angles to the direction of the shear stress. Figure 3.16b shows, for comparison, a corresponding view of an edge dislocation. Here the dislocation line mn moves in the same direction as the shear stress, and slip is propagated through the crystal in this direction. In both instances the direction and magnitude of slip are shown by the vector **b**, which is called the *Burgers vector*. The Burgers vector may be one or more atomic distances.

The mechanism of yielding which we have been discussing requires that at least some of the atomic bonds be re-formed continuously so that the crystal has almost the same form after yielding as before. It is therefore most commonly found in metallic crystals, since metallic bonds are indiscriminate and can form between any two atoms. Recently, however, a similar type of slip has been produced in nonmetallic crystals—ionic and covalent.* The concept of dislocations thus appears to have some application to these crystals, although it originated with metals and is an important factor in accounting for their high ductility.

During distortion of a crystal there is, of course, constant thermal agitation among its atoms. As atom B in Fig. 3.15a moves away from atom C, it is possible that the bond will be broken ahead of time, i.e., at a slightly lower stress than normal because of the thermal energy present. As the temperature increases and the thermal energy increases, the stress at which the bond is broken decreases. Thus thermal activation accounts for the fact that yielding begins at lower stresses when the temperature rises.

3.7 YIELDING IN POLYCRYSTALS AND AMORPHOUS MATERIALS

Most crystalline materials are aggregates of many small crystals (sometimes called *grains*). The individual crystals are oriented at random in all possible directions, and consequently the planes and directions of easiest slip vary throughout the material. When a tensile stress is applied along the axis of a polycrystalline bar, however, the maximum shearing stress will still be on planes at 45° with the axis. This stress will coincide with the

---

* Parker, Earl R., "Modern Concepts of Flow and Fracture" (1957 Edward de Mille Campbell Memorial Lecture) *Transactions* Am. Soc. Metals **50**, 100 (1958).

planes of easy slip in some but not in the majority of crystals. Hence there will be "weak" and "strong" crystals, and slip will generally start in the weak ones—those most favorably oriented for slip.

After slip has begun in certain crystals, its continued progress through the material involves slip in adjacent crystals, and because of their different orientations a greater stress is required. The polycrystalline mass is stronger than a single favorably oriented crystal, and slip does not follow exactly the planes of maximum shear but accommodates itself partially to the various directions of easy slip encountered.

Another factor in the greater strength of polycrystalline materials is the crystal (grain) boundaries themselves. Generally speaking, the crystal boundaries offer more resistance to slip than the interiors of the crystals, partly because of the differences in slip directions between crystals described above. However, the difference in orientation between two adjacent crystals also results in a region of atomic disorder between them, in the grain boundary. If the difference is great (high-angle boundary), there is much disorder, and the energy of the boundary region is high compared with that of the interior of the crystal. Consequently impurity atoms precipitate in the boundary region, with the net result that slip through the boundaries may be very difficult because dislocations are impeded both by atomic disorder and the impurity atoms.

Because some of the crystals in a polycrystalline material are always oriented with their slip directions in the plane of maximum shear, they will try to yield at a stress comparable to that for a single crystal. If the surrounding crystals are elastic enough, they will permit minute amounts of yielding in these weak crystals. This microscopically localized yielding cannot be detected in the overall effect, and the action still appears to be elastic until a number of such crystals have yielded. Thus general yielding begins very gradually, and the exact end of the elastic range becomes uncertain. The observed limit of elasticity and the proportional limit therefore depend on the accuracy of measurements.

Amorphous materials yield by a variety of mechanisms. In thermoplastic polymers, for example, yielding takes place when the long-chain molecules slip past each other. Sometimes molecular bonds are re-formed as fast as they are broken, but no strengthening results. Consequently so long as the stress is maintained, the molecules will continue to slip. This is a true *viscous flow* in the material. The applied stress actually determines, not the strain, but the *rate of strain*, and the behavior should properly be expressed by a diagram of stress vs strain rate, or strain vs time (see Chapter 8). Nevertheless the behavior of most thermoplastic polymers under ordinary short-time loading is very similar to that of other materials. Consequently the common stress-strain diagram is quite universally used to provide important engineering information.   Viscous flow does make the speed of testing of major importance, whereas in metals and similar materials it is usually of minor importance, except at elevated temperatures.   The effects of viscous flow under elevated temperatures and long-time loading are covered in Chapters 7 and 8.

Polymers often contain certain amounts of crystallinity which affects their yielding characteristics.   In thermoplastics the chain molecules are lined up in many small parallel groups (Fig. 3.17).   These *crystallites* are

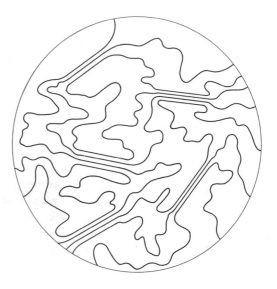

Fig. 3.17   Crystallites in a thermoplastic, formed by spontaneous lining up of molecules in small parallel groups.

surrounded by the matrix of disordered molecules.   If a polymer of this type is elongated inelastically, the molecules tend to line up more and more in the direction of elongation.   The resultant increase in the number of crystallites is responsible for the strengthening of drawn filaments like nylon.   The most highly crystalline polymers are the thermosetting types. Cross-linking between long molecules produces a three-dimensional network of considerable order.

Crystallinity in polymers always strengthens them and inhibits viscous flow.   Thus their behavior in yielding becomes more like that of other crystalline materials.

In certain materials yielding results in only a few of the bonds being re-formed while others are permanently broken.   This behavior may cause a general weakening of the material.   Concrete, wood, and some plastics yield in this manner.   Other mechanisms may also be involved, such as friction and interlocking between the particles in an aggregate, and fragmentation of particles.

3.8   STRAIN-HARDENING

In most ductile materials it is observed that as yielding progresses, an ever-increasing stress is required to produce further yielding. The stress-strain diagram of Fig. 3.10c illustrates how stress always increases with increasing strain. The cause is *strain-hardening,* a phenomenon in which the mechanical properties of ductile materials change when they are strained beyond the elastic range.

Strain-hardening in crystalline materials is largely accounted for by dislocations. They interact in many ways because of the localized stresses surrounding them in the crystal. A complete analysis of these stresses and their interactions can be made only on the basis of the theory of elasticity. However, a good picture of certain elementary interactions can be obtained by simple reasoning.

Let us consider the interactions between like and unlike parallel dislocations on the same plane. The stress pattern around a dislocation can be visualized by reference to Fig. 3.15a. We see that above the dislocation the vertical planes of atoms have closer than normal spacing to make room for the extra plane of atoms. At the same time the vertical planes of atoms below the dislocation have been pulled farther apart. These displacements of the atomic planes produce, among other things, horizontal normal stresses, compressive above and tensile below the dislocation. Distortion of the crystal fades out rapidly as we move away from the dislocation in any direction. In fact it almost vanishes after a few atomic distances. The bulk of the crystal is so large compared with the dislocation that infinitesimal adjustments among the other atoms are sufficient to accommodate the dislocation. The stress pattern therefore is largely localized in the atoms immediately surrounding the dislocation.

Similar dislocations such as those in Fig. 3.18a will, of course, have identical stress patterns. If for any reason they should approach each other, the overlapping of these patterns would cause increased compressive stresses above and increased tensile stresses below the common plane, and a resulting increase in strain energy. Consequently repulsive forces act between the two dislocations. Dislocations like those in Fig. 3.18b are clearly opposite in sense. They are distinguished by sign—the one at *A* being *positive* and the other *negative.* Interaction between two such dislocations is opposite to that of the two similar dislocations described above. As they approach each other the compressive stresses of one meet the tensile stresses of the other. The result is that all stresses are cancelled, the extra plane of one dislocation lines up directly over the extra plane of the other, and both dislocations disappear. Unlike dislocations therefore attract and cancel each other, thereby reducing the strain energy in that region.

The effect of these two elementary interactions on slip can now be examined. Suppose that, under the influence of a shear stress, several like

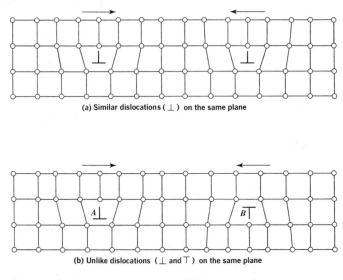

(a) Similar dislocations (⊥) on the same plane

(b) Unlike dislocations (⊥ and ⊤) on the same plane

Fig. 3.18   Interaction of two dislocations on the same plane. The symbol ⊥ is used for an edge dislocation: the vertical line indicates the extra plane of atoms, and the horizontal line indicates the plane of slip.

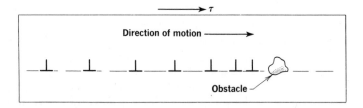

Fig. 3.19   Motion of a row of dislocations along a slip plane.

dislocations are moving along a slip plane (Fig. 3.19).   Suppose also that one of the dislocations is stopped by an obstacle that it cannot break through or bypass.   Because of repulsion, other dislocations can only approach to a certain spacing under the action of the applied stress.   Furthermore, a back stress is set up that stops any Frank-Read sources (p. 79) that may have been acting on that plane.   The entire slip on that plane is thus brought to a halt when one dislocation is stopped by an obstacle.

To produce further slip the shear stress will have to be increased to overcome the obstacle or bypass it in some way.

That the interaction of unlike dislocations also impedes slip can be seen by simply noting that two such dislocations tend to annihilate each other, and two sources of slip are eliminated every time this happens.

The interactions between dislocations in real crystals are far more complex than these examples. The most important interactions are those between nonparallel dislocations associated with simultaneous slip on more than one slip plane (multiple slip). They account for the fact that cubic crystals strain-harden more rapidly than hexagonal crystals. The latter, having only one set of slip planes—the base planes of its hexagonal unit cell—usually slip on this one set of planes only (simple slip). Cubic crystals, on the other hand, have several slip planes and are prone to multiple slip. In fact it is only with the greatest difficulty that cubic crystals can be deformed in such a way that slip takes place on only one plane. Slip on intersecting planes and the resulting interaction of nonparallel dislocations is clearly a controlling factor in strain-hardening. Unfortunately the mathematical difficulties in the analysis of these interactions are thus far almost insurmountable.

In polycrystalline materials dislocations find additional obstacles in the form of crystal boundaries and inclusions of foreign matter. Thus polycrystals have a higher rate of strain-hardening than single crystals.

3.9   THE PLASTIC RANGE

The range of mechanical behavior in which yielding and strain-hardening take place is often referred to as the plastic range. The strain that results from yielding is irrecoverable. In addition to this *plastic strain*, however, there is a recoverable elastic strain. To provide the necessary internal stresses to balance the external loads the atoms must always be separated a certain amount from their equilibrium spacings. As yielding progresses the atoms are shifted to new equilibrium positions, but they must also be displaced slightly from these new positions to develop the necessary interatomic forces. Thus there are always two distinct mechanisms—elastic and plastic—involved in producing strain. The corresponding parts of the total strain are the elastic and plastic components. The elastic component usually continues to increase at the same rate, governed by Hooke's law, while the plastic component increases more rapidly with increased stress.

A very important difference between the two components of strain is their effect on the volume of the material. Elastic strain, consisting in a separation of the atoms, naturally produces a certain increase in volume. This dilatation is equal to $\epsilon_x(1 - 2\,\mu)$ (Eq. 3.4), or about $\epsilon_x/3$ for many materials. Plastic strain, on the other hand, is accompanied by no significant volume change because it involves only place changes among atoms and no direct separation. Thus the value of μ for the plastic strain is $\frac{1}{2}$ and the lateral strain is half the axial.

The process of yielding in the plastic range is localized at many points throughout the material at any given instant. As each point yields, the cross-section of the member is reduced slightly, but at the same time the material is strain-hardened. Thus, although the stress increases slightly because of the smaller area, the material is capable of withstanding it and the next yielding occurs at a different location. The overall effect of this more-or-less random yielding is that on a macroscopic scale the strain remains uniform along the length of the member. On a microscopic scale there is continued competition between the increased strength owing to strain-hardening and increased stress owing to area reduction. The former overcompensates for the latter, and the strain remains essentially uniform.

Since plastic strain increases so rapidly compared with elastic strain, the latter can soon be neglected (Example 3.2). The entire action is then governed by the laws for plastic strain at essentially constant volume, and the effective value of μ approaches $\frac{1}{2}$ for all materials.

EXAMPLE 3.2

The proportional limit of a certain steel is 30,000 psi. At 45,000 psi the strain is 0.0615 in./in.; at 60,000 psi it is 0.2020 in./in. Compare the elastic and plastic strains at these three stresses.

At 30,000 psi:
Since this is the proportional limit stress, there is no plastic strain; the elastic strain is

$$\epsilon_e = \frac{30,000}{30 \times 10^6} = 0.0010 \text{ in./in.}$$

At 45,000 psi:
  Elastic strain

$$\epsilon_e = \frac{45,000}{30 \times 10^6} = 0.0015 \text{ in./in.}$$

  Plastic strain

$$\epsilon_p = 0.0615 - 0.0015 = 0.0600 \text{ in./in.}$$

$$\frac{\epsilon_e}{\epsilon_p} = \frac{1}{40} \text{ or } 2.5\%.$$

At 60,000 psi:
  Elastic strain

$$\epsilon_e = \frac{60,000}{30 \times 10^6} = 0.0020 \text{ in./in.}$$

  Plastic strain

$$\epsilon_p = 0.2020 - 0.0020 = 0.2000 \text{ in./in.}$$

$$\frac{\epsilon_e}{\epsilon_p} = \frac{1}{100} \text{ or } 1\%.$$

Plastic Instability

In many materials the rate of strain-hardening decreases with increased strain. Thus it often happens that at some value of strain the strengthening effect of strain-hardening no longer compensates for the increased stress caused by the reduction in area. When this condition is reached at some location in the material, the plastic strain continues to increase at this location because the *stress* increases, owing to area reduction, faster than the *strength* increases, owing to strain-hardening. This behavior occurs with no increase in load and is an unstable process. It is also highly localized, with all further elongation taking place at this location, so that a constriction or *neck* begins to form. As deformation goes on, the *rate* of strain-hardening continues to decrease locally, and with the ever-decreasing area the load required to cause further deformation continues to drop. This process goes on until rupture.

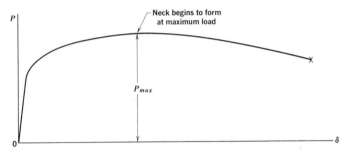

Fig. 3.20   Typical load vs elongation diagram for a ductile metal.

The behavior described above, which occurs in many ductile materials, is termed *plastic instability*. It is characterized by a *maximum* in the conventional stress-strain (or load-elongation) curve. Mathematically it is defined by the condition

$$dP = 0, \text{ or } d(\sigma A) = 0. \tag{3.14}$$

Both stress and area are variables, a fact that will be discussed in more detail in Art. 3.11. Thus the above equation can be written

$$A \, d\sigma + \sigma \, dA = 0. \tag{3.14a}$$

The first term represents the increase in load owing to strain-hardening—positive, since $d\sigma$ is positive; the second term represents the decrease in load owing to reduction in area—negative, since dA is negative. Until the maximum load is reached, the first term is larger than the second (absolute value) because of the overcompensation mentioned above, and $dP > 0$. At the maximum load the two effects are just equal, and beyond it the second term becomes predominant, so that $dP < 0$. The mathematical treatment of plastic instability will be taken up again in Art. 3.12 following the treatment of true stress and true strain. Figure 3.20 shows the variation of load with elongation for a typical ductile metal exhibiting plastic instability.

Loading and Unloading

When a member is unloaded after being loaded into the plastic range, the elastic part of the strain is recovered as the atoms return to their current equilibrium positions. The plastic strain remains as a permanent increase in length, or *permanent set*, in the member. This behavior can be illustrated by plotting a stress-strain diagram (Fig. 3.21). Since the

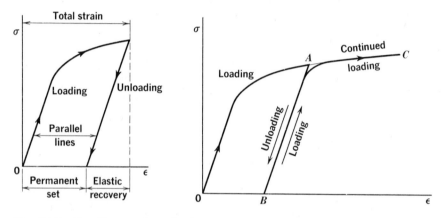

Fig. 3.21   Loading and unload-ing in the plastic range.   *Fig. 3.22   Repeated loading.*

forces that pull the atoms back together when the load is removed are the same interatomic forces that had to be overcome in the first elastic elongation, the stiffness is the same. Hence the slope of the unloading line is the same as that of the original elastic line. If, after unloading, the member is loaded again, the atoms will simply be displaced to the positions they occupied just before they were unloaded, after which further yielding takes place as if nothing else had happened. Figure 3.22 shows the complete picture: loading along the curve OA, unloading from A to B, loading again from B back to A, followed by continued loading along an extension of the curve OA toward C. It should be noted that for the loading curve BAC the proportional limit is A; it is considerably higher than the original proportional limit for the material, another effect of strain-hardening.

The foregoing description of what happens upon repeated loading is ap-

proximate to a certain extent.   In most materials the atoms are prevented
by internal friction from returning immediately to their equilibrium positions upon unloading.   Some part of the elastic deformation persists and
disappears only after some time has passed.   This *elastic aftereffect* is
hardly noticeable in crystalline materials under ordinary conditions, but
in amorphous materials like polymers it is pronounced.   The result is that
the stress-strain diagram does not follow a straight line with unloading and
reloading, but describes a narrow loop as in Fig. 3.23.   The area of the loop

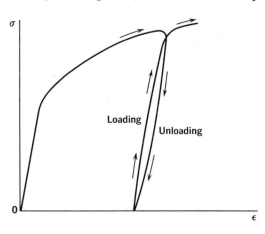

*Fig. 3.23   Hysteresis loop
in unloading and reload-
ing.*

represents energy lost during a cycle of unloading and reloading, as does
the area between the two curves for rubber (Fig. 3.9).   The energy lost
in one cycle is usually small, and its greatest importance lies in repeated
cycling, as in mechanical vibrations (see Chapter 7).

   For ordinary static loading conditions encountered in the laboratory and
in many applications, the approximation of linear unloading and reloading
curves is quite satisfactory as well as useful.

Rupture

   The plastic range ends with the rupture of the member, usually after
the member has necked down to some extent; the break occurs at the
smallest section of the neck.   The stress distribution at this section is
complicated because the surface is no longer cylindrical but curves outward
above and below.   This outward curvature causes the axial stresses to
curve outward, too, thereby producing a component of stress radially outward in the neck.   The very center of the neck is in a state of triaxial tension, which encourages a brittle type fracture in this region (see Chapter 6).
Rupture starts, then, with a small crack in the very center of the neck, as
shown in Fig. 3.24.   The crack spreads rapidly outward, but as it does so

the radial stress diminishes.   By the time the crack has spread nearly to the circumference there is only a narrow ring of material like a tube left to support the load.   This tube is in a state very close to simple tension and fails by shearing action all the way around.   The result is the *cup-cone*

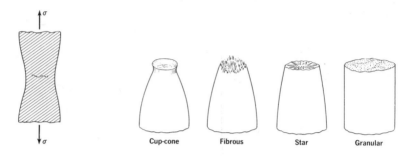

Fig. 3.24   Crack formed
in center of neck.

Fig. 3.25   Typical ten-
sile fractures of metals.

form of ductile fracture.   Figure 3.25 shows the cup-cone and other types of fracture found in various materials.

Some materials can be roughly identified by their fractures.   Mild steel fails in a pronounced cup-cone, while in steels with increasing carbon

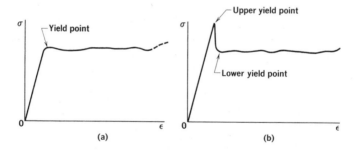

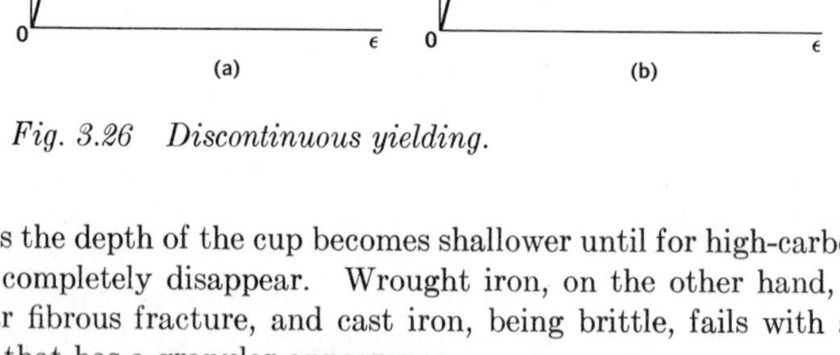

Fig. 3.26   Discontinuous yielding.

contents the depth of the cup becomes shallower until for high-carbon steel it may completely disappear.   Wrought iron, on the other hand, has an irregular fibrous fracture, and cast iron, being brittle, fails with a plane surface that has a granular appearance.

3.10   DISCONTINUOUS YIELDING

In certain materials yielding does not begin gradually but comes suddenly and results in a large plastic deformation at a more-or-less constant stress without any strain-hardening. The stress-strain diagram for this type of behavior is a discontinuous curve (Fig. 3.26a). The point on the curve at which yielding begins is called the yield point. Sometimes yielding is especially abrupt and is even followed by a sharp drop in the stress that can be sustained by the material (Fig. 3.26b). The peak stress is then called the *upper yield point* and the lower stress the *lower yield point*.

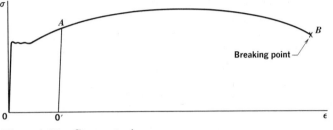

Fig. 3.27 Stress-strain diagram for mild steel.

Although this type of yielding does not ordinarily occur in many materials, it is of great importance because it is characteristic of mild steel, one of the most common structural materials. (Mild steel is the name often used for plain carbon structural steels having carbon contents in the neighborhood of 0.20 per cent.) A complete stress-strain diagram for a typical mild steel tension member is illustrated in Fig. 3.27. Other materials

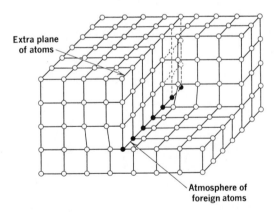

Fig. 3.28 Cutaway view of dislocation, showing row, or atmosphere, of foreign atoms.

which sometimes yield discontinuously include molybdenum, cadmium, brass, aluminum, and zinc.

Discontinuous yielding is caused by the presence of small amounts of foreign atoms in the material, usually carbon or nitrogen. The foreign atoms, in solution, occupy more-or-less unstable interstitial positions in the lattice. (As noted in Art. 2.9, the carbon atoms in steel are on the borderline for size compared with the iron atoms and hence are an especially tight fit in the interstitial positions.) These foreign atoms naturally tend to migrate to vacancies in the lattice or to regions of higher energy such as dislocations. Many of them find stable positions in the spaces just below the extra planes of atoms in edge dislocations. Therefore they line up in these spaces and effectively anchor the dislocations against movement. Such a line of foreign atoms is called an *atmosphere* (Fig. 3.28). Most of the dislocations in mild steel are locked by their atmospheres of carbon or nitrogen atoms. Consequently, although the body-centered cubic structure of iron (ferrite) has many planes and directions of easy slip and should yield at a low stress, it is prevented from doing so by the immobility of its dislocations.

When a shear stress is applied on a slip plane in mild steel, it must pull the dislocations away from their atmospheres before slip can take place. The relation between applied stress and the resulting displacement of a dislocation from its line of foreign atoms is given by the equation*

$$\tau(x) = \frac{Cx}{(x^2 + r_0^2)^2}, \tag{3.15}$$

where x is the displacement, r_0 is a constant of the order of one atomic spacing, and C is a combination of constants. Figure 3.29 illustrates the

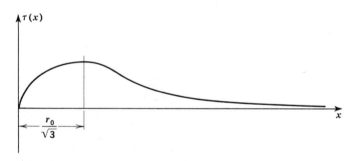

Fig. 3.29 *Variation of stress on an anchored dislocation.*

variation, in which the stress is largest when the dislocation has been displaced $r_0/\sqrt{3}$. As the dislocation moves farther away, it does so at a decreased stress. Thus a high stress is required to initiate yielding but a low stress will continue it—and we have the upper and lower yield points.

The carbon and nitrogen atmospheres in mild steel are materially aided

---

* Cottrell, A. H., *Dislocations and Plastic Flow in Crystals*, Clarendon Press, Oxford, 1953, p. 142.

in causing the high yield stress by another characteristic: between the ferrite grains are small crystals of cementite or iron carbide (Fe_3C), a very hard material. It forms a hard film along the crystal boundaries and provides an additional obstruction to dislocations. Thus even when freed from their atmospheres, they are prevented from propagating slip from one crystal to the next until still higher stresses are reached.

The beginning of discontinuous yielding is highly localized. Slip is nucleated at macroscopic or microscopic imperfections which act as stress-raisers. As the applied stress increases, the stress at some such point or points reaches the limit necessary to release the dislocations and yielding starts. Local yielding has the effect of spreading the imperfection that was responsible for its beginning. As it spreads, the yielded region is preceded by stress concentrations, as in the propagation of a crack.* Thus yielding is propagated through materials in much the same manner as brittle fracture. Since the basic mechanism is one of slip, however, propagation tends to follow the planes of maximum shear (45° to the axis of the applied stress). Soon it has traversed the entire specimen, and a band may be seen on its surface if it has been polished beforehand. Such visible surface markings are called *Lüders lines* (Fig. 3.30). The presence of the

Fig. 3.30   Lüders lines on polished mild steel bar in tension.

first band with its stress concentrations causes the next band to start at the same low stress, so that yielding goes on at approximately constant stress. The stress does not begin to rise again until the slip bands have covered the entire bar. The elongation that takes place during this yielding is often 15 to 20 times the elastic elongation that preceded it.

The Lüders lines that appear on the surface of low-carbon steel as it yields are slight depressions or irregularities in the surface. The originally smooth surface becomes rough to the touch, often an undesirable condition. For example, in the deep-drawing of annealed steel sheets for automobile

---

* Zener, Clarence M., "A Theoretical Criterion for the Initiation of Slip Bands," *Phys. Rev.* **69**, 128 (1946); also Cottrell, A. H., *Dislocations and Plastic Flow in Crystals*, Clarendon Press, Oxford, 1953, pp. 104–107.

body parts, the formation of Lüders lines produces objectionable irregularities called *stretcher strains.* Cold-rolled sheets do not have these lines because the material has been carried past the range of discontinuous yielding in the direction of the plane of the sheet by the rolling process. In other words the material has been elongated in the plane of the sheet to a point like point A in Fig. 3.27, after which its stress-strain diagram is represented by $O'AB$.

Since the beginning of discontinuous yielding, like the fracture strength of brittle materials, depends on the presence of imperfections (other than dislocations), it is subject to the same variations. Like the fracture strength, the stress required to initiate yielding exhibits a random distribution of observed values, with considerable scatter (Art. 3.4). Also as in fracture strength, a size effect has been observed, large members yielding at considerably smaller stresses than small members. The stress required to continue yielding once it has started (the lower yield point stress) is, on the other hand, relatively stable. Since this process involves yielding and flow of material, it is more like the ordinary yielding process and more-or-less independent of imperfections other than dislocations themselves.

3.11 STRESS AND STRAIN

Before the inelastic properties of materials are discussed, the significance of stress and strain must be clearly understood. For properties in the elastic range no serious ambiguity results from the use of the definitions given in Eqs. 3.1 and 3.2. The elastic reduction in area is so small as to be almost negligible (for steel, with $\mu = 0.3$ and $\sigma_{pl} = 50,000$ psi, the reduction is only 0.1 per cent), and strains are of the same order of magnitude (about 0.1 per cent). The area and length used in defining stress and strain can therefore be the original dimensions of the member, from which $\sigma = P/A_0$ and $\epsilon = \delta/l_0$. Stress and strain defined in this manner are called *conventional, nominal,* or *engineering* stress and strain. These are the quantities used throughout the usual courses in mechanics of materials.

When dealing with the plastic range, however, it must be recognized that both the reduction in area and the strain can become very large. It is at once clear that conventional stress is not the actual stress in the plastic range. In reality it is simply a measure of the load on a standard tension member. As such it has considerable use as a means of comparing materials in terms of standardized tensile behavior, even in the range of yielding and rupture. It has long been the stress in terms of which the mechanical properties are specified.

Conventional strain also has long been the standard measure used in stress-strain diagrams. Its deficiencies are not so obvious as those of conventional stress. An extreme example will serve to illustrate. Suppose that a member 10 inches long has been elongated to *twice* its original length ($l = 2\,l_0 = 20$ inches, so that the conventional strain is 1.00, or 100 per cent). Now imagine that a small additional elongation is given to the member, say 1 inch. According to the conventional strain the member has been strained an additional 10 per cent, and yet its 20-inch length has only been elongated by $\frac{1}{20}$th, or 5 per cent. Thus, while conventional strain is perfectly satisfactory for some purposes, it may not always mean just what we think it does.

In recent years engineers and scientists have been turning more and more to the so-called *true stress* and *true strain* (also called *natural strain*) as proper measures of the mechanical behavior of materials in all ranges, even the elastic range.

True stress is defined by

$$\sigma' = \frac{P}{A},$$

where A is the actual area of the cross-section corresponding to the load P. Figure 3.31 compares true stress with conventional stress, both plotted

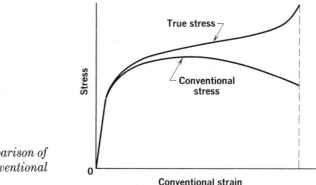

Fig. 3.31   Comparison of true and conventional stress.

against conventional strain, for an aluminum alloy. The monotonic increase of true stress up to the breaking point illustrates that strain-hardening continues throughout the plastic range. After the onset of plastic instability, or necking, at the ultimate load, true stress is computed using the smallest cross-section—that at the center of the neck. Because of the shape of the neck the stress in this cross-section is not uniform, and the true stress represents only the average value. The true stress in the neck continues to rise until rupture. The drop in load that accompanies necking is reflected in a corresponding drop in conventional stress.

True strain differs from conventional strain in that each increment of strain is based on the actual length at the time of the increment instead of on the original length. The instantaneous conventional strain is defined as

$$\epsilon = \frac{\delta}{l_0} = \frac{l - l_0}{l_0}, \tag{3.2}$$

in which l is the instantaneous length and l_0 the original length. The increment of conventional strain resulting from an infinitesimal increase in length, dl, from l to l_1, is given by

$$d\epsilon = \epsilon_1 - \epsilon = \frac{l_1 - l_0}{l_0} - \frac{l - l_0}{l_0}$$

$$= \frac{l_1 - l}{l_0},$$

or

$$d\epsilon = \frac{dl}{l_0}.$$

The total conventional strain, ϵ, can be obtained from the increment by integration, as follows:

$$\int_0^\epsilon d\epsilon = \int_{l_0}^l \frac{dl}{l_0},$$

or

$$\epsilon = \frac{l - l_0}{l_0}$$

as above. True strain is defined in such a way that the increment caused by an increase in length, dl, is based on the instantaneous length, l:

$$d\epsilon' = \frac{dl}{l},$$

where ϵ' is the true strain. The total true strain is found by integration:

$$\int_0^{\epsilon'} d\epsilon' = \int_{l_0}^l \frac{dl}{l}$$

or

$$\epsilon' = \log_e \frac{l}{l_0}. \tag{3.16}$$

Figure 3.32 is a comparison of true and conventional strain in which strain is plotted against the length ratio l/l_0. Note that for uniform *tensile* strains true strain is always less than conventional. The difference is especially noticeable in compression, when true strain is always *greater* than conventional strain. For example, if the length of a member could be compressed to zero, the conventional strain would appear to be -1, whereas the true strain, being the logarithm of zero, is infinite, a much more logical result.

Since conventional strain is

$$\epsilon = \frac{l - l_0}{l_0} = \frac{l}{l_0} - 1,$$

it follows that

$$\frac{l}{l_0} = 1 + \epsilon,$$

and true strain can be expressed as

$$\epsilon' = \log_e (1 + \epsilon). \tag{3.16a}$$

As an example, suppose $l_0 = 2$ inches and $l = 2.5$ inches. Then $\epsilon = (2.5 - 2)/2 = 0.25$, while $\epsilon' = \log_e (1.25) = 0.223$. An increase in length of 0.1 inch beyond the 2.5-inch length would be a conventional strain increment of $0.1/2 = 0.05$, but a true strain increment of only $0.1/2.5 = 0.04$ (approximately).

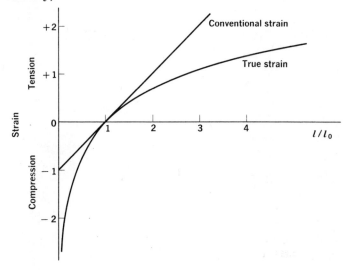

Fig. 3.32   Comparison of true and conventional strain.

When the strain is nonuniform (e.g., the highly localized strain occurring in the neck) the only really significant strain is the local strain at a given section. In the definition of true strain (Eq. 3.16) the length, l_0, then becomes an infinitesimal length centered on this section.

Direct measurement of highly localized strains is difficult. The required infinitesimal length l_0 can be approximated only by the use of a very short measuring device (Art. 3.16). At large plastic strains, however, it is possible to measure local strains quite easily and accurately through the use of the following principles.

At large plastic strains the volume remains essentially constant if we neglect elastic deformations as noted in Art. 3.9.   Consider a segment of the member having length l_0; the original volume of that part is A_0l_0. After some plastic elongation has taken place, the length is l and its area is A, giving a volume Al.   For constant volume we have

$$Al = A_0l_0 \text{ or } \frac{l}{l_0} = \frac{A_0}{A}. \tag{3.17}$$

This equation applies to every segment of the member, but for that part in which the neck forms, the length l_0 must be taken as infinitesimal be-

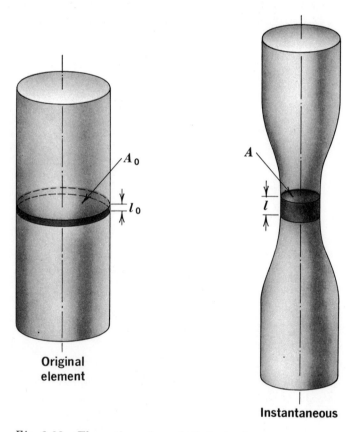

Original
element

Instantaneous

Fig. 3.33   Elongation of an infinitesimal element in the neck.

cause, as noted above, the strain is nonuniform, and furthermore the neck is far from cylindrical (Fig. 3.33).

Substituting Eq. 3.17 in Eq. 3.16, we have

$$\epsilon' = \log_e \frac{A_0}{A} \tag{3.16b}$$

for large plastic strains. It should be emphasized that this expression for true strain holds only so long as the volume remains constant. For small plastic strains the elastic volume change introduces a significant error.

The ratio of A_0/A is an indication of the reduction in area. The *conventional* reduction in area is defined as

$$q = \frac{A_0 - A}{A_0} = 1 - \frac{A}{A_0},$$

which is positive when A is *less* than A_0. The increment of q is $dq = -dA/A_0$. The *true* reduction in area, q', is analogous to true strain in that its increment is based on the instantaneous area rather than on A_0. Thus $dq' = -dA/A$, from which

$$q' = \int_{A_0}^{A} -\frac{dA}{A} = \log_e \frac{A_0}{A}. \tag{3.18}$$

We see by comparing Eqs. 3.18 and 3.16b that true strain and the true reduction in area are identical for large plastic strains.

EXAMPLE 3.3

Given $\sigma' = 20,000$ psi and $\epsilon' = 0.300$, compute the corresponding values of conventional stress and strain, σ and ϵ, assuming constant volume.

Solution:

$$\sigma' = \frac{P}{A}; \sigma = \frac{P}{A_0}$$

$$\epsilon' = \log_e \frac{A_0}{A}$$

$$\frac{A_0}{A} = e^{\epsilon'}$$

$$\sigma = \frac{P}{A_0} = \sigma' \frac{A}{A_0} = \sigma' e^{-\epsilon'}$$

Therefore

$$\sigma = 20,000 \, e^{-0.300} = 20,000(0.741)$$

$$= 14,820 \text{ psi.}$$

$$\epsilon = e^{\epsilon'} - 1 = e^{0.300} - 1 = 0.350.$$

Figure 3.34 is a comparison of stress-strain diagrams for an aluminum alloy, using conventional and true values. Corresponding points on the two diagrams are connected to show their relation one to the other. It should be noted that until the maximum load is reached, the points on the true stress-strain curve are always to the left of those on the conventional curve.   After this point, however, because of the high local strains in the neck, the curve for true strain overtakes that for conventional strain and at the breaking point is far to the right.

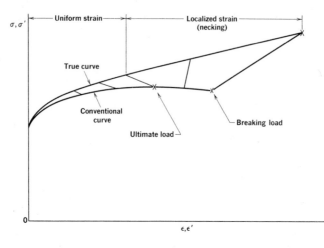

Fig. 3.34   Comparison of conventional and true stress-strain curves for an aluminum alloy.

Both conventional stress and strain and true stress and strain have applications in engineering and research.   In the elastic range conventional stress and strain are usually used, although true stress and strain are really the correct values.   For strong, stiff materials like metals the maximum error in using the conventional values is about 0.1 per cent for both stress and strain.   However, some investigators have used the true values even here to ensure the highest accuracy.

In the plastic range, as already pointed out, conventional stress and strain are only approximations, becoming less accurate with increasing strain.   Here, too, true stress and strain are really the correct values so long as necking does not take place.   However, if a neck does form, these, too, become approximations since neither the stress nor the strain is uniform on any cross-section in the neck.   They do give average values and thus come closer to representing the true situation than conventional stress and strain.

Both types have advantages and disadvantages.   The decision of which to use in any given analysis depends on many factors.   In the study of combined stresses and metal forming, such as drawing and rolling, true stress and strain are almost universally used.   Similarly, they are used in attempts to correlate the theories for different forms of loading, as in all scientific investigations of mechanical properties. In the specification of mechanical properties for design conventional stress and strain are still largely accepted except for certain special properties.

3.12   INELASTIC PROPERTIES

The inelastic properties most commonly used in engineering practice— *yield strength, tensile strength, secant modulus, tangent modulus, ductility,* and *toughness*—are measured in terms of conventional stress and strain.

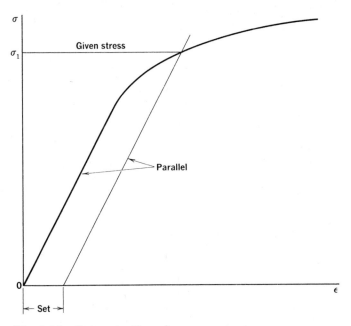

Fig. 3.35   Determination of permanent set for a given stress.

Yield strength is the stress at which yielding begins in a ductile material. Since it usually begins very gradually, the very first plastic strain is extremely minute and cannot actually be measured by any known method. Consequently it is necessary to specify a certain measurable amount of yielding as the beginning of yielding. The actual value of the yield strength, then, will depend upon this arbitrarily selected amount of yielding. A value of yield strength given without this qualifying amount is ambiguous and can be used only as a rough approximation.

The plastic strain at a given stress on a member in tension is the same as the permanent set that remains if the member is unloaded from that stress. It can easily be determined from a stress-strain diagram by drawing a line from the point corresponding to the given stress parallel to the elastic part of the curve. The point at which this line crosses the strain axis gives the value of the yield strain or permanent set (Fig. 3.35). If we want to know the stress at which a certain yield strain will have occurred, the process can simply be reversed. The specified yield strain can be measured on the strain axis and a line drawn at this *offset*, parallel to the elastic line; the stress at which this line crosses the stress-strain curve is the required yield stress. This is the *offset yield strength*, σ_y, the most commonly used measure of the beginning of yielding and the end of the elastic range. Various standard offsets are used under various conditions and with different materials. Probably the one used most frequently is 0.2 per cent. Since the offset is actually a strain, it is dimensionless and can be expressed alternatively as a per cent or a decimal fraction. Thus 0.2 per cent and 0.002 (in./in.) strain mean the same thing. Another way of looking at it is to say that after the member is loaded to its 0.2 per cent offset yield strength and then unloaded, it will be found to be 0.2 per cent

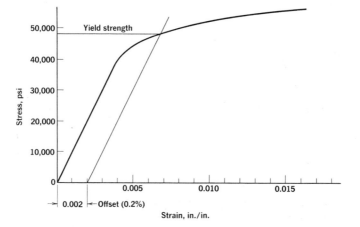

Fig. 3.36 Determination of offset yield strength for an aluminum alloy.

longer than originally. Figure 3.36 illustrates the determination of the offset yield strength for an aluminum alloy using a 0.2 per cent offset.

In the special case of discontinuous yielding the first plastic strain is easily detected since it comes so abruptly. At the *yield point* in a tension test the load suddenly stops increasing, and the stress at which this happens is the *yield point stress* (or simply the yield point). Sometimes the load may drop sharply at the yield point to a more-or-less steady value at which yielding continues. The material is then said to have an *upper yield point* and a *lower yield point* defined by corresponding stresses σ_{uy} and σ_{ly}. These

stresses are illustrated in the stress-strain diagrams in Fig. 3.37. In view
of the inherent variability of the stress at which yielding begins—the upper
yield point—and the relative stability of the lower yield point, the latter

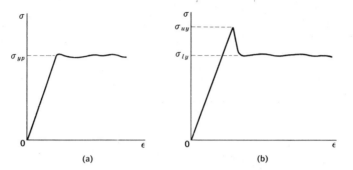

Fig. 3.37   *Yield points in discontinuous
yielding.*

is a better measure of elastic strength and is so used. Typical yield
strengths and yield points are given in Table 3.3.

Table 3.3   **Typical Values of Yield Strength of
Engineering Materials**

MATERIAL	YIELD STRENGTH AT 0.2% OFFSET, $\sigma_y(0.2\%)$, psi	YIELD POINT (LOWER), σ_{ly}, psi
Alloy steel[a]	215,000	—
Aluminum alloy[b]	70,000	—
Structural steel[c]	—	40,000
Aluminum[d]	3,500	—

[a] Manganese-silicon steel.
[b] Alloy 7075-T6 (heat-treated).
[c] C1020 hot-rolled.
[d] Commercial soft aluminum, 1100-O (annealed).

The yield strength is used as the basis for a design or working stress
whenever it is intended that a member remain elastic under load. Since
elastic action is usually desired, the yield strength is used in a majority of
engineering applications. A suitable factor of safety, n_y, is applied to
obtain the working stress as follows:

$$\sigma_w = \frac{\sigma_y}{n_y}. \tag{3.19}$$

The factor of safety used depends largely upon the previous experience and
judgment of the engineer. Working stresses are specified in various build-

ing codes.   Here the appropriate factor of safety has been determined by the organization responsible for the code and represents the combined experience of many engineers.   Values of the factor of safety vary widely: they are large when loading is uncertain and materials somewhat undependable, approximately one (actually no safety factor) in certain aircraft applications where weight is all-important.

Tensile strength is the maximum conventional stress that can be sustained by the material.   It is the *ultimate strength in tension* and corresponds to the maximum load in a tension test.   It is measured by the highest point on the conventional stress-strain diagram.   Figure 3.38 illus-

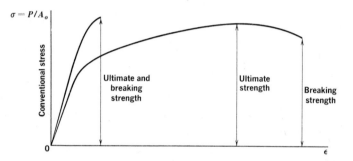

Fig. 3.38   Ultimate and breaking loads.

trates two possibilities, one a ductile material, the other a brittle material. For the ductile material the load drops after the ultimate load because of necking.

In brittle materials the ultimate strength is a logical basis for working stresses.   Like yield strength, it is used with a factor of safety, n_u, as follows:

$$\sigma_w = \frac{\sigma_u}{n_u}. \tag{3.20}$$

Here σ_u is the ultimate strength, obtained either from published tables (handbooks, etc.) or from actual experimental observation.   Because of the scatter in the strengths of brittle materials (Art. 3.4), the value from either source is usually rather uncertain.   This uncertainty, plus the fact that brittle fracture is a complete failure while yielding may simply redistribute the stress, makes it necessary to choose a higher factor of safety than that used with the yield strength.

In ductile materials the ultimate strength is sometimes used as a basis for working stress when actual rupture is the principal concern and some permanent deformation may be tolerated.   The design of riveted joints is a case in point.   The full strength of the joint is not realized until the stresses have been equalized by considerable yielding in the various parts. In pressure vessels and piping systems some increase in diameter is often permissible. Actual bursting is the thing that must be avoided. Here, too, the use of an ultimate stress is appropriate in design.

The ultimate strength in ductile materials defines the onset of plastic instability, as described in Art. 3.9. It is not a true "strength" in the ordinary sense of the word, but nevertheless it is an important mechanical property. Typical values are given in Table 3.4.

Table 3.4   Typical Tensile Strengths of Engineering Materials

MATERIAL	TENSILE STRENGTH, σ_u, psi
Alloy steel[a]	230,000
Tungsten carbide cermet	130,000
Aluminum alloy[b]	80,000
Structural steel[c]	70,000
Alumina ceramics	30,000
Acrylics[d]	8,000

[a] Manganese-silicon steel.
[b] Alloy 7075-T6 (heat-treated).
[c] C1020 hot-rolled.
[d] Plexiglas, Lucite.

The secant modulus as a measure of stiffness is identical with that described under nonlinear elastic properties (Eq. 3.9),

$$E_{sec} = \frac{\sigma}{\epsilon}.$$

Since the relation between stress and strain can always be written as $\sigma = E_{sec}\epsilon$, where E_{sec} is a variable coefficient, this equation is useful in the analysis of plastic behavior. For example, analytical expressions for stress concentration factors beyond the elastic range have been developed using the secant modulus. The following formula was derived by E. Z. Stowell[*] for the stress concentration factor (plastic) at a small circular hole in a large plate:

$$K_p = 1 + 2\frac{(E_{sec})_a}{(E_{sec})_\infty}$$

where $(E_{sec})_a$ is the secant modulus corresponding to the maximum stress which occurs at the sides of the hole and $(E_{sec})_\infty$ is the secant modulus corresponding to the average stress at a considerable distance from the hole. For linear conditions the stress concentration factor for a circular hole is 3. For a large stress E_{sec} is always smaller than for a small stress, and hence K_p is always less than 3.[†]

---

[*] Stowell, Elbridge Z., *Stress and Strain Concentrations at a Circular Hole in an Infinite Plate,* National Advisory Committee for Aeronautics Technical Note 2073, Washington, April 1950.

[†] The calculation of K_p requires a trial-and-error procedure.

As for the nonlinear elastic curve it is sometimes necessary to know the "instantaneous" stiffness or tangent modulus, E_t, measured by the slope of the curve at a given stress. One of the most important applications of the inelastic tangent modulus is in the buckling of short columns that are stressed beyond the elastic range in compression. This application will be taken up in Chapter 4. The tangent modulus is given by Eq. 3.10

$$E_t = \left[\frac{d\sigma}{d\epsilon}\right]_\sigma.$$

Figure 3.39 shows a curve of tangent modulus vs stress, calculated from the accompanying stress-strain curve.

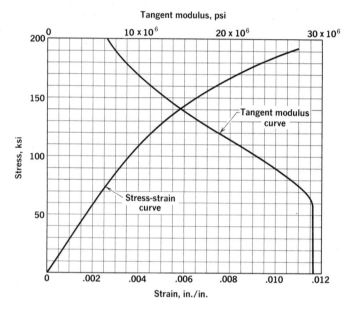

Fig. 3.39   Tangent modulus vs stress, computed from stress-strain curve for chromium-nickel steel in tension.

One of the most desirable features of metals is their ductility. Because of this property they can be drawn, extruded, rolled, and otherwise formed into an almost unlimited variety of shapes of great use in engineering. Even more important, their ductility provides an additional margin of safety beyond the elastic range, often preventing serious mechanical failure. For example, under a momentary large overload on some part, a structure will yield locally if the material is ductile, and the overstresses will be distributed among other parts of the structure, preventing complete collapse.

It is therefore important to know the relative ductilities of materials.

Two standard measures are obtained from the conventional tension test: one is the *per cent elongation* in a specified length of the tension member at rupture; the other is the *per cent reduction in area* of its smallest cross-section at rupture.

The per cent elongation is usually based on a 2-inch length including the neck, but other lengths are also used.   Since the largest part of the plastic strain is localized in the neck with relatively little in other parts of the member, the per cent elongation varies with the length used.   An example will illustrate.   A steel bar is elongated until it breaks.   Segment A of the bar, located at the neck, was originally $\frac{1}{2}$ in. long but is 1 in. long after fracture—a 100 per cent elongation.   The other parts of the bar are elongated uniformly by 10 per cent so that each inch becomes 0.1 in. longer after fracture.   In a 2-inch length including the neck, therefore, the total elongation is 0.5 in. for segment A, plus 0.15 in. for the other one and one-half inches (1.5×0.1).   The per cent elongation in 2 in. is therefore $100 \times (0.5 + 0.15)/2 = 32.5$ per cent.   In an 8-inch length, also including segment A, the elongation is 0.5 in. plus 7.5×0.1 in., and the per cent elongation in 8 in. is $100 \times (0.5 + 0.75)/8 = 15.6$ per cent, less than half as much as that in 2 in.   Hence it is essential that the length be specified in giving the per cent elongation.   The per cent elongation has little or no basic significance; its primary use is to compare the ductilities of materials.

The per cent reduction in area is found by measuring the cross-sectional area of the member before loading (A_0) and that of the neck after fracture (A) and comparing them as follows:

$$\text{Per cent reduction in area} = \frac{A_0 - A}{A_0} \times 100. \qquad (3.21)$$

For specimens of the same size and shape this quantity provides a good ductility rating.   There is no ambiguity as in per cent elongation.   Typical ductilities of engineering materials are shown in Table 3.5.

Table 3.5   Typical Ductilities of Engineering Materials

MATERIAL	ELONGATION IN 2 IN., PER CENT	REDUCTION IN AREA, PER CENT
Structural steel[a]	35	60
Aluminum[b]	25	80
Aluminum alloy[c]	10	30
Alloy steel[d]	10	20
Acrylics[e]	4	0

[a] C1020 hot-rolled.
[b] Commercial soft aluminum, 1100-O (annealed).
[c] Alloy 7075-T6 (heat-treated).
[d] Manganese-silicon steel.
[e] Plexiglas, Lucite.

Toughness is the overall capacity of a material to absorb energy.   Like the modulus of resilience, the *modulus of toughness* is measured by the unit strain energy absorbed—this time to rupture.   Equation 3.7, developed for

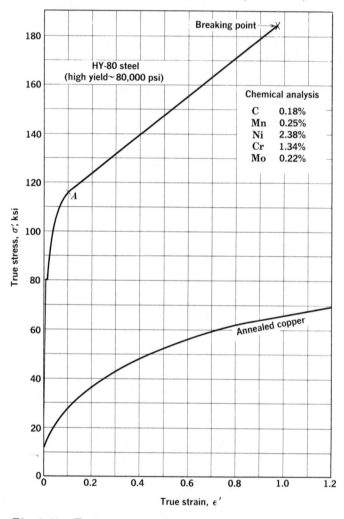

Fig. 3.40   True   stress-strain   curves   for
copper and steel.

nonlinear elasticity, can be used here since no restrictions are placed on the variation of stress and strain.   In the plastic range the energy absorbed per unit volume is therefore

$$u = \int_0^{\epsilon_r} \sigma d\epsilon,$$

where ϵ_r is the strain at rupture. The integral represents the total area under the stress-strain diagram from beginning to end. The modulus of toughness can be computed by counting squares or by the use of a planimeter. An approximate value sometimes used is obtained by multiplying the maximum stress, σ_u, by ϵ_r.

Since it involves the highly localized strain after necking, the modulus of toughness should include the length of the member used in computing it.

Properties in Terms of True Stress and Strain

A number of mechanical properties either *require* evaluation in terms of true stress and strain or can be studied more successfully on that basis. Before discussing them we shall examine some of the characteristics of the true stress-strain diagram for tension. Figure 3.40 shows two typical curves. Since true stress and strain are primarily applicable to the plastic range, the scale is made to include this range in its entirety. The elastic range is so small as to be invisible on the graph.

The true stress-strain diagram shows clearly the variation in the rate of strain-hardening, an important property in the analysis of plastic instability (Art. 3.9) and forming operations. The rate of strain-hardening at any given strain is equal to the slope of the σ'-ϵ' curve at that point, and is sometimes called the *modulus of strain-hardening*.

Attempts have been made to find an equation that would describe the relation between true stress and strain. It has been found that for many metals the observed data can be fitted approximately by the empirical equation[*]

$$\sigma' = k\epsilon'^n \quad (n < 1), \tag{3.22}$$

where k and n are constants that depend on the material. The degree of accuracy with which this equation fits a given set of data can best be seen in a log-log plot. Taking the logarithms of both sides of the equation, we have

$$\log \sigma' = \log k + n \log \epsilon'. \tag{3.22a}$$

This equation represents a straight line on the log-log plot, with n the slope of the line and $\log k$ its intercept on the $\log \sigma'$-axis at $\epsilon' = 1$. In Fig. 3.41 data from Fig. 3.40 are plotted in this way, with lines fitted according to Eq. 3.22a. In some instances the fit is reasonably good, as in the curve for annealed copper; in others the approximation is quite large. It should be noted that the upper curve in Fig. 3.40 can best be fitted by a straight line from A (the point of maximum load) to its end at the breaking point, a fairly common situation. It is frequently found that the first part of such a curve can be fitted closely by Eq. 3.22.

---

[*] Marin, Joseph, *Engineering Materials—Their Mechanical Properties and Applications*, Prentice-Hall, Inc., Englewood Cliffs, N. J., 1952, p. 53.

When the actual true stress-strain curve can be satisfactorily approximated by Eq. 3.22, the various properties and relations between them can be expressed mathematically. The material constant, k, representing the *stress* at a strain of unity, is called the *strength coefficient.* The exponent n, being related to the *slope*, is called the *strain-hardening exponent.*

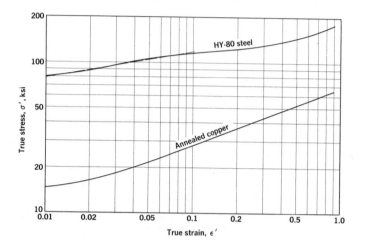

Fig. 3.41   Data from Fig. 3.40, plotted on
logarithmic coordinates.

The condition of *plastic instability*, expressed by Eqs. 3.14 or 3.14a, can now be specified in more precise terms. From Eq. 3.14a we can write

$$\frac{d\sigma'}{\sigma'} = -\frac{dA}{A}. \tag{3.14b}$$

Since, at the onset of plastic instability, fairly large plastic strains have occurred, we can assume that the volume remains essentially constant, and make use of Eq. 3.17, $Al = A_0 l_0 = $ constant. As described in Art. 3.9, A decreases while l increases. Differentiating Eq. 3.17 gives

$$A \, dl + l \, dA = 0$$

or

$$-\frac{dA}{A} = \frac{dl}{l}, \tag{3.17a}$$

which, by definition, is equal to the increment of true strain, $d\epsilon'$ (Art. 3.11). Substituting $d\epsilon'$ for $-dA/A$ in Eq. 3.14b, we have

$$\frac{d\sigma'}{\sigma'} = d\epsilon'$$

or

$$\frac{d\sigma'}{d\epsilon'} = \sigma'. \tag{3.14c}$$

According to this equation, plastic instability occurs when the slope of the true stress-strain curve equals the true stress at that point. It is worthwhile noting that this result is completely independent of any assumed equation of the curve. Using Eq. 3.22, the left side of the above relation becomes

$$\frac{d\sigma'}{d\epsilon'} = kn\epsilon'^{(n-1)},$$

and substitution in Eq. 3.14c gives the following equality:

$$kn\epsilon'^{(n-1)} = k\epsilon'^{n}$$

or

$$\epsilon' = n. \tag{3.23}$$

Thus the true strain at which a neck begins to form in simple tension—the onset of plastic instability—is equal to the strain-hardening exponent. This analysis for simple tension can be adapted to other forms of loading, such as in pressure vessels and piping systems, where the condition of plastic instability gives the value of the *bursting pressure*, an important factor in design.*

Specifications of *ductility* can be made in terms of true stress and strain with much more significance than in terms of conventional values. One such measure of ductility is the *true strain at maximum load*, which gives the maximum *uniform* strain. Another is the *true fracture strain*, which is equivalent to the *true reduction in area* at fracture.

$$\epsilon'_f = q'_f = \log_e \frac{A_0}{A_f}, \tag{3.24}$$

where the subscript f indicates fracture.

Toughness in the most severely strained region is measured by the area under the true stress-strain diagram to rupture. This area represents the energy per unit volume actually put into the material at the smallest part of the neck.

EXPERIMENTAL METHODS

The study of engineering materials, like every other scientific study, depends ultimately on experimental research. Here we are interested pri-

---

* The M. W. Kellogg Company, *Design of Piping Systems*, 2nd ed., John Wiley & Sons, Inc., New York, 1956, pp. 5–7; Weil, N. A., "Rupture Characteristics of Safety Diaphragms," *J. App. Mech.* **26,** 621–624 (1959).

marily in experiments of the engineering type.   Experiments by physicists, chemists, and metallurgists in the fundamentals of the solid state are, of course, of basic importance but beyond the scope of this text.   The dividing line between them and experiments that can be classified as engineering is, however, becoming less distinct as time goes on, and there are large areas of overlap.   Thus many of the experimental methods discussed here will also have use in other fields of basic science.

3.13   RESEARCH AND STANDARD TESTS

Experiments on materials are made for various purposes.   Of first importance are those through which the physical laws governing mechanical behavior of materials are investigated.   Since time is required to develop valid physical laws, and the demands of engineering are immediate, a second type of experiment is of almost equal importance.   In this type the expected conditions of use for the particular material are imitated as closely as possible, but in a simplified and standardized form, and the performance observed.   In this way many of the mechanical properties are determined.   Sometimes the results of these experiments provide valuable help in investigating basic physical laws.   They often lead to the discovery of new uses for materials.

A third type of experiment is used when the physical laws are known and the constants occurring in these laws must be evaluated.   Experimental determination of the modulus of elasticity for use in Hooke's law is an example.

Still a fourth type is the one used most often in industry: *control testing.* Here the purpose is to provide routine information on the quality of a product.   The need for accuracy is usually the least in these tests, but speed is of utmost importance.   The analysis of results becomes largely a problem in statistics.

Since so much of the experimental work with materials is to test their quality or their response to certain conditions of loading, it has become common usage to refer to all experiments with materials as "materials testing."   This term hardly seems appropriate to the scientific study of materials, but it is widely used nevertheless.

In the following sections we take up experiments in simple tension. This form of experiment has been highly standardized to enable comparison of results and improve their reproducibility.   Since the behavior of materials in tension often varies with the size and shape of the specimen, the rate of loading, and the temperature, standardization has been found necessary for all types of tension experiments.   The American Society for Testing Materials (ASTM), as the principal standardizing agency, publishes every three years a set of volumes called the ASTM *Standards.*   In these books are to be found complete descriptions of methods of testing as well as specifications for materials. They will be referred to repeatedly in the following discussion.* Each description or specification is given a designation, such as E8-57T: the first letter indicates the classification (E—miscellaneous subjects); following is the number of that particular standard; the number following the dash is the year it was adopted or last revised; the *T* means that it is a tentative standard, still subject to further revision. To ensure reference to the proper version of each standard, the date is usually included in its designation. Earlier or later versions often differ from the one cited only in minor respects.

Special equipment used in mechanical testing of materials includes machines for applying a measured load to a specimen (*testing machines*), and devices for measuring the resulting deformation (*strainometers*). Other equipment used is that ordinarily found in any laboratory, such as thermometers, micrometers, and balances.

3.14 TESTING MACHINES

Many kinds of machines are in use for applying measured loads to specimens. Loads ranging from a few grams to millions of pounds can be obtained with the various machines available. Application of the load, however, is only half the problem. The other half is weighing the load with the necessary precision. The *loading mechanism* and the *weighing mechanism* constitute the two principal components of a testing machine.

Loading is done either mechanically or hydraulically. *Mechanical* loading systems use screws to apply the load, as in a screw jack. A suitable frame is provided in which to mount the specimen. One part of the frame is driven by screws, and the other part is supported by some sort of weighing system (Fig. 3.42a). *Hydraulic* loading systems use a piston activated by hydraulic pressure in a cylinder, as in a hydraulic jack. The piston drives part of the mounting frame, while the other part is either fixed or supported by the weighing system (Fig. 3.42b and c). Hydraulic machines are usually less expensive than the mechanical or screw type and can be made to have higher capacities. Screw machines are seldom made to exert loads of more than 400,000 lb, while hydraulic machines capable of exerting 5,000,000 lb and more have been constructed.

Weighing systems can also be classified as *mechanical* or *hydraulic*, at least in the larger machines. Other types that are coming into common use for low loads include electrical cells and air cells. The mechanical system is simply a balance scale, constructed to withstand high loads. One

---

* A booklet entitled *Selected ASTM Engineering Materials Standards* for use in college curricula is also published by ASTM. Many of the standards referred to here will be found in this booklet.

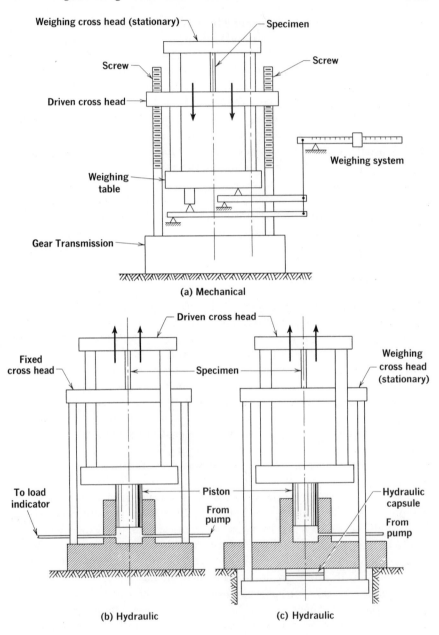

Fig. 3.42 Schematic diagram of mechanical and hydraulic loading systems.

part of the mounting frame—usually in the shape of a table—is supported by knife edges that rest on a lever system connected to a load indicator (Fig. 3.42a). The load indicator is usually one of three types: a *horizontal balance beam* having a movable poise like that on a common platform scale; a vertical pendulum connected either directly, by a linkage, or electrically to the hand on a load dial; an *elastic load-sensing element* (e.g., a torque bar), connected electrically to the load dial. In the first type it is necessary, in reading the load, to bring the poise to a position on the beam where it will balance the load. The beam is calibrated in pounds, depending on the position of the poise. To obtain a continuous series of load readings the beam must be kept in balance at all times during the experiment. Considerable skill is required, a factor that has led to the use of other load indicators. In the second type the pendulum automatically swings up enough to balance the load, and its position is then indicated on a load dial. In the third type the elastic load-sensing element simply deforms in proportion to the load, and this deformation is indicated on the load dial. With either of these latter two arrangements the load can be read directly on the dial, which is calibrated in pounds.

Hydraulic weighing systems are of two main types. In the first the load is measured by a pressure gage attached directly to the hydraulic cylinder. The only difficulty is that the force must be transmitted to the specimen from the oil in the cylinder by means of the piston, and some force is lost on the way, in the form of friction. Friction can be minimized by extremely careful machining (lapping) of the piston and cylinder walls. High precision has been claimed for some machines of this type. It is the simplest type because there is no separate weighing mechanism, and one side of the mounting frame can be fixed (Fig. 3.42b). The second type consists of a hydraulic capsule having no connection with the hydraulic loading system. The weighing part of the mounting frame is attached to the capsule, which is firmly supported on the foundation (Fig. 3.42c). When the load is applied to the specimen, it is transmitted by the frame to the capsule, squeezing out a minute quantity of oil. This oil is forced into a bourdon tube, which in turn is connected directly or indirectly to the hand on the load-indicating dial.

Mechanical weighing systems are usually incorporated in machines using mechanical loading, and hydraulic weighing systems in those using hydraulic loading. However, machines sometimes use mixed systems—mechanical loading with hydraulic weighing, and vice versa. Electrical and air-operated weighing cells are incorporated in various types of machines, and are available as attachments for measuring small loads on existing machines. Air cells use compressed air controlled by the load through special valves. Electrical units use an elastic element which deforms under load, and deformation is measured electrically.　Electrical measurement of deformation will be discussed under electric strain gages (Art. 3.16).

The frame in which the specimen is mounted is equipped to hold various types of specimens in tension.　(Most machines of this type are also arranged so that specimens can be loaded in compression or bending and are therefore called *universal* testing machines.)　By reference to Fig. 3.42

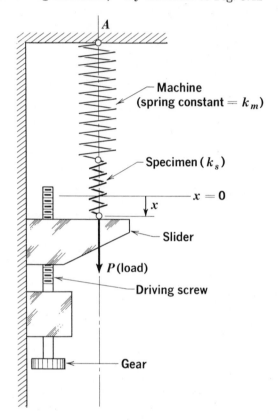

Fig. 3.43　Schematic representation of testing machine and specimen by springs in series (spring constants k_m and k_s).

the various parts can be seen.　The horizontal parts of the frame, extending between the columns or screws, are called *crossheads* or *platens*.　The specimen is fastened in grips in the movable and fixed crossheads.　Grips are usually either simple clamps that squeeze the ends of the specimen tightly enough so that they can apply an axial force, or holders to which the specimens are positively attached by means of shoulders, pins, or screw threads.

The movable crosshead is driven by an electric motor (or occasionally by a hand crank) through a system of gears and screws, or by a pump and a hydraulic piston.　Controls are provided through which the rate of motion of the crosshead can be governed. In the mechanical-type machine the control consists of a variable-speed motor, or a clutch-and-gear transmission. In hydraulic machines control is provided by needle valves. When there is no specimen in the machine, a given control setting always results in a certain fixed speed of the movable crosshead, called the *idling speed*.

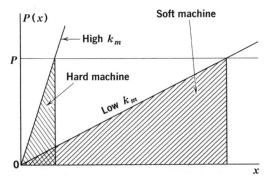

Fig. 3.44 Comparison of hard and soft testing machines. Shaded areas represent stored energies at a given load, P:

$$U = \frac{k_m x^2}{2} = \frac{P^2}{2k_m}.$$

When a specimen is being loaded, the load is transmitted to the entire machine, and it deforms elastically along with the specimen. The deformation of the machine is often greater than that of the specimen. Furthermore, under increasing load the speed of a motor tends to decrease. Consequently, unless the machine is provided with automatic controls, the speed of the movable crosshead is considerably less under load than its idling speed. So long as the specimen remains elastic, however, a fixed control setting does provide an approximately constant crosshead speed and therefore an approximately constant rate of elongation. This fact can be shown by the following calculation. The action of a testing machine can be illustrated by two springs in series (Fig. 3.43). The upper spring, whose stiffness is k_m, represents the machine itself, fastened to the foundation at A. The other spring, k_s, represents the specimen. For a fixed control setting, neglecting any change in the speed of the motor, the total elongation of the spring, x, increases at a constant rate, $\dot{x}$ (the idling speed). Now $x = x_m + x_s$ where x_m and x_s are the corresponding elongations of the two springs. Differentiating we have, $\dot{x} = \dot{x}_m + \dot{x}_s$, from which we see that the total rate is made up of the two separate rates of elongation.

Since, at any instant, the load $P = k_m x_m = k_s x_s = kx$, where k is the equivalent total stiffness $= k_m k_s/(k_m + k_s)$, we have $k_m \dot{x}_m = k_s \dot{x}_s = k\dot{x}$. Thus if $\dot{x}$ is constant, $\dot{x}_s$ is also constant. It also follows that $\dot{x}_s/\dot{x} = k/k_s = k_m/(k_m + k_s)$. For example, if $k_s = k_m$, the rate of elongation of the specimen will be half the idling speed of the crosshead.

A testing machine having a high stiffness, k_m, is called a *hard* machine; one having a low k_m is called a *soft* machine. It is often important to use a hard machine to reduce the deformation of the machine itself and thereby increase its response to the material being tested. In instability experiments like measuring the discontinuous yielding of mild steel it is important to reduce the energy stored in the machine during the test. This excess energy is always ready to upset the unstable equilibrium of the specimen if triggered by some outside impulse or shock. A hard machine stores less energy than a soft one; Fig. 3.44 compares the energy stored in each at a given load as given by the area under the load-deformation diagram.

3.15   ACCURACY AND SENSITIVITY

As is true in all measurements, the measurement of load is never absolutely accurate. The reading obtained for a given load is always in error by some small amount. Increasingly greater care in observation will make the difference between the observed and actual load smaller, but never zero. The word *accurate* must therefore be interpreted as a relative term. ASTM defines it as follows: "A testing machine is said to be accurate if the indicated load is within the specified permissible variation from the actual load."* The actual load, though not really measurable, can be approached very closely by the use of standards such as those kept at the National Bureau of Standards in Washington, D. C.

The permissible variation from the actual load depends on the use to which the testing machine is to be put. The ASTM *Standards* specify that the error shall not exceed 1 per cent.* Most commercial testing machines meet this specification. A so-called "precision" testing machine usually has a guaranteed accuracy of 0.5 per cent in a specified loading range, while its actual accuracy can be 0.1 per cent or better in certain parts of the range. Testing machines must have their accuracy verified periodically by comparison with known standards, and must be adjusted if necessary. Use of corrections to compensate for errors is not permissible.

Sensitivity is an indication of the response of the machine to small changes in load. *It should not be confused with accuracy.* A machine that responds quickly and definitely to small changes in load is a sensitive machine. However, if the loads or changes in load that it indicates are not within

---

* ASTM E4-57T.

the permissible error from the actual values, it is not an accurate machine. On the other hand, a machine that does *not* respond to small changes in load can hardly be expected to give accurate results.   In other words, the accuracy of a machine may be limited by low sensitivity but is not necessarily improved by high sensitivity.

Sensitivity is measured in a number of ways.   The usual measure is the increment of load corresponding to the smallest division or fraction of a division that can be read on the dial.   The fraction that can be read or estimated depends on the size of the smallest division and the thickness of the pointer.   It is usually one-half, one-fifth, or one-tenth.   (A slide rule provides a good example of the estimation of fractions of divisions of varying sizes.)   For example, if the smallest division represents 10 lb and it is possible to estimate the position of the pointer to the nearest fifth of a division, the sensitivity is 2 lb.   Sensitivity may also be expressed as per cent of the total load measured.   Thus if the total load above were 1000 lb, the sensitivity could be thought of as 0.2 per cent.

A number of factors are not taken into account in the measure of sensitivity outlined above.   Most important is friction or lost motion in the mechanism of the pointer or elsewhere in the machine.   Such defects could prevent the pointer from responding to changes in load as small as that indicated by the usual sensitivity measurement.   The only way to check for such conditions is to apply known increments of load equal to the apparent sensitivity and observe the response of the pointer at various points in its range.   Failure to take precautions against parallax may also reduce the sensitivity of the readings.   Still another factor not taken into account is the speed of response, which is sometimes indicated by the number of seconds required for the pointer to reach full range from zero.

3.16 STRAINOMETERS

In observing the deformation of a tension specimen it must be possible to measure very small changes in length with great accuracy.   The total elastic elongation of a standard tension specimen of a strong metal may not exceed 0.002 inch.   If ten readings are desired in the elastic range, each increment of elongation will be only 0.0002 inch.   To measure each increment within 1 per cent it must be possible to measure changes in length of 0.000002 inch, or 2 microinches (millionths of an inch).   The purpose of a strainometer is to magnify these small changes in length so that they can be observed.

Strain can be magnified in two ways: by measuring the deformation over a long "gage length," l_0; or by amplifying the motion of the measuring points attached to the specimen.   The latter is the principal source of strain magnification.   A gage length of 10 inches provides a multiplication of only 10, and longer lengths are seldom used.   Magnification of 1000 or more can be obtained by various multiplying devices incorporated into strainometers. As a general rule the larger the magnification, the smaller the overall range.

Strainometers take a wide variety of forms. The three general types in most common use are *mechanical, optical,* and *electrical.*

Mechanical Strainometers

A system of mechanical levers is used to magnify the elongation of the specimen. A simple arrangement giving a 5:1 multiplication or *gage factor* is shown in Fig. 3.45. Further multiplication is obtained by attaching a dial indicator between the ends of the levers. The dial indicator trans-

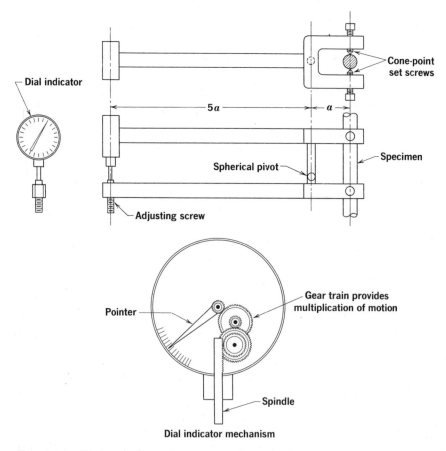

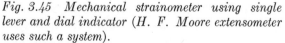

Fig. 3.45 Mechanical strainometer using single lever and dial indicator (H. F. Moore extensometer uses such a system).

forms the linear motion of its spindle to rotation of its hand by means of an ordinary rack and pinion. Figure 3.46 shows a more complex system giving a 1000:1 multiplication. The strainometer is attached to the desired portion of the specimen by means of knife edges or cone-point set-

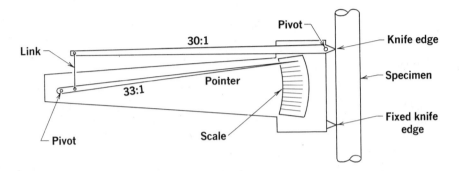

Fig. 3.46   Mechanical strainometer using multiple levers to give 1000:1 multiplication (Huggenberger tensometer uses such a system).

screws. It is the relative motion of these points as the specimen elongates that is magnified by the levers. The distance between these points is the gage length, l_0. The most common value of l_0 is 2 inches, although distances of 1, 8, and 10 inches are also used.

Strainometers especially adapted to measure elongation are called *extensometers.*

Available ranges in mechanical strainometers vary from 0.15 per cent (0.0015 in./in.) for the Huggenberger Tensometer to as much as 10 per cent (0.10 in./in.).

The pivots in the system of levers are a source of friction in the mechanical strainometer. Friction is minimized by using knife edges or very carefully made small pivots or jeweled bearings. Continuous vibration of the strainometer or repeated light tapping (for example with a pencil) will reduce the effects of friction by transforming it into kinetic friction, which is somewhat less than static friction. Looseness in the pivots causes lost motion. Both friction and lost motion contribute to inaccuracies in this type of strainometer. With proper construction and use, however, it provides quite satisfactory accuracy for much experimental work. It has the advantages of durability and relatively low cost.

A special variety of mechanical strainometer is that used with automatic recording apparatus. In the usual type the lever arm from the movable knife edge is attached to an iron core that moves inside a coil when the

specimen is strained.   The position of the core determines the inductance
of the coil for any given strain.   Magnification is primarily electrical, in
the form of amplification of the signal from the coil.   A change in the
elongation of the specimen produces a corresponding rotation of the re-
corder drum about its axis to a new position; the load can also be recorded
by moving the stylus in the direction parallel to the axis of the drum.
Thus a complete load-elongation diagram can be obtained.

Optical Strainometers

Optical levers have the advantage of complete absence of weight.   Consequently large magnifications can be obtained optically with a minimum
number of mechanical bearings, correspondingly low friction, and little lost
motion.   Optical strainometers therefore are of highest accuracy.   An
elementary form of this type, the Marten's mirror extensometer, is illustrated in Fig. 3.47.   The only mechanical bearings are the two knife edges

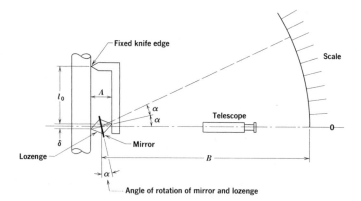

Fig. 3.47   Martens mirror extensometer.

on the lozenge* which supports the mirror.   The magnification is the ratio
of the scale reading to the elongation, δ.   For small elongations the scale
reading is double the angle of rotation of the mirror times B, the distance
from the mirror to the scale.   The elongation equals the angle of rotation
times A, the distance from knife edge to knife edge on the lozenge.   Consequently the magnification is given by $2\,\alpha B/\alpha A = 2\,B/A$.   If, for example, A is 4.50 mm and B is 112.5 cm (45 in.), the magnification is 500.
The smallest reading that can be made on the scale is 0.1 mm (by means

---

* Lozenge: a four-sided prism having sharp edges.

of a telescope), which represents a δ of 0.0002 mm (0.000008 in.). Hence the sensitivity, based on the usual measure (Art. 3.15), is 8 μin.

The Tuckerman optical strain gage is a refined form making greater use of optical principles and resulting in a more compact instrument.

In addition to high accuracy, the optical strainometer offers the advantage of fast response to dynamic strains. The only moving mass is the small lozenge and mirror, and it can be made extremely light. One disadvantage is the high cost of optical systems. Optical strainometers are also rather difficult to use and require considerable experience. Because of their high sensitivity their range is limited. The Tuckerman strain gage, for example, has a range of 0.0002 inch elongation.

Electrical Strainometers

Several ways of measuring strains electrically have been developed. The most widely used electrical strainometer is the *bonded electric resistance-wire strain gage*. Its operation is based on the change in resistance of a material under strain (see Chapter 11). A very small wire is cemented to the specimen, parallel to the axis of loading. Because of the size of the wire, the cement is very strong by comparison, so that the wire is in effect an integral part of the specimen (hence the word *bonded*). As the specimen is strained under load, the wire is strained by exactly the same amount. Thus the wire becomes a true strain gage, measuring strain directly.

For a number of metals the resistance increases in direct proportion to the strain, according to the equation $R = R_0 + K_s R_0 \epsilon$. Here R_0 is the normal resistance of the wire, without strain, and K_s is a constant called the *gage factor*. From the above equation K_s is given by

$$K_s = \frac{(R - R_0)/R_0}{\epsilon}, \qquad (3.25)$$

the ratio of the unit resistance change to the corresponding strain. For a given material the value of K_s may be found experimentally by making a series of observations of resistance at known strains. If we plot $(R - R_0)/R_0$ against ϵ and fit a straight line to the points, K_s may be computed from the slope of the line. When K_s is known, the wire can be used for measuring strain.

In practice the bonded electric resistance-wire strain gage is made in the form of a grid of wire (Fig. 3.48) to increase the resistance over that of a single strand. Wire 0.001 inch in diameter is usually used, and a piece of thin paper is cemented between the wire and the specimen for insulation.

The most commonly used commercial gage of the kind in this country is the SR-4, manufactured by Baldwin-Lima-Hamilton Corporation. The wire grid is cemented on a paper backing, and connecting wires are attached. They can be cemented directly to the specimen according to instructions contained in each package. The gage factor for each lot of gages is determined in the factory by calibrating a statistically selected sample of the lot. The gage factor, resistance, and lot number are shown on each package. Many different types are available to suit the purposes for which they are used.

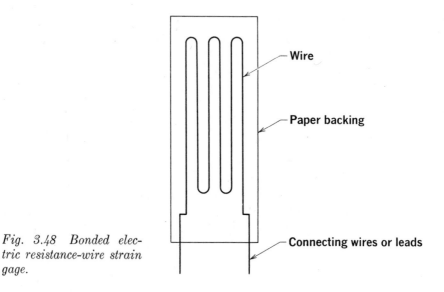

Fig. 3.48 Bonded electric resistance-wire strain gage.

Most gages are made of wires having a gage factor of 2.0. These wires also have low temperature coefficients of resistance, a desirable feature. When higher output is required, as in measuring dynamic strains, wire having a gage factor of 3.5 is often used. Its higher temperature coefficient of resistance is acceptable if the duration of test is short, as for dynamic strain.

Ordinarily the SR-4 strain gage is used with an SR-4 strain indicator, an electronic device for measuring the change in resistance of the gage. The readings given by the indicator are calibrated directly in terms of strain, in microinches per inch. It is necessary only to set the proper gage factor on a dial before taking readings.

The SR-4 indicator incorporates certain features of the Wheatstone bridge. Four resistances are arranged in a circuit similar to that of Fig. 3.49. Resistance A is the strain gage mounted on the specimen. Resistance R is the adjustable resistance. In principle the resistance of A is found by adjusting R until the bridge is balanced and the galvanometer reads zero (the null-reading method). This arrangement also makes it possible to compensate for any change in length of the specimen as a result of temperature change. A strain gage identical to A is used for resistance C, on the opposite side of the bridge. If C is cemented onto a piece of the same material as the specimen, any changes in length owing to temperature will be the same in both, and the resulting change in the resistances of A and C will also be the same, holding the bridge in balance. Gage C is called a *compensating* or *dummy* gage.

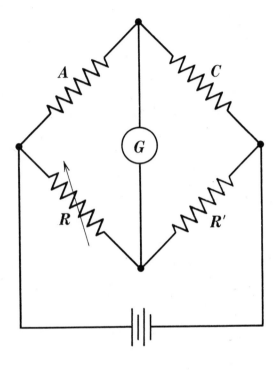

Fig. 3.49 Wheatstone bridge circuit for use with electric resistance-wire strain gage: A *is the active gage;* R *is the adjustable resistance;* C *is the compensating gage;* R' *is the fourth leg of the bridge.*

The bonded electric resistance-wire strain gage is undoubtedly more widely used than any other strainometer. Its advantages include:

Accuracy: the gage factor of the SR-4 strain gage is guaranteed to be correct within 1 per cent. An error of 1 per cent in the gage factor would produce a 1 per cent error in all strains measured, assuming the gage to be linear. Thus a strain of 0.001 would be in error by 10 microinches per inch, while a 10 per cent strain (0.10) would be in error by 0.001 inch per inch. This is a systematic error. Random errors occur in the reading of the instruments and in the instruments themselves. It is generally assumed that in the elastic range, at least, observations are correct to the nearest 10 microinches per inch when sufficient care is used. Results reproducible to 2 or 3 microinches per inch can sometimes be obtained in very carefully conducted tests. The SR-4 is therefore one of the more accurate strainometers.

Sensitivity: the least reading on the SR-4 strain indicator is 1 microinch per inch, which can be estimated fairly closely.   It thus ranks among the most sensitive gages.

Short gage length: gage lengths as small as $\frac{1}{16}$ inch make it possible to measure local strains.

Negligible mass: good for dynamic strain measurements.

Remote reading and recording possible with suitable electrical equipment.

No knife edges or setscrews against the surface of the specimen.

Disadvantages are:

High first cost of electronic equipment.

Not reusable; increases experimental operating costs.

Time required for cementing gages; can be speeded up by drying with heat lamps according to instructions.

The total usable range of the SR-4 gage is at least 0.01 inch per inch (1 per cent).   Special SR-4 "post-yield" gages offer ranges up to 10 per cent.

Other electrical strainometers include unbonded resistance-wire gages, inductance gages, and capacitance gages.   Information on these will be found in texts and handbooks on testing and experimental stress analysis.

3.17   THE TENSION TEST

The tension test has for many years been the most widely used experimental procedure for the study of mechanical behavior.   It is often called the basic mechanical test, and much of our present knowledge has come from it.   In the idealized state of static tension it is assumed that (a) the stress is uniformly distributed across each cross-section of the member, (b) the stress is constant from cross-section to cross-section along the length of the member, and (c) the load changes so slowly that no dynamic effects are present.   In the standard tension test these conditions are approached as closely as possible within the practical limitations of the equipment available.   A specimen of some standard form is loaded slowly with an axial load, and a series of observations of load and deformation are made.

Deformation may be axial elongation or lateral contraction (or both). In the tension test for conventional stress and strain, it is necessary only to measure the elongation with a strainometer.   The true stress-strain tension test is more involved since the lateral contraction must be measured, and sometimes the elongation as well.   This is the main reason for the widespread use of conventional stress and strain.   In fact all standardized tension tests are for conventional stress and strain.

Tests for Conventional Stress and Strain

Since methods differ somewhat from material to material, the ASTM *Standards* present a number of standard methods: E8-57T, for example,

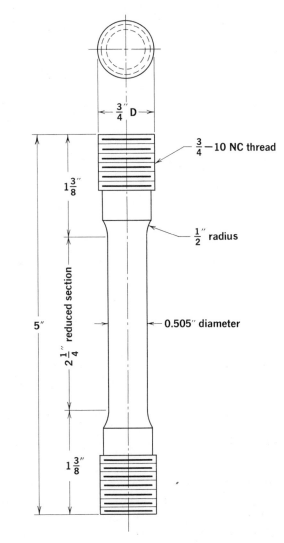

Fig. 3.50 Common form of ASTM standard tension specimen.

covers metallic materials, D638-58T covers plastics, C190-58 covers cement mortar, and D143-52 covers timber. Many of the methods used for metallic materials, however, apply also to others, and consequently this discussion will be based on that test.

Specimens.   Specimens are nearly always cylindrical or prismatic, with substantially constant cross-sectional area for uniformity of stress.   The ends are usually enlarged for added strength so that rupture will not take place near the grips, where the stress distribution is complicated.   The experimental measurements are all made on the central portion (the *reduced*

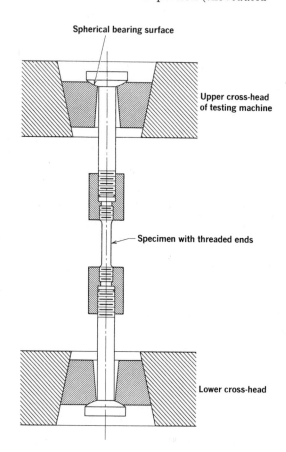

Spherical bearing surface

Upper cross-head of testing machine

Specimen with threaded ends

Lower cross-head

Fig. 3.51 Self-aligning specimen holders.

section).   In cylindrical specimens this portion is commonly $\frac{1}{2}$ inch in diameter and $2\frac{1}{4}$ inches long.   The ends are $\frac{3}{4}$ inch in diameter and are threaded to screw into specimen holders on the testing machine.   Since abrupt changes in cross-section cause stress concentrations, the transition from the central portion to the larger ends must be made by fillets of large radius (Fig. 3.50).   The $2\frac{1}{4}$-inch central portion allows the use of a 2-inch gage length.   It is often tapered very slightly (0.003–0.005 inch) toward the center to help ensure rupture near the center.   Rectangular specimens are used for plate or sheet materials.   Their proportions are similar to those of the cylindrical type. The ends are gripped by jaws in the testing machine. A number of other types and sizes are in common use for various purposes. Details are given in the appropriate ASTM *Standards*.

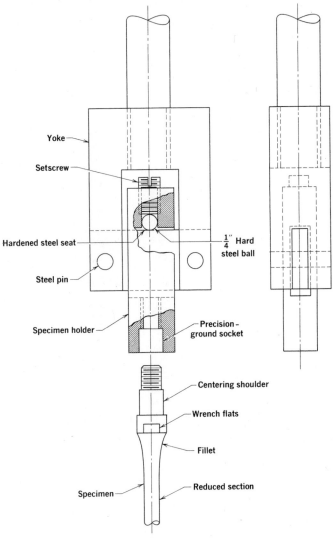

Fig. 3.52 Precision specimen holder for reducing eccentricity.

Loading. Before the specimen is placed in the testing machine its dimensions must be measured with care. The diameter of a $\frac{1}{2}$-inch specimen is usually measured to the nearest 0.001 inch (for more detailed instructions see ASTM E8-57T).   The gage length is fixed by the extensometer, the gage points or knife edges of which are at the proper spacing.   The range of most extensometers is much less than the total extension of a ductile specimen, and consequently some other means must be used to measure the elongation far into the plastic range.   A pair of gage marks is usually

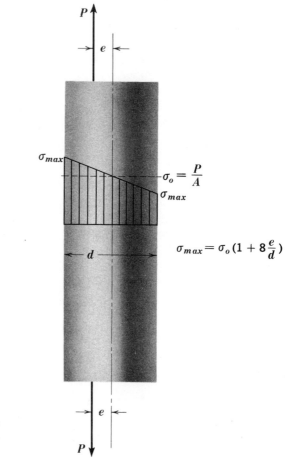

$$\sigma_o = \frac{P}{A}$$

$$\sigma_{max} = \sigma_o \left(1 + 8\frac{e}{d}\right)$$

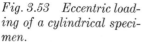

Fig. 3.53   Eccentric loading of a cylindrical specimen.

punched on the surface of the specimen so that changes in their spacing can be measured with dividers for large elongations.   These gage marks are also necessary if the final elongation is to be obtained.

The specimen is placed in the testing machine by using the appropriate grips, care being taken to align it carefully with respect to the axis of loading. Specimen holders for threaded-end specimens are usually "self-aligning," having a spherical bearing at each end (Fig. 3.51).   Even with this arrangement, there may be some eccentricity. The spherical bearings must be properly lubricated so that they will adjust themselves at the lowest loads; at high loads even well-lubricated surfaces are subject to friction, which may prevent proper alignment. Furthermore, very slight errors in the threads on the ends of the specimens will introduce some eccentricity in the loading. It is possible to design special holders for small loads which use a steel ball at each end and are machined to very close tolerances (Fig. 3.52) so that eccentricity is reduced to a minimum. Other methods of gripping (such as clamps) usually introduce large eccentricities.

The effect of eccentric loading is greater than one would assume at first thought. Consider a cylindrical specimen in which the axis of loading is parallel to the axis of the specimen but displaced from it by an eccentricity e (Fig. 3.53). In the elastic range the maximum stress is

$$\sigma_{max} = \frac{P}{A} + \frac{Mc}{I} = \frac{P}{A} + \frac{Pec}{A\rho^2}$$

$$= \sigma_0 \left(1 + \frac{ec}{\rho^2}\right), \tag{3.26}$$

where $M = Pe$ is the moment about the neutral axis for bending, c is the distance from the neutral axis to the extreme fiber, ρ is the radius of gyration about the neutral axis, and $\sigma_0 = P/A$ is the average stress on the cross-section. For the cylindrical specimen of diameter d, $c = d/2$, the radius, and $\rho^2 = d^2/16$. Then

$$\sigma_{max} = \sigma_0 \left(1 + 8\frac{e}{d}\right), \tag{3.26a}$$

and the per cent error in assuming that the stress is constant (σ_0) is $(8\ e/d) \times 100$. For example, an eccentricity of 0.005 inch in a $\frac{1}{2}$-inch specimen means an error of 8 per cent (i.e., the maximum stress is 8 per cent higher than the average for an eccentricity of only 1 per cent of the diameter).

The effect of small eccentricities on ductile specimens is not so serious as on brittle specimens. It is usually important, however, to measure the average strains when some eccentricity is present. For this reason extensometers are often attached to opposite sides of the specimen. The *averaging* type is arranged to average the strains in a single instrument. With other types two extensometers must be used.

After the specimen is properly aligned, a small initial load is usually applied to hold it firmly while the extensometer is being attached. The type of extensometer used depends on the gage length of the specimen, the accuracy and range desired, and whether the strains are to be recorded autographically. As mentioned before, extensometers have a limited range. The problems connected with measuring a long range of strains are just as great as those of measuring very small strains. Modern plastics often necessitate very long-range measurements, and special extensometers are needed.

The load is increased at a slow enough rate that dynamic effects may be assumed to be negligible, and the specimen can always be considered to be in a state of equilibrium. This is not always possible. For certain materials the rate of increase to guarantee these conditions would be much too slow to be practical. Some materials continue to flow for long periods of time after the load has been increased and held at a certain value. To wait for equilibrium conditions would require almost unlimited time. Consequently a certain specified rate must be maintained at all times for these materials to ensure comparable results. The ASTM standard test methods give rates for various materials. This rate may be expressed in terms of increase in load (dP/dt), stress $(d\sigma/dt)$, or strain $(d\epsilon/dt)$, or in terms of crosshead speed.

For metals the rate of strain should be held steady in the plastic range. This can usually be done by keeping the testing machine controls at approximately the same setting throughout this part of the test. Testing machines are sometimes equipped with electronic controls which automatically hold one of the various rates constant.

Operation of a testing machine and other instrumentation requires experience, but there are some points that the beginner should remember. The load indicator should be zeroed before each test. The operator should always be ready to stop the increase of load instantaneously: needle valves on hydraulic machines should not be opened too wide at first; in machines having clutches, the operator should be ready to disengage the clutch at a moment's notice. When needle valves are shut off, great care must be taken not to use too much force. Finger-tip tightness is sufficient, and more force wears out the valves quickly.

If a stress-strain diagram is to be plotted, the load and extensometer readings must be obtained at regular intervals. Intervals of load or extensometer reading are chosen before the start of the test to provide the desired number of readings. At each interval of the chosen variable the corresponding value of the other variable is recorded.

EXAMPLE 3.4

A steel specimen is to be tested. Its elastic strength is estimated to be 30,000 psi, corresponding to a strain of 0.001 in./in. It is desired to obtain ten points in the elastic range. Determine convenient increments to be used for observations.

Solution: If we use equal intervals of strain, the strain increment is 0.001/10 or 0.0001 in./in. With a gage length of 2 in. the increment of elongation is 0.0002 in. The gage (multiplication) factor of the extensometer is 5, and its

dial reads in 0.001-in. divisions.   Hence the increment of extensometer reading is $0.0002 \times 5/0.001 = 1$ division.   If equal intervals of load are to be used,
it is necessary only to find the load corresponding to the 30,000-psi stress and
divide by ten.   If the diameter is 0.505 in., the area is 0.200 in.² (a commonly
used size).   The increment of load is then $30,000 \times 0.2/10 = 600$ lb.

For ductile materials the stress-strain diagram has a "knee" at the end
of the elastic range (curve 1, Fig. 3.54).   To obtain information about this
region it is best to use equal increments of extensometer reading, corresponding to equal increments of strain (vertical lines, Fig. 3.54).   The

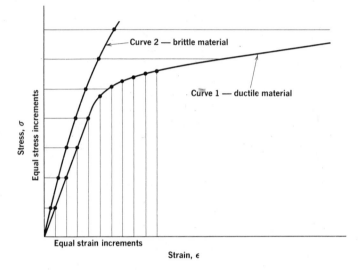

*Fig. 3.54   Stress-strain curves constructed
from readings at equal increments of strain
(curve 1) and equal increments of stress
(curve 2).*

horizontal lines represent equal increments of stress (or load); few points
are obtained by this method.   For brittle materials (curve 2) equal increments of load are obviously satisfactory.

As soon as it nears the end of its operating range the extensometer should
be removed (before this if there is any reason to believe that the specimen
might rupture prematurely).   Observations of strain can then be continued
with the dividers and gage points, using a steel scale and a magnifying glass
if necessary.

Particular loads, such as yield point load (if any), ultimate (maximum)
load, and breaking load, are recorded during the progress of the experiment.
If it is carried all the way to rupture, the final elongation and cross-sectional
area can be measured (see ASTM Standard E8-57T, Sections 28 and 29).

The character of the fracture is often a revealing piece of information and should be described.*

The extensometer readings must be converted to strain by applying the gage factor and gage length unless an SR-4 strain gage was used. The following examples will illustrate the procedure.

EXAMPLE 3.5

A dial reading of 48.4 is obtained, and the dial reads in thousandths. Thus its spindle travelled 0.0484 in. The extensometer has a gage factor of 4— hence the actual elongation is 0.0484/4 = 0.0121 in. Finally, the gage length is 2 in., from which the strain is 0.0121/2 = 0.00605 in./in., rounded off to 0.0061.

EXAMPLE 3.6

An SR-4 strain gage is used which has a gage factor of 2.2 and a length of $1\frac{1}{2}$ in. If an SR-4 strain indicator is used, the gage factor is set on the proper dial and neither it nor the length enter into any calculations. At zero load the strain reading is 638 μin./in. plus 9 on the "thousands" dial, or $9{,}638 \times 10^{-6}$. At a given load the reading is 1,264 μin./in. plus 11 on the thousands dial or $12{,}264 \times 10^{-6}$. Neither reading is an actual strain because this instrument is never zeroed. The strain at the given load is $12{,}264 \times 10^{-6} - 9{,}638 \times 10^{-6} = 2{,}626 \times 10^{-6} = 0.002626$ in./in., which would be rounded off to 0.00263.

If a Wheatstone bridge circuit is used, as shown in Fig. 3.49, the gage factor must be used to compute strain. The resistance change observed is that in the variable resistance, R. If the bridge remains balanced while R and the gage resistance, R_A, are varied simultaneously, we have the relation

$$\frac{\Delta R}{R} = \frac{\Delta R_A}{R_A}.$$

From Eq. 3.25,

$$\epsilon = \frac{\Delta R_A/R_A}{K_s} = \frac{\Delta R/R}{K_s}.$$

EXAMPLE 3.7

The SR-4 strain gage in Example 3.6 is used with a Wheatstone bridge. At zero load the bridge is balanced, and R reads 120 ohms. At the given load, to bring the bridge into balance, R must be adjusted to 120.694 ohms. From this the strain may be computed:

$$\epsilon = \frac{0.694/120}{2.2} = 0.00263.$$

The need for highly accurate resistances and sensitive measuring instruments is obvious.

---

* Davis, Harmer E., Troxell, George E., and Wiskocil, Clement T., *The Testing and Inspection of Engineering Materials*, 2nd ed. (McGraw-Hill Civil Engineering Series) McGraw-Hill Book Company, Inc., New York, Toronto, London, 1955, p. 111.

Presentation of Data

Variation of stress and strain in the tension test can best be presented in the form of a stress-strain diagram. The conventional diagram is plotted from conventional stresses and strains computed from the loads and extensometer readings. Sometimes the load is plotted directly, without converting to stress, since the only difference between the two is a constant factor—the original area. The same applies to the extensometer reading, which is sometimes plotted directly, without any computation. Extensometer readings are often converted to elongation, which is plotted instead of strain.

It is common engineering practice to plot the stress on the vertical axis and the strain on the horizontal axis to give curves of the type shown in various illustrations throughout the text. The mechanics of constructing the diagram involves selecting the proper type of graph paper, choice of scales, location of the axes on the sheet, plotting points, drawing the curve, and indicating pertinent facts about the experiment in a title.

For plotting the variables directly, a graph paper having 20 divisions to the inch, with every fifth division emphasized, is recommended. Smaller divisions are difficult to see, and larger divisions make interpolation more difficult.

There are two considerations in choosing scales: the size of the resulting graph, and the ease of interpolation. It is usually desirable to make the graph as large as possible, allowing for suitable margins on all sides. It is equally important that the values of both variables be readable at any point on the curve—both at and between the plotted points. For this reason scales chosen should involve factors like 2, 5, 10, or sometimes 4. The following are examples of good scales: 2 in. = 1000 lb; $\frac{1}{2}$ in. = 0.001 in./in.; 1 in. = 5000 psi; 5 major divisions ($\frac{1}{2}$-in. each) = 1000 psi. *Scales involving the factor 3 must not be used.* They are often tempting because they may make the largest possible graph for the sheet, but interpolation of values is very awkward to say the least. (Examples of bad scales are 1 in. = 3000 psi; or 3 major divisions = 0.001 in./in.)

EXAMPLE 3.8

In a tension test the ultimate stress is found to be 60,000 psi, and the strain at the breaking point 0.15. The graph paper has 14 major divisions one way and 20 the other. Using the latter as the horizontal direction we see that if we let one major division represent 0.01, we will use 15 major divisions, leaving 5 for margins. In the vertical direction we try dividing the 60,000-psi range of stress by the available 14 divisions; however, we readily see that if we use only 12 divisions, we will have a scale in which one major division represents 5000 psi and 2 divisions will be left for margins. These are good scales for this graph. It would not be practical to reverse the directions and place the

14 divisions horizontally because we would have to go to a smaller scale to get 0.15 into the 14 divisions.

Another important consideration is the resultant size of the elastic range on the graph.   If the material is steel and has a yield point of 30,000 psi, the elastic range covers only 0.001 in./in. strain.   Use of the scales above would confine the elastic range to one-tenth of a major division, too small a size if any information is desired from the elastic range.   A separate graph would have to be drawn to show only the elastic range at a larger scale.   A possible choice of scales would be 1 major division = 0.0002. This larger-scale curve could be drawn on the same sheet with the overall curve and the same stress scale used for both.   The yield point would be at a point about 5 divisions horizontally and 6 divisions vertically from the origin.

When the scales have been chosen and the extent of the graph is known, the axes should be drawn so that the graph will be approximately centered on the sheet.   The top of the graph should always be either at the top of the sheet or next to the binding holes, so that it can be read from either the lower or the right-hand side of the sheet.   Each axis should be drawn in pencil on one of the major division lines (heavy lines on the graph paper). The scales are shown alongside the axes.   Examples are: Stress, psi (or ksi); Strain, in./in.   Notations such as psi $\times$ 10^{-3} or in./in. $\times$ 10^3 should not be used, as they are apt to be confusing.   The intersection of the two axes should represent the actual origin of coordinates so that each scale is shown completely, from zero to the maximum value.

After the axes have been properly located and the scales indicated, the experimental data should be plotted with great care.   In plotting, use a sharp-pointed pencil to make a fine dot at each point.   These dots are then emphasized either by enclosing in small circles or enlarging to make larger circular dots centered on the original point.   When more than two curves are shown on the same sheet, other symbols may be used.

The curve representing the variation is drawn as a heavy line, using instruments (French curve or straightedge, as required)—never freehand. Whether it should follow the plotted points exactly or be drawn as a smooth averaging curve depends upon the characteristics of the variation. Usually a certain amount of averaging is necessary because the points deviate slightly from the true curve owing to experimental error.   The points representing the elastic range in mild steel, for example, should be averaged by a straight line, while those in the yielding region may sometimes be followed more closely, using an irregular curve connecting most of the points.

Generally speaking points near or at the origin are least reliable.   The effects of friction and lost motion in the instruments are most pronounced in the low ranges, and the readings are thus subject to greater errors than at higher loads.   As a result the fitted curve often does not pass through the origin of coordinates even though the first point may have been observed as zero stress and zero strain.   Provided the load indicator was properly zeroed before the test, it can be assumed that the zero axis for stress (the horizontal axis) is correct.   The *true origin* for the curve is therefore at the point where the curve crosses the horizontal axis.   For computations from the graph, all strains should be measured from this point.   It is not necessary to change the graph but merely to apply a correction equal to the strain reading at the true origin to all other strain readings.

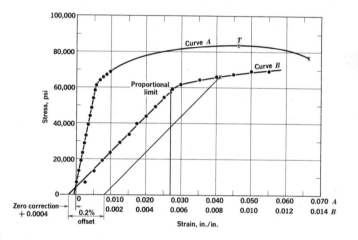

Fig. 3.55   Conventional stress-strain diagram constructed from experimental data for 7075 aluminum alloy: curve A is drawn at the smaller scale to show the entire curve to the breaking point; curve B is drawn at the larger scale to facilitate measurement in the elastic range.

Figure 3.55 illustrates these principles and rules for constructing the stress-strain diagram.

Important information that should be contained in the title includes type of test (tension, compression, etc.), material being investigated (complete description), name of person constructing graph, date, and, if desired, the variables represented (e.g., Stress-Strain Diagram).   Other information may be required under various circumstances.

When the diagram is complete, various properties may be computed from it.   The following example, based on the curve for 7075 aluminum alloy (Fig. 3.55) illustrates the computation of some common properties.

EXAMPLE 3.9

Given the data presented graphically in Fig. 3.55, compute the following properties.

Proportional limit stress: The point marked proportional limit on curve B is selected as the end of the linear part of the curve.   The stress at this point is $\sigma_{pl} = 58,000$ psi.

Modulus of elasticity: To find the slope of the elastic line the proportional limit on curve B is again used.   The strain at this point is 0.0054 plus the correction 0.004, or $\epsilon_{pl} = 0.0058$ in./in.   The modulus of elasticity is therefore

$$E = \frac{\sigma_{pl}}{\epsilon_{pl}} = \frac{58,000}{0.0058} = 10 \times 10^6 \text{ psi.}$$

Modulus of resilience:

$$u = \frac{\sigma_{pl}\epsilon_{pl}}{2} = \frac{(58,000)(0.0058)}{2} = 168.2 \text{ in. lb/in.}^3$$

Yield strength at 0.2 per cent offset: Since 0.2 per cent = 0.002, an offset line is drawn parallel to the elastic line of curve B, starting at 0.002 corrected strain $(0.002 - 0.0004 = 0.0016$ on the indicated scale).   The offset line intersects curve B at point Y, which represents the offset yield strength,

$$\sigma_y(0.2\%) = 65,000 \text{ psi.}$$

Tensile strength: On curve A the highest point, T, represents the tensile or ultimate strength,

$$\sigma_u = 90,000 \text{ psi.}$$

Errors

Each observation in an experiment is subject to some small error in measurement (Art. 3.15).   The effect of any small change in a measurement on the final result can often be studied by the following method.

Suppose the purpose of the experiment is to compute the value of a property y.   If the formula for y in terms of the observed variables x_1, x_2, x_3 . . . is of the form

$$y = cx_1^m \cdot x_2^n \cdot x_3^q \cdot \ldots , \qquad (3.27a)$$

we can take logarithms of both sides to give

$$\log y = \log c + m \log x_1 + n \log x_2 + q \log x_3 + \ldots .$$

Since $d(u + v) = du + dv$, $d(\text{const}) = 0$, and $d(\log x) = dx/x$, we can write

$$\frac{dy}{y} = m\frac{dx_1}{x_1} + n\frac{dx_2}{x_2} + q\frac{dx_3}{x_3} + \ldots . \qquad (3.27b)$$

The left side of this equation represents the relative change in y. On the right side each term represents the effect of a small relative change in one of the observations needed to compute y.

EXAMPLE 3.10

The formula for the modulus of elasticity, E, computed from the observations of a tension test, can be written

$$E = \frac{4\,Pl}{\pi d^2 \delta},$$

where P is the load, l the gage length, d the diameter of the specimen, and δ its elongation. If we take the logarithms of both sides and write the differential, we have

$$\frac{dE}{E} = \frac{dP}{P} + \frac{dl}{l} - 2\frac{dd}{d} - \frac{d\delta}{\delta}.$$

Thus if the load is 8000 lb, an error of $+100$ lb in reading the load will make an error in E of

$$+\tfrac{100}{8000} = +0.0125 = +1.25\%.$$

Similarly an error of $+0.002$ in. in the 0.500-in. diameter will make an error in E of

$$-2\left(\frac{0.002}{0.500}\right) = -0.008 = -0.8\%.$$

The maximum overall error would occur if the signs of the individual errors were such that all the terms in Eq. 3.27b had the same sign. In the above example this would mean positive errors in P and l, negative errors in d and δ (or the reverse), a very unlikely situation. It can be shown by probability theory that the maximum probable error is given by

$$\text{Maximum probable}\left(\frac{dy}{y}\right) = \sqrt{\left(m\frac{dx_1}{x_1}\right)^2 + \left(n\frac{dx_2}{x_2}\right)^2 + \left(q\frac{dx_3}{x_3}\right)^2 + \ldots}$$

If the error in measuring the 2-in. gage length is 0.01 in. and that in the 0.0028-in. elongation is 0.0001 in., the maximum probable error is

$$\text{Maximum probable}\left(\frac{dE}{E}\right) = \sqrt{\left(\frac{100}{8000}\right)^2 + \left(\frac{0.01}{2.00}\right)^2 + \left(2\frac{0.002}{0.500}\right)^2 + \left(\frac{0.0001}{0.0028}\right)^2}$$

$$= 0.0384 = 3.84\%.$$

If the property y is given by the more general expression

$$y = f(x_1, x_2, x_3 \ldots),$$

the probable relative error in y is given by*

---

* Davis, Harmer E., Troxell, George E., and Wiskocil, Clement T., *The Testing and Inspection of Engineering Materials*, 2nd ed. (McGraw-Hill Civil Engineering Series) McGraw-Hill Book Company, Inc., New York, Toronto, London, 1955, p. 277.

$$\text{Maximum probable} \left(\frac{dy}{y} \right) = \sqrt{ \left[\left(\frac{x_1}{y} \frac{\partial y}{\partial x_1} \right) \left(\frac{dx_1}{x_1} \right) \right]^2 + \left[\left(\frac{x_2}{y} \frac{\partial y}{\partial x_2} \right) \left(\frac{dx_2}{x_2} \right) \right]^2 + \cdots }$$

Tests for True Stress and Strain

This type of test is largely limited to the investigation of ductile materials. The methods used have not yet been standardized. However, some parts are the same as those used in the tension test for conventional stress

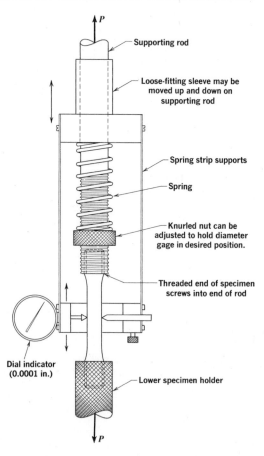

Fig. 3.56   Diameter gage.

and strain. Standard specimens lend themselves well to true stress-strain experiments. The diameter should be uniform along the reduced section, however, and not tapered. It should be machined to a uniform diameter within at least 0.0005 in., and 0.0001 in. if possible.

An extensometer may or may not be used on the specimen, depending upon how complete and how accurate the diagram needs to be. In a large part of the plastic range the law of constant volume holds within the usual limits of accuracy, and Eq. 3.16b can be used to compute true strain. Here the variable is the cross-sectional area, A, which can be found from the diameter of the specimen. Since the same A is used to compute true stress, only two variables need be observed: load and diameter. Figure 3.56 shows a diameter gage that has been found satisfactory. It is supported on the specimen holder above the specimen so that it is always horizontal, and can be moved up or down easily on the specimen.

In the early part of the plastic range the elastic strain is an important factor, and the error in assuming constant volume may be significant. Since the strain is uniform in this region, Eq. 3.16a can be used to advantage. Strain is measured by means of an extensometer and converted to true strain. The extensometer and the dial indicator must be constructed so that the former can be removed when it reaches the end of its useful range.

The conduct of the test is similar to that of the test for conventional strain. The specimen is carefully measured and placed in the machine. The load is increased slowly, and simultaneous values of load and deformation are recorded at intervals. Since the lateral contraction in the elastic range is so small ($\mu\epsilon_x d = 0.3 \times 0.001 \times 0.5 = 0.00015$ in. for a half-inch mild steel specimen), it can be detected only by a very sensitive diameter gage. The elastic range is often entirely omitted in true stress-strain tests.

During the early stages of the test the diameter gage should be held at the center of the specimen. As soon as necking begins to be discernible, the gage should be moved to the point of smallest diameter. If the specimen is of uniform diameter within the suggested tolerances, the true strain reading will not be disturbed by moving the gage. Thereafter it should be continually adjusted up or down the axis so that it always measures the diameter of the smallest cross-section. Special care must be taken at the breaking point to avoid damage to the diameter gage.

The true strain at rupture is usually so large compared with the elastic strain that the two cannot be shown on the same scale. If we wish to show elastic strain and the early part of the plastic range, as well as the later plastic strain, we must draw two curves at different scales of strain.

EXAMPLE 3.11

Let us calculate true stress and strain for a specimen of a ductile metal having an original diameter of 0.5040 in., from which $A_0 = 0.1995$ in.^{2} The diameter gage, which reads in ten-thousandths of an inch, is set to read 0.5040 in., and the load is applied. At a load of 9,500 lb, well within the plastic range, the diameter reads 0.4860 in. Thus $A = 0.1855$ and the true stress is $\sigma' = 51,200$ psi. To calculate true strain a five-place table of natural logarithms can be used, or a table of common logarithms with a conversion factor. Using common logs, we first find $\log_{10} A = 9.26834 - 10$ and subtract this from $\log_{10} A_0$, giving $\log_{10} A_0/A = 0.03160$. The conversion factor is $1/M = 2.3026$, from which $\epsilon' = \log_e A_0/A = 0.0728$.

If necking has not begun, the conventional strain may be calculated. Combining Eqs. 3.2 and 3.17, we obtain $\epsilon = (A_0/A) - 1$. Using the above value of $\log_{10} A_0/A$ we have $A_0/A = 1.0755$, or $\epsilon = 0.0755$.

BIBLIOGRAPHY

Marin, Joseph, *Engineering Materials—Their Mechanical Properties and Applications*, Prentice-Hall, Inc., Englewood Cliffs, N. J., 1952.
Chapter 1 deals with static properties in tension and compression.

Timoshenko, S., *Strength of Materials—Part II—Advanced Theory and Problems*, 3rd ed., D. Van Nostrand Company, Inc., Princeton, N. J., 1956.
Chapter X—Mechanical Properties of Materials—includes good discussion of behavior in tension.

Freudenthal, Alfred M., *The Inelastic Behavior of Engineering Materials and Structures*, John Wiley & Sons, Inc., New York, 1950; Nadai, A., *Theory of Flow and Fracture of Solids*, Vol. I, 2nd ed. (Engineering Societies Monographs) McGraw-Hill Book Company, Inc., New York, Toronto, London, 1950.
Discussion of inelastic behavior for the advanced student.

Cottrell, A. H., *Dislocations and Plastic Flow in Crystals*, Clarendon Press, Oxford, 1953.
Thorough treatise on dislocation theory.

Goldman, J. E., Ed., *The Science of Engineering Materials*, John Wiley & Sons, Inc., New York, 1957.
Chapters 7, 8, and 9 discuss dislocations and their effects on mechanical properties.

Davis, Harmer E., Troxell, George E., and Wiskocil, Clement T., *The Testing and Inspection of Engineering Materials*, 2nd ed. (McGraw-Hill Civil Engineering Series) McGraw-Hill Book Company, Inc., New York, Toronto, London, 1955.
Excellent reference book on experimental methods.

PROBLEMS

3.1 Sketch an *elastic* stress-strain curve in which energy is dissipated.

3.2 Give an explanation for the fact that polymers, as typified by acrylics in Table 3.1, have lower values of E by one or two orders of magnitude than most metals.

3.3 Derive the formula for the modulus of resilience for the linear case (Eq. 3.8) by considering the work done by the average force acting on a unit cube of material in a bar under simple tension.

3.4 Explain the difference in meaning between the term *modulus of resilience* as applied to metals and the term *resilience* as applied to rubber.

3.5 A member made of cold-worked columbium is 15 in. long and has a rectangular cross-section $\frac{1}{4}$ in. by $\frac{3}{4}$ in. For a tensile load of 5000 lb, determine the total change in (a) length, (b) cross-sectional dimensions, and (c) volume. Assume elastic behavior, with $E = 22.7 \times 10^6$ psi and $\mu = 0.28$.

3.6 A solid rod of an acrylic plastic is 20 in. long and $\frac{5}{8}$ in. in diameter. For a tensile load of 500 lb, determine the total change in (a) length, (b) diameter, and (c) volume. Assume elastic behavior, with $E = 400,000$ psi and $\mu = 0.4$.

3.7 A member whose diameter is 15 mm elongates 0.37 mm in a gage length of 10 cm under a load of 3000 kg in tension. Find (a) the modulus of elasticity and (b) the strain energy per unit volume at this load, in both metric and English units. What material has approximately this value of E?

3.8 Plot the points represented by the following data and draw a stress-strain curve through them (the linear portion of the curve passes through the first two points, extending some distance beyond the second). From this stress-strain curve determine (a) the modulus of elasticity, (b) the proportional limit, (c) the modulus of resilience, (d) the yield stress at 0.1 per cent offset. Name a material that might have such a stress-strain diagram.

STRESS, psi	STRAIN, in./in.
0	0
33,600	0.0008
46,000	0.0012
50,000	0.0016
52,000	0.0020
54,000	0.0025

3.9 Repeat Problem 3.8 for the following data (the linear portion of the curve ends at the second point). Convert answers to English units.

STRESS, kg/cm²	STRAIN, cm/cm
0	0
3060	0.0015
2500	0.0017
2600	0.0030
2400	0.0050

3.10 Using the following data for rubber, construct a stress-strain diagram and determine (a) the secant modulus and the tangent modulus at $\sigma = 200$ psi (loading), (b) the resilience, and (c) the hysteresis loss per cycle in in.-lb/in.³ (The areas under the curves may be measured by counting squares on the graph paper.)

LOADING		UNLOADING	
STRESS, psi	STRAIN, in./in.	STRESS, psi	STRAIN, in./in.
0	0.00	300	4.25
60	0.40	240	4.15
120	1.25	180	3.90
180	2.42	120	3.13
240	3.55	100	2.00
300	4.25	60	0.70
		0	0.00

3.11 A member 15 in. long is to be designed to withstand a load of 6000 lb in tension. Three choices of materials are available: an aluminum alloy, for which $E = 10 \times 10^6$ psi and $\sigma_y = 52,000$ psi; a magnesium alloy, for which $E = 6.5 \times 10^6$ psi and $\sigma_y = 28,500$ psi; molded nylon, for which $E = 410,000$ psi and $\sigma_y = 8000$ psi. Determine the necessary cross-section for each material, using a factor of safety of 1.50. Compute the weight of each member and the total amount of strain energy stored by each at the 6000-lb load.

3.12 A structural member for a nuclear reactor is to be made of cold-worked zirconium for which $E = 14 \times 10^6$ psi and $\sigma_y = 58,000$ psi. The load for which it is to be designed is 60,000 lb in simple tension. (a) Using a safety factor, $n_y = 3$, determine the cross-sectional area required. (b) Determine the necessary cross-sectional area if the member is 2 ft long and its total elongation is limited to 0.03 in. (c) Select the area to meet both requirements, strength and elongation.

3.13 A crystal composed of a single row of body-centered cubic unit cells is subjected to a tensile stress, σ, along its axis. The planes of easy slip are the diagonal planes making 45° with the axis, i.e., the (110) planes. The *direction* of easy slip in any (110) plane is the [111] direction (a body diagonal of the cube). If the crystal begins to yield when $\sigma = 350$ psi, what is the critical resolved shear stress?

3.14 A crystal composed of a single row of face-centered cubic unit cells is subjected to a tensile stress, σ, along its axis. The planes of easy slip are the octahedral planes, i.e., the (111) planes. The *directions* of easy slip in any (111) plane are the face diagonals of the cube, e.g., the [110] direction. If the critical resolved shear stress is 35 kg/cm², find the stress, σ, to cause yielding.

3.15 Prove that the maximum value of $\tau(x)$ in Eq. 3.15 occurs at $x = r_0/\sqrt{3}$, as shown in Fig. 3.29.

3.16 Wool fibers are believed to be composed of molecules whose natural configuration is crumpled, or zigzag. Sketch the probable shape of the stress-strain curve for a wool fiber.

3.17 The original diameter of a tension specimen is 0.505 in.   At a certain load the diameter is found to be 0.388 in.   Compute the true and conventional strains at this point, assuming constant volume.

3.18 Specify the range in which the annealed copper stress-strain relation fits Eq. 3.22 closely.   For this range compute the strength coefficient, k, and the strain-hardening exponent, n.*

3.19 Repeat Problem 3.18 for HY-80 steel.*

3.20 By measuring the slope of a true stress-strain curve, such as that for annealed copper, at several stresses, a curve of $d\sigma'/d\epsilon'$ vs σ' can be plotted.   From such a curve it is determined that $d\sigma'/d\epsilon' = \sigma'$ when $\sigma' = 48,500$ psi.   According to Eq. 3.14c, this value defines the onset of plastic instability, or the maximum load.   (a) Compute the conventional stress corresponding to this true stress.   (b) Compute the corresponding conventional strain.*

3.21 Repeat Problem 3.20 for HY-80 steel.   The point of maximum load is that marked A on the curve.   Does point A fit the criterion expressed by Eq. 3.14c?*

3.22 Estimate the toughness of annealed copper by counting squares on the true stress-strain diagram and compare it with the toughness of HY-80 steel.*

3.23 The true stress-strain data for a certain metal plot as a straight line on a log-log graph.   The end points of the line are determined by the following coordinates: $\sigma_1' = 25,000$ psi, $\epsilon_1' = 0.01$; $\sigma_2' = 70,000$ psi, $\epsilon_2' = 0.20$.   Determine the equation of the true stress-strain curve between these points and plot the curve on linear coordinates.

3.24 Compute the toughness of the material of Problem 3.23 by integrating the true stress-strain equation from $\epsilon' = 0$ to $\epsilon' = 0.20$.   (Assume that the equation holds for strains below 0.01, and that 0.20 is the true fracture strain.)

3.25 Compare the magnitudes of the elastic and plastic strains at point T in the curve for 7075 aluminum alloy (Fig. 3.55).

3.26 (a) Investigation shows that under a load of 50,000 lb a certain testing machine, including the specimen-gripping devices, deforms 0.070 in.   Compute the stiffness of this machine.   (b) Compute the stiffness of a tension specimen of beryllium, considered as a round rod 0.250 in. in diameter and 1.50 in. long ($E = 44 \times 10^6$ psi).   (c) If the machine is set at an idling speed of 0.050 in./min, determine the approximate rate of elastic elongation of the beryllium specimen.   What is its strain rate in in./in./sec.?

3.27 A tension test is conducted to determine the elastic properties of a molded phenolic plastic.   The specimen diameter is 0.400 ± 0.001 in.; the gage length is 1 ± 0.01 in.; the load at the proportional limit is 500 ± 20 lb; and the corresponding elongation is 0.0030 ± 0.0001 in.   (a) Determine the modulus of resilience, u_r.   (b) Compute the probable maximum relative error in u_r.

3.28 From Fig. 3.55 measure the secant modulus at several different strains and plot a curve of E_{sec} vs ϵ.

---

* Problems 3.18–3.22 refer to the true stress-strain diagrams of Figs. 3.40 and 3.41.

3.29 Figure 3.57 shows the stress-strain curves for 4 different steels. From these curves, determine (a) which is the toughest, (b) which is the most ductile, (c) which is the strongest, and (d) which is the stiffest.

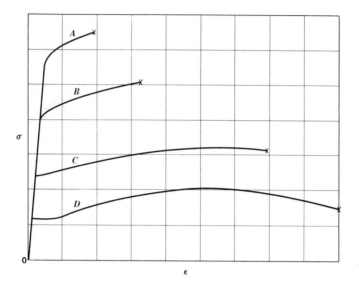

Fig. 3.57   Comparative stress-strain curves for four steels.

3.30 Two extensometers are used to measure the strain in a bar in simple tension. At a certain load, extensometer A indicates a strain of 0.004765 and extensometer B a strain of 0.0049.   If the correct value of strain is known to be 0.00485, which extensometer is the most sensitive?   Which is the most accurate?

3.31 If the load on a member in simple tension is slowly increased, what are the two possible mechanisms by which elastic action in the member may be terminated?

3.32 Approximately what fraction of members made of a brittle material should be expected to fail if loaded to the *average* ultimate strength of the material? Suggest a rational basis for a more conservative value of ultimate strength for a brittle material.

3.33 Why should the results of tests using standard laboratory specimens be treated with caution in the design of structures using brittle materials?

3.34 Explain on an atomic basis why slip takes place easily in ductile materials and not in brittle materials.

3.35 Explain the mechanism of plastic deformation in single crystals of ductile materials.

3.36 What is the general explanation for the fact that both slip and brittle fracture take place at stresses far below the theoretical cohesive strength of a material?

CHAPTER 4

STATIC
COMPRESSION

Behavior of materials in static compression is in many ways similar to that in static tension. There are enough important differences, however, to merit separate discussion of this common form of loading. Stress-strain diagrams often differ for tension and compression, as does the amount of ductility exhibited by a material and the mode of failure. Behavior in the elastic range is important for brittle materials, which are better adapted to compression than to tension. Behavior in the plastic range is involved in hardness measurements and technological forming operations such as rolling and extruding as well as in simple compression applications. It is in the plastic range that the differences between compression and tension are the greatest.

ELASTICITY

4.1 ELASTIC ACTION IN COMPRESSION

In nonporous solids of simple structure (e.g., crystals) elastic action in compression is exactly the same as elastic action in tension but in the reverse direction. The curve of stress vs atomic spacing (Fig. 3.3) is continuous through the equilibrium point, with no abrupt change in slope or curvature on either side. For a given applied stress the atoms develop the necessary repulsive forces to balance the stress at approximately the same displacements as in tension. The extent of the elastic range is so small (Art. 3.1) that the curvature of the stress-displacement curve is not ordinarily noticeable. Thus the elastic stress-strain curve in compression is a linear extension of that in tension (Fig. 4.1). The only difference between the two diagrams is their extent, to be discussed in Art. 4.3 under inelastic action.

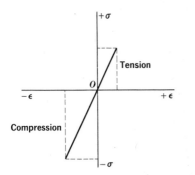

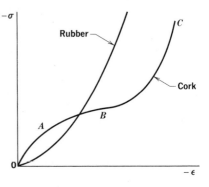

Fig. 4.1 Elastic stress-strain diagram in tension and compression for a material following Hooke's law.

Fig. 4.2 Elastic stress-strain curves for rubber and cork in compression.

The idealized elastic behavior just described is approached quite closely by crystalline materials, including polycrystals, if they are substantially homogeneous and isotropic. Materials having other structures often behave quite differently, with the result that the mechanism of elastic compression varies considerably from that of elastic extension.

Elastic extension of long-chain polymers such as rubber has been discussed on p. 65. At first it consists primarily of the uncoiling of molecules for which, because of thermal agitation, the coiled configuration has the highest probability. Before long the forces between molecules and between atoms in the molecules become involved, and the material stiffens, as is seen from the stress-strain diagram of Fig. 3.5. In compression the mechanism seems to be a combination of both effects, the material stiffening more and more rapidly as it is compressed. The resulting stress-strain diagram is illustrated in Fig. 4.2.

Materials having complex structures, like concrete, also tend to behave differently in tension and compression. Fibrous or cellular materials such as wood and cork represent the extreme in different behavior. Here the cell walls are rather stiff until the compressive load becomes high enough to buckle them.   Then their stiffness decreases sharply, as shown from A to B in Fig. 4.2.   Clearly no such buckling can occur in tension.   As the cells are compacted, a point is reached where stiffness increases again and the line curves upward toward C.   The compression stress-strain diagram looks quite like the stress-strain diagram for rubber in tension.

Plastic foams tend to behave similarly to rubber in compression.

4.2 ELASTIC PROPERTIES IN COMPRESSION

Modulus of elasticity E; Poisson's ratio μ; proportional limit stress σ_{pl}; and modulus of resilience u_r are measured in exactly the same way as in tension.   The secant modulus E_{sec} and tangent modulus E_t may be important in nonlinear elastic cases.

BEYOND THE ELASTIC RANGE

4.3 INELASTIC ACTION IN COMPRESSION

It is obvious that *failure* of a homogeneous, nonporous material cannot result simply from pushing the atoms closer together.   Unlike the situation in tension, where a definite maximum exists in the atomic bond curve, there is no limit to the amount of repulsive force that can be built up between atoms.   Consequently it might be said that the true compressive strength of such a material is infinite, and that the action produced by normal stress is always elastic.

Inelastic action in compression must therefore be accounted for by the shearing stresses which act on inclined planes.   These stresses are given by Eqs. 3.11 and 3.12 for compression as well as tension.   In homogeneous nonporous materials the shearing stresses produce slip on the inclined planes according to the same laws as in tension.

Ductile Materials

In ductile materials, whose atomic or molecular bonds can be re-formed easily, slip leads to yielding at a stress approximately the same as the tensile yield stress.   This applies to discontinuous as well as continuous yielding, as evidenced by the fact that mild steel has upper and lower yield points in compression that are usually the same as those for tension.

Brittle Materials

In brittle materials, whose atomic or molecular bonds cannot be re-formed easily, slip leads to fracture, in which the bonds are permanently ruptured.

Fracture may be in the form of either complete failure along a single shear plane or a multitude of small failures on shear planes in all directions (fragmentation).   The usual failure is somewhere between these two extremes.

The axial stress required to cause fracture of a brittle material is much greater in compression than in tension.   In tension, fracture usually takes place by separation or cleavage on a plane at right angles to the axis of loading.   Because it is initiated by stress-raisers in the form of cracks, holes, and other imperfections, the stress is well below that necessary to cause slip on the 45° shear planes.

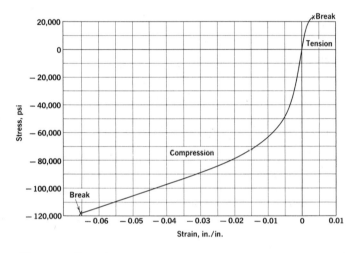

Fig. 4.3   Complete   stress-strain   diagram for gray cast iron.

In compression these imperfections cease to act as stress-raisers.   Instead, any cracks or holes in the material tend to close up and their effect vanishes.   The stress can then reach the larger values needed to initiate slip.   Factors that tend to weaken the material include dislocations and imperfections so oriented as to act as shear stress-raisers.   They are far less effective than the stress-raisers in tension.   The strength of a material in compression is often increased, too, by the internal friction acting along the shear planes between microscopic or macroscopic particles.   Concrete, soils, and other granular materials are examples of this effect.*

The net result is that brittle materials are stronger in compression than

---

* Taylor, D. W., *Fundamentals of Soil Mechanics*, John Wiley & Sons, Inc., New York, 1948, Chs. 13–15.

in tension, sometimes by a large factor, as illustrated in Table 4.1, which compares tensile and compressive strengths for some brittle materials, and in Fig. 4.3, a complete stress-strain diagram for gray cast iron.

Table 4.1   Comparative Tensile and Compressive Strengths of Brittle Materials

MATERIAL	TENSILE STRENGTH, σ_{ut}, psi	COMPRESSIVE STRENGTH, σ_{uc}, psi	RATIO $\dfrac{\sigma_{uc}}{\sigma_{ut}}$
Gray cast iron	24,000	120,000	5
Concrete (28-day)[a]	400	5,000	12.5
Acrylics (Plexiglas, Lucite)	10,600	17,000[b]	1.6
Alumina ceramics (95% alumina)	30,000	300,000	10

[a] 1:3 mix (by volume), 7.8 sacks per cu yd, water-cement ratio 0.64 (by volume).
[b] Stress at which excessive deformation or rupture occurs.

Although this discussion is concerned with simple uniaxial compression, it is desirable to mention *hydrostatic compression*. Hydrostatic compression is a state of stress in which equal compressive stresses act in all directions on the material, like the pressures on an object submerged in water. Its effect is to push the atoms and molecules closer together in all directions. A given group of atoms remains in exactly the same configuration but is merely reduced in volume. There is no distortion of the atomic structure and hence *no tendency to slip*. If the stresses always remain exactly equal in all directions as the stress increases, this situation may continue to any level of stress. Since a simple crowding together of the atoms cannot cause failure, we see that failure is usually impossible under an ideal state of hydrostatic compression, as discussed in greater detail in Art. 6.8.

Porous or Cellular Materials

Inelastic behavior of porous or cellular materials like wood, cork, or plastic foams is a continuation of the elastic behavior discussed in Art. 4.1. The individual collapse of cells owing to rupture of the cell walls can hardly be classed as a shearing failure, although some shear effects may be involved in small regions. Hence this failure may be classed as purely compressive. The collapse of the cells or pores is a definite failure and may easily cause excessive permanent deformation or even leave the material unusable.

4.4 THE PLASTIC RANGE

The plastic range in compression extends from the end of the elastic range to final failure.   Strain in this range can be divided into elastic and plastic components, each governed by different laws.   As in tension, elastic strain is accompanied by a volume change while plastic strain is not.   Thus the value of μ for plastic strain is again $\frac{1}{2}$, and the member expands laterally with a strain half that of the axial compressive strain.

Plastic instability, so troublesome in tension, is no problem in compression.   Both the area of the cross-section and the strength of the material increase with compressive plastic strain, the former because of the Poisson effect and the latter because of strain-hardening.   Therefore the load, which is the product of the area and the true stress, always increases throughout the plastic range.   The plastic range is potentially much longer in compression than in tension.

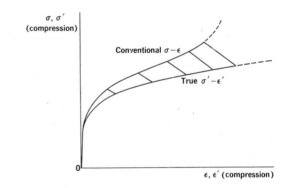

Fig. 4.4 Comparison of compression stress-strain curves for a ductile material in the plastic range, using conventional and true stresses and strains.

For a given material the shape of the stress-strain diagram in compression depends on whether conventional or true stress and strain are used. Figure 4.4 shows typical curves of both kinds for a ductile material in compression.   Note that the conventional curve is higher than the true curve, instead of lower, as in tension, because the actual area increases instead of decreasing.   For most ductile metals the true stress-strain diagram in compression is quite similar to that in tension—up to the point corresponding to the maximum load in tension.   The conventional diagrams are, of course, different in tension and compression, but even here the differences are not great in the early part of the plastic range, and for simplicity they are often assumed to be identical.

Some materials behave quite differently in tension and compression. For example, a material may have only a limited ductility in tension and a great ductility in compression.   Figure 4.5 shows comparative curves for such a material, an acrylic plastic.

Load Reversal

In crystalline materials loading into the plastic range in compression, followed by unloading, produces the same results as in tension.   The elastic strain is recovered, and the plastic strain remains as a permanent set (Art. 3.9).   When the material is loaded again, we find the proportional limit and yield strength raised to higher values of compressive stress (Fig. 4.6).

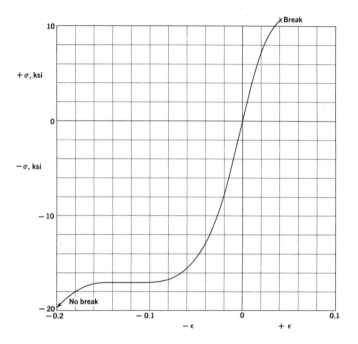

Fig. 4.5   Stress-strain curve in compression and tension for an acrylic plastic (Plexiglas).

When the load is *reversed*, however, an interesting new effect appears. Figure 4.7 shows the virgin stress-strain diagram ($B'A'OAB$) for a ductile metal in both tension and compression.   The yield stresses at A and A' are of equal magnitudes.   A member made of this metal is loaded in tension to the point B and then unloaded.   Because of strain-hardening, B represents the new tensile yield strength of the metal.   After it is unloaded to C, the member is loaded again, but this time in compression. It is now observed that *the compressive yield strength has been decreased at the same time that the tensile yield strength was increased.* It is now at D instead of A'. This is the well-known *Bauschinger effect,* discovered by Johann Bauschinger in 1886.

The Bauschinger effect involves two factors. One is the nonuniformity of yielding in a polycrystalline metal. Because the crystals are oriented at random throughout the metal, they yield by different amounts so that on a microscopic scale the stress varies slightly from crystal to crystal. When the member is unloaded, it contracts until the average stress is zero,

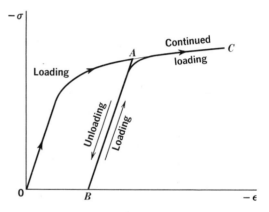

Fig. 4.6   Repeated load-ing in compression.

but the crystals that yielded the least do not quite return to zero and remain in tension, while those that yielded the most go beyond zero and are under compression. Thus there are microscopic residual stresses called *Heyn stresses** or *textural stresses*† throughout the metal, some tension and some compression. When the material is compressed after having been elongated, the crystals that already have compressive residual stresses will yield at a lower-than-normal stress, and therefore the *overall yield stress* is lowered.

These residual stresses do not account for all the observed effect in poly-crystals, however, nor do they explain the effect in single crystals. Another factor is the behavior of dislocations, which can be stated in an elementary way as follows. When the material yields in tension, the dislocations move through the crystal structure until they come to obstacles that slow their

---

* Seitz, Frederick, *The Physics of Metals*, 1st ed. (Metallurgy and Metallurgical Engi-neering Series) McGraw-Hill Book Company, New York, London, 1943, p. 147.

† Freudenthal, Alfred M., *The Inelastic Behavior of Engineering Materials and Struc-tures*, John Wiley & Sons, Inc., New York, 1950.

progress or stop them entirely.   As other dislocations approach, they, too, are slowed or stopped, and strain-hardening takes place.   When the load is removed, the elastic strains are recovered, but the dislocations still remain immobile.   When a compressive stress is applied, however, the shearing stresses are the reverse of those in tension and try to move the dislocations

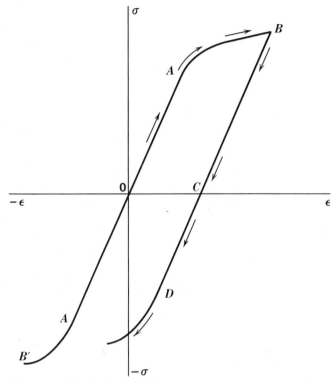

Fig. 4.7   Effect of reversal of stress on the yield stress.   B′A′OAB represents the virgin σ−ε curve for a ductile material having yield stresses of equal magnitudes in tension and compression (A and A′).

in the opposite direction.   This is the direction from which they previously came, and they are under some strain from having been crowded together behind the various obstacles.   Consequently they move more easily in this reverse direction and at a lower-than-normal stress.   This mechanism explains the Bauschinger effect in single crystals and at least part of that in polycrystals.

An important consequence of the Bauschinger effect is seen in cold-working of metals.   Cold-rolled steel, for example, is strengthened by applying the principle of strain-hardening.   Running a bar of mild steel through rollers compresses it laterally and causes it to elongate (principle of constant volume).   Elongation causes an increase in tensile yield strength *longitudinally*, but lateral compression causes a decrease in tensile yield strength *across* the bar.

4.5   INELASTIC PROPERTIES IN COMPRESSION

The most commonly used inelastic properties in compression are yield strength (or yield point, if applicable), compressive strength, secant modulus, tangent modulus, and toughness.   Most of these are defined in the same way as the corresponding tensile properties (Art. 3.12).   For ductile metals properties in compression are often inferred from the tensile properties by assuming that the stress-strain diagrams are identical in tension and compression.   The compressive strength of ductile materials has very little meaning since no fracture occurs.   An arbitrary definition is sometimes used, in which the value depends on the degree of distortion regarded as constituting complete failure,* but this is actually a yield stress at a large total strain.   The compressive strength of brittle materials is defined as *the maximum compressive stress which a material is capable of developing, based on original area of cross-section.*†   This strength is a real ultimate strength.

The tangent modulus, E_t, has an important application in the design of short columns to resist buckling.   Euler's column formula gives the critical load for a column, if we assume linear elasticity:

$$P_{cr} = \frac{\pi^2 EI}{l^2}. \tag{4.1}$$

Here E is the modulus of elasticity in compression, I the moment of inertia of the cross-section, and l the column length, which may be modified to suit the given end conditions.‡   Equation 4.1 may be expressed in terms of stress by dividing by the cross-sectional area, A, to give

$$\sigma_{cr} = \frac{\pi^2 E}{(l/\rho)^2}, \tag{4.2}$$

where $\rho = \sqrt{I/A}$ is the radius of gyration of the cross-section, and l/ρ is called the *slenderness ratio*.

---

* ASTM E9-52T, Section 1.
† ASTM E6.
‡ For a discussion of column theory, see any good text on mechanics of materials.

If the stress given by Eq. 4.2 exceeds the compressive proportional limit stress of the material, these equations are no longer directly applicable but must be modified to take into account inelastic action. This condition is reached as the slenderness ratio is reduced, the limiting value being $l/\rho = \pi\sqrt{E/\sigma_{pl}}$. Columns for which l/ρ is less than this value are classified as *short columns*.

Since Hooke's law does not apply to the buckling of short columns, we must use the stiffness associated with small increments of increasing load in place of the modulus of elasticity, E. The incremental stiffness is measured by the tangent modulus, E_t. If E_t is substituted for E in Eq. 4.1, the resulting critical loads are found to agree well with experiment. Thus Eqs. 4.1 and 4.2 become, for short columns,

$$P_{cr} = \frac{\pi^2 E_t I}{l^2} \qquad (4.1a)$$

and

$$\sigma_{cr} = \frac{\pi^2 E_t}{(l/\rho)^2}. \qquad (4.2a)$$

Application of these equations to actual columns involves evaluating E_t, which itself depends on the stress, σ_{cr}. An indirect approach must therefore be used. From a graph such as Fig. 3.39 several pairs of corresponding values of E_t and σ_{cr} are selected (it is assumed that this graph holds for compression as well as tension). For each pair of values the corresponding value of l/ρ is computed from Eq. 4.2a. A graph can now be plotted showing σ_{cr} as a function of l/ρ, and from this the critical stress can be selected for any given slenderness ratio.

EXPERIMENTAL METHODS

4.6 THE COMPRESSION TEST

Loading in compression offers certain advantages over loading in tension in some types of investigation. It also presents some new difficulties. The advantages will be discussed first, followed by an analysis of the difficulties and ways of minimizing them.

A load in compression is much easier to apply to brittle materials than one in tension. The problem of gripping brittle materials in tension is serious. If screw threads are used, it is difficult to prevent fracture in the threads or at the fillets because of the pronounced effect of stress concentrations on brittle materials. On the other hand, if clamp-type grips are used, with wedge blocks to provide automatic clamping, the transverse clamping pressure becomes serious, tending to cause compressive failure (shear or crumbling) in the grips.   These difficulties, coupled with their weakness in tension, make brittle materials less useful in tensile applications than in compression.

Wood, because of its cellular structure and directional grain, also offers major difficulties in the application of loads in tension.   In the direction of the grain it is actually quite strong in tension—sometimes stronger than in compression.   Any grips that might be used to apply a load in this direction must either clamp the ends of the member or hook onto some projection.   The transverse clamping pressure causes compression failure and the projections shear off easily, so that application of the load is very difficult, and wood is not often used in tension.   (Timber fasteners are an important part of the development of timber structures.)   The same difficulties apply to other cellular or porous materials.

An axial compressive force, however, is easily applied by means of two parallel flat plates, one at each end of a cylindrical or prismatic specimen. Consequently the compression test is commonly used in investigating brittle and cellular materials.

For ductile materials the compression test makes it possible to investigate much larger plastic strains than the tension test.   With no problems of plastic instability as in tension, the plastic range becomes theoretically unlimited.   The compression test might therefore be used to study the effects of forming (rolling, extruding, etc.) ductile metals.

Lateral Instability and End Restraint

Two main difficulties of the compression test are *lateral instability* and *end restraint*.   Lateral instability arises from simple column action.   Its effect is to produce lateral deflections and consequent nonuniform stress in the member.   These conditions may be followed by complete collapse at a load less than the true compressive strength of the material.   From Eq. 4.2a the critical stress on a column is $\sigma_{cr} = \pi^2 E_t/(l/\rho)^2$.   To ensure against buckling failure the critical stress must be greater than the compressive stresses to be used in the test.   Consequently the slenderness ratio, l/ρ, must be small enough.   For a circular cross-section $\rho = d/8$, where d is the diameter, and the slenderness ratio is therefore proportional to l/d. The ratio l/d must be kept small if lateral instability is to be avoided.

End restraint is caused by the lateral expansion that accompanies axial compression.   As a cylindrical specimen is shortened by the pressure of the plates on its ends, its diameter increases by the amount $\epsilon_y d = |\mu\epsilon_x d|$ (Eq. 3.3).   Expansion of the ends of the specimen is hindered, however, by friction between the ends and the compression plates (Fig. 4.8); sometimes it may be prevented entirely.   This condition is known as end restraint. Its effect is to hold the ends of a compression specimen near their original diameter while the center portion expands, resulting in a barrel-shaped specimen (Fig. 4.9).

End restraint produces a transverse compression on the material near the ends of the specimen, as shown in Fig. 4.8.   This transverse compression is greatest at the end surfaces and diminishes toward the midsection of the specimen; at a distance from the ends roughly equal to one diameter (of the specimen) it decreases to zero.   The transverse compressive stress combines with an equal part of the axial compressive stress to form a hydrostatic pressure.   Since hydrostatic pressure cannot produce failure

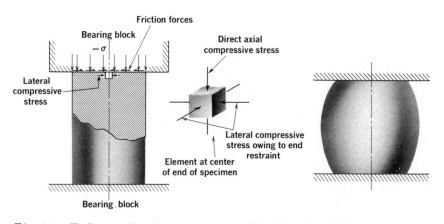

Fig. 4.8   End restraint in compression.

Fig. 4.9   Barrel-shaped specimen resulting from end restraint.

(Art. 4.3), the material near the ends of the specimen is in effect strengthened.   The stress distribution in the ends of the specimen becomes *triaxial* (stresses in three dimensions) and is far from the state of simple compression desired in the test.

There are a number of ways of dealing with the combined effects of end restraint and lateral instability.   One is simply to ignore the former and make the specimen short enough to eliminate all possibility of buckling, as is done in the standard quality control tests of brittle materials when a comparison of results on different specimens is all that is required.   Here the exact state of stress is considered unimportant.   The standard specimen is often a 2-inch cube or the ASTM *short specimen*, 1 inch long and $1\frac{1}{8}$ inches in diameter ($l/d = 0.9$).*   Many tests of this kind are described in the ASTM *Standards*.   They are simple to conduct and, when standardized, provide useful comparisons between materials.

A second method is to make use of the fact that end restraint disappears

---

* ASTM E9-52T.

at a distance approximately one diameter from the end of a cylindrical specimen. The specimen is made long enough to provide a suitable middle region that will be free of the effects of end restraint (simple compression). The length of this region is approximately $l - 2d$, where l is the overall length of the specimen. Thus the lower limit for l is $2d$. The *medium-length specimen* specified by ASTM has an l/d ratio of 3,* giving a region of simple compression in the center about one diameter long. This length is usually adequate for measuring strains, but for more accurate results ASTM *long specimens* are used; these have l/d ratios of 8 or 10.* As l/d

Fig. 4.10 *Uranium compression specimens with grooved ends: (left) before testing; (middle) after testing, with improper lubricant and groove configuration; (right) after testing, with proper lubricant and groove configuration. (Reprinted courtesy Dr. John E. Hockett, Los Alamos Scientific Laboratory, Los Alamos, New Mexico)*

becomes larger, the danger of lateral buckling increases, and with it the need for precise machining of specimens and special precautions for reducing eccentricity in loading. The actual selection of proportions for a compression specimen becomes a compromise between large l/d to avoid end effects and small l/d to avoid buckling. Usually the most satisfactory compromise is $l/d = 3$, the ASTM medium-length specimen.

One of the most common compression tests is that specified for concrete in ASTM Standard C39. In this test the minimum l/d ratio of 2 is used. Standard dimensions are $l = 12$ in. and $d = 6$ in. (For concrete using small gravel, and for mortar, smaller sizes are used, but still in the ratio $l/d = 2$). The cylinders are molded in various types of container, and the ends are capped to ensure flat, parallel surfaces.

---

* ASTM E9-52T.

A third method of dealing with end restraint is to lubricate the ends to reduce friction. The contact pressures are so high that special lubricants, such as paraffin, must be used. The results are somewhat uncertain, however, because the lubricant tends to flow outward under pressure and produces the same effect as friction, only in the reverse direction. Compression specimens are often split longitudinally by the lateral tension produced at the ends by lubricants. The result is a weakening instead of a strengthening of the specimen.

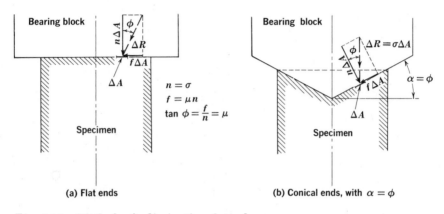

Fig. 4.11   Method of eliminating lateral compressive stresses in compression tests.

An improvement used successfully by several investigators is as follows. Fine concentric grooves are made in the ends of the specimen, covering the surface completely. A suitable lubricant applied to the ends is retained by the grooves, which prevent outward flow. The barrelling effect in ductile specimens can be completely eliminated by this method. However, the shape and size of the grooves and the type of lubricant used are critical, and can only be determined experimentally at present. Figure 4.10 shows a specimen before being compressed, and two similar specimens after compression, one with improper lubricant and the other with proper lubricant.

A fourth method involves shaping the bearing plates and the ends of the specimen to introduce an outward thrust just balancing the friction force. Figure 4.11a shows the forces acting on an element, ΔA, of a specimen having plane ends: $n =$ the normal pressure per unit area, equal to σ here; $f =$ the friction force per unit area. If we assume that the outward expansion force of the cylinder is sufficient actually to cause some slipping between the end and the compression plate, the resultant ΔR will be inclined at the angle of friction, ϕ, with the normal as shown. From Fig. 4.11b it can be seen that if the surface of contact is in the form of a cone, the resultant ΔR can be made parallel to the axis of the cylinder. The angle α must be made equal to ϕ, and thus ΔR will be equal to $\sigma\Delta A$, resulting in simple compression. The only difficulty is in determining the angle of friction for any given materials and surface conditions. In general it can only be approximated. However, for careful investigations the method can give good results.

Conduct of Experiments

Compression tests for measuring stress and strain may be either conventional or true stress-strain types. Their conduct is similar to that of

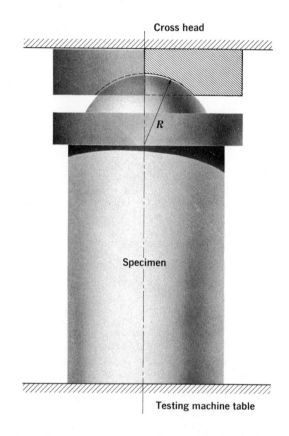

Fig. 4.12 Self-aligning compression plate.

the corresponding tension tests. Specimens are usually plain right cylinders or prisms whose ends are made as nearly flat and parallel as possible to avoid eccentric loading. Occasionally specimens have enlarged ends to add to their lateral stability, but these are of doubtful value because they also extend the effects of end restraint farther from the ends. When specimens are capped, as are concrete cylinders, care must be taken to use a hard enough material for the caps.   A cap that is too soft will tend to flow outward under pressure and cause longitudinal splitting.

A universal testing machine, fitted with compression plates, is usually used to apply the load.   The lower compression plate is fixed on the table of the machine while the upper plate is attached to the crosshead.   Since it is impossible to make specimens having perfectly parallel ends, it is desirable to provide some adjustment in the compression plates so that they can be made to apply a uniform stress over each end of the specimen.   The simplest adjustable compression plate is one having a spherical seat.   It is arranged as shown in Fig. 4.12, at the top of the specimen, the spherical surface having its center in the top surface of the specimen.   The surfaces of the compression plates must be hard enough that plastic deformation in the plates will be negligible.

Before the specimen is placed in the machine, it should be measured in accordance with standard procedures (for metallic materials see ASTM Standard E9).   The greatest care must be exercised in placing the specimen to see that its centerline coincides with the axis of the machine (as well as with the axis of the spherical-seated bearing block, if any).   Effects of eccentricity are even more pronounced in compression than in tension because of the lateral instability involved.   Thus it is almost always necessary to measure strains at two or more points around the specimen. Usually an averaging strainometer is sufficient for this, but sometimes three or four equally spaced strainometers are desirable.

After the specimen is properly aligned, a small initial load is usually applied to hold it firmly while the strainometer is being attached.   A strainometer especially made for use in compression is often referred to as a *compressometer*.   SR-4 electric strain gages can also be used in compression; they have approximately the same range as in tension.

From this point on, the conduct of the compression test is almost identical with that of the tension test described in Art. 3.17.   The observations are the same as those taken in the tension test, for both the conventional and true stress-strain tests.

As in the tension test, maintaining a constant rate of strain is often important.   In fact, materials usually tested in compression are those most susceptible to changes in strain rate.   Brittle and cellular materials like plastics, wood, concrete, and ceramics often have considerable viscous flow and do not readily reach equilibrium conditions under high loads.   Various rates are specified in the standard tests.

Since the majority of compression tests are made on other than ductile materials, they are usually carried all the way to final fracture.   Figure 4.13 shows typical fractures of wood, cast iron, and concrete.   All are seen to be of the shear type.   However, other influences can also be detected.   In cast iron and concrete the shear surfaces tend to run from corner to corner of the specimen—not on the 45° plane of maximum shear; this is evidence of the effect of end restraint, which strengthens the material in a cone-shaped region at each end and leaves a weakness around the edge

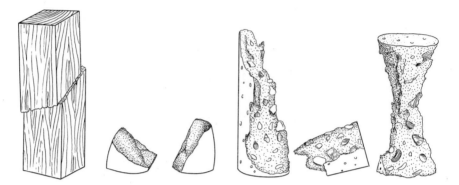

Fig. 4.13   Compression fractures of wood, gray cast iron, and concrete, illustrating failure by slip on planes near those of maximum shear.

of the specimen, from which the shear cracks spread, meeting in the center. Cylindrical specimens of concrete tend to fail along conical shear surfaces, forming the typical hourglass fracture of concrete.   The directionality of the grain affects the shear failure in wood, but nevertheless the shear plane is usually about 45°.

BIBLIOGRAPHY

Marin, Joseph, *Engineering Materials—Their Mechanical Properties and Applications*, Prentice-Hall, Inc., Englewood Cliffs, N. J., 1952, Ch. 1.

Timoshenko, S., *Strength of Materials—Part II—Advanced Theory and Problems*, 3rd ed., D. Van Nostrand Company, Inc., Princeton, N. J., 1956, Ch. X.

Davis, Harmer E., Troxell, George E., and Wiskocil, Clement T., *The Testing and Inspection of Engineering Materials*, 2nd ed. (McGraw-Hill Civil Engineering Series) McGraw-Hill Book Company, Inc., New York, Toronto, London, 1955, Ch. 4.

Nadai, A., *Theory of Flow and Fracture of Solids*, Vol. I, 2nd ed. (Engineering Societies Monographs), McGraw-Hill Book Company, Inc., New York, Toronto, London, 1950, Ch. 20.

PROBLEMS

4.1 Compare the proportional limit, modulus of resilience, and ductility of gray cast iron in tension and compression, from Fig. 4.3.

4.2 Repeat Problem 4.1 for Plexiglas, from Fig. 4.5 (omit ductility).

4.3 From Fig. 4.3, measure the values of the secant modulus for several different strains and plot a curve of E_{sec} vs ϵ for gray cast iron.

4.4 The maximum tensile stress for a certain ductile steel is 60,000 psi (conventional). The corresponding conventional strain is 0.080 in./in. Assuming that the *true* stress-strain diagrams are identical for tension and compression, compute the *conventional* stress and strain in compression corresponding to the values given in tension (assume constant volume).

4.5 From Fig. 3.39 read and tabulate the values of E_t corresponding to stresses from 60 to 200 ksi at intervals of 20 ksi. Using Euler's formula for pin-ended columns ($\sigma_{cr} = \pi^2 E/(l/\rho)^2$), with E_t in place of E, compute the value of l/ρ for each of the tabulated values of σ. Plot a curve of σ_{cr} vs l/ρ and compare with Euler's curve based on an elastic modulus for steel of 29×10^6 psi. (Note: this problem assumes that the tension and compression curves for this steel are identical.)

4.6 Without the aid of the text describe three ways in which a material may fail in compression.

4.7 Explain what is meant by the Bauschinger effect.

4.8 Discuss the two main difficulties connected with the compression test and tell how their effects may be minimized.

4.9 Explain the purpose of the swivel head commonly used in compression tests. Make a sketch showing the proper arrangement of such a head.

4.10 Name materials for which the secant modulus in compression is (a) always less than the tangent modulus; (b) always greater than the tangent modulus; (c) greater at some stresses, and less at others, than the tangent modulus. Sketch stress-strain curves for the materials named.

4.11 Construct a stress-strain curve for concrete in compression, determined by the following data:

STRESS, psi	STRAIN, in./in.
0	0
2000	0.00050
4000	0.00110
6000	0.00200

(a) Determine the initial (tangent) modulus of elasticity.   (b) Determine the secant modulus and tangent modulus at 4800 psi.

4.12 Referring to the diagram used in Problem 4.11, and assuming that 6000 psi is the fracture stress, determine the total energy necessary to break a cylinder 4 in. in diameter and 8 in. long, made of this concrete.

CHAPTER 5

STATIC
BENDING

Members loaded so that one side is elongated while the other side is compressed are said to be loaded in bending. The majority of members used in engineering are subject to some bending. The reaction of the material is to build up internal stresses to resist the elongation and compression. On every cross-section of the member there are normal stresses that vary from tension on one side to compression on the other.

PURE BENDING

In the simplest form—pure bending—the normal stresses are the only ones present on the cross-section; shearing stresses are absent. Pure bending is thus an example of uniaxial stress and as such is an application of the principles of simple tension and compression. The only additional factor is the variation of stress across the cross-section, and it is with this factor that we are primarily concerned.

A member is subject to pure bending when it is loaded by two equal and opposite couples at its ends (Fig. 5.1a). The bending moment, M, is constant along the length of the beam, and the shear is zero. A common form of loading producing pure bending is shown in Fig. 5.1b; the two loads are at equal distances from the end supports, and M varies according to

167

the bending moment diagram of Fig. 5.1c. The center portion, BC, is seen to be in pure bending since the moment is constant in this portion. As is usual in all bending problems, it is assumed that the supports and the means of applying the load are such that no longitudinal restraint is imposed.

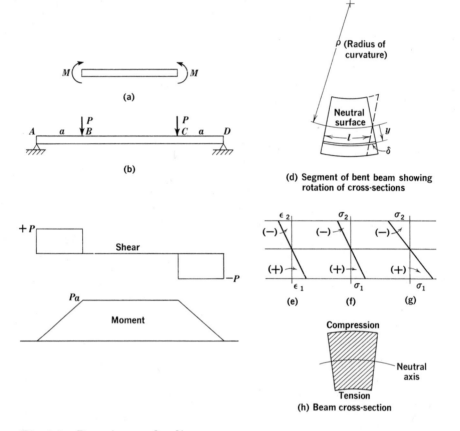

Fig. 5.1 *Beam in pure bending.*

We shall consider only the case of pure bending where the loads are applied in a plane of symmetry so that bending takes place parallel to this plane. We shall also assume that cross-sections remain plane during bending—even beyond the elastic range. This is a common assumption that experience has shown to hold with reasonable accuracy. For convenience the beam may be thought of as composed of longitudinal elements of infinitesimal cross-section, or "fibers," each of which is in a state of simple tension or compression.

5.1 ELASTIC ACTION IN PURE BENDING

The necessary relations between bending moment, stress, and deflection for prismatic beams made of materials which follow Hooke's law and have the same elastic properties in tension and compression may be derived by elementary theory.

Keeping in mind the assumptions stated above, consider a short segment of the beam in Fig. 5.1a contained between two cross-sections. As the moment is applied, the upper fibers are shortened and the lower fibers elongated, causing the cross-sections to rotate (Fig. 5.1d). The strain in any fiber is given by the ratio of its change in length, δ, to the original length of the segment, l. It can easily be seen that δ, and therefore the strain, ϵ_x, is zero somewhere in the middle of the beam and varies linearly in each direction from this point. The variation of strain is shown in Fig. 5.1e. The neutral surface, or location of zero strain, intersects each cross-section at its neutral axis, passing through the centroid of the cross-section. This statement may be verified by summing the internal axial forces and setting them equal to zero, as follows.

From the geometry of the deformation (Fig. 5.1d) we have the proportion

$$\frac{\delta}{y} = \frac{l}{\rho}$$

or
$$\epsilon_x = \frac{y}{\rho} \text{ (Fig. 5.1e).} \tag{5.1}$$

It follows from Hooke's law that

$$\sigma_x = E\epsilon_x = E\frac{y}{\rho} \tag{5.2}$$

as shown in Fig. 5.1f. The force on each element in the cross-section is $\sigma_x \, dA$, where dA is the area of the element. If we sum these forces and set them equal to zero, for equilibrium

$$\int dF_x = \int_A \sigma_x \, dA = \frac{E}{\rho} \int_A y \, dA = 0,$$

from which, since $\int y \, dA = A\bar{y}$, we find that $\bar{y} = 0$. Thus the neutral axis passes through the centroid.

The stress caused by the moment M is found by summing the moments about the neutral axis of the cross-section,

$$M = \int_A (\sigma_x \, dA)y = \frac{E}{\rho} \int_A y^2 \, dA = \frac{EI_z}{\rho}, \tag{5.3}$$

where I_z = the moment of inertia of the cross-section about the neutral axis. Since $\sigma_x = Ey/\rho$, it follows that

$$\sigma_x = \frac{My}{I_z} \text{ or } (\sigma_x)_{max} = \frac{Mc}{I_z}, \tag{5.4}$$

where c = the distance from the neutral axis to the extreme fibers.   This is the *flexure formula*.

The behavior of a material in pure bending is represented by relations between various force and deformation variables.   Since stress is not constant across the cross-section, the use of stress as the force variable requires the choice of some particular value like $(\sigma_x)_{max}$.   Consequently it is just as significant, and much easier, to use the moment, M, or the load, P, as

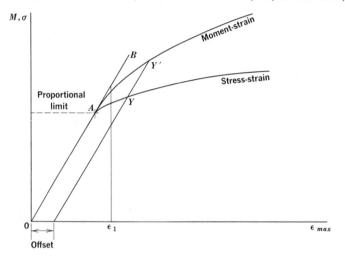

Fig. 5.2   Moment-strain and stress-strain diagrams compared.

the force variable.   The maximum strain provides a good deformation variable because it is simple to measure, and the variation of strain is always linear across the cross-section.   The maximum deflection is also widely used because of its ease of measurement.   For our further discussions we shall use the moment-strain relation (analogous to the stress-strain relation in simple tension).   For materials following Hooke's law the flexure formula gives

$$M = \frac{I_z}{c}(\sigma_x)_{max} = \frac{EI_z}{c}(\epsilon_x)_{max}. \tag{5.5}$$

This is the equation of the elastic line, OA (Fig. 5.2).

The value of E used above is the same as that found in simple tension or compression.   The other elastic properties in bending, such as the elastic resilience and the end of the elastic range, can be predicted from the corresponding properties in simple tension.

The resilience can also be expressed in terms of the work done by the applied moments up to the proportional limit. The average work per unit volume is equal to half the product of the moment and the angular displacement, divided by the volume of the beam:

$$u = \frac{M_{pl}\theta_{pl}}{2\,AL},\tag{5.6}$$

where A = the area of the cross-section, L = the length of the beam in pure bending, and θ_{pl} = the angular rotation of one end of the beam with respect to the other, at the proportional limit. Since θ_{pl} is the same as the angle between the radii to the ends of the beam,

$$\theta_{pl} = \frac{L}{\rho_{pl}} = \frac{L}{c}\,(\epsilon_{max})_{pl}.$$

The resilience can then be expressed in terms of moment and strain as

$$u = \frac{M_{pl}(\epsilon_{max})_{pl}}{2\,Ac},\tag{5.6a}$$

which is equal to the area under the moment-strain diagram divided by the product Ac. The resilience as calculated from either of the two equations above is useful for comparing beams of different materials but identical geometry. Varying the proportions of the beams will change the value of resilience and render the comparison meaningless.

If the material were perfectly brittle, the flexure formula could be used all the way to rupture. The stress computed from Eq. 5.4, using the rupture moment, is

$$\sigma_r = \frac{M_r c}{I_z}\tag{5.7}$$

and is called the *modulus of rupture*. Since no material is actually perfectly brittle, stress σ_r is never quite equal to the maximum stress in the beam at rupture. It is nevertheless a commonly used property for materials like ceramics, cast iron, concrete, wood, and brittle plastics, even though some of these have considerable inelastic deformation before rupture.

Accompanying the change in length of the longitudinal fibers is a lateral strain, just as in simple tension and compression (the Poisson effect). The fibers on the tension side of the beam contract laterally and those on the compression side expand. The strain in the z-direction is $\epsilon_z = -\mu\epsilon_x$. Since ϵ_x varies linearly across the cross-section, ϵ_z does likewise. Consequently the beam becomes wider on the compression side and narrower on the tension side (Fig. 5.1h). A transverse curvature is produced in the opposite direction from the longitudinal curvature (anticlastic curvature).

If we make the beam wider while holding its depth fixed, the interference between the two curvatures increases. For wide plates the two curvatures become incompatible, and little if any of the transverse curvature remains.

The material has been prevented from expanding or contracting in the
z-direction by a stress σ_z. Thus the bending of plates involves stresses in
two directions, called *biaxial stresses*. The effect of these biaxial stresses
on ductility will be studied in Chapter 6.

Elastic bending of materials having nonlinear stress-strain relations, like
rubber and certain plastics, will be treated in Art. 5.3 along with the plastic
bending of metals and other ductile materials.

5.2   YIELDING IN PURE BENDING

The atomic mechanism of yielding in pure bending is the same as in
simple tension: slip along planes in the general direction of the maximum
shearing stress, at 45° with the axis of the beam.   When the extreme fibers
(those farthest from the neutral axis) reach the strain at which yielding
begins in simple tension, local yielding takes place just as in a bar in tension
(Arts. 3.5 and 3.7).   As bending continues, yielding progresses gradually
inward toward the neutral surface.   The stress in each fiber follows the
stress-strain relation for simple tension, and the stress distribution begins
to look like that in Fig. 5.1g.

Since initial yielding affects the stress only in small parts of the cross-
section—those near the extreme surfaces of the beam—the effect on the
moment-strain diagram is slight.   Figure 5.2 is a typical moment-strain
diagram for a ductile metal.   On the same diagram is the stress-strain
curve for the same metal in simple tension.   The scales of stress and
moment have been adjusted so that the proportional limits, σ_{pl} and M_{pl},
coincide.   The extension of line OA toward B represents the values of
moment or stress that would pertain if the material continued to behave
elastically.   How the moment and the corresponding stress vary with
yielding can thus be compared, both with one another and with the elastic
values.

At strain ϵ_1, for example, slightly beyond the elastic range, the stress in
simple tension is already 10 per cent below the corresponding elastic stress,
while the moment is only about 1 per cent below the corresponding elastic
moment.   Thus it is difficult to detect the initial yield in bending.   And
the offset yield strength is of little value for bending if computed for the
same offset used in tension, as can be seen by comparing the values found
by the offset construction shown in Fig. 5.2.   The yield stress at Y is only
about 10 per cent higher than the proportional limit stress at A, while the
moment at Y', for the same offset, is fully 50 per cent higher than the
proportional limit moment.   Using a smaller offset is some improvement,
but greater accuracy is then required.

Since the gradual departure from linearity in the moment-strain diagram
makes the location of the proportional limit very uncertain, it can be seen

that the moment-strain diagram does not provide a good indication of the elastic strength in bending.   An easier and more reliable way of determining the elastic strength is to compute it from the corresponding property measured in simple tension.   Thus the proportional limit moment, M_{pl}, can be computed quite accurately from σ_{pl} by means of Eq. 5.4.   The yield moment, M_y, can be computed similarly from σ_y, although here a small amount of inelastic deformation is involved and the value obtained is approximate.

Materials that yield discontinuously, such as mild steel, present some additional problems.   The stress in each fiber still follows the stress-strain relation for simple tension up to a point.   However, because of the con-

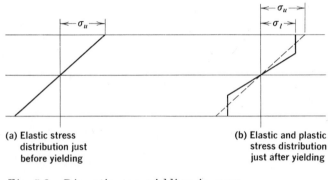

(a) Elastic stress
    distribution just
    before yielding

(b) Elastic and plastic
    stress distribution
    just after yielding

Fig. 5.3   Discontinuous yielding in pure bending.

centration of the maximum stress in the extreme fibers (Fig. 5.3) and the support given by the inner fibers, the beam usually does not begin to yield until somewhat higher stresses are reached than are ordinarily observed in tension.   When yielding does begin at some point, owing to an imperfection, it forms a small slip band starting at the extreme surface and progressing inward toward the neutral surface in the form of a wedge.   This wedge acts like a notch having stress concentrations at its tip, and the inner fibers therefore yield at stresses comparable to the lower yield point in tension. There is an abrupt change in shape of the stress distribution from that in Fig. 5.3a to that in Fig. 5.3b.   As in simple tension, highly localized yielding occurs at more and more points along the beam until the entire beam has yielded.

The sudden change in stress distribution as yielding begins means that the moment-strain curve departs more abruptly from its elastic line. Again, as in tension, a distinct size effect is noted, small beams having higher yield strengths than large ones (Fig. 5.4).   Smaller beams also yield more abruptly than larger ones.

5.3 PURE BENDING WITH NONLINEAR RELATIONS BETWEEN STRESS AND STRAIN

If the stress-strain diagram for a material is nonlinear (Fig. 5.5a), the stress distribution across the beam will be as shown in Fig. 5.5b.   The curves in a and b have the same shape and differ only in scale.   In Fig. 5.5a the horizontal axis represents the strain, ϵ_x, while in Fig. 5.5b the vertical axis represents distance from the neutral axis, y; in each the other

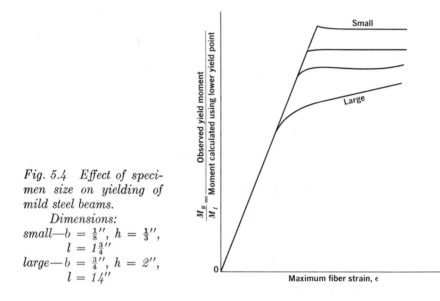

Fig. 5.4   Effect of specimen size on yielding of mild steel beams.
Dimensions:
small—$b = \frac{1}{8}''$, $h = \frac{1}{3}''$,
$l = 1\frac{3}{4}''$
large—$b = \frac{3}{4}''$, $h = 2''$,
$l = 14''$

axis is stress.   Since ϵ_x is proportional to y (on the assumption that plane sections remain plane even beyond the elastic range), it follows that the scales of the two curves are proportional.   If the maximum strain $(\epsilon_x)_{max}$ is known, the stress distribution curve can be constructed as follows. From Eq. 5.1

$$\epsilon_x = \frac{(\epsilon_x)_{max}}{c} y. \tag{5.8}$$

If we compute ϵ_x for several values of y, the corresponding values of σ_x may then be picked off the stress-strain diagram and plotted to give the stress distribution.

The example illustrated in Fig. 5.5 is a beam that has not only a vertical plane of symmetry, in which the loads are applied, but a horizontal plane of symmetry as well.   The cross-section may be a rectangle, circle, I-section, or any other shape having two axes of symmetry.   Since the material illustrated has identical stress-strain diagrams in tension and com-

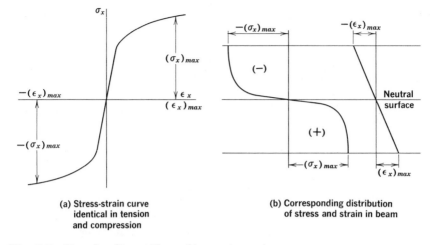

(a) Stress-strain curve
identical in tension
and compression

(b) Corresponding distribution
of stress and strain in beam

Fig. 5.5   Pure bending with nonlinear stress.

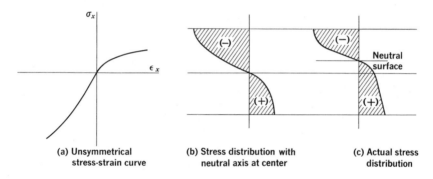

(a) Unsymmetrical
stress-strain curve

(b) Stress distribution with
neutral axis at center

(c) Actual stress
distribution

*Fig. 5.6   Pure bending with unsymmetrical non-
linear stress.*

pression, the neutral axis coincides with the horizontal axis of symmetry;
the stress distributions are identical in tension and compression, with a
resultant of zero, as required for equilibrium.

For materials having stress-strain diagrams that differ in tension and
compression (Fig. 5.6a) the stress distribution is also changed. If the
neutral axis remained at the axis of symmetry (Fig. 5.6b), the resultant
of the tensile stress would differ from that of the compressive stress. To
satisfy the conditions of equilibrium the neutral axis must shift toward the
side having the higher stress, equalizing the stress distributions (Fig. 5.6c).
As bending continues, the neutral axis must continually change its position
to preserve equilibrium. A similar situation develops when the beam has
no horizontal plane of symmetry, as for example, a T-section. In both

circumstances the neutral axis moves away from the centroid as bending progresses.

Nonlinear stress-strain relations include both nonlinear elastic materials and materials stressed into the plastic range.   In either instance the flexure formula (Eq. 5.4) has no real significance, having been developed for conditions of linear elasticity.   The relation between moment and stress must be worked out for each stress distribution.   The resultants of the tensile and compressive distributions, being equal and opposite forces, form a couple.   For a rectangular section the moment arm of the couple is the distance between the centroids of the stress distributions (shaded areas, Fig. 5.7).   The moment of the couple, T or C multiplied by the *arm*, must always equal the applied moment

$$M = Ta. \tag{5.9}$$

Beams of brittle materials (i.e., materials of low ductility, Fig. 3.10b) usually develop stress distributions like those of Fig. 5.7.   Actually the ductilities of such materials may be enhanced in bending by reason of the statistical nature of brittle fracture.   In a beam the maximum stress is concentrated in two very small regions adjacent to the extreme surfaces.

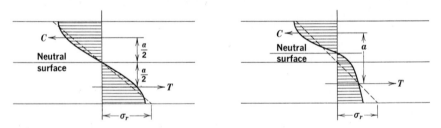

Fig. 5.7   Typical stress distributions in brittle materials in pure bending.

This concentration has the same effect on fracture strength as a very small specimen has in tension—the fracture strength is increased.   The actual tensile stress in the extreme fibers when failure takes place may be expected to be somewhat higher than the simple tensile strength.   Compressive failure never occurs because the compressive strength of brittle materials is so much higher than their tensile strength.

The relation between actual rupture stress and the *modulus of rupture* can now be studied.   If we assume that one of the diagrams in Fig. 5.7 represents the stress distribution at rupture, the moment, Ta, must equal M_r.   Use of the flexure formula to compute the stress implies a linear stress distribution like the dashed lines in Fig. 5.7, which does not actually exist.   Like the actual distribution, the linear distribution would have a moment equal to M_r.   Thus the modulus of rupture, σ_r, found from Eq. 5.7, is the maximum stress of the hypothetical linear distribution. It is always greater than the actual maximum tensile stress by a considerable margin: 80 per cent for cast iron, 50 to 100 per cent for concrete.

Final failure in beams made of ductile materials usually involves either excessive deformation or lateral buckling of some kind.

Beams of mild structural steel are of particular interest because of their wide use and because of the discontinuous behavior of this material. After yielding has progressed some distance from the outer surfaces, the stress distribution has the appearance of that in Fig. 5.8a. The maximum stress,

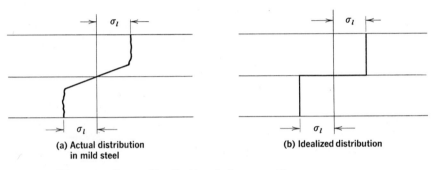

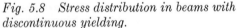

(a) Actual distribution   (b) Idealized distribution
in mild steel

Fig. 5.8   Stress distribution in beams with discontinuous yielding.

σ_l, is approximately constant over the depth of yielding. At the limit, as the yielded region approaches the center of the beam, the stress distribution can be represented by two rectangles (Fig. 5.8b). This distribution is referred to as the fully plastic condition, and the corresponding moment can easily be computed. So long as strain-hardening does not occur, the moment cannot increase beyond this value, which is therefore called the *ultimate moment, M_u.*

For a rectangular section the ultimate moment is found to be

$$M_u = \left(\sigma_l \cdot \frac{bh}{2}\right) \cdot \frac{h}{2} = \sigma_l \frac{bh^2}{4}, \tag{5.10a}$$

where σ_l is the lower yield point stress, b is the width of the cross-section, and h its depth. The moment at which yielding *begins* (neglecting the upper yield stress, if any) is, from Eq. 5.4,

$$M_y = \sigma_l \frac{I}{c} = \sigma_l \frac{bh^2}{6}. \tag{5.10b}$$

Comparing the two we find

$$\frac{M_u}{M_y} = 1.5, \tag{5.11}$$

or the ultimate moment is 50 per cent higher than the yield moment.

The value of the ratio M_u/M_y depends on the shape of the beam cross-section and is called the *shape factor*. For circular cross-sections $M_u/M_y = 1.7$; for standard I-sections $M_u/M_y \approx 1.18$. The shape factor is important in determining the margin remaining beyond the initial yield moment, and is used in *plastic design* of steel structures.

5.4 RESIDUAL STRESSES

After a beam has been bent into the plastic range, removal of the load leaves it with internal *residual* stresses. The reason is that the stress-strain diagram for unloading is different from that for loading (Fig. 3.21). Imagine a rectangular beam of a ductile metal, loaded until the stress distribution is as shown in Fig. 5.9b. If the load is reduced slowly, the

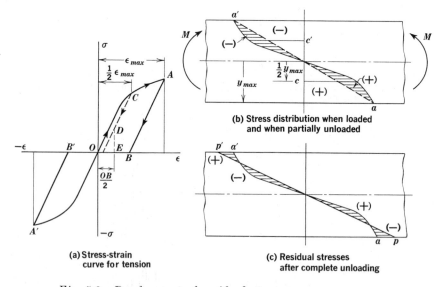

(b) Stress distribution when loaded and when partially unloaded

(a) Stress-strain curve for tension

(c) Residual stresses after complete unloading

Fig. 5.9   Development of residual stresses in a beam.

outer fibers, which were stressed to points A and A' on the stress-strain diagram (Fig. 5.9a), read zero stress at B and B' while the strain is still equal to $\overline{OB}$ and $\overline{OB'}$. Now the assumption that plane sections remain plane in pure bending has been found to hold for all conditions—plastic bending and unloading included. Thus the strain at any point in the cross-section is always proportional to the distance from the neutral axis. In the loaded state, then, the stress and strain at a point c, half-way to the outer fibers, is given by point C on the graph. Likewise, when the strain

in the outer fibers has been reduced to $\overline{OB}$ (i.e., when the stress in the outer
fibers is zero) the strain at point c is $\frac{1}{2} \overline{OB} = \overline{OE}$.   Consequently the stress
at point c, reducing along line CD, is not yet zero, but has a value equal
to $\overline{ED}$.   To find the stresses at other points in the cross-section we need
only remember that the reduction of stress at all points is linear.   Hence
the same effect could be obtained if a linear distribution of stress were
subtracted from the original distribution.   Such a distribution is shown by
dashed line aa' in Fig. 5.9b.   Points a and a' are located by making the
stresses at these points the same in the superimposed linear distribution
as in the original plastic distribution.   Subtracting the linear distribution
from the original plastic distribution leaves the shaded area between them,
representing the remaining distribution of stress in the cross-section.

When the load is removed completely, the moment of the stress distribution must be zero.   The stress all across the section is reduced still further,
so that the stress in the outer fibers changes sign and produces an opposite
moment to balance that of the remaining stress.   Line pp' in Fig. 5.9c
represents the necessary superimposed linear stress distribution.   The result is that in most parts of the unloaded beam the stress is not zero.   On
the lower, or tension side, there are residual compressive stresses in the
outer fibers, tensile in the interior; on the upper, or compression side, there
are residual tensile stresses in the outer fibers, compressive in the interior.
The net moment of the distribution is zero.

Residual stresses are also produced by thermal expansion, as discussed
in Chapter 12.   The presence of residual stresses is important from the
standpoint of fatigue (Chapter 9) and other forms of mechanical behavior.

EXPERIMENTAL METHODS

5.5 EXPERIMENTS IN PURE BENDING

In investigating experimentally the behavior of materials under pure
bending it is first necessary to satisfy the conditions assumed earlier—loading in a plane of symmetry, freedom from longitudinal restraint, and constant moment with zero shear in the portion of the beam under consideration.

The usual experimental setup is as illustrated schematically in Fig. 5.10.
At least one of the supports should be in the form of a hard roller, which
allows the greatest possible freedom longitudinally.

The loads are applied through a loading beam resting on two rollers on
top of the beam under investigation.   Rockers are sometimes used in place
of rollers, as in the ASTM standard test for flexural strength of concrete

(ASTM C78).   Rockers can be made to allow for some adjustment laterally, to fit beams that are slightly twisted from one end to the other.

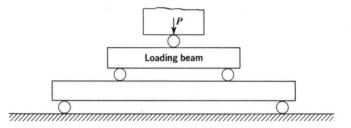

Fig. 5.10 Experimental setup for pure bending.

Constant moment and zero shear are provided by accurate spacing of the supports and loading points.   The loading beam itself must be loaded carefully at the midpoint between its two supporting rollers.   These in

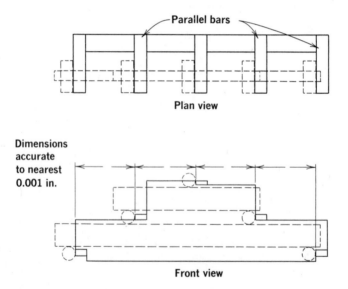

Fig. 5.11 Jig for setting up pure-bending experiment.

turn must be carefully spaced at equal distances from the supports for the main beam.   Sometimes rollers are used for both sets of supports to ensure complete symmetry in all respects.

Loading in a vertical plane of symmetry requires precision in the machining of both the loading beam and the experimental beam as well as the supporting rollers.   A further requirement is that the rollers be perpendicular to the axis of the beam.   This and the need for accurate spacing of the rollers can be fulfilled by using a specially constructed jig (Fig. 5.11) in setting up the beam.

Loads are often applied at the quarter points or third points, but any location can be used so long as the loads are at equal distances from the supports.   There are always local stresses near the loading points, but they disappear a short distance away (roughly equal to the depth of the beam). The center portion should be long enough to leave a sizable portion free from the local stresses.   A good minimum length for the center portion is 4 times the depth.

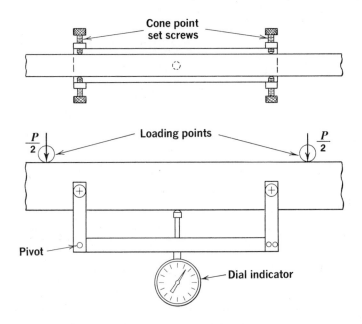

Fig. 5.12   Frame for measuring deflection in pure bending.

Experimental observations usually include *load* and either *deflection* or *strain*.   The deflection measured is that of the portion of the beam that is in pure bending.   It is therefore measured by a device like that of Fig. 5.12.   The frame is supported by pins or setscrews attached to the beam within the pure-bending portion and at the neutral surface.   The effects of shear in the end portions are thereby eliminated.   Deflection is measured by a standard dial indicator calibrated in either thousandths or ten-thousandths of an inch.

Strain is most conveniently measured by SR-4 strain gages attached to the top and bottom of the beam, although other types of strainometers are also used. With the SR-4 gage it is possible to detect deviations from linearity as small as 4 μin./in. in the moment-strain relation. This deviation corresponds to an offset of 0.0004 per cent and provides a good indication of the bending proportional limit. However, great care is required throughout the experiment to obtain such sensitivity.

There are few standard tests using pure bending. The flexure test for concrete, ASTM C78, is one. The only observation in this test, however, is maximum load, from which the modulus of rupture is computed. Most of the standardized bending tests involve midpoint loading, which is accompanied by transverse shear.

BENDING WITH SHEAR

5.6 TRANSVERSE SHEAR

Transverse shear transforms the stress in a beam from a uniaxial to a biaxial state. The longitudinal fibers are no longer under simple tensile or compressive stresses. Furthermore, because of the variation of moment along the length of the beam, the state of stress changes from point to point. The situation is indeed complex.

In the elastic analysis of beams it is assumed that the effects of transverse shear and those of the normal or bending stresses can be considered separately. In the inelastic range this cannot be done without introducing a certain degree of approximation. The degree depends upon the relative magnitudes of the two stresses, which in turn depends upon the physical proportions of the beam and the amount of inelastic bending involved. No attempt will be made to go into this subject here although the effects of combined stresses in simpler cases will be studied in Chapter 6.

The principal importance of bending with shear, in the study of materials, is its wide use as a standard test. It is so used primarily because of the ease with which the test can be made. Large, easily measured deflections or failure require only small loads to produce. The standardized tests are useful in comparing materials to be used in bending applications.

Bending tests with shear are also used to analyze the performance of full-sized members. They provide a direct means of evaluating the effects of such factors as shape on the structural stability of the member. They may also provide a detailed picture of the stress distribution in the member if elaborately carried out.

Bending properties determined by standard flexure tests with midpoint loading include stiffness, measured by E; strength, mainly the modulus of rupture for brittle materials; resilience; toughness; and ductility. It must be remembered that these properties are not measured under simple stress conditions and consequently they usually differ radically from the corresponding properties under simple tension. They are useful in the engineering design of beams, if used with judgment, and in comparison of materials. They are not of much scientific value in studying the material.

Two examples will serve to illustrate. The modulus of elasticity for short beams is found to be smaller than that for long beams of the same depth because the shear in a short beam is larger compared with the moment. The added deflection caused by shear gives the appearance of greater flexibility in the short beam, and this is not taken into account in the deflection formulas used for computing E.

The modulus of rupture found by midpoint loading is 10 to 20 per cent higher than that found by third-point loading (pure bending). In midpoint loading the maximum stresses are concentrated in the region close to the load, whereas in pure bending they are spread over a much larger portion of the span. The result is the same as for small and large specimens: the smaller is stronger than the larger.

Many standard flexure tests are contained in the ASTM *Standards*, for such materials as cast iron, plain concrete, bricks, plaster board, timber, plastics, and insulating materials. As in specifications for tension and compression tests of materials of this kind, rates of loading are often specified. Formulas for calculating the required properties are included in the standards.

The ductility of a material is frequently measured in terms of the amount of bending necessary to cause failure (analogous to per cent elongation at failure in tension). Since ductile materials do not fracture readily when bent, various means have been devised for inducing fracture—in a standardized way. The *cold-bend test* utilizes very sharp angles of bend to cause cracking in the tension surface. A bar of the material under investigation is bent around a pin of given size (ratio of pin diameter to thickness of specimen), and the angle at which cracking begins is observed (ASTM Standards A7, A15, A16). In other tests a notch is cut in the tension side of the bar to ensure fracture. The angle of bend at fracture is a measure of ductility. The work done by the applied load to fracture is a measure of toughness.

184   *Engineering Materials Science*

BIBLIOGRAPHY

Marin, Joseph, *Engineering Materials—Their Mechanical Properties and Applications*, Prentice-Hall, Inc., Englewood Cliffs, N. J., 1952, Ch. 2.

Davis, Harmer E., Troxell, George E., and Wiskocil, Clement T., *The Testing and Inspection of Engineering Materials*, 2nd ed. (McGraw-Hill Civil Engineering Series) McGraw-Hill Book Company, Inc., New York, Toronto, London, 1955, Ch. 5.

PROBLEMS

5.1 A small tungsten carbide flexure specimen has a circular cross-section 0.300 in. in diameter. Compute the slope of the elastic moment-strain diagram ($E = 78 \times 10^6$ psi).

5.2 Repeat Problem 5.1 for a fused silica glass flexure specimen having a rectangular cross-section 0.800 in. wide by 0.200 in. high ($E = 10 \times 10^6$ psi).

5.3 Compute the resilience of the beam in Problem 5.1, assuming that $(\epsilon_{max})_{pl} = 0.001$ in./in.

5.4 Compute the resilience of the beam in Problem 5.2, assuming that $(\epsilon_{max})_{pl} = 0.0001$ in./in.

5.5 Determine the ratio between the resilience of a beam, as given by Eq. 5.6a, and the *modulus of resilience* of a member in simple tension, based on the same proportional limit stress and strain. Evaluate this ratio for a rectangular cross-section.

5.6 The stress-strain diagram for a certain titanium alloy in tension can be approximated by two straight lines defined by the following points: 0, the origin; A, $\sigma_1 = 150,000$ psi, $\epsilon_1 = 0.010$ in./in.; B, $\sigma_2 = 170,000$ psi, $\epsilon_2 = 0.050$ in./in. A beam made of this material has a rectangular cross-section 1 in. wide by 2 in. high. Assuming that the stress-strain relation in compression is the same as that in tension, compute the moments corresponding to the stresses at points A and B.

5.7 What elastic stress would produce the same moment as that computed for the stress at point B in Problem 5.6? What residual stresses will remain in the beam after unloading from the stress at point B? (Illustrate by a sketch.)

5.8 Under what conditions would you expect the apparent modulus of elasticity in bending to be different from the modulus of elasticity in tension for the same material?

5.9 Show that the shape factor for mild steel beams of circular cross-section is 1.7, as stated in Art. 5.3.

5.10 Find the shape factor for a mild steel beam of square cross-section, loaded in the plane of the diagonal of the square.

5.11 Explain the purpose of the experimental loading arrangement in Fig. 5.10.

CHAPTER 6

COMPLEX
STATIC
STRESSES

Thus far our study of the mechanical behavior of materials has been limited to forms of loading that produce essentially simple uniaxial stress distributions. Materials used in engineering applications are often loaded in ways that produce more complex stress distributions. Circular shafts loaded in torsion, thin-walled tubes under internal pressure, wide plates loaded in bending, notched bars in tension, all are examples in which stresses are complex to some degree. In each instance the loading appears outwardly simple. This situation is a common one; even in "simple compression" we have seen that a highly complex state of stress can exist in part or all of the specimen.

The term *complex stress distribution*, as used here, includes distributions that are not uniaxial, plus those in which sharp variations occur in the stress. Thus biaxial and triaxial states of stress are included, as well as stress concentrations. (The stress around an indentation made in a hardness test (Chapter 10) is an example in which both occur.)

The effects of stresses of this kind on the behavior of materials are always interesting, frequently unexpected, and sometimes disastrous. A number of factors are involved. The effect of shearing stress on the yielding and fracture of materials has already been discussed for simple stresses. Its contribution in complex cases, and the effects of peak stresses, will be studied in this chapter. Effects of rate of strain and temperature will be taken up in Chapter 7.

STRESS ANALYSIS

Before particular forms of loading are discussed, a brief summary of the analysis of combined stresses and strains is in order.

6.1 COMBINED STRESSES

Biaxial Stresses

Consider biaxial stresses σ_x and σ_y acting on the faces of the rectangular element in Fig. 6.1. The subscripts x and y indicate that the planes on

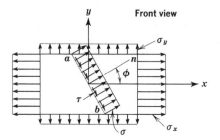

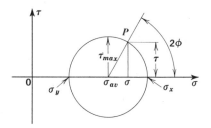

Fig. 6.1   *Element under biaxial tension stresses.*
         Fig. 6.2   *Mohr's circle for biaxial tension stresses.*

which these stresses act are those perpendicular to the x- and y-axes, respectively. Thus σ_x is the normal stress acting on planes parallel to the yz plane, and σ_y is the normal stress acting on planes parallel to the xz plane. Since the applied stresses are biaxial, there is no stress on the xy plane ($\sigma_z = 0$).

As a consequence of the applied stresses σ_x and σ_y, both normal and shearing stresses act on inclined planes. Plane ab is representative of those which are perpendicular to the xy plane but inclined to the x-axis. The angle of inclination is indicated by the angle ϕ between the normal, n, and the x-axis. Each of the applied stresses contributes to the normal stress, σ, on plane ab in accordance with Eq. 3.11:

$$\text{From } \sigma_x: \qquad \sigma = \sigma_x \cos^2 \phi$$
$$\text{From } \sigma_y: \qquad \sigma = \sigma_y \cos^2 \theta$$
$$= \sigma_y \cos^2 (\phi - 90°)$$
$$= \sigma_y \sin^2 \phi$$
$$\text{From both } \sigma_x \text{ and } \sigma_y: \sigma = \sigma_x \cos^2 \phi + \sigma_y \sin^2 \phi.$$

Similarly for τ, using Eq. 3.12:

From σ_x: $\tau = \sigma_x \cos\phi \sin\phi$

From σ_y: $\tau = \sigma_y \cos\theta \sin\theta$

$$= \sigma_y \cos(\phi - 90°) \sin(\phi - 90°)$$

$$= -\sigma_y \sin\phi \cos\phi$$

From both σ_x and σ_y: $\tau = \sigma_x \cos\phi \sin\phi - \sigma_y \sin\phi \cos\phi$.

These equations can be expressed more conveniently as

$$\sigma = \frac{\sigma_x + \sigma_y}{2} + \frac{\sigma_x - \sigma_y}{2} \cos 2\phi \tag{6.1}$$

and

$$\tau = \frac{\sigma_x - \sigma_y}{2} \sin 2\phi. \tag{6.2}$$

From these equations the stresses on any plane perpendicular to the xy plane can be calculated. The maximum shearing stress on such a plane occurs when $\sin 2\phi = 1$, or $\phi = 45°$, and is given by

$$\tau_{max} = \frac{\sigma_x - \sigma_y}{2}. \tag{6.3}$$

The normal stress accompanying τ_{max} is $(\sigma_x + \sigma_y)/2$, the average of the two applied stresses.

Mohr's Stress Circle

The above results can be represented graphically by Mohr's stress circle (Fig. 6.2). The abscissas represent normal stress, σ, and the ordinates shearing stress, τ. The values of σ_x and σ_y are laid off on the σ-axis and a circle drawn using $\sigma_x - \sigma_y$ as the horizontal diameter. The stresses on any inclined plane are given by the coordinates of the corresponding point on the circle. Point P, for example, being at the angle 2ϕ from the σ-axis, represents the stresses on plane ab in Fig. 6.1. By geometry it can be verified that the coordinates of this point are the same as the stresses found from Eqs. 6.1 and 6.2. This calculation is left as an exercise for the student.

From Eq. 6.2 the value of τ is the same for all angles ϕ for which $\sin 2\phi$ is the same, i.e., all angles differing by 90°. Thus the shearing stresses on planes at right angles are always equal.

Triaxial Stresses

Stresses such as those which we have been discussing are often called *plane stresses* because all are parallel to a common plane (the xy plane

here).   These stresses do, however, set up normal and shearing stresses on
other planes *inclined* to the *xy* plane.   In this sense there is no such thing

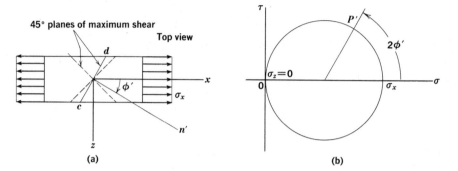

Fig. 6.3   Stresses on planes inclined to plane of applied stress.

as a plane stress system.   All stress distributions are actually three-
dimensional, or *triaxial*.

Figure 6.3a is a plan view of the rectangular element of Fig. 6.1.   Plane
cd, perpendicular to the *xz* plane, has its normal, *n'*, inclined at the angle ϕ'
to the *x*-axis.   The normal and shearing stresses acting on this plane are
given directly by Eqs. 3.11 and 3.12:

$$\sigma = \sigma_x \cos^2 \phi'$$

$$\tau = \frac{\sigma_x}{2} \sin 2 \phi'.$$

The maximum value of τ for planes perpendicular to the *xz* plane is then

$$\tau_{max} = \frac{\sigma_x}{2} \tag{6.3a}$$

and acts on the 45° planes shown by dashed lines in Fig. 6.3a.

A similar analysis shows that on planes perpendicular to the *yz* plane
there are stresses

$$\sigma = \sigma_y \cos^2 \phi''$$

and

$$\tau = \frac{\sigma_y}{2} \sin 2 \phi'',$$

where ϕ'' is the angle between the *y*-axis and the normal, *n''* (Fig. 6.4a).
Here we have

$$\tau_{max} = \frac{\sigma_y}{2} \tag{6.3b}$$

for planes perpendicular to the *yz* plane and at 45° to the *y*-axis.

A comparison of Eqs. 6.3, 6.3a, and 6.3b shows that if σ_x and σ_y are of the same sign, the first value found for τ_{max} (Eq. 6.3) will *not* be the absolute maximum shearing stress acting in the material. If σ_x and σ_y are both positive and $\sigma_x > \sigma_y$, the absolute maximum shearing stress will be $\sigma_x/2$ (Eq. 6.3a). Since the maximum shearing stress is such an important factor in the behavior of materials, the importance of considering all three dimensions is evident.

The Mohr's circle for planes perpendicular to the xz plane is shown in Fig. 6.3b. Point P' represents the stress acting on plane cd. Similarly the Mohr's circle in Fig. 6.4b is for planes perpendicular to the yz plane, and point P'' represents the stress acting on plane ef.

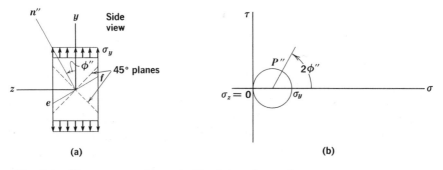

(a)   (b)

Fig. 6.4   Stresses on planes inclined to plane of applied stress.

In each of the Mohr's circles shown, the intersections of the circles with the σ-axes represent directions in which shearing stresses are zero. At these intersections the normal stresses have their largest and smallest values. The directions represented by these points are 90° apart since $2\phi = 180°$. The maximum and minimum normal stresses are called *principal stresses*. It can be shown that in every state of stress there are three principal directions, at right angles to each other, along which the principal stresses act. Each principal stress represents the maximum or minimum normal stress for one set of plane stresses represented by one of the Mohr's circles. No shearing stresses act on the principal planes. In the biaxial stress system above the principal stresses are σ_x, σ_y, and σ_z, the last being zero.

The three principal directions are often designated by orthogonal axes 1, 2, and 3 and the principal stresses by σ_1, σ_2, and σ_3. It is customary to follow the convention that σ_1 is the algebraic maximum, σ_3 the algebraic minimum, and σ_2 the intermediate value. Thus

$$\sigma_1 \geqslant \sigma_2 \geqslant \sigma_3. \tag{6.4}$$

Figure 6.5 shows a cubical element having principal stresses σ_1, σ_2, and σ_3 acting on its six faces.   The Mohr's circle for planes perpendicular to the 1-2 plane is shown in Fig. 6.6a.   As usual, the maximum shearing stress

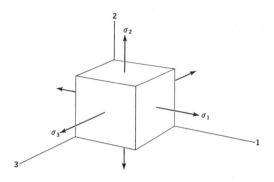

Fig. 6.5   Principal stresses on cubical element subject to triaxial stresses.

occurs on those planes making an angle of 45° with the 1-axis, as shown by the shaded planes in Fig. 6.6b.   Calling this particular maximum shearing stress τ'_{max}, we see from the Mohr's circle that

$$\tau'_{max} = \frac{\sigma_1 - \sigma_2}{2}. \tag{6.5}$$

Similarly Figs. 6.6c and 6.6d show the Mohr's circle for planes perpendicular to the 2-3 plane and the corresponding planes of maximum shear. This maximum shearing stress is

$$\tau''_{max} = \frac{\sigma_2 - \sigma_3}{2}. \tag{6.6}$$

Finally, Figs. 6.6e and 6.6f show the Mohr's circle for planes perpendicular to the 3-1 plane and the planes of absolute maximum shear:

$$\tau_{max} = \frac{\sigma_1 - \sigma_3}{2}. \tag{6.7}$$

In Fig. 6.6g all three Mohr's circles are superimposed to form the composite diagram of the complete triaxial state.   The stress on any plane perpendicular to one of the principal planes can be found by using the corresponding Mohr's circle or by applying Eqs. 6.1 and 6.2.   The stresses on a plane perpendicular to the 1-2 plane, for example, are given by

$$\sigma = \frac{\sigma_1 + \sigma_2}{2} + \frac{\sigma_1 - \sigma_2}{2} \cos 2\phi \tag{6.1a}$$

and

$$\tau = \frac{\sigma_1 - \sigma_2}{2} \sin 2\phi. \tag{6.2a}$$

The mean stress is defined as

$$\sigma_m = \frac{\sigma_1 + \sigma_2 + \sigma_3}{3}. \tag{6.8}$$

Figure 6.7 shows the Mohr's circles for three common states of stress: simple tension, simple compression, and equal biaxial tension.

6.2 ANALYSIS OF STRAIN

The strains in the directions of the principal stresses can be computed by considering the effect of each stress separately and adding them algebraically. Consider strain ϵ_1 in the direction of the largest principal stress, σ_1: stress σ_1 acting alone would produce a strain σ_1/E; stress σ_2 acting alone

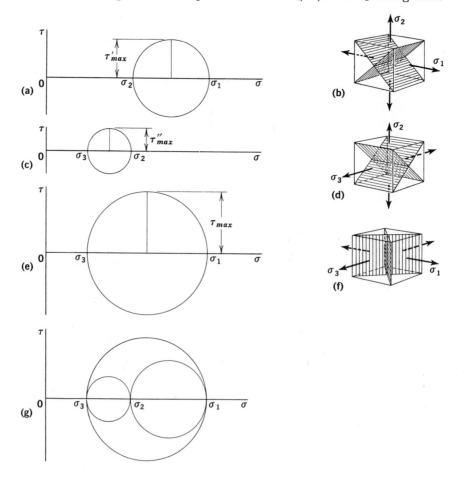

Fig. 6.6   Mohr's circles for triaxial stresses.

would produce a contraction in the direction of σ_1 given by $-\mu\sigma_2/E$; and stress σ_3 acting alone would produce a contraction in the direction of σ_1 given by $-\mu\sigma_3/E$. Consequently the net strain in the direction of σ_1 is

$$\epsilon_1 = \frac{\sigma_1}{E} - \mu\frac{\sigma_2}{E} - \mu\frac{\sigma_3}{E}. \tag{6.9}$$

Applying similar reasoning to the other principal directions leads to these expressions for the three principal strains:

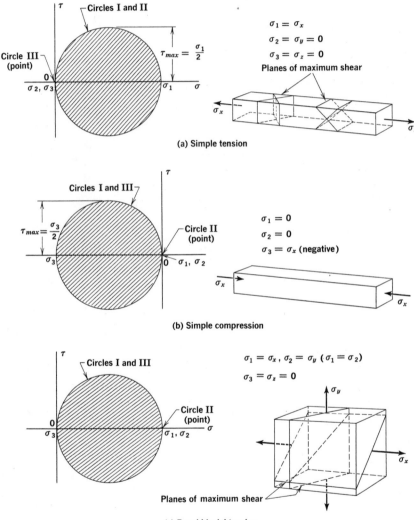

(a) Simple tension

(b) Simple compression

(c) Equal biaxial tension

Fig. 6.7 Mohr's circles for three typical stress distributions.

$$\left.\begin{array}{l} \epsilon_1 = \dfrac{1}{E}\left[\sigma_1 - \mu(\sigma_2 + \sigma_3)\right] \\[2mm] \epsilon_2 = \dfrac{1}{E}\left[\sigma_2 - \mu(\sigma_3 + \sigma_1)\right] \\[2mm] \epsilon_3 = \dfrac{1}{E}\left[\sigma_3 - \mu(\sigma_1 + \sigma_2)\right]. \end{array}\right\} \qquad (6.10)$$

Note that the last two expressions can be obtained from the first by cyclic permutations of the subscripts, i.e., the subscripts of the σ's are always in the order 1-2-3, 2-3-1, 3-1-2.

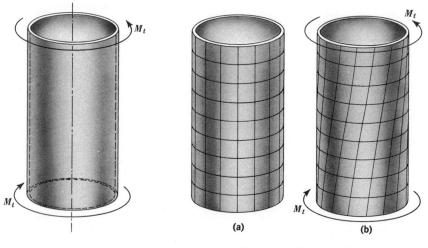

Fig. 6.8   Thin-walled   tube   in torsion.

Fig. 6.9   Thin-walled tube showing rectangular grid on surface.

We shall now discuss the behavior of materials under several common forms of loading which produce complex stress distributions.

TORSION—PURE SHEAR

One of the simplest examples of complex stress distribution is that produced by torsion of a thin-walled tube of circular cross-section.   Figure 6.8 shows such a tube twisted about its axis by the action of equal and opposite moments applied at its ends.   When the tube is replaced by a solid circular shaft, the situation is complicated by the fact that the stress varies from zero at the center to a maximum at the outer surface.   Both solid and hollow members are used in torsion, for instance, as rotating shafts to transmit power and as components of control systems. Of equal importance is the use of torsion in determining shearing properties of materials.

6.3 ELASTIC ACTION IN TORSION

Thin-Walled Tube

If a rectangular network of lines is inscribed on the surface of the thin-walled tube of Fig. 6.8, as illustrated in Fig. 6.9a, the elastic distortion of the tube can be pictured as in Fig. 6.9b. Figure 6.10a shows the atomic

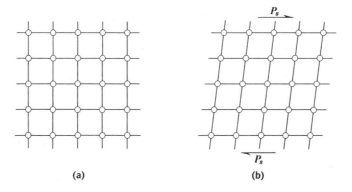

(a)   (b)

Fig. 6.10   Schematic representation of distortion of crystal structure in pure shear.

structure as it might be at some point in a crystalline material, and Fig. 6.10b shows the distortion produced in this structure as a result of torsion. Schematically this figure illustrates the mechanism of elastic distortion referred to as *pure shear*. So long as the distortion is small enough that none of the atoms (or molecules) slips to new equilibrium positions, the action will be completely elastic and the tube will return to its original shape upon release of the load.

The internal force necessary to push the planes of atoms past each other is the *shearing force*, P_s. If the force is equally distributed among all atoms, the force per unit area, or *shearing stress*, is

$$\tau = \frac{P_s}{A}.\tag{6.11}$$

In the thin-walled tube, force P_s is distributed around the cross-section (Fig. 6.11a). Since it must balance the applied moment at the end of the tube, it follows that its resultant must be a couple. From the symmetry of the cross-section it can be concluded that the stress that makes up P_s must be distributed uniformly around the circumference.

To find the relation between shearing stress, τ, and the applied moment, M_t, we equate the moment of the stress distribution to M_t. The shearing force acting on a small element of the cross-section, ΔA, is $\Delta P_s = \tau \Delta A$ (Fig. 6.11b). The moment of this force about the center is $(\Delta P_s) \times r = \tau r \Delta A$, where r is the radius of the tube. (It is assumed that the term *thin-walled tube* means one whose wall thickness is very small compared with its radius so that the inside and outside radii are almost the same and

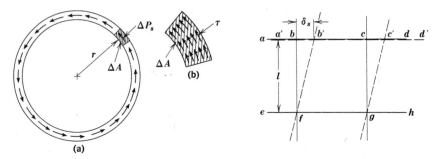

Fig. 6.11   Section of thin-walled tube.

Fig. 6.12   Shearing distortion.

the variation of stress across the wall thickness can be neglected. In an actual tube the radius used would usually be the mean radius, r_m.) The total moment of the shearing forces is then $\Sigma\, r\Delta P_s = \Sigma\, \tau r \Delta A = \tau r A$ since all ΔA's are at the same radius and τ is constant. It follows that

$$\tau = \frac{M_t}{Ar}, \tag{6.12a}$$

or, since $A = 2\,\pi rt$, where t is the wall thickness,

$$\tau = \frac{M_t}{2\,\pi r^2 t}. \tag{6.12b}$$

The above derivation applies equally to any section along the length of the tube, from which we conclude that the shearing stress is uniform along its length. Equation 6.12a is analogous to $\sigma = P/A$ for simple tension.

The distortion produced by the shearing stress is illustrated by Fig. 6.12, which shows a small rectangle taken from the grid of lines on the surface of the tube (Fig. 6.9). If this rectangle is small enough, it can be considered as a plane surface. The shearing displacement, δ_s, is the displacement of one line, say the top line, ad, relative to a parallel line, say eh. The shearing strain, γ, is the *unit* shearing displacement: δ_s divided by the distance, l, between the parallel lines.

$$\gamma = \frac{\delta_s}{l}. \tag{6.13}$$

From this definition γ is seen to be equal to the tangent of the angle of rotation of lines originally perpendicular to the two parallel lines such as bf. For strains small enough that the angle and its tangent may be taken as equal, γ is often thought of as the angle itself (bfb').

Since the shearing stress is uniform along the length of the tube, we can say that the strain is also uniform along its length. The longitudinal lines in the grid of Fig. 6.9b will consequently have a uniform inclination along

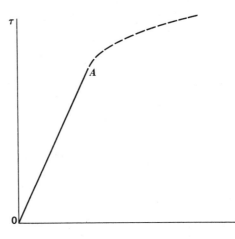

Fig. 6.13   Elastic $\tau - \gamma$ diagram.

the length of the twisted tube. We can derive the relation between the shearing strain and the angle of twist by considering a unit length of the tube. The shearing displacement of one end of this unit length relative to its other end is $\delta_s = r\theta$, where θ is the angle of twist per unit length. (If ϕ is the total angle of twist in the length l, then $\theta = \phi/l$.) From Eq. 6.13

$$\gamma = \frac{\delta_s}{1} = r\theta. \tag{6.14}$$

The behavior of a material in pure shear can be studied by applying a slowly increasing moment to a tubular torsion specimen and making observations of load and angle of twist at regular intervals. If these readings are converted to stress and strain by use of Eqs. 6.12b and 6.14, a shearing stress-strain diagram can be plotted. As in simple tension, if the mechanism of displacement of the atoms or molecules is simple, the elastic behavior will be linear and follow a form of Hooke's law

$$\tau = G\gamma, \tag{6.15}$$

where G is the *modulus of elasticity in shear* (sometimes called the *modulus of rigidity*). Materials that follow Hooke's law in tension usually do so in shear. Figure 6.13 is an elastic τ-γ diagram for such a material. The

slope of the line gives the value of G, and the end, point A, represents the
proportional limit.   Table 6.1 gives a few typical values of G.

Table 6.1   Typical Values of G for a Few
Engineering Materials

MATERIAL	MODULUS OF ELASTICITY IN SHEAR, G, psi
Molybdenum	16,100,000
Steel	11,800,000
Aluminum	3,800,000
Lead	700,000

As in simple tension, the modulus of resilience in torsion represents the
capacity of the material to absorb energy elastically.   It is given by the
strain energy per unit volume at the proportional limit.   Consider a unit
cube having shearing stresses equal to the shearing proportional limit acting
on its upper and lower surfaces.   The force on its upper surface is τ_{pl},
and the displacement of that surface relative to the lower surface is γ_{pl}.
The work done during the displacement, as τ increases from 0 to τ_{pl}, is u_r:

$$u_r = \frac{\tau_{pl}}{2} \times \gamma_{pl}, \tag{6.16a}$$

or, using Eq. 6.15,

$$u_r = \frac{\tau_{pl}^2}{2\,G}. \tag{6.16b}$$

(None of the other shearing stresses does work during the displacement.)
The actual state of stress in the material in the torsion tube can be
analyzed by applying the concepts of Arts. 6.1–6.3 to a small element of
the tube.   If the element is small enough, its surfaces can be considered
plane and its shape as a rectangular prism.   The shearing stress, τ, acts
on its upper and lower faces, as shown in Fig. 6.14, and is balanced by
equal shearing stresses on the sides, as required for equilibrium (Art. 6.1).
No normal stresses act on any of the four sides, and of course the inner and
outer surfaces, being free surfaces, have no stress.
Considering the distribution as one of plane stress and taking x horizontal
(circumferential) and y vertical (axial) (Fig. 6.14a), it can be shown that
the principal stresses are

$$\sigma_{max} = \tau \text{ and } \sigma_{min} = -\tau \tag{6.17}$$

at angles of 45° and 135° with the x-axis (Fig. 6.14b).   The Mohr's circle
is centered at the origin and has a radius equal to τ (Fig. 6.15a).
Considering the three-dimensional aspects of the state of stress, we see
that the principal stresses are $\sigma_1 = \tau$, $\sigma_2 = 0$, and $\sigma_3 = -\tau$.   (This can be

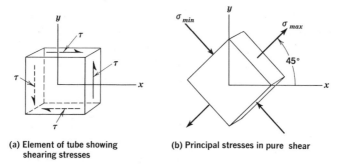

(a) Element of tube showing
   shearing stresses

(b) Principal stresses in pure shear

Fig. 6.14   State of stress in a tube under torsion.

verified by substitution in the appropriate form of Eqs. 6.1a and 6.2a with $\phi = 45°$.)   In the corresponding Mohr's circle diagram (Fig. 6.15b), circles II and III (compare Fig. 6.6g) have been added.   The maximum shearing stress acting on the element is, from Eq. 6.7,

$$\tau_{max} = \frac{\sigma_1 - \sigma_3}{2} = \tau.$$

The strains in the principal directions are given by Eq. 6.10.   Noting that $\sigma_3 = -\sigma_1$,

$$\epsilon_1 = \frac{1}{E}(\sigma_1 + \mu\sigma_1) = \frac{\sigma_1}{E}(1 + \mu)$$

$$\epsilon_2 = \frac{1}{E}[\mu(-\sigma_1 + \sigma_1)] = 0$$

$$\epsilon_3 = \frac{1}{E}(-\sigma_1 - \mu\sigma_1) = -\frac{\sigma_1}{E}(1 + \mu).$$

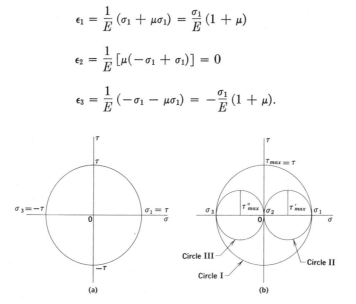

Fig. 6.15   Mohr's circles for pure shear.

The first of these expressions gives us the form of Hooke's law for the maximum principal stress

$$\sigma_1 = \frac{E}{1 + \mu} \, \epsilon_1, \tag{6.18}$$

from which we can determine the relation between the two moduli of elasticity, E and G. The relation between normal strain, ϵ_1, and shearing strain, γ, is shown in Fig. 6.16. When the square element is given a

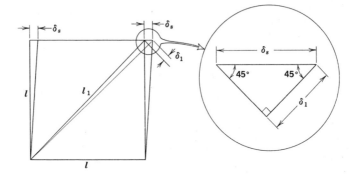

Fig. 6.16   *Relation between normal strain and shearing strain in pure shear.*

shearing deformation, δ_s, its diagonal is elongated by an amount δ_1. The shearing strain is $\gamma = \delta_s/l$, while the normal strain on the diagonal is $\epsilon_1 = \delta_1/l_1$. From the geometry of the figure we have, for small strains, $l_1 = l\sqrt{2}$ and $\delta_1 = \delta_s/\sqrt{2}$, from which

$$\epsilon_1 = \frac{\delta_s}{2\,l} = \frac{\gamma}{2}. \tag{6.19}$$

If we replace σ_1 by τ and ϵ_1 by $\gamma/2$, Eq. 6.18 becomes

$$\tau = \frac{E}{2(1 + \mu)} \, \gamma. \tag{6.20}$$

If we compare this equation with Eq. 6.15, we see that

$$G = \frac{E}{2(1 + \mu)}. \tag{6.21}$$

Thus the two moduli are not independent, and if E and μ are known, G can be calculated. If μ is taken as $\frac{1}{3}$, $G = \frac{3}{8} E$. For aluminum G is approximately 3,800,000 psi, which is close to $\frac{3}{8}$ of the value of E (Table 3.1).

The strain in the direction of the thickness of the tube, ϵ_2, was shown to be zero. Consequently the thickness is unchanged during torsion.

Because there is no normal stress in either the circumferential or the axial direction, there is no strain in either of these directions, and the radius and length also remain unchanged.

Solid Shaft

In view of the conclusions reached above, a solid circular bar in torsion can be considered as a set of concentric thin-walled tubes. Since there are no changes in dimension radially, tangentially, or axially, there will be no

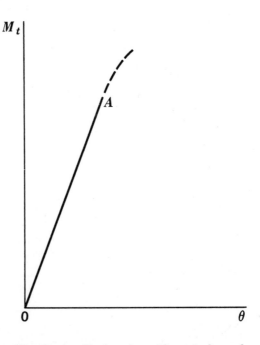

Fig. 6.17   Elastic torque-angle of twist diagram.

normal stresses in any of these directions. Each tube will act independently to carry its share of the applied moment. That part of the moment carried by a tube of radius ρ and area dA will be, from Eq. 6.12a,

$$dM_t = \tau_\rho \rho \, dA.$$

The shearing strain in this tube is, from Eq. 6.14, $\gamma_\rho = \rho\theta$, and if Hooke's law is followed,

$$\tau_\rho = G\rho\theta. \tag{6.22}$$

Hence

$$M_t = \int_{\rho=0}^{\rho=r} (G\rho\theta)\rho \, dA = G\theta \int_{\rho=0}^{\rho=r} \rho^2 \, dA,$$

or

$$M_t = G\theta I_p, \tag{6.23}$$

where $I_p = \pi r^4/2$ is the polar moment of inertia of the circular cross-section about its center. Since, from Eq. 6.22, $G\theta = \tau_r/r$, we have

$$M_t = \frac{\tau_r I_p}{r}, \tag{6.24}$$

where τ_r is the shearing stress at the surface.

Behavior of materials in torsion is often represented by plotting the moment and the angle of twist directly, without converting them to stress and strain. Figure 6.17 is an elastic torque-angle of twist diagram. The slope of the line is GI_p, from which G can be calculated. The end of the diagram, point A, represents the proportional limit in torsion.

6.4 INELASTIC ACTION IN TORSION

When distortion of the material becomes so great that some of the atomic or molecular bonds are broken, the action becomes inelastic. As in simple tension, both normal and shearing strain are involved, and there are two possibilities for inelastic action: fracture and yielding.

Fracture

Brittle fracture in torsion, like brittle fracture in tension, is caused by the maximum tensile stress. Hence it occurs on planes at 45° to the shearing direction, and the result is a helical fracture, as illustrated in Fig. 6.18.

Fig. 6.18 Fracture of gray cast iron in torsion, illustrating helical form.

The classic example, used in countless classrooms, is a piece of chalk broken by twisting its ends with the fingers. Other materials having strong tendencies toward brittleness, like ceramics, cast iron, and concrete, break in the same way.

The mechanism of brittle fracture is the same in tension and torsion. A characteristic distribution of imperfections causes a characteristic distribution of strengths for a given material. The strength is relatively unaffected by the presence of the compressive stress at right angles to the tensile stress. Consequently the tensile stress at failure in torsion averages approximately the same as that in simple tension.

Yielding

Yielding, on the other hand, involves a shearing process, and is associated with the maximum shearing stress, τ_{max} (which has been called simply τ for the thin-walled tube and τ_r for the solid bar) (pp. 196 and 202). When τ_{max} reaches a certain critical value such as that necessary to move dislocations in a crystalline material, yielding begins. To a first approximation the critical value of shearing stress is the same for all states of stress. In simple tension it is half the tensile yield stress, $\tau_0 = \sigma_y/2$. In torsion, or pure shear, yielding will begin when τ_{max} is approximately equal to τ_0. Denoting this value of τ_{max} by $(\tau_y)_s$, where the subscript s stands for *pure shear*, we can write the criterion for yielding in the form

$$(\tau_y)_s = \tau_0. \qquad (6.25)$$

Since in pure shear the maximum shearing stress and the maximum normal stress are equal, it follows that

$$(\sigma_y)_s = \frac{\sigma_y}{2}, \qquad (6.25a)$$

where $(\sigma_y)_s$ is the maximum tensile stress at yielding in pure shear and σ_y is the yield stress in simple tension. *We conclude that yielding in pure shear takes place when the maximum tensile stress is only half that required to produce yielding in simple tension.* Thus materials yield more easily in pure shear, and continued yielding is less likely to be interrupted by fracture, which is governed by tensile stress. The *apparent ductility* of materials is enhanced by torsion. Note that this is not because of any change in the material itself, but only in the way the stress is applied; hence the use of the word "apparent" in referring to it.

Strength Theories

For simplicity it was assumed above that the critical shearing stress for yielding is the same for all states of stress. In many practical problems this assumption is quite accurate and is used as a basis for predicting the yield stress for various forms of loading. It is the basis of the *maximum shear stress theory* originated by the French engineer Tresca about 1870. It is expressed mathematically as

$$(\tau_{max})_y = \tau_0. \qquad (6.26)$$

The critical shearing stress for yielding actually varies somewhat with the state of stress acting in the material. It is influenced by the values of the other maximum shearing stresses, τ'_{max} and τ''_{max} (Art. 6.2).   Another theory in which these shearing stresses are included has been developed and found wide application.   Known as the *distortion energy theory*, or *octahedral shear stress theory*, it was originated by Huber in 1904.*   It can be expressed mathematically in many ways.   One form is

$$(\tau_{oct})_y = (\tau_{oct})_0, \tag{6.27}$$

where τ_{oct} is the shear stress acting on the octahedral plane, i.e., that making equal angles with the principal stress axes—in crystal notation, the (111) plane of a cubic crystal.   The left side represents the stress for yielding in any state of stress, while the right side is that for simple tension.

The two theories of yielding can be expressed in terms of the principal stresses for comparison.   From Eq. 6.7, $\tau_{max} = (\sigma_1 - \sigma_3)/2$ (assuming $\sigma_1 > \sigma_2 > \sigma_3$).   As noted above $\tau_0 = \sigma_y/2$, where σ_y is the tensile yield stress.   Hence in accordance with the maximum shear stress theory, Eq. 6.26 reduces to

$$\sigma_1 - \sigma_3 = \sigma_y. \tag{6.26a}$$

The octahedral shear stress is given by†

$$\tau_{oct} = \tfrac{1}{3}\sqrt{(\sigma_1 - \sigma_2)^2 + (\sigma_2 - \sigma_3)^2 + (\sigma_3 - \sigma_1)^2}.$$

To evaluate this expression for yielding in simple tension, we let $\sigma_1 = \sigma_y$ and $\sigma_2 = \sigma_3 = 0$, from which $(\tau_{oct})_0 = \sqrt{2}\,\sigma_y/3$.   Substituting in Eq. 6.27 we obtain, in accordance with the octahedral shear stress theory,

$$(\sigma_1 - \sigma_2)^2 + (\sigma_2 - \sigma_3)^2 + (\sigma_3 - \sigma_1)^2 = 2\,\sigma_y^2. \tag{6.27a}$$

For pure shear, where $\sigma_1 = -\sigma_3 = \tau$ and $\sigma_2 = 0$, Eqs. 6.26a and 6.27a reduce to

$$(\tau_y)_s = \frac{\sigma_y}{2} \text{ and } (\tau_y)_s = \frac{\sigma_y}{\sqrt{3}},$$

respectively.   The ratio of the second to the first is 1.15; thus the shear stress for yielding, as given by the more accurate maximum octahedral shear stress theory, is 15 per cent greater than that given by the maximum shear stress theory.   This variation is the maximum difference between the results of the two theories, and for most states of stress the difference is considerably less than 15 per cent.

---

* Timoshenko, S., *Strength of Materials—Part II—Advanced Theory and Problems*, 3rd ed., D. Van Nostrand Company, Inc., Princeton, New Jersey, 1956, pp. 451–455. Credit for originating the theory is shared by von Mises, who also developed it independently of Huber, but not until 1913.   The theory was redefined by Hencky in 1925.

† Timoshenko, S., *Strength of Materials—Part II—Advanced Theory and Problems*, 3rd ed., D. Van Nostrand Company, Inc., Princeton, New Jersey, 1956, p. 455.

EXAMPLE 6.1

A cube of annealed cobalt is subjected to principal stresses which are in the following proportion: $\sigma_1:\sigma_2:\sigma_3 = 2:1:0$. Determine the magnitude of σ_1 for yielding, according to (a) the maximum shear stress theory; (b) the octahedral shear stress theory. The tensile yield stress is 42,500 psi.

Solution: From Eq. 6.26a

$$\sigma_1 - 0 = \sigma_y,$$

or

$$\sigma_1 = 42{,}500 \text{ psi.}$$

From Eq. 6.27a

$$\left(\sigma_1 - \frac{\sigma_1}{2}\right)^2 + \left(\frac{\sigma_1}{2} - 0\right)^2 + (0 - \sigma_1)^2 = 2\,\sigma_y^2,$$

$$\tfrac{3}{2}\sigma_1^2 = 2\,\sigma_y^2,$$

$$\sigma_1^2 = \tfrac{4}{3}\,\sigma_y^2,$$

or

$$\sigma_1 = 1.154\,\sigma_y$$

$$= 49{,}000 \text{ psi.}$$

6.5   THE PLASTIC RANGE IN TORSION

It was pointed out in the preceding article that materials appear to be more ductile in torsion than in simple tension. Materials that exhibit no significant plastic deformation in simple tension are sometimes found to have a sizable plastic range in torsion.

Thin-Walled Tubes

For a thin-walled tube the relations between moment and stress and between angle of twist and strain are the same after yielding as before because they are not based on the assumption of elasticity but only on equilibrium and geometry. Thus Eqs. 6.12b and 6.14 still hold in the plastic range.

$$\tau = \frac{M_t}{2\,\pi r^2 t}. \tag{6.12b}$$

$$\gamma = r\theta. \tag{6.14}$$

The diagram of τ vs γ is therefore geometrically similar to that of M_t vs θ for the thin tube. Figure 6.19 shows a typical shear stress-strain diagram for a ductile metal. Yielding takes place more or less gradually, as in simple tension. The proportional limit stress is subject to the same uncertainties as in tension.

As might be expected, materials that yield discontinuously in simple tension do likewise in pure shear. The upper and lower yield points can be obtained from the shearing stress-strain diagram in the same way as in simple tension.

Torsion in the elastic range has no effect on the dimensions of a member of circular cross-section, whether tubular or solid (Art. 6.4). The deformation is a pure distortion, in which the atoms are, in effect, simply pushed past each other. This behavior is inherent in the pure shear deformation involved in torsion and does not depend on elasticity. Thus the dimensions remain essentially constant, even in the plastic range, as borne out by experimental observations.

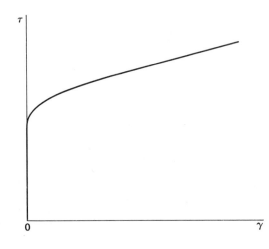

Fig. 6.19 Shear stress-strain diagram for a ductile metal, determined by torsion of a thin-walled tube.

Since there is no change in dimensions, the problems of plastic instability and necking, so bothersome in simple tension, never appear in torsion. For a thin tube, for example, $M_t = \tau r A$, and the increment of moment can be expressed as

$$dM_t = \tau r \, dA + \tau A \, dr + rA \, d\tau. \tag{6.28}$$

Since both area and radius remain constant, their differentials vanish, leaving $dM_t = rA \, d\tau$. Neither r nor A is zero, and τ increases throughout the plastic range. Consequently dM_t is never zero, and M_t never decreases.

That shearing stress increases throughout the plastic range follows from the close association of strain-hardening with shearing strain (Art. 3.8). As a result of the steady progress of strain-hardening, the shearing stress in torsion, like the true stress in simple tension, increases monotonically.

Owing to the absence of plastic instability and necking the plastic range in torsion is much longer than in simple tension. The net result is that plastic strains in torsion are possible far beyond the limits of any other

simple form of loading. The useful plastic range in compression is restricted by end restraint and lateral instability (Art. 4.6). In bending,
because of lateral strains, the shape of the cross-section changes significantly at sharp curvatures, and there is also a definite limit to the total
amount of bending that is possible. None of the methods discussed so far,
therefore, provides information about the large plastic strains that can be
obtained in torsion.

On the other hand, torsion has two characteristics that prevent its being
the ideal means of loading for experimental research. One is the ease with
which localized buckling can take place in thin-walled tubes. The diagonal

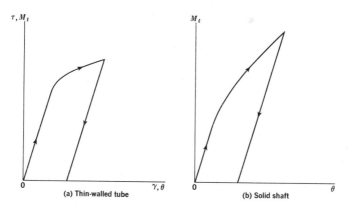

*Fig. 6.20   Loading and unloading in tor-
sion.*

compressive stress is the responsible factor; its effects can be reduced by
suitable precautions, described under experimental methods.

The other difficulty is rotation of the principal axes in torsion. If a line
is scribed on the surface of the member in the form of a helix making a
constant angle of 45° with the axis, this angle will gradually increase as
the member is twisted, indicating rotation of the material in the member.
The principal stresses, however, always remain at 45° with the axis of the
member. Hence the principal axes rotate gradually *with respect to the
material* as the plastic strain increases. This effect is not observed in
uniaxial stress, and it does alter the behavior of the material slightly.

At large distortions plastic elongation in the diagonal direction tends to
produce a fiber structure oriented in the same way as the helical line mentioned in the preceding paragraph. This fiber structure is anisotropic and
affects further plastic deformation and mode of failure. It explains the
failure of ductile materials by shear on a right section. Since the shearing
stress is equally large on the longitudinal planes, it might be expected that

failure would take place indiscriminately on either transverse or longitudinal planes.   However, the fiber structure, having rotated to nearly a circumferential direction by the time of failure, makes the longitudinal planes stronger by comparison, so that failure usually takes place on a transverse plane.

Because of this anisotropy there is also a good chance that other stresses and strains will appear in the last stages of plastic deformation.   There may even be some reduction in area, and changes in length have been observed at large strains.

The mechanism of unloading in the plastic range in torsion or pure shear is the same as in simple tension.   Unloading is almost entirely elastic, so that the shear stress-strain diagram follows an unloading line that is parallel to the original elastic line (Fig. 6.20a).   This pattern is also reflected in the M_t–θ diagram, both for thin-walled tubes and solid shafts (Fig. 6.20a and b).

If, after a metal specimen is unloaded, the twisting moment is reversed and increased in the opposite direction, a Bauschinger effect will be observed.*   Yielding will begin at a lower stress than in the first direction. The mechanism by which this phenomenon takes place is the same at that described in Art. 4.4.   The fact that dislocations piled up at obstacles during the first distortion are easier to move in the opposite direction upon reversal of stress, together with the effect of microscopic residual stresses in the crystals, explains the reduction in the shearing yield stress.

Solid Shaft

Torsion of a solid circular shaft is far more difficult to analyze in the plastic range than torsion of a thin-walled tube.   In the first place, when the surface begins to yield, the interior of the shaft is still elastic.   The situation is similar to that in pure bending (Art. 5.2).   The overall effect of yielding in the outer fibers alone is very slight at first; the resulting departure from linearity in the M_t–θ diagram is almost imperceptible. Consequently the proportional limit found from solid specimens is uncertain.   Similarly the offset yield strength at ordinary offsets is usually of little value; the moment found is so far beyond the true end of the elastic range for the material that it can be quite misleading.   The only remedy is to select a much smaller offset, lowering the yield moment and making it a better indication of actual yield strength.   As in bending, increased accuracy in observations is required.

In the plastic range use of the solid circular shaft does not permit easy

---

* Liddicoat, R. T., and Potts, Philip O., *Laboratory Manual of Materials Testing*, The Macmillan Company, New York, 1952, p. 128.

computation of shearing stress as does the thin-walled tube.   Methods have been devised for computing the stress from the M_t–θ diagram, but they involve advanced theory* and even then are only approximate over a large part of the range.   The difficulty stems from nonlinear distribution of shearing stress in the cross-section, as illustrated in Fig. 6.21.

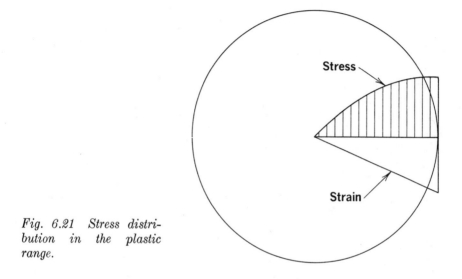

Fig. 6.21   Stress distribution   in   the   plastic range.

The principal use of information derived from torsion experiments with solid specimens is to compare the behavior of similar materials or the effects of varying environment, such as temperature and strain rate.†   For such purposes a simple comparison of torque-angle of twist diagrams often provides useful information.

Failure

In a solid shaft of ductile material, failure starts with the formation of a circumferential shear crack in the outer, most heavily strained surface. Because of slight variations in the material, this crack is somewhat irregular.   As twisting continues, the surfaces of the crack rub past each other like small cams and gradually force the center of the bar apart so that it

---

* Nadai, A., *Theory of Flow and Fracture of Solids*, Vol. I, 2nd ed. (Engineering Societies Monographs) McGraw-Hill Book Company, Inc., New York, Toronto, London, 1950, p. 349.

† Work, Clyde E., and Dolan, Thomas J., *The Influence of Temperature and Rate of Strain on the Properties of Metals in Torsion*, University of Illinois Bulletin, Vol. 51, No. 24, November 1953, University of Illinois, Urbana, Illinois.

finally breaks in tension.   Although the cross-section of the bar may not decrease perceptibly, as soon as the crack begins to form the load begins to drop.   Consequently the moment-angle of twist diagram of a solid shaft sometimes turns down at the end, like the tensile stress-strain diagram.   The resemblance, however, is purely coincidental.

6.6   INELASTIC PROPERTIES IN TORSION

Yield Strength

Offset yield strength is determined in the same manner as in simple tension (Art. 3.12).   Depending on whether the diagram plotted is of τ vs γ or M_t vs θ, the offset is in terms of strain or angle of twist.   For a shear stress-strain diagram from a thin-walled tube the offset can be the same as that used in simple tension (e.g., 0.2 per cent).   For a torque-twist diagram of a solid bar, a smaller offset should be chosen and converted to unit angle of twist.   For example, if we take an offset of 0.05 per cent strain (one-fourth the usual value), we find, for a 1-inch diameter specimen, $\theta = \gamma/r = 0.0005/0.5 = 0.001$ rad/in.

For materials like mild steel, that yield discontinuously, upper and lower yield points are taken directly from the shear stress-strain diagram for a thin-walled tube.

Ultimate Strength

If buckling can be prevented, the stress in a thin-walled tube can be expected to reach its maximum at the breaking point.   This stress is then the ultimate shearing strength of the material.   Solid specimens are often compared by means of the *modulus of rupture*, τ_u, defined as the stress computed from Eq. 6.24 using the maximum or rupture moment, $(M_t)_u$:

$$\tau_u = \frac{(M_t)_u r}{I_p}.$$

Since Eq. 6.24 is based on Hooke's law, the modulus of rupture cannot represent an actual stress except in the limiting case of a perfectly brittle material.   It is used simply as a convenient means of comparing maximum moments for members of identical size and shape.   The need for standardization of experimental specimens is obvious.

Ductility

Ductility is measured from angle of twist, shearing strain, or per cent elongation of the outer fibers at rupture.   Angle of twist, ϕ, at rupture is observed directly but can be used only for comparing specimens of identical size and shape.   Strain at rupture is computed from Eq. 6.14,

$$\gamma_r = r\theta = \frac{r\phi}{l}.$$

Per cent elongation of the outer fibers at rupture is found by comparing the initial length of a longitudinal straight line on the surface of the specimen with its final length after it has been twisted into a helix. If we call the initial length l, the final length is $l' = \sqrt{l^2 + (r\phi)^2} = l\sqrt{1 + (r\theta)^2}$. The per cent elongation is then

$$\frac{l' - l}{l} \times 100 = (\sqrt{1 + (r\theta)^2} - 1) \times 100.$$

Thus the three measures of ductility are directly related. The most useful one is obviously *strain at rupture*, γ_r, since it is independent of specimen length and easy to compute.

Toughness

As in simple tension, toughness is indicated by the work needed to rupture the specimen, per unit volume. It is measured from the area under the shear stress-strain diagram to the breaking point.

EXPERIMENTAL METHODS (PART A)

6.7 TORSION

Testing Machines

Specially designed testing machines are used for torsion tests. They usually consist of a rigid frame supporting two chucks for gripping the ends of the specimen, plus the necessary loading and weighing apparatus. The chucks must be accurately aligned on a common axis to avoid bending. The load is applied by rotating one chuck about the axis while the other measures the amount of torque being applied to the specimen. Power for turning the movable chuck is supplied by motor or by hand crank through a system of gears. Capacities of the order of 100,000 in.-lb of moment are common. The moment is measured by lever systems, pendulums, or hydraulic capsules in a manner similar to that used in tension-testing machines.

Gripping mechanisms may be self-tightening jaws for round specimens, positive holders for square or other shapes, or special grips for use in reversed or alternating torsion.

Specimens

Specimens must have ends suitable for gripping. They are usually larger than the center portion, and if a thin-walled tube is used, the ends must be plugged to prevent crushing. Large-radius fillets must be provided at the change in cross-section to reduce stress concentrations, which are as serious in shear as in tension. A suitable design for a solid specimen is shown in ASTM A260 for cast iron, the only torsion test that has been standardized by ASTM. If torsion tests of solid specimens in the plastic range are to provide any significant information, the use of standard

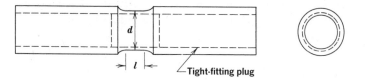

(a) Short specimen for measurements in the plastic range

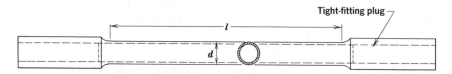

(b) Long specimen for measurements in the elastic range

Fig. 6.22   Thin-walled tubular specimens for torsion, showing recommended proportions.

specimens is essential. Only in this way can different materials or different testing conditions be compared meaningfully.

Thin-walled tubular specimens are used to study shearing properties, both elastic and inelastic. To minimize the variation of stress between the inside and outside of the wall, its thickness must be as small as possible. And for measuring the angle of twist accurately a long length is desirable. Both these factors, however, tend to encourage local buckling of the tube. The design of tubular specimens is therefore a compromise. Experience has shown that the ratio of diameter to wall-thickness (d/t) cannot be much greater than 20 if the entire plastic range is to be covered. Thus the stress in the inner surface will be about 90 per cent of that in the outer surface. Tests have been successfully carried out with tubes in which $d/t = 30$, but even with the greatest care, buckling takes place before the end of the plastic range.

As another precaution against buckling, it is necessary to keep the length of the reduced section to a minimum. For tests covering the entire plastic range, this length should be no more than about half the diameter. Longer specimens, having l/d as large as 10, can be used for experiments in the elastic range. Figure 6.22 shows recommended proportions for tubular specimens.

Deformations

Shearing deformation in torsion is usually measured by a device or gage which indicates the angle of twist of one end of a specified gage length, l, with respect to the other. Such torsion indicators, or *troptometers*, consist of pointers or mirrors attached to collars clamped on the specimen, and indicate the angle on a graduated scale. The collars are held in place by three cone-point setscrews bearing on the specimen at points 120° apart around its circumference. Since there is always some twisting of the ends of the specimen adjacent to or even in the grips, neither end of the gage length remains fixed. Consequently if one scale is used, it must be attached to one of the collars so that it can rotate with it. Two fixed scales can be used instead; the angles of rotation of the two ends are subtracted to arrive at the net angle of twist in the gage length.

Strain gages are used to measure the normal strains, ϵ_1 and ϵ_3, in the directions of the principal stresses. Electric resistance-wire strain gages are useful for this purpose because of the ease with which they can be attached at 45° to the axis. When the normal strains are known, Eq. 6.19 can be used to compute the shearing strain, $\gamma = 2\,\epsilon_1$.

Conduct of the Torsion Test

Before the specimen is placed in the testing machine, its dimensions must be measured with care. The diameter is usually measured to the nearest 0.001 inch. Wall thickness of the tube should be measured to at least the same accuracy and preferably to a greater one (say 0.0001 inch). The wall thickness of a tube is sometimes difficult to hold constant. In the specifications for the tubular specimen permissible limits should be set for variation of wall thickness around the circumference and along its length. A number of measurements of wall thickness should be taken and averaged. Special devices may be needed for precision measurements. A straight line is often scribed or marked on the surface of the reduced section, parallel to the axis of the bar, to aid in measuring the total angle of twist at rupture. The troptometer should have suitable spacers to ensure proper gage length.   If not, circumferential lines can be marked at each end of the gage length and the setscrews positioned on these lines.

When the troptometer has been attached, the specimen is inserted in the chucks of the testing machine with care being taken that each end is properly centered.   The grips must be tightened in such a way that no bending is introduced during tightening.

The load is normally applied at a rate slow enough that dynamic effects are negligible.   In some materials, e.g., plastics, maintaining a constant rate of loading throughout the test is very important.   In other materials an increase in rate of loading changes the behavior of the material noticeably only if it is large.

During the loading period readings of moment and angle of twist are taken at regular intervals.   Increments of either moment or angle should be decided upon before the beginning of the test.   The same principles apply as for the conventional tension test (Art. 3.17).

The rupture of a ductile specimen in torsion is so gradual that the troptometer can be safely left in place.   If properly designed, it can also remain unaffected by the more sudden failure of a brittle specimen.

Presentation of Data and Results

The results of the torsion test are usually plotted as graphs.   For a solid specimen the moment is plotted directly in inch-pounds, and the angle of twist in radians per inch of gage length.   If the total angle, ϕ, is measured in degrees and the gage length in inches, θ, in radians per inch, is given by $\theta = (\phi/l) \times (\pi/180)$.

For tubular specimens the results may be plotted directly, as above, or converted to shear stress and strain and then plotted.   Equations 6.12b and 6.14 are used for this purpose.   The radius used in Eq. 6.12b should be the mean radius, $r_m = (d - t)/2$ where d is the outside diameter of the specimen.   The resulting stress is the mean stress at the middle of the wall thickness

$$\tau_m = \frac{M_t}{2 \, \pi r_m t}.$$

The corresponding strain is

$$\gamma_m = r_m \theta.$$

These values are used for most purposes, including determination of shearing modulus of elasticity and measurements in the plastic range.

If the beginning of yielding is being investigated, the use of average stress may lead to serious errors.   In the elastic range the variation of the stress across the wall thickness is linear (Fig. 6.23a).   The maximum stress at the outer surface is given by the proportion

$$\frac{\tau_{max}}{d/2} = \frac{\tau_m}{r_m}.$$

$$(6.29)$$

If $d/t = 10$, we find that $\tau_{max}/\tau_m = \frac{10}{9}$. Consequently the maximum stress in the cross-section when yielding begins is 11 per cent greater than the

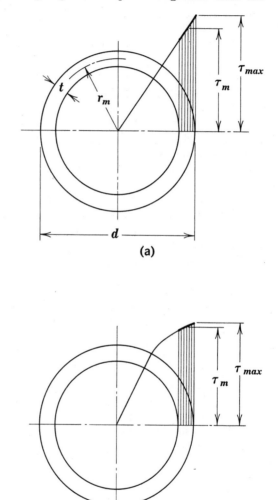

(a)

(b)

Fig. 6.23   *Variation of stress across the thickness of a tubular specimen in torsion.*

mean stress. If thinner tubes can be used, the error will be reduced somewhat, but it is still advisable to apply a correction by use of the above equation.

In the plastic range the variation of stress across the wall thickness decreases (Fig. 6.23b) because of the decreased slope of the shear stress-strain diagram.   The variation of τ_m with γ_m is considered an adequate representation of the shearing behavior of the material in the plastic range.

Detailed instructions on plotting graphs of this kind are given in Chapter 3.

TRIAXIAL STRESSES

We have seen that in torsion materials tend to be more ductile than in simple tension.   Apparent changes in ductility—owing to variations in the relative value of the maximum shearing stress, but not to any actual changes in the material itself—occur under a variety of forms of loading. In addition there are sometimes changes in the actual ductility of the material which are caused by variations in the magnitude of the mean stress.   A number of important stress distributions will be examined with particular attention to their apparent and actual effects on ductility.

6.8   HYDROSTATIC COMPRESSION

Hydrostatic compression is the state of stress that exists in a body submerged in a liquid under pressure p.   The pressure is the same in all directions and is always normal to any surface on which it acts.   No shearing stresses are possible because the static shearing resistance of the liquid is zero.   Hydrostatic compression is also produced by other forms of loading.

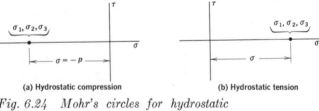

(a) Hydrostatic compression   (b) Hydrostatic tension

Fig. 6.24   Mohr's circles for hydrostatic stress.

Since in hydrostatic compression the normal stresses are all equal, any three orthogonal directions can be chosen as the principal directions, and we have $\sigma_1 = \sigma_2 = \sigma_3 = \sigma$, where $\sigma = -p$ is the *hydrostatic stress*.   The Mohr's circles for this state of stress degenerate to a single point at $\sigma = -p$ (Fig. 6.24a).

In an idealized sense the atomic mechanism of hydrostatic compression in a homogeneous nonporous material is simple.   The atoms and molecules are merely pushed together; their configuration remains geometrically similar at all times.   The repulsion is increased in the same proportion in all bonds, but there is no distortion and no tendency for atoms to change bonds.   As a result the action remains purely *elastic*, and no inelastic behavior of any kind can occur.   Obviously the apparent ductility of all such materials is zero in pure hydrostatic compression because of the complete absence of shearing stresses.   In real materials, with their irregularity and imperfections, some small permanent readjustments may occur even under ideal hydrostatic compression.   These effects are usually slight and will be neglected here.

Volume Change

Materials which follow Hooke's law in simple tension and compression do so in hydrostatic compression at moderate pressures.   Hooke's law for hydrostatic compression is

$$\sigma = K \frac{\Delta V}{V},$$ (6.30)

where $\Delta V/V$ is the unit volume change, or volume strain, and K is the *volume modulus of elasticity*, often called the *bulk modulus.*

The relation between K and the other elastic constants can be derived as follows.   Imagine a rectangular prism of dimensions a, b, and c, under hydrostatic stress σ.   If we take the directions of the edges of the prism as the principal directions and remember that $\sigma_1 = \sigma_2 = \sigma_3 = \sigma$, Eq. 6.10 shows that the strains in these directions are equal and are given by

$$\epsilon = \frac{\sigma}{E} (1 - 2\,\mu).$$

(Since $\sigma = -p$, the strains are all negative, or contractions.)   As a result of these strains the dimensions of the prism become $a(1 + \epsilon)$, $b(1 + \epsilon)$, and $c(1 + \epsilon)$, so that the new volume is

$$\begin{aligned} V_1 &= abc(1 + \epsilon)^3 \\ &= V(1 + 3\,\epsilon + 3\,\epsilon^2 + \epsilon^3), \end{aligned}$$

where V is the original volume.   If the strain ϵ is small, its powers may be neglected in comparison with 1, and the change in volume is

$$\Delta V = V(3\,\epsilon)$$

or
$$\frac{\Delta V}{V} = 3\,\epsilon = 3\,\frac{\sigma}{E}(1 - 2\,\mu).$$ (6.30a)

Substitution in Eq. 6.30 gives

$$\sigma = 3\,K\,\frac{\sigma}{E}(1 - 2\,\mu)$$

or
$$K = \frac{E}{3(1 - 2\,\mu)}.$$ (6.31)

The units of K are psi.   It should be noted that if $\mu = \frac{1}{3}$, K and E have the same numerical value as well as the same units.   Since μ is close to $\frac{1}{3}$

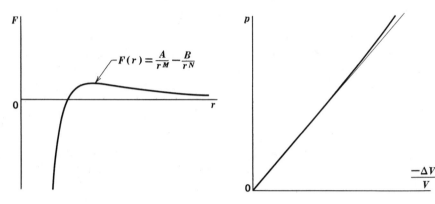

Fig. 6.25   Typical   atomic   bond curve.

Fig. 6.26   Pressure   vs   volume strain diagram for high pressures.

for *metals*, the bulk modulus may be approximated for this class of materials by using the value of E.   Some common values of K are given in

Table 6.2   Approximate Values of the Bulk   Modulus   for   Some Representative Engineering Materials[a]

MATERIAL	BULK MODULUS, K, psi
Steel	24,000,000
Copper	20,000,000
Aluminum	10,000,000
Glass (silica)	5,000,000
Hard rubber	1,000,000
Cesium	660,000

[a] These are typical values for comparison. Measured values vary somewhat with the composition of the material and its previous treatment.

Table 6.2.   The reciprocal of K is sometimes used.   It defines the *compressibility* of a material and is denoted by k.*

---

* Nadai, A., *Theory of Flow and Fracture of Solids*, Vol. I, 2nd ed. (Engineering Societies Monographs) McGraw-Hill Book Company, Inc., New York, Toronto, London, 1950, p. 33.

High Pressures

As the pressure is increased and the atoms or molecules are pushed closer together, the repulsive forces in the bonds increase more rapidly, as shown by the downward curvature of the curve of Fig. 6.25 (see also Figs. 2.3 and 2.10). This effect is gradual and is not usually noticeable at moderate pressures. From the scale of the bond curves (Art. 3.1, Fig. 3.3) it is seen that the range of pressures in which the bonds can be considered linear is quite large for most purposes, perhaps of the order of 10,000 psi. At higher pressures the nonlinearity of the bond curves produces an upward curvature in the pressure vs volume strain diagram (Fig. 6.26). The deformation remains purely elastic, however, and yielding and rupture are still impossible.

The behavior of materials at high hydrostatic pressures has been investigated by P. W. Bridgman,* T. C. Poulter,† and others, with results that are of great general interest. The technological advances resulting from these investigations have made it possible to obtain working pressures of more than 1,500,000 psi. At these high pressures the upward curvature in the pressure vs volume strain diagram is pronounced and can be interpreted in terms of a variable bulk modulus, analogous to the secant modulus of elasticity in tension. Bridgman has suggested an equation of the form‡

$$\frac{\Delta V}{V_0} = -ap + bp^2.$$

If we compare this equation with Eq. 6.30 and recall that $\sigma = -p$, the expression corresponding to K is $1/(a - bp)$, and K is seen to be a function of p. For iron, Bridgman found $a = 5.87 \times 10^{-7}$ and $b = 2.10 \times 10^{-12}$ for p measured in kilograms per square centimeter. At zero pressure

$$K = \frac{1}{5.87 \times 10^{-7}} \text{ kg/cm}^2$$

$$= 24.2 \times 10^6 \text{ psi,}$$

which corresponds to the value given in Table 6.2.

For homogeneous nonporous materials $\partial K / \partial p$ is positive, in accordance with the upward curvature of the pressure vs volume strain curve. Zwik-

---

* Bridgman, P. W., *Studies in Large Plastic Flow and Fracture with Special Emphasis on the Effects of Hydrostatic Pressure*, 1st ed. (Metallurgy and Metallurgical Engineering Series) McGraw-Hill Book Company, New York, Toronto, London, 1952, pp. 118–124.

† Nadai, A., *Theory of Flow and Fracture of Solids*, Vol. 1, 2nd ed. (Engineering Societies Monographs) McGraw-Hill Book Company, Inc., New York, Toronto, London, 1950, pp. 35, 36.

‡ *Ibid.*, p. 33.

ker* has shown that $\partial K/\partial p$ for various elements, as derived from their atomic bond equations (Eq. 2.1), is in good agreement with experimental values.   This fact helps confirm the values taken for M and N in the bond equations.

In some *glasses* $\partial K/\partial p$ is negative, an indication that they become more compressible at high pressures.   This behavior is related to their open structure, which tends to collapse under pressure.   Some crystals go through transformations to more compact crystal forms, giving rise to negative values of $\partial K/\partial p$.   Porous materials and others of more complex structure behave as described in Art. 4.1 and do not follow the comparatively simple laws discussed above.

Experiments with materials under high hydrostatic compressive stresses superimposed on simple compression or tension show that ductility is actually somewhat improved by increasing the mean pressure.   Since the atoms are pushed closer together by this pressure, they are evidently able to form new bonds more easily during slip.   Larger plastic strains are possible as a result.   Not only do normally ductile materials become more ductile, but normally brittle materials like cast iron and marble become ductile under high pressures.   An example of a great increase in ductility is that undergone by Carboloy, which was used by Bridgman for pistons to transmit high pressures.†   In tests of a very brittle grade—999—under hydrostatic pressures of about 425,000 psi he found that a superimposed uniaxial compressive stress could deform the Carboloy plastically by 10 per cent before fracture.   The compressive stress required was of the order of 2,000,000 psi.   Probably the effect of flaws in the material was greatly reduced by the hydrostatic pressure, through closing up of cracks and holes, so that the material could withstand such a high compressive stress before failure.

Transverse Compression

When transverse compressive stresses are added to a simple uniaxial compression of the same order of magnitude, there is an *apparent loss* of ductility.   It can be explained in terms of hydrostatic compression: the transverse compression combines with an equal part of the axial compression to form a hydrostatic component which does not contribute to yielding. If the stresses are not too large, the increase in ductility resulting from the

---

* Zwikker, C., *Physical Properties of Solid Materials*, Interscience Publishers, Inc., New York, 1954, pp. 90–96.

† Bridgman, P. W., *Studies in Large Plastic Flow and Fracture with Special Emphasis on the Effects of Hydrostatic Pressure*, 1st ed. (Metallurgy and Metallurgical Engineering Series) McGraw-Hill Book Company, New York, Toronto, London, 1952, pp. 118–124.

increase in mean pressure will not be great enough to be significant.   The
net result is that the axial compressive stress can be raised to higher values
before yielding takes place, thereby increasing the apparent strength and
decreasing the amount of yielding for a given stress.

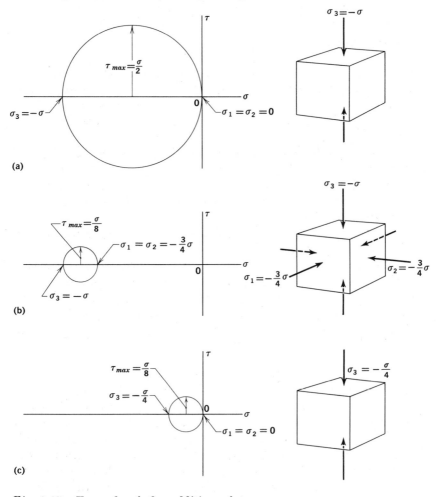

(a)

(b)

(c)

*Fig. 6.27   Example of the addition of transverse
compressive stresses to simple compression.*

For example, consider a member subjected to a simple compression
$\sigma_3 = -\sigma$ ($\sigma_1 = \sigma_2 = 0$).   The maximum shearing stress is $\sigma/2$.   The
Mohr's circle in Fig. 6.27a represents the situation graphically.   If transverse compressive stresses $\sigma_1 = \sigma_2 = -3\,\sigma/4$ are added, the situation is
changed to that shown in Fig. 6.27b.   The maximum shearing stress is now

only $\sigma/8$, the same as under a simple compressive stress only one-fourth as large (Fig. 6.27c). Since the shearing stress is only one-fourth its original magnitude, yielding is correspondingly more difficult.

End restraint in the ordinary uniaxial compression test (Art. 4.6) is an effect similar to that described above.

6.9 HYDROSTATIC TENSION

While a state of pure hydrostatic tension (equal tensile stresses in all directions) rarely, if ever, occurs, it is important as a limiting case, since it represents the opposite extreme from hydrostatic compression. At both extremes the shearing stress is zero (Fig. 6.24b). Consequently *no inelastic behavior can occur.*

In hydrostatic tension the atoms and molecules are pulled farther apart in all directions, just as they are pushed together in hydrostatic compression. However there is a limit to the strain that can be placed on the bonds, and failure by cleavage can take place on interatomic planes—a completely brittle failure.

The stress required for such failure follows the same general rules as those governing brittle fracture in simple tension (Art. 3.4). Materials that are normally brittle in simple tension should have the same average strength in hydrostatic tension. Normally ductile materials, however, are ductile because their cleavage strength is high relative to their yield strength. Consequently they should be stronger in hydrostatic tension than in simple tension.

Transverse Tension

When transverse tensile stresses are superimposed on a simple uniaxial tension, a state of triaxial tension results, with an apparent loss of ductility. The transverse tension combines with an equal part of the axial tension to form a hydrostatic tension component which does not contribute to yielding. The net result is that the axial tension can be raised to higher values before yielding, thereby increasing the apparent strength and decreasing the amount of yielding that will take place before the fracture stress is reached.

Imagine a member subjected to a uniaxial tension $\sigma_1 = \sigma$ ($\sigma_2 = \sigma_3 = 0$). The yield stress in simple tension is σ_y, so that the critical shear stress for yielding is $\tau_0 = \sigma_y/2$ (Art. 6.4). Now superimpose the transverse stresses $\sigma_2 = \sigma_3 = \alpha\sigma$, where α is a fraction between 0 and 1. The maximum shearing stress becomes $\tau_{max} = (\sigma_1 - \sigma_3)/2 = (1 - \alpha)\sigma/2$. If we assume the maximum shear criterion (Eq. 6.26), yielding will now take place when $\tau_{max} = \tau_0$, or $(1 - \alpha)\sigma/2 = \sigma_y/2$, from which

$$(\sigma_y)_1 = \frac{\sigma_y}{1 - \alpha} = \beta\sigma_y. \tag{6.32a}$$

Here $(\sigma_y)_1$ is the yield stress for the triaxial distribution, and β is the *triaxiality factor*,

$$\beta = \frac{1}{1 - \alpha}, \tag{6.32b}$$

which indicates the amount by which triaxial tension raises the yield stress.

6.10 TRIAXIALITY CAUSED BY CONSTRAINT

Elastic Constraint

Triaxial tension is a byproduct of many forms of loading. Here is a simple example in which it is produced by *elastic constraint*. A tension member is built up of three parts, as in Fig. 6.28a. The end sections are

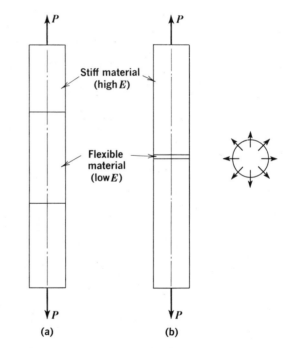

Fig. 6.28 Composite tension member.
                                   (a)   **(b)**

made of some stiff material such as steel ($E = 30 \times 10^6$ psi), and the center section is of a flexible material such as lead ($E = 2 \times 10^6$ psi). If a tensile load is applied to the composite member, producing an elastic strain in the center section, the axial strain in the center section will be much larger than in the end sections (15 times for these two materials). The lateral contraction caused by the Poisson effect will be in the same proportion, and will be unhindered except near the junctions between the three sections. For a member like that in Fig. 6.28b, however, in which the center section is only a thin disk, lateral contraction in the center section will be almost entirely prevented.   The end sections, acting almost like rigid members, exert stresses pulling outward on the material in the disk.   A rough idea

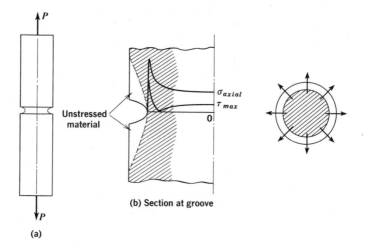

(b) Section at groove

(a)

Fig. 6.29   Tension member with circumferential groove.

of the magnitudes of the transverse stresses can be obtained by assuming that the transverse principal strains are zero and applying Eq. 6.10:

$$\epsilon_2 = \frac{1}{E}\left[\sigma_2 - \mu(\sigma_3 + \sigma_1)\right] = 0$$

$$\epsilon_3 = \frac{1}{E}\left[\sigma_3 - \mu(\sigma_1 + \sigma_2)\right] = 0,$$

from which

$$\sigma_2 = \sigma_3 = \sigma_1\left(\frac{\mu}{1 - \mu}\right).$$

Here σ_1 is the axial stress, and σ_2 and σ_3 are the transverse principal stresses. The factor $\mu/(1 - \mu)$ corresponds to α as defined in the last section.   The triaxiality factor is then

$$\beta = \frac{1}{1 - \alpha} = \frac{1}{1 - \dfrac{\mu}{1 - \mu}} = \frac{1 - \mu}{1 - 2\mu}.$$

If $\mu = \frac{1}{3}$, we have $\alpha = \frac{1}{2}$ and $\beta = 2$.   Thus σ_1 would have to be twice that in simple tension to cause yielding in the presence of this triaxiality.

It should be pointed out that the above analysis is approximate only since lateral contraction will not be prevented entirely, especially near the surface of the member.   If this were taken into account, the effect would be to reduce σ_2 and σ_3.   Thus α is actually considerably less than the value found above, and consequently β is smaller also.   A similar effect occurs in tension members having grooves and notches.   Consider, for example, a cylindrical member having a circumferential groove around its center (Fig. 6.29a).   If such a member is loaded in simple tension, a triaxial stress distribution is set up in the region of the groove.   The material immediately above and below the groove carries practically none of the axial stress (Fig. 6.29b), and it therefore tends to resist deformation.   The material in the center of the member, which carries all the tensile load, tries to contract laterally because of the Poisson effect, but it is hindered by the resistance of the unloaded material.   The result is that there are tensile stresses acting radially outward on the inner material.   Just as in the example of the composite member (Fig. 6.28b), these radial stresses produce a state of triaxial tension.   This example is another instance of elastic constraint.

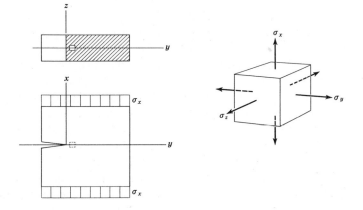

Fig. 6.30   Notched plate.

A similar effect takes place at a notch in the edge of a flat plate (Fig. 6.30).   Lateral contraction of the material at the root of the notch is hindered by the mass of unloaded material above and below the notch, in both the width and thickness directions (y and z in Fig. 6.30).   The triaxial stress distribution is confined to the mid-thickness of the plate because at the two surfaces the transverse stress, σ_z, must reduce to zero.

It follows that triaxiality will be greater for thicker plates than for thin ones, often an important consideration.*

Plastic Constraint

The triaxiality produced by elastic constraint is relatively small, as shown in the first example; the effect of a groove or a notch, when the material is the same throughout, is even smaller.   A much larger effect results when the yield stress is exceeded.   This effect is known as *plastic constraint*.† It is similar to elastic constraint, and can be explained on a similar basis.   Consider the composite member of Fig. 6.28a.   If the stress exceeds the yield stress of the center section, plastic elongation will take place, accompanied by lateral contraction.   Since volume remains constant in the plastic range (Art. 3.9), the lateral strain will be half the axial strain.   If the center section is reduced to a thin disk, as in Fig. 6.28b, lateral contraction will again be prevented.   The result is a triaxial stress distribution having larger transverse stresses than in elastic constraint and consequently a larger triaxiality factor, β.   The same observations apply to grooved and notched members.

Plastic constraint can also be analyzed in terms of actual yielding. Yielding always progresses along planes of maximum shear, at 45° with the principal stresses.   In the example above yielding begins in the thin lead disk but at once encounters the hard steel on either side and can go no farther.   Yielding cannot continue in the lead until the stress is large enough to start yielding in the steel as well.   Thus the stress for overall yielding of the composite member may be many times that for lead alone.

In the grooved tension member we find a situation analogous to that of the composite member.   Figure 6.29b shows the shearing stress to be fairly large right at the bottom of the groove, although it almost vanishes in the interior of the member.   Consequently yielding begins in a very small region at the bottom of the groove.   This time, instead of running into stronger material, yielding is stopped by material of the same kind having practically zero shearing stress.   Thus a condition of plastic constraint again arises.

It can be shown on the basis of theory of plasticity that the stress required to cause yielding in the presence of a groove can be as high as *three times* that for simple tension.   The ratio is called the *plastic constraint factor*, q, and takes the place of β in Eq. 6.32a:

---

* Parker, Earl R., *Brittle Behavior of Engineering Structures*, John Wiley & Sons, Inc., New York, 1957, p. 9.
† Orowan, E., "Fracture and Notch Brittleness in Ductile Materials," reprint of Part V of *Brittle Fracture of Mild Steel Plates*, report of a conference held at Cambridge University, October 26, 1945, pp. 4, 5.

$$(\sigma_y)_1 = q\sigma_y, \qquad (6.32c)$$

where q may be as high as 3. Note that this factor is considerably greater than the corresponding triaxiality factor for elastic constraint but that local plastic deformation is required before its full value can be realized.

A similar plastic constraint occurs at the tip of every notch or crack.

6.11 NOTCHES

The effect of a sharp notch on the stresses in a tension member is twofold: the stress acting in the material is raised to a peak value at the base of the notch, determined by the elastic stress concentration factor; and the yield stress for the material is raised by the action of the elastic and plastic constraints. Combination of these effects makes brittle fracture more likely in the presence of a sharp notch than in an unnotched member. If, for example, the stress for brittle fracture is twice the tensile yield stress, $(\sigma_f)_1 = 2\,\sigma_y$, and the full plastic constraint factor is developed ($q = 3$) so that $(\sigma_y)_1 = 3\,\sigma_y$, overall yielding will not occur because σ_1 will reach $(\sigma_f)_1$ before it reaches $(\sigma_y)_1$. Consequently when the peak stress reaches $(\sigma_f)_1$ or twice the tensile yield stress, brittle fracture will take place.

Other important factors entering into the general problem of *notch effect*, such as strain rate and temperature, will be taken up in the next chapter.

6.12 BIAXIAL TENSION

Biaxial tension is a special form of triaxial stress in which $\sigma_3 = 0$. Considerable evidence exists that materials lose some of their ductility under biaxial tension. One of the most common forms is found in thin-walled cylinders under internal pressure. Here the circumferential stress is the largest principal stress,

$$\sigma_1 = \frac{pr}{t},$$

and the axial stress is the intermediate principal stress,

$$\sigma_2 = \frac{pr}{2\,t},$$

where p is the internal pressure, r the inner radius of the tank, and t the wall thickness.* The stress in the radial direction actually varies from $-p$ on the inner surface to zero on the outer surface, but it is usually considered negligible, so that σ_3 is taken as zero.

---

* The analysis of thin-walled cylinders with closed ends under internal pressure is given in most elementary textbooks on mechanics of materials.

If we subject a thin-walled cylinder to internal pressure and superimpose either axial tension or compression, the total axial stress can be varied over a wide range to produce various combinations of biaxial stress (see Art. 6.13 for a detailed discussion). Many investigations of this kind have been made,* and their results usually indicate a loss of ductility compared with simple tension. Brittle fractures occur at stresses much lower than the ultimate strength found in simple tension for the same material. This is especially true for equal biaxial tensions ($\sigma_1 = \sigma_2$).

Spectacular failures of pressure vessels, both cylindrical and spherical, are of this type. The fractures are brittle and occur at relatively low stress levels. It must be mentioned, however, that in almost every instance other factors are also involved: stress-raisers in the form of holes, welded attachments, or other discontinuities; low temperatures; thermal gradients; and defective materials.

Another example in which biaxial stresses are involved in unexpected failures is in the bending of wide plates in forming operations. As mentioned in Art. 5.1, if anticlastic curvature is entirely prevented, the transverse strain is forced to remain zero everywhere except very close to the edges of the plate. Thus a transverse tension is set up on the tension side, equal to μ times the longitudinal bending stress. Again it should be mentioned that other factors are involved, such as the stress gradient across the thickness of the plate, possible flaws in the plate surface, and perhaps even low temperatures.

As a final example of biaxial stresses associated with brittle fracture, we shall consider a problem that arose in connection with the use of polyethylene sheaths for telephone cables. Polyethylene is usually thought of as a tough, pliable material, but soon after the sheaths were first used, brittle fractures were discovered. They occurred at bends and other discontinuities, and many of the fractures could not be traced to any recognized source of trouble, such as environmental deterioration. Tests indicated that the material satisfied all standard specifications. From experience with other materials it was suspected that since biaxial stresses were set up at bends, the failures might be traced to this condition. A series of special tests (bulge tests, Art. 6.13) showed conclusively that the material was indeed less ductile under biaxial tension than in simple tension. It was also found that an increase in molecular weight, which is closely associated with an increase in the average lengths of the polymer chains, provided greater ductility (Fig. 6.31). When polyethylene of higher molecular weight was substituted for the original material, the trouble was completely eliminated.

---

* Timoshenko, S., *Strength of Materials—Part II—Advanced Theory and Problems*, 3rd ed., D. Van Nostrand Company, Inc., Princeton, New Jersey, 1956, Art. 81.

EXPERIMENTAL METHODS (PART B)

6.13 TRIAXIAL STRESSES

High Pressures

Experiments with materials under high hydrostatic pressures require highly specialized equipment and techniques. The experiments must be made inside a pressure chamber, and when pressures of 1,000,000 psi and more are used, containment presents many problems. Massive walls, reinforced by externally applied pressure, are required. Furthermore, because the energy stored in the pressure chamber increases with its volume, it must be made very small (perhaps only $\frac{1}{2}$ inch in diameter and 4 inches long). The specimens and any auxiliary equipment used with them must be unusually small and precisely made.

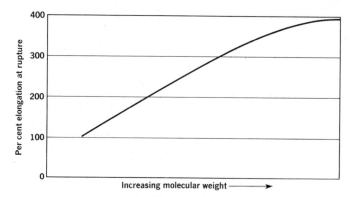

Fig. 6.31   *Increased ductility accompanying increase in molecular weight of polyethylene.   (Reprinted by permission from Hopkins,* Bell Laboratories Record, *Vol. XXXVI, No. 1, January 1958, p. 8, published by Bell Telephone Laboratories)*

High pressures are produced in the pressure chamber by means of a piston fitted into one end.   Here another problem presents itself: preventing leakage around the piston.   The usual method is to make the force acting on the piston act also on the packing, forcing it into tighter and tighter contact with the cylinder wall as the force increases.   Figure 6.32 illustrates the method as developed by Bridgman.   The piston is in two parts, A and B, which can slide freely on each other.   A ring of packing between the two parts transmits the force from one part to the other. Since the area of the packing is so much smaller than that of the end of the piston, the pressure on the packing is much higher than that in the pressure chamber by a constant factor.   Thus an effective seal is formed which improves in direct proportion to the pressure which it must contain.

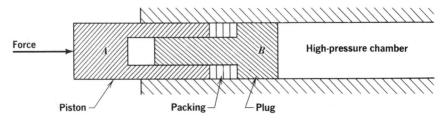

Fig. 6.32   High-pressure piston, illustrating self-tightening packing.

This brief description is intended only to give a general idea of the factors involved in high-pressure experiments.   Details of the equipment and its use are too numerous to be included in this text.   The reader is referred to the writings of Bridgman* and others, where fairly complete descriptions of equipment and test procedures can be found.

Thin-Walled Tubes

To date most experiments with combined stresses have been made on thin-walled tubes.   Many different combinations of stresses can be produced by applying loads of various types.   Since radial stress in a thin-walled tube is always either zero or negligible, stresses are always limited to biaxial distributions.   Even with this restriction, much useful information can be obtained from experiments on thin-walled tubes.

Loads applied include axial tension or compression, internal pressure, and torsion.   Again special equipment is involved, but the problems are not so great as with high pressures.

The ends of the specimen must be adapted for applying various loads: screw threads for applying tension or compression, plugs with oil-pressure fittings for applying internal pressure, and keyways or flattened areas for applying torsion.   A specimen combining all three features is illustrated in Fig. 6.33.   Problems of sealing against internal pressures are involved, too, but are not serious because the pressures used are comparatively low.

---

* Bridgman, P. W., *The Physics of High Pressure*, 2nd ed., The Macmillan Company, New York, 1950.

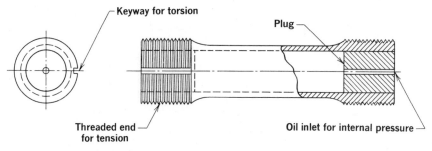

Fig. 6.33   Specimen for combined tension, internal pressure, and torsion.

Equipment for applying tension is the same as that discussed in Ch. 3. Internal pressures are applied by means of standard motor-driven or hand-operated hydraulic pumps, equipped with standard dials for measuring

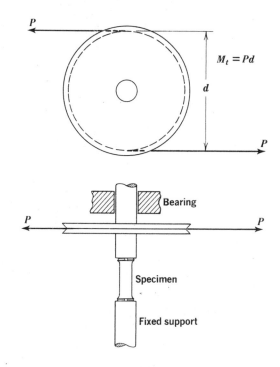

Fig. 6.34   Method of applying torsion to combined stress specimen.

pressure. Torsion is applied as shown in Fig. 6.34. A wheel is attached to one end of the specimen, and two cords or wires are wound around it as shown. Equal forces are then applied to the ends of the cords by dead weights, worm gears, or hydraulic pistons. The magnitudes of the forces

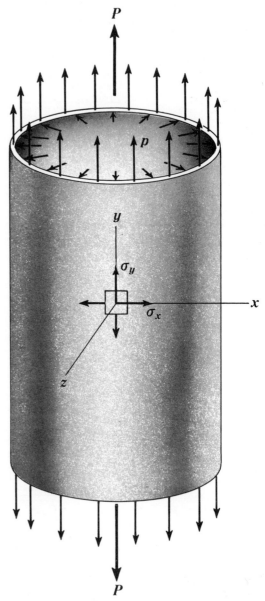

Fig. 6.35 Thin-walled tube under internal pressure, p, and axial tension, P.

are measured by dynamometers in the force system.   A couple is thus applied to the specimen as in the torsion test described in Art. 6.7.

The stresses acting in the thin-walled tube are analyzed by the methods outlined in Art. 6.1.   Consider, for example, a tube under internal pressure and simple tension (Fig. 6.35).   In the circumferential direction the stress is, from Art. 6.12,

$$\sigma_x = \frac{pr}{t},$$

where p is the internal pressure, r the inner radius of the tube, and t the wall thickness.   The axial stress is the sum of the stresses resulting from internal pressure and simple tension, P:

$$\sigma_y = \frac{pr}{2t} + \frac{P}{2\pi rt}.$$

As noted before, $\sigma_z = 0$.

For $P = 0$, σ_x is the largest principal stress ($\sigma_x = 2\sigma_y$) and can be called σ_1, while σ_y is σ_2 and σ_z is σ_3.   As P increases, σ_y approaches the value of σ_x. When $P/2\pi rt = pr/2t$, or $P = \pi r^2 p$, the two are equal and a state of equal biaxial tension exists.   For larger values of P, σ_y is the larger of the two and must be called σ_1, while σ_x is σ_2 and σ_z is still σ_3.

The variation between stresses can be represented in terms of n, the ratio of σ_x to σ_y.   In the above example n varies from 2 to 0 as P increases. By applying compression (P negative), σ_y can be reduced to zero, so that $n = \infty$.   One well-known series of such experiments was carried out by E. A. Davis in 1945.[*]

If torsion is applied with internal pressure or simple tension, a shearing stress τ_{xy} is added to the normal stresses as found above.   From Eq. 6.12b, the shearing stress is

$$\tau_{xy} = \frac{M_t}{2\pi r^2 t}.$$

Here σ_x and σ_y are not the principal stresses because of the shearing stresses on the x- and y-planes.   It can be shown that the principal stresses are

$$\left.\begin{aligned}
\sigma_1 &= \frac{\sigma_x + \sigma_y}{2} + \sqrt{\left(\frac{\sigma_x - \sigma_y}{2}\right)^2 + \tau_{xy}^2} \\[2mm]
\sigma_2 &= \frac{\sigma_x + \sigma_y}{2} - \sqrt{\left(\frac{\sigma_x - \sigma_y}{2}\right)^2 + \tau_{xy}^2} \\[2mm]
\sigma_3 &= \sigma_z = 0.
\end{aligned}\right\} \tag{6.33}$$

(If the expression for σ_2 happens to be negative, then σ_2 and σ_3 must be interchanged to satisfy the condition $\sigma_1 \geqslant \sigma_2 \geqslant \sigma_3$ (Eq. 6.4).

---

[*] Davis, E. A., "Yielding and Fracture of Medium-Carbon Steel under Combined Stress," *J. App. Mech.* **12**, A-13-A-24 (1945) (Am. Soc. Mech. Engrs. *Transactions* **67** (1945)); Davis, E. A., "The Effect of Size and Stored Energy on the Fracture of Tubular Specimens," *J. App. Mech.* **15**, 216–221 (1948) (Am. Soc. Mech. Engrs. *Transactions* **70** (1948)).

The same general considerations discussed in Art. 6.7 govern the design of specimens.   For accurate results the wall thickness-to-diameter ratio should be small and the length-to-diameter ratio large.   However, to avoid

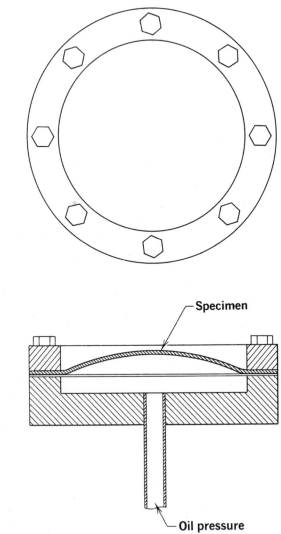

Fig. 6.36   Bulge test apparatus.

buckling there are definite limits beyond which it is impractical to go.   If axial compression is to be used, even greater restrictions must be applied because of the increased tendency toward buckling.

Deformations must be measured in terms of change in length, angle of

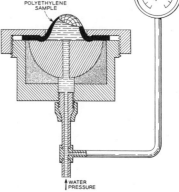

Fig. 6.37   Deformation and failure of polyethylene sample in bulge test. (Reprinted by permission from Hopkins, Bell Laboratories Record, Vol. XXXVI, No. 1, January 1958, p. 6, published by Bell Telephone Laboratories)

Fig. 6.38   Apparatus for bulge test of polyethylene. (Reprinted by permission from Hopkins, Bell Laboratories Record, Vol. XXXVI, No. 1, January 1958, p. 7, published by Bell Telephone Laboratories)

twist, and increase in diameter.   Many different devices have been used, but all involve the same principles discussed for simpler loadings.   For additional details the reader is referred to various technical papers on combined stress testing.*

---

* Marin, Joseph, *Mechanical Properties of Materials and Design*, 1st ed., McGraw-Hill Book Company, New York, Toronto, London, 1942.

Bulge Tests

Another type of experiment for determining combined stresses is the *bulge test*. In its simplest form a plate or sheet of the material is clamped between two circular rings and pressure applied to one side by means of a liquid (Fig. 6.36). The bulging produced by the pressure creates a state of equal biaxial tension in the material. The specimen is usually marked with a rectangular or polar grid so that large strains can be measured. Smaller strains may be measured by electric resistance-wire strain gages cemented to the surface. Deflections may also be measured at various points by dial indicators.

The bulge test is useful mainly for studying the ductility of materials under biaxial tension when large plastic deformations are involved. Figure 6.37 shows the bulge test of polyethylene mentioned in Art. 6.12; Figure 6.38 shows the arrangement of specimen and equipment. The specimen is a disk 3 inches in diameter and 0.1 inch thick, clamped in a holder having an opening 1.8 inches in diameter. The rectangular grid stencilled on the surface has original spacing of 0.1 inch. For a material of low molecular weight the elongation under biaxial stress was as low as 28 per cent, whereas under uniaxial tension the same material satisfied specifications by elongating to as much as five times its original length.

BIBLIOGRAPHY

Timoshenko, S., *Strength of Materials—Part II—Advanced Theory and Problems*, 3rd ed., D. Van Nostrand Company, Inc., Princeton, N. J., 1956, Ch. X.
   A good discussion of strength theory is found in Art. 82.

Marin, Joseph, *Engineering Materials—Their Mechanical Properties and Applications*, Prentice-Hall, Inc., Englewood Cliffs, N. J., 1952.
   Chapter 3 contains a more detailed discussion of the effects of combined stresses.

Nadai, A., *Theory of Flow and Fracture of Solids*, Vol. I, 2nd ed. (Engineering Societies Monographs) McGraw-Hill Book Company, Inc., New York, Toronto, London, 1950.
   For the advanced student.

Ridenour, Louis N., Ed., *Modern Physics for the Engineer*, McGraw-Hill Book Company, Inc., New York, Toronto, London, 1954.
   Chapter 11, by David T. Griggs, contains a good general discussion of effects of high pressure on properties of materials.

Bridgman, P. W., *Studies in Large Plastic Flow and Fracture with Special Emphasis on the Effects of Hydrostatic Pressure,* 1st ed. (Metallurgy and Metallurgical Engineering Series) McGraw-Hill Book Company, Inc., New York, Toronto, London, 1952.

    Accepted authority on high-pressure effects; extensive experimental data with conclusions.

PROBLEMS

6.1 The principal stresses acting on a rectangular element of a solid are as follows: $\sigma_x = +6000$ psi, $\sigma_y = +10,000$ psi, $\sigma_z = -4000$ psi. (a) Construct the set of Mohr's circles for this state of stress. (b) Find the three maximum shearing stresses τ_{max}, τ'_{max}, τ''_{max} and show the planes on which they act by a suitable sketch. (c) Find the mean stress.

6.2 Repeat Problem 6.1 for the following stresses: $\sigma_x = -2000$ psi, $\sigma_y = -2000$ psi, $\sigma_z = +2000$ psi. (Such a state is sometimes referred to as *3-dimensional pure shear.*)

6.3 If the material in Problem 6.1 is aluminum ($E = 10 \times 10^6$ psi; $\mu = 0.33$), compute the principal strains.

6.4 If the material in Problem 6.2 is lead ($E = 2 \times 10^6$ psi; $\mu = 0.43$), compute the principal strains.

6.5 From the data in Tables 3.1 and 6.1 compute Poisson's ratio for the following materials: steel, aluminum, lead.

6.6 A thin-walled copper tube is tested in torsion. Its mean radius is 0.75 in., and its wall thickness is 0.040 in. Compute the slope of the elastic diagram of twisting moment vs unit angle of twist (θ) ($G = 6.4 \times 10^6$ psi).

6.7 Equation 6.24 can be applied to the torsion of tubes by noting that $I_p = \pi r_0^4/2 - \pi r_i^4/2$, where r_0 is the outer radius and r_i the inner radius. When the wall thickness of the tube is large, the stress determined in this way is the correct value, while that found by Eq. 6.12b is approximate. Derive an expression for the ratio between the correct and approximate values, in terms of the ratio of the wall thickness to the mean radius (t/r_m). For what ratio, t/r_m, is the approximate value in error by 1 per cent? [Hint: In Eq. 6.24 express r_0 and r_i in terms of r_m and t, and use r_m in Eq. 6.12b.]

6.8 The following data are obtained in a torsion test of a thin-walled tube specimen, where ϕ is the total angle of twist in the length, l:

M_t, in.-lb	ϕ, degrees	M_t, in.-lb	ϕ, degrees
0	0	1890	1.50
1367	0.40	1960	2.00
1590	0.60	2040	3.00
1775	1.00		

Dimensions of the tube are: $r_m = 0.500$ in., $t = 0.050$ in., $l = 3.00$ in.   Convert the above data to shearing stress and strain and plot the $\tau - \gamma$ curve for the material.   Determine the following shearing properties: modulus of elasticity, G; proportional limit, τ_{pl}; modulus of resilience, u_r; yield stress at 0.2% offset.   What material might have these properties?

6.9 The tensile yield strength of annealed uranium is 25,000 psi.   If a thin-walled tube of this material is loaded in torsion, find the magnitude of the maximum principal stress at which yielding should begin according to (a) the maximum shear stress theory; (b) the octahedral shear stress theory.

6.10 A cube of annealed uranium is subjected to principal stresses which are in the following proportion: $\sigma_1 : \sigma_2 : \sigma_3 = 2 : 0 : -1$.   Determine the magnitude of σ_1 for yielding, according to (a) the maximum shear stress theory; (b) the octahedral shear stress theory, assuming a tensile yield stress of 25,000 psi, as in the previous problem.

6.11 The tensile yield stress of a magnesium-thorium-zirconium alloy is 14,500 psi.   A cube of this alloy is subjected to principal stresses which are in the proportion $\sigma_1 : \sigma_2 : \sigma_3 = 1 : -1 : -1$.   Determine the magnitude of σ_1 for yielding, according to (a) the maximum shear stress theory; (b) the octahedral shear stress theory.

6.12 Explain why the problem of plastic instability does not affect torsion.

6.13 Compute the bulk modulus of each of the following materials: (a) brass ($E = 14.5 \times 10^6$ psi, $\mu = 0.37$); (b) gray cast iron ($E = 12.0 \times 10^6$ psi, $\mu = 0.18$); (c) hard rubber ($E = 0.65 \times 10^6$ psi, $\mu = 0.42$).

6.14 Bridgman proposes the following equation for the compressibility of lead: $\Delta V / V_0 = 10^{-7} p(23.73 - 17.25 \times 10^{-5} p)$, where p is in kg/cm². From this equation compute the value of the bulk modulus, K, *in psi*, (a) at zero pressure; (b) at 1000 atmospheres.

6.15 A mild steel member yields at 35,000 psi in simple compression.   If a transverse pressure equal to half the axial stress is added, determine the *axial* stress needed to cause yielding according to the maximum shear stress theory.

6.16 Repeat Problem 6.15 using the maximum octahedral shear stress theory.

6.17 An annealed titanium member yields at 82,000 psi in simple tension.   If transverse tensile stresses equal to $\frac{2}{3}$ the axial stress are added, determine the *axial* stress needed to cause yielding according to the maximum shear theory. Evaluate the triaxiality factor, β.

6.18 Explain the reason for the apparent loss of ductility of materials when transverse tensile or compressive stresses are superimposed on simple axial stresses of the same sign.

6.19 If transverse stresses of *opposite* sign are superimposed on a simple axial tension or compression, what would happen to the apparent ductility of the material?   Why?

6.20 Explain why the triaxiality at the base of a notch in the side of a flat plate is greater for a thick plate than for a thin one.

6.21 A thin-walled tube is subjected to a combination of internal pressure, axial tension, and torsion. Determine the principal stresses for the following dimensions and loads: $r_m = 1.125$ in., $t = 0.060$ in., $p = 300$ psi, $P = 500$ lb, $M_t = 1000$ in.-lb.

CHAPTER 7

DYNAMIC
AND
THERMAL
EFFECTS

Dynamic loading is important in many engineering applications such as impact, high accelerations, and mechanical vibrations. The increased use of plastics having time- and temperature-dependent properties produces additional problems concerning rate of loading. Even in slow-speed static loading, if a member contains a notch, the local increase in strain rate at the root of the notch has important consequences.

Thermal effects include those of both high- and low-temperature environments. We do not need to look far to find numerous examples of both in engineering. Room temperature may be classed as either high or low, depending on conditions. For example, the transition from ductile to brittle behavior in steel, usually considered a low-temperature effect, may occur at or even above room temperature. On the other hand, in low-melting point materials room temperature produces high-temperature effects such as creep. Examples of extremes in temperature are also plentiful. The low temperatures encountered in the polar regions or in outer space may cause drastic changes in mechanical properties. Equipment for liquefying gases poses extreme problems in low-temperature effects.   In the high-temperature range are problems encountered in internal combustion engines, steam piping systems, rocket motors, and re-entry of space vehicles.

The response of materials to changes in rate of loading is similar in important respects to their short-time response to changes in temperature. The yield strength of steel, for example, may be doubled *either* by raising the loading rate or lowering the temperature.   Tar will flow in the familiar manner if the temperature is high enough, *or* if it is deformed slowly enough, whereas it will deform elastically and fracture when deformed at a low temperature *or* too high a rate.   Some materials are relatively unaffected by changes in rate and temperature, but others, like the examples above, are so sensitive that their sensitivity is in itself an important property.

As evidenced by their similarities, the effects of variation in rate of loading and temperature are closely interrelated.   This interrelation is suggested by the Arrhenius equation (Eq. 2.4), by which the rates of certain processes are related to temperature.   In a number of physical processes, including diffusion, discontinuous yielding, and the deformation of polymers, the Arrhenius equation has been shown to be a controlling factor. Rate of loading and short-time temperature effects are therefore discussed together in this chapter, as is their connection with brittle fracture.   Long-time effects, special high-temperature effects, and repeated loading will be taken up in chapters on creep and fatigue.

DYNAMIC EFFECTS

7.1 RATE OF LOADING

The term *rate of loading* is used in the sense of any convenient characteristic rate accompanying the application of load to a member.   In a conventional tension test (Art. 3.17) the rate may be that at which the load or the stress is increased, the rate at which the strain is increased, or the rate of crosshead motion on the machine.   The most generally useful rate is the strain rate

$$\dot{\epsilon} = d\epsilon/dt \ (\text{or} \ \dot{\gamma} = d\gamma/dt).$$

For a material which follows Hooke's law the rates of change of stress and strain are, of course, proportional; a constant rate of increase of one means a constant rate of increase of the other.   In ordinary "static" loading the strain rate is usually of the order of 10^{-4} (in./in.)/sec; if we take aluminum as an example, it corresponds to a stress rate of 1000 psi/sec or a loading rate of 200 lb/sec for a standard $\frac{1}{2}$-in. specimen.

7.2 ELASTIC AFTEREFFECT

Even at low rates of loading there are important time effects. The first is the *elastic aftereffect*, or *delayed elasticity*, a transient variation of strain with time. One of the simpler elastic aftereffects is thermoelastic action. When a member is elongated, its volume increases, accompanied by a drop in its temperature. This phenomenon is the converse of thermal expansion (see Chapter 12, Thermal Properties). If elongation takes place slowly enough that thermal equilibrium is maintained, absorption of heat from its surroundings holds the temperature of the member constant and the process is isothermal. If, on the other hand, elongation is rapid and there is insufficient time for heat transfer, the process is adiabatic, and the temperature of the member is lowered. If, after a member is loaded adiabatically to a certain stress, the stress is held constant while the member is allowed to absorb heat, a further expansion takes place until the total elongation is the same as in the isothermal process. The two processes are illustrated by the stress-strain diagram of Fig. 7.1a. Isothermal

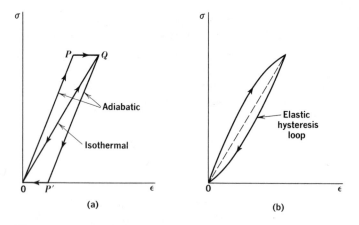

Fig. 7.1   Thermoelastic effect.

elongation is represented by line OQ and adiabatic elongation by line OP. This effect is very small and can be detected only by very precise measurements; the distance between points P and Q in Fig. 7.1a is greatly exaggerated for illustration.

The same processes can be observed in unloading from point Q. Isothermal unloading follows the line QO, whereas adiabatic unloading follows the line QP', parallel to OP, and only after some time returns to the origin. In a smooth cycle of loading and unloading a curve something like that of Fig. 7.1b is traced out instead of the parallelogram $OPQP'$. During such a cycle energy is dissipated equal to the area inside this loop (Art. 3.3), which is called an *elastic hysteresis loop.*

The size and shape of the hysteresis loop varies with the frequency of cyclic loading. At very low frequencies the rate of loading and unloading is slow, and the action may be nearly isothermal; the width of the hysteresis loop is negligible, and little or no energy is lost. At very high frequencies the loading and unloading rate may be high enough to be substantially adiabatic; here, too, the width of the loop is negligible and no energy is lost. At some frequency between these two extremes the energy lost rises to a maximum.

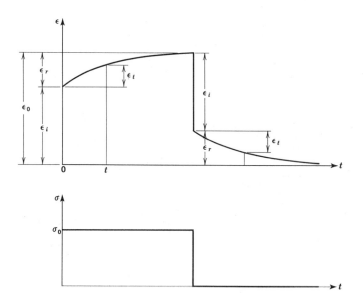

Fig. 7.2   Elastic aftereffect.

Figure 7.2 illustrates elastic aftereffect in general. If, at $t = 0$, a constant stress σ_0 is suddenly imposed on the member as illustrated by the step-function for σ vs t, the stress is accompanied by an instantaneous strain ϵ_i (e.g., the adiabatic strain in the thermoelastic case). The transient strain, ϵ_t, follows at a decreasing rate until the total strain is ϵ_0 (e.g., the isothermal strain in the thermoelastic case). When the load is removed, the process is exactly reversed. The strain decreases instantaneously by the same amount as it increased in loading, ϵ_i. The transient strain, ϵ_t, again follows at a decreasing rate until the total strain is zero.

The rate at which the transient strain increases is usually expressed in terms of the *retardation time,* the time required for ϵ_t to reach a certain arbitrary fraction of ϵ_0.   Similarly, the *relaxation time* is that required for ϵ_t to decrease to a certain arbitrary fraction of ϵ_0 after the load is removed. Relaxation time will be discussed in more detail in Art. 7.4.

Thermoelastic effect is only one of a number of causes of transient elastic strain.   Others include atomic diffusion, magnetoelastic effect (Art. 11.5), the uncoiling of long-chain molecules in polymers, and heterogeneity.

As discussed in Art. 2.7, atomic diffusion is a process by which atoms migrate to positions of lower energy, thereby relaxing the atomic structure and allowing further strain.   In unloading the atoms may migrate back to their original positions, and if so the entire action is elastic.   Steel is an example in which the interstitial carbon atoms normally occupy positions at the centers of the cube edges in the body-centered unit cells of iron. One such atom is illustrated in Fig. 7.3.   As noted in Art. 2.9, the carbon

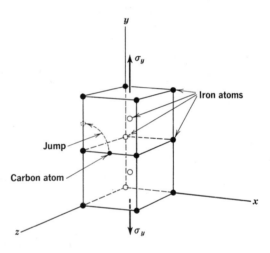

Fig. 7.3   Mechanism of atomic diffusion in steel.

atoms are slightly too large to fit into these positions without distorting the lattice.   Under zero stress they tend to distribute themselves equally among the cube edges in the x-, y-, and z-directions.   If a stress is applied in the y-direction, the spacing between atoms is increased in that direction, leaving more room for the carbon atoms.   At the same time the bonds in the x- and z-directions shorten (the Poisson effect).   Thus some of the carbon atoms in the x and z cube edges are, in effect, squeezed out and jump to the elongated y cube edges (Fig. 7.3).   As each atom jumps, the whole crystal elongates a little more in the y-direction to produce a transient strain.   The rate at which strain proceeds depends on the number of atoms remaining in the x and z cube edges; it decreases as more atoms jump.   It also depends on the diffusion rate, which in turn is governed by the Arrhenius equation (Eq. 2.4), and is therefore affected by temperature.

The higher the temperature, the higher the diffusion rate, and the more rapid the transient strain. The strain continues until no more atoms jump. Upon release of the stress the structure gradually returns to its equilibrium condition with the carbon atoms equally distributed in all three directions. The effect is therefore elastic.

The uncoiling of long-chain molecules in rubber has already been discussed briefly in Art. 3.1. This uncoiling is not an instantaneous process but requires some time after stress is first applied. The rate at which the molecules uncoil under stress is roughly governed by the Arrhenius equation, from which we see that the rate is strongly temperature-dependent. In ordinary thermoplastics the aftereffect is measurable at room temperature; for rubber it is very large. It is this effect which accounts for the high mechanical hysteresis of rubber (Art. 3.3).

Most of the elastic aftereffects are quite small, like the thermoelastic effect. The area of a single hysteresis loop is almost insignificant compared with the total strain energy in the material at maximum strain. When mechanical vibrations are involved, however, the energy lost in each loop is multiplied by the number of cycles, and the total energy dissipated may become large. The mechanism which produces elastic aftereffect is often called *internal friction*. The energy dissipated through internal friction in vibrating members *damps* the vibrations. Materials having high internal friction and hence high damping capacity are often desirable. Damping causes transient vibrations to die out quickly and reduces the amplitude of resonant vibrations. It should also be remembered, however, that the energy dissipated goes into heat and may cause overheating of the part. These two effects must be balanced in designing for vibrations.

Internal friction is measured quantitatively in many different ways. One is to measure $\Delta u/u$, where u is total strain energy per unit volume at the maximum strain ($u = \sigma_{max}^2/2E$), and Δu is the energy dissipated per cycle, given by the area of the hysteresis loop; $\Delta u/u$ is commonly called the *specific damping capacity*. Not only does it vary from material to material, but the magnitude of the internal friction varies over a wide range for a given material, depending on the frequency, temperature, and previous treatment of the material.* To give some idea of the order of magnitude of internal friction it may be noted that for metals the range of $\Delta u/u$ is approximately 0.0001 to 0.05, while for rubber it can be as large as 0.6. Impurities in metals have a pronounced effect, and their presence may increase the internal friction by a factor of 1000 or more. Molecular materials generally have higher damping capacities than crystalline mate-

---

* Zener, Clarence, *Elasticity and Anelasticity of Metals*, The University of Chicago Press, Chicago, Illinois, 1948, pp. 55ff; Zwikker, C., *Physical Properties of Solid Materials*, Interscience Publishers, Inc., New York, 1954, p. 117.

rials because configurational changes in large molecules are more sluggish than among the atoms of a crystal.

The most important characteristic of the elastic aftereffect is its transient nature; it proceeds at a decreasing rate, which approaches zero fairly rapidly.

7.3 VISCOUS FLOW

Another important time effect, viscous flow, differs from aftereffect in that it is a continuing deformation. It also is highly temperature-dependent although it occurs at room temperature in many materials.

Viscous flow is characterized by a steady increase of deformation at constant stress. An ideal viscous liquid acted upon by a constant shearing stress is deformed at a constant rate of shearing strain given by

$$\dot{\gamma} = \frac{1}{\eta}\,\tau, \qquad (7.1a)$$

where η is the coefficient of viscosity for the liquid*. Ideal viscous deformations in solids are governed by the same law. If a member is loaded in tension, the viscous deformation occurs at the rate

$$\dot{\epsilon} = \frac{1}{\phi}\,\sigma, \qquad (7.1b)$$

where ϕ is the coefficient of viscosity for *tension* for the material.† A liquid or solid that obeys this linear law is referred to as *Newtonian*.

The mechanism of viscous flow in solids is one in which particles slide past one another without any strengthening effect. One such mechanism was mentioned in Art. 3.7 in connection with the yielding of thermoplastic polymers. Wood and concrete are subject to a similar effect. In most solids, however, other forms of deformation accompany viscous flow. There is always an instantaneous elastic deformation, and if the material is partially crystalline, there will be plastic yielding and strain-hardening as well. The result is a more-or-less complex stress-strain relation, but one that is time-dependent.

The effect of rate of loading on the stress-strain diagram of a viscous material can be illustrated as follows. Imagine a perfectly viscous material in which strain is governed by Eq. 7.1b, $\dot{\epsilon} = \sigma/\phi$. If a member of

---

* Viscosity is usually expressed in *poises*. One poise $= 1$ (dyne/cm²)/(1/sec).

† Nadai, A., *Theory of Flow and Fracture of Solids*, Vol. I, 2nd ed. (Engineering Societies Monographs) McGraw-Hill Book Company, Inc., New York, Toronto, London, 1950, p. 396.

this material is loaded by a stress which increases uniformly with time, i.e., $\sigma = kt$, we can write

$$\frac{d\epsilon}{dt} = \frac{kt}{\phi}.$$

Integrating, we get

$$\epsilon = \frac{k}{\phi} \cdot \frac{t^2}{2} + C,$$

and if, at $t = 0$, $\epsilon = 0$, then $C = 0$. Substituting $t = \sigma/k$ in this equation, we find

$$\sigma = \sqrt{2 k\phi} \; \epsilon^{\frac{1}{2}}.$$

Figure 7.4 is a family of such stress-strain curves for various values of k, the rate of increase of stress. If the material is only partly viscous, the stress-strain relation is complicated by the elastic part of the strain and

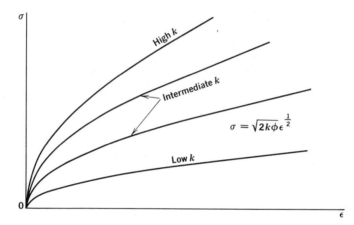

Fig. 7.4 Variation in shape of stress-strain diagram for various rates of loading $(d\sigma/dt = k)$.

by other kinds of yielding. Nevertheless the general effect of increasing the stress rate, k, is the same: the stress-strain diagram is raised so that a higher stress is required to produce the same amount of yielding. The effect is similar to that of triaxiality (Chapter 6).

The dependence of stress on the rate of strain is clearly shown by Eq. 7.1b, written $\sigma = \phi\dot{\epsilon}$. As the strain rate is increased, the stress increases in direct proportion.

Rate of loading is an important variable both in wholly and partially viscous materials. If a valid comparison is to be made between tests on materials of this type they must be conducted at a standardized constant rate of loading.   The ASTM *Standards* specify suitable standard rates for such materials as plastics, rubber, wood, and concrete.

7.4   MECHANICAL MODELS

It is sometimes helpful in studying time effects to depict a solid by means of a mechanical model.   For example, the ideal viscous solid can be represented by a dashpot (Fig. 7.5a).   If we call the applied force σ, to cor-

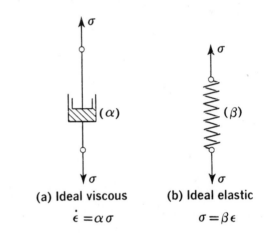

(a) Ideal viscous

$$\dot{\epsilon} = \alpha \sigma$$

(b) Ideal elastic

$$\sigma = \beta \epsilon$$

Fig. 7.5   Elementary mechanical models.

respond to the stress in the solid, and the resulting displacement of the plunger ϵ, to correspond to the strain, then, since rate of displacement is proportional to force, we can write $\dot{\epsilon} = \alpha\sigma$, where α is the dashpot constant. When this equation is compared with Eq. 7.1b, we see that $\alpha = 1/\phi$. Similarly an ideal elastic solid can be represented by a linear spring (Fig. 7.5b).   Here $\sigma = \beta\epsilon$, where β is the spring constant.   When we compare this equation with Hooke's law, we see that $\beta = E$.   These two basic model elements are used in various combinations to represent idealized behavior of materials.

Maxwell Model

A solid whose deformation is partly ideal elastic and partly ideal viscous can sometimes be represented by the so-called Maxwell model, which consists of a dashpot and spring connected in series (Fig. 7.6a).*   When a force (or stress) σ is applied, the spring responds instantaneously, elongat-

---

* Freudenthal, Alfred M., *The Inelastic Behavior of Engineering Materials and Structures*, John Wiley & Sons, Inc., New York, 1950, p. 233.

ing by an amount σ/β. At the same time the dashpot begins to move at a rate $\alpha\sigma$. The displacement of the plunger at any time t is given by $\int \alpha\sigma \, dt$. Since the total elongation of the model is the sum of the two elongations, we have

$$\epsilon = \frac{\sigma}{\beta} + \int \alpha\sigma \, dt.$$

By differentiating both sides with respect to time we obtain the differential equation of the Maxwell model,

$$\frac{\dot{\sigma}}{\beta} + \alpha\sigma = \dot{\epsilon}. \tag{7.2}$$

This equation can also be thought of as the differential equation for an ideal solid, called a *Maxwell body.*

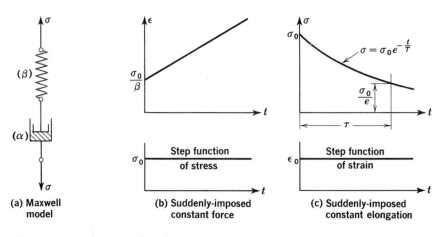

(a) Maxwell model   (b) Suddenly-imposed constant force   (c) Suddenly-imposed constant elongation

Fig. 7.6   *Ideal Maxwell body.*

This equation will now be used to examine two important forms of loading. The first consists in attaching a given weight to the Maxwell model, or applying a step-function of stress, as illustrated in Fig. 7.6b. When the stress, σ_0, is first applied, the spring is instantaneously elongated by the amount σ_0/β. Thereafter, σ remains constant, so that $\dot{\sigma}$ is zero, and Eq. 7.2 becomes

$$\dot{\epsilon} = \alpha\sigma_0. \tag{7.2a}$$

Thus ϵ increases linearly with time, as shown.

If, on the other hand, the model is stretched suddenly and held at a fixed elongation, i.e., a step-function of strain, ϵ_0, is applied, the initial stress will be $\beta\epsilon_0$. Since ϵ remains constant, $\dot{\epsilon} = 0$, and Eq. 7.2 becomes

$$\frac{\dot{\sigma}}{\beta} + \alpha\sigma = 0. \tag{7.2b}$$

The solution of this equation is

$$\sigma = \beta\epsilon_0 e^{-(\alpha\beta)\,t}, \tag{7.3}$$

showing that the stress relaxes exponentially (Fig. 7.6a). The relaxation time, τ, can now be defined more explicitly than in Art. 7.2 as the time required for the stress to reduce to a fraction, $1/e$, of its original value. Thus Eq. 7.3 can be written

$$\sigma = \sigma_0 e^{-\frac{t}{\tau}}, \tag{7.3a}$$

for when $t = \tau$, $\sigma = \sigma_0/e$. Since $e = 2.718$, σ reduces to $0.368\,\sigma_0$ by the end of the relaxation time. We also see that $\tau = 1/\alpha\beta$. The problem of stress relaxation will be discussed in more general terms in Art. 8.8.

Combination Models

Elastic aftereffect (Art. 7.2) can be depicted as a combination of three or more elements (springs and/or dashpots). For the idealized case a combination such as that shown in Fig. 7.7 can be used.* Here the initial

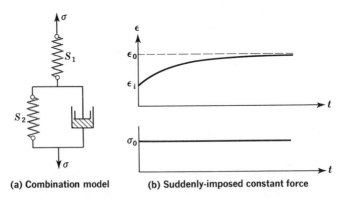

(a) Combination model   (b) Suddenly-imposed constant force

Fig. 7.7   Elastic aftereffect.

application of a force σ_0 produces an instantaneous elongation, ϵ_i, of spring S_1. If the force is maintained at σ_0, spring S_2 and the dashpot will begin to elongate together. Their rate of elongation is at first proportional to σ_0, but as spring S_2 takes up more and more of the force, the rate of elongation

---

* Orowan, E., "Creep in Metallic and Non-Metallic Materials," reprinted from the *Proceedings of the First National Congress of Applied Mechanics*, American Society of Mechanical Engineers, New York, 1951, p. 454.

decreases. Thus elongation approaches a maximum determined by the spring constant of S_2. The variation of elongation with time is similar to the variation of strain shown in Fig. 7.2.

The behavior of any viscoelastic material can be simulated by a multiunit model (Fig. 7.8). Each unit has its own relaxation time corresponding to

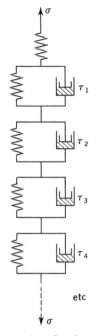

Fig. 7.8   Model representing a viscoelastic material.

that of some mechanism in the actual material. Such models are commonly used in the study of polymers.*

7.5   YIELDING AND FRACTURE

The influence of rate of loading on yielding and fracture of ductile metals is still another time effect. Yielding of crystalline materials depends primarily on the passage of dislocations through crystals. A certain stress is required to put the dislocations in motion, after which they move at a definite velocity which increases with the stress. Thermal energy in the crystal aids the applied stress in starting motion. The rate at which dislocations are set in motion through the aid of thermal energy is given by

---

* Goldman, J. E., Ed., *The Science of Engineering Materials*, John Wiley & Sons, Inc., New York, 1957, pp. 473–475.

the Arrhenius equation (Eq. 2.4).   The activation energy is strongly affected by the stress; the higher the stress, the lower the activation energy needed.   Consequently if the strain is increased slowly, thermal energy will play an important part in producing additional strain, and the stress needed can be relatively low.   If, on the other hand, the strain is increased rapidly, there will not be time for the thermal energy to have much effect, and the stress needed will be relatively high.   We are therefore led to the following conclusion, which has been confirmed by many experiments: *the plastic stress-strain curve of a ductile metal is raised by increasing the strain rate.*

This effect, too, is temperature-dependent through the Arrhenius equation, being more pronounced at temperatures near the melting point of the metal.   The effect is fairly small at room temperature for most metals. For example, increasing the strain rate by a factor of 100 increases the yield stress of copper by only 10 or 15 per cent at room temperature.   At temperatures near the melting point, however, the same increase in strain rate can double the yield stress.

The range of strain rates covered by various investigators in "short-time" tests is from 10^{-6} to 10^3 (in./in.)/sec.   If we remember that in ordinary static testing the strain rate is of the order of 10^{-4} (in./in.)/sec, the lower value is quite slow.   At this rate approximately half an hour would be required to complete the elastic deformation of structural steel.   The other end of the range corresponds to what is commonly thought of as *impact* loading.   For example, if a 2-in. specimen is struck by a falling weight moving at 17 ft/sec, so that the specimen is elongated at that rate, the strain rate will be $17 \times \frac{12}{2} = 102$ (in./in.)/sec.   In going from 10^{-6} to 10^3 (in./in.)/sec, increases in yield stress as high as 40 per cent have been observed in metals like copper at room temperature.   Figures 7.9a and b show the variation of the ultimate stress in tension, as a function of strain rate, for pure copper and pure aluminum as reported by Nadai and Manjoine.*

Mild steel is of particular interest because of its wide use and special behavior.   The yield point of mild steel is subject to striking variations with strain rate.   Figure 7.10 shows the results of tests by Manjoine† in which yield stress is increased by a factor of 3 over its static value by a strain rate of 300 (in./in.)/sec.   The corresponding dynamic stress-strain curves are shown in Fig. 7.11.   Note that the yield point is the most affected property; other properties, including ultimate stress, are affected more nearly like those for other metals.

---

* Nadai, A., *Theory of Flow and Fracture of Solids*, Vol. I, 2nd ed. (Engineering Societies Monographs) McGraw-Hill Book Company, Inc., New York, 1950, p. 24.

† Manjoine, M. J., "Influence of Strain and Temperature on Yield Stresses of Mild Steel," *J. App. Mech.* **1944**, A-211–A-218 (Am. Soc. Mech. Engrs. *Transactions* **66** (1944)).

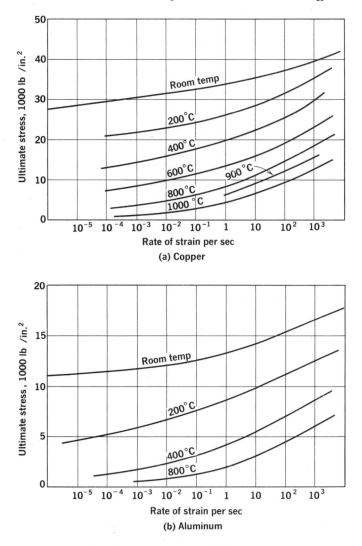

*Fig. 7.9   Effect of strain rate on ultimate stress of pure copper and pure aluminum at various temperatures. (Adapted from Nadai and Manjoine, J. App. Mech., ASME Trans., **63**, A-82 (1941))*

The sensitivity of the yield point of mild steel to variations in strain rate is closely associated with the causes of discontinuous yielding.   The general mechanism by which stress varies with strain rate is similar to that described for all metals; however, it was pointed out (Art. 3.10) that in mild steel dislocations are immobilized by atmospheres of carbon and nitrogen. The time delay before enough dislocations are released to cause yielding is much greater than in other metals. Thus the stress can reach much higher values before general yielding begins than in other metals.

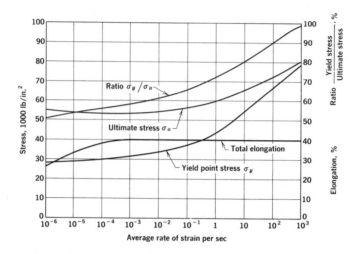

*Fig. 7.10 Influence of rate of strain on tensile properties of mild steel at room temperature. (Reproduced from Manjoine, J. App. Mech., ASME Trans., **66**, A-214 (1944) by permission of the publisher, The American Society of Mechanical Engineers, 29 West 39th Street, New York 18, New York)*

The importance of increased yield strength at higher strain rates is its effect on ductility.   Rate of loading has comparatively little effect on the *cleavage fracture strength* of materials.   The stress required for cleavage between atomic planes depends primarily on the cohesive strength of the material and the characteristic distribution of imperfections in the material (Art. 3.4).   These two factors are not influenced by rate of loading. Hence increasing the rate of loading has the same general effect as increasing the triaxiality of stress: both tend to raise the yield stress while leaving the cleavage fracture stress relatively unchanged.   The result is decreased ductility and a greater tendency to brittle fracture.   Both crystalline and amorphous materials are affected.

There is some evidence that at extremely high strain rates, such as those involved in the impact of projectiles and in explosive forming, the strength

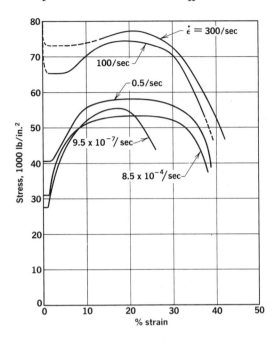

Fig. 7.11 Stress-strain curves of mild steel at room temperature for various rates of strain. (Reproduced from Manjoine, J. App. Mech., ASME Trans., 66, A-215 (1944) by permission of the publisher, The American Society of Mechanical Engineers, 29 West 39th Street, New York 18, New York)

of materials takes a sudden drop. Experiments at rates higher than 10^3 (in./in.)/sec are very difficult to evaluate, however, because the time of loading becomes smaller than the natural period of vibration of the specimen or of the weighing device. Badly distorted observations of load and deformation may result.* The possibility of such a drop in strength, plus the uncertainty in both strain rate and stress involved in impact, precludes the use of any increase in strength in actual engineering design.

THERMAL EFFECTS

7.6 HIGH AND LOW TEMPERATURES

As already pointed out, thermal activation is an important factor in a number of processes involving solid materials. Hence they depend to a great extent on the Arrhenius equation

$$\Phi = Ae^{-\frac{E_a}{kT}}. \tag{2.4}$$

---

* Manjoine, M., and Nadai, A., "High-Speed Tension Tests at Elevated Temperatures," *Proceedings* Am. Soc. Test. Mats. **40**, 831 (1940).

It is clear that changes in temperature have a marked effect on the rates of such processes, such as diffusion (Art. 2.7) and yielding (Art. 7.5). Viscous flow is another such process, in which the viscosity follows roughly the above equation.*

Diffusion—migration of atoms and molecules through the solid—goes on at all temperatures whenever a metastable condition exists. As a result inequalities such as internal stresses, segregation of atoms, and irregular grain sizes tend to be ironed out and a more homogeneous structure produced. The process is much more rapid at high temperatures than at low.

Heat Treatments

Various heat treatments take advantage of this increase in diffusion rate with temperature to produce changes in the material in a relatively short time. When it is suspected that a material contains residual stresses as a result of forming or other treatment, it can be *stress relieved* by heating to a high temperature. The atoms or molecules are given sufficient thermal energy to activate them under the steady action of the stress. As they move to new positions, the stress is gradually reduced. Acrylic plastic parts, for example, are stress relieved at various stages of their manufacture to prevent surface cracking or crazing, which would damage their transparency. A temperature of 150–180°F for half an hour is sufficient. However, the rate of application and removal of heat is very important: the temperature is raised slowly to the final temperature, at which the parts are held for the required time, and then allowed to return slowly to room temperature. Low-carbon steel is stress relieved at 1100–1250°F, the temperature being raised by 200°F or less per hour, held for 1 hour, and lowered by 200°F or less per hour (a total time of at least 12 hours).

When a metal has been heavily deformed, as in cold-rolling or forming, the grains are distorted and broken up, leaving a very inhomogeneous structure which contains high residual stresses. Such a metal can be *recrystallized* by suitable heating. In the process of diffusion, the old grains are replaced by an entirely new network of strain-free grains of more-or-less regular size. The metal is thereby softened, its ductility increased, and its strength lowered. Since the rate at which diffusion progresses depends on the temperature (Eq. 2.4), the recrystallization temperature depends to some extent on the time allowed. For ordinary times, such as one hour, it is usually between 35 and 50 per cent of the absolute melting temperature (°K or °R, Art. 2.7).

Recrystallization and stress relief are part of the general process of

---

* Goldman, J. E., Ed., *The Science of Engineering Materials*, John Wiley & Sons, Inc., New York, 1957, p. 475.

annealing. If the metal is held at a high temperature after recrystallization is complete, the new crystals continue to grow. The larger crystals gradually take over the smaller ones and in time may become larger than the original grains. As a result the metal becomes still softer and weaker.

Mechanical Properties

The immediate effect on materials of changes in temperature is reflected in their mechanical properties, such as yield strength, viscous flow, and ultimate strength (since plastic yielding is involved). Figure 7.12 shows the variation of strength with temperature for several materials and illustrates the downward trend of both yield stress and ultimate stress with increasing temperature. Occasionally a curve of this kind will show a positive slope for a short interval, followed by a maximum at some temperature. Such behavior is usually associated with structural changes within the material, such as polymorphic transformations.

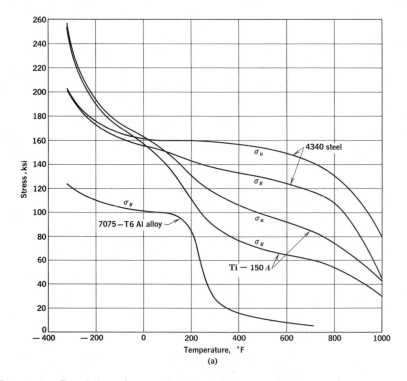

Fig. 7.12 Strengths of several materials as a function of temperature. Curves in (a) reproduced by permission from Wright Air Development Center report TR 55-150, Part 7, 1957 (4340 steel); Alcoa Structural Handbook, published by the Aluminum Company of America, Pittsburgh, Pa., in 1958, p. 79 (7075-T6 aluminum alloy); and Air Force Technical Report 4662, Part 4 (Titanium 150-A).

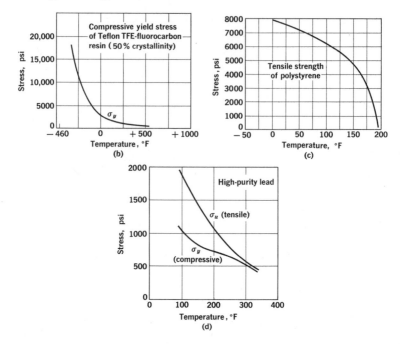

Fig. 7.12 (cont'd) Part (b) is from DuPont literature. Part (c) is reproduced by permission from Technical Data on Plastics, *published 1952 by the* Manufacturing Chemists Association, Inc., Washington, D.C. *Part (d) is reproduced by permission from* Wright Air Development Center report TR 57-695, 1958.

The stiffness of most materials also decreases with increasing temperature, partly because of the increase in certain elastic aftereffects at higher temperatures, which cause increased relaxation and an apparent decrease in stiffness. Figure 7.13 shows the variation of E with temperature for a few materials.

Variations in temperature are often divided into two classifications: *elevated temperatures*—above room temperature, and *low temperatures*—below room temperature. This is an important classification since room temperature is the basis for human living environment and is therefore the most easily controlled temperature for experimental purposes. It can, however, be misleading; there are other critical temperatures so far as materials are concerned, and they may be high or low compared with room temperature. The really important range of temperature is that through which the material is a solid. The lower limit is, of course, always absolute zero; the upper limit is the melting point for metals and ceramics, and the melting or disintegration points for polymers, wood, and similar materials. This upper limit is the principal critical temperature. Other critical temperatures include those for recrystallization in metals, softening and flow

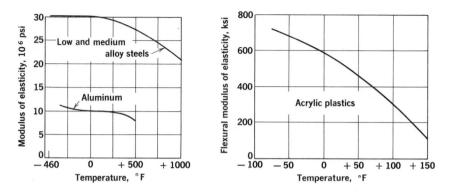

Fig. 7.13 Stiffness of several materials as a function of temperature. (Adapted from data furnished in Technical Data on Plastics, *published by the Manufacturing Chemists Association, Washington, D. C., in 1957,* Alcoa Structural Handbook, *published by the Aluminum Company of America, Pittsburgh, Pa., in 1958, and Wright Air Development Center reports TR55-150 and 58-386)*

in thermoplastics, ductile-brittle transition in metals, and the fictive temperature* in glass. These temperatures mark the dividing lines between ranges in which materials behave in certain characteristic ways.

The classification *elevated temperature* actually covers a wide variety of temperature ranges. In metals, high-temperature behavior may be said to begin at the recrystallization temperature, which is roughly 35 to 50 per cent of the absolute melting temperature. (In low-melting alloys this temperature may be considerably less than room temperature.) It is in this range that creep becomes important (see Chapter 8). There is also an upper limit on the temperature that should be allowed for various applications; it may range from 50 to 80 per cent of the absolute melting point.†

Materials whose melting points are very high relative to room temperature are called *refractories*. They may be either metallic or nonmetallic (ceramic materials), though they are usually the latter. The dividing line between refractories and other materials is rather vague; ASTM defines refractories only as "materials . . . used to withstand high temperatures." Generally speaking, refractories have melting points above 3000°F. Their absolute maximum service temperatures may be as high as 90 per cent of their absolute melting temperatures. In refractories the elevated temperature range may start at temperatures higher than the melting points of other materials.

---

* Goldman, J. E., Ed., *The Science of Engineering Materials*, John Wiley & Sons, Inc., New York, 1957, p. 503.

† Jahnke, L. P. and Frank, R. G., "High-Temperature Metallurgy Today," *Metal Prog.* **74**, No. 5, 79 (1958).

The melting or distintegration points of polymers are quite low relative to those of most other materials. High-temperature behavior may be said to start at the *softening point* for thermoplastics. At temperatures below the softening point the material is hard, or "rigid," and its elastic behavior is similar to that of thermosetting polymers and metals. At temperatures above the softening point the molecules begin to uncoil during deformation, and the material becomes soft rather than rigid, exhibiting large transient elastic strains. The applications of a polymer depend largely on its softening temperature relative to the temperature of its surroundings. The *flow temperature* is that above which viscous flow (Art. 7.3) predominates, and determines the requirements for molding the plastic. Maximum service temperatures are based on these considerations among others.

Table 7.1 gives melting points and maximum recommended service temperatures of a few reference materials ranging from refractories to polymers and low-melting metals.

Table 7.1   Maximum Service Temperatures of Several Materials, Compared with Their Melting Points

MATERIAL	MELTING POINT, T_M, °F	MAXIMUM SERVICE TEMPERATURE, T_S, °F	PER CENT ABSOLUTE MELTING POINT[a]
Refractories			
Zirconia (ZrO_2)	4710	4530	96
Alumina ceramics (95%)	3686	3000	83
Tungsten	6170	2550	45
Molybdenum	4760	2650	59
Metals and Alloys			
Titanium	3100	1200	46
Steel (austenitic)	2800	1600	63
Aluminum	1220	550	60
Lead	620	—	—
Plastics			
Nylon	455	290	83
Acrylics	300	170	83

[a] $\dfrac{T_S + 460}{T_M + 460} \times 100.$

Low-temperature behavior is usually defined on the basis of transition from ductile to brittle behavior. It will be discussed in detail later, when it will be shown that not all materials are affected by this phenomenon. The transition temperature may range from near absolute zero to well above room temperature.

Porous materials exhibit a special low-temperature effect: freezing and thawing. Concrete, for example, almost always contains water in its pores, and at temperatures below 32°F the water is transformed to ice, which has a larger volume. This swelling within the pores causes deformations in the concrete and small amounts of cracking. Repeated thawing and freezing has a weakening effect on concrete. Brick is also subject to damage from freezing and thawing.

The effect of changes in temperature on the *cleavage fracture strength* of materials is also related to thermal activation energy. Under an applied normal stress the bonds in the vicinity of imperfections are highly stressed and are the first to break. Fluctuation of thermal energy in the material may cause some of these highly stressed bonds to break prematurely and set off a cleavage fracture. From the Arrhenius equation it follows that cleavage becomes easier with increased temperature. Here, however, propagation of the cleavage crack is largely controlled by the stress concentrations at imperfections, whereas the motion of dislocations in slip is entirely an atomic phenomenon and much more closely related to thermal energy. The result is that the cleavage fracture stress decreases by only a relatively small amount with increasing temperature.

DUCTILE AND BRITTLE STATES

7.7 DUCTILE-BRITTLE TRANSITION

Three main factors have been shown to influence yielding and fracture:

Triaxiality: The yield stress increases with increasing triaxiality; the fracture stress is relatively unaffected (Art. 6.10).

Rate of loading: The yield stress increases with increasing strain rate; the fracture stress is relatively unaffected (Art. 7.5).

Temperature: The yield stress decreases with increasing temperature; the fracture stress also decreases, but by only a small amount.

Figure 7.14 illustrates these statements; from it the basis for transitions from ductile to brittle behavior can be deduced. Consider a material which is loaded at point A, representing a given triaxiality, strain rate, or temperature. As the stress is increased along line AA', the yield stress of the material is encountered first at Y_A. Consequently the material will be in a ductile state, and the final failure will be a ductile one, not governed by the laws of brittle cleavage. The point F_A is never reached. Now consider loading at point B, a higher triaxiality or strain rate, or a lower temperature. Here the stress moves upward along line BB' and encounters the cleavage fracture stress first at F_B. Obviously the point Y_B will never be reached, and the material is in a brittle state. The transition value of triaxiality, strain rate, or temperature is represented by point C. To the right of this transition the material is in a *ductile state* and to the left it is in a *brittle state*. In the neighborhood of C there will usually be some yielding followed by a partially brittle fracture. Thus the transition phenomena occur over a range of values rather than at a single point. The width of the range depends on the material.

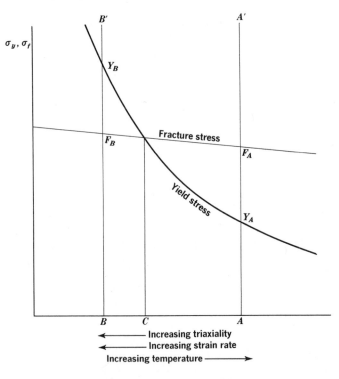

Fig. 7.14 Generalized variation of yield stress and fracture stress with various factors.

This discussion deals with general principles only and does not attempt to go into all the details that must be considered to give the complete picture. Figure 7.14 is not drawn to any particular scale, but simply indicates yield and fracture stress variations *qualitatively*. A completely brittle material may be thought of as having its yield stress curve so high that it does not intersect the fracture curve at all, except possibly at temperatures near its melting point. Other materials will be in a ductile or brittle state, depending on the considerations outlined above.

Evidence has already been given that ductile materials tend to become brittle as *triaxiality* increases (Arts. 6.9–6.11). Impact loadings of unnotched members provide evidence of a transition *strain rate*, above which ductile materials become brittle.   Low-temperature tests on unnotched specimens under static loading bear out the existence of a transition *temperature*.*   Any one of these three factors alone must usually be either extremely high or extremely low to bring about a transition in behavior. Some materials, however, are unusually sensitive to one or more, and moderate values are sufficient (Art. 7.9).

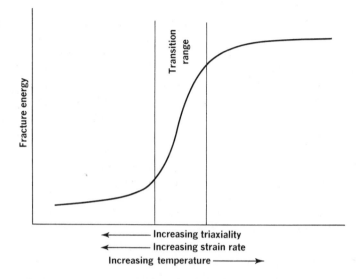

Fig. 7.15   Generalized transition curve for ductile-brittle transition.

The transition phenomenon can also be illustrated by the curve of Fig. 7.15.   The energy that must be put into a material to fracture it is given by the area under the stress-strain diagram (toughness; Art. 3.12).   It follows that brittle materials require far less energy for fracture than ductile materials of approximately the same strength.   The transition from ductile to brittle behavior is therefore accompanied by a drop in fracture energy. Figure 7.15 shows the variation of fracture energy with the three variables of Fig. 7.14.

* Parker, Earl R., *Brittle Behavior of Engineering Structures*, John Wiley & Sons, Inc., New York, 1957, p. 38; Eldin, A. S., and Collins, S. C., "Fracture and Yield Stress of 1020 Steel at Low Temperatures," *J. App. Phys.* **22**, 1296–7 (1951).

7.8 NOTCH EFFECT

The behavior of a member containing a notch involves all the factors discussed in Art. 7.7, together with stress concentration (Art. 6.11).

The part played by stress concentration is to raise the stress at the root of the notch and provide the large stress necessary to produce fracture. It also provides a high local strain rate, which raises the yield stress of the material at this point. If K_t is the theoretical elastic stress concentration factor and σ_{av} is the average stress at the section containing the notch, the maximum stress in the elastic range is $\sigma_{max} = K_t \sigma_{av}$. It follows that $\epsilon_{max} = K_t \epsilon_{av}$; differentiating this expression we find $\dot{\epsilon}_{max} = K_t \dot{\epsilon}_{av}$ and show that the local strain rate at the root of the notch is multiplied by the same concentration factor as the stress. If, for example, a member is elongated at a rate of 100 (in./in.)/sec and contains a notch for which $K_t = 5$, the local strain rate will reach 500 (in./in.)/sec. The yield stress may be raised to as much as 3 times its static value in some materials.

The triaxiality of stress at the notch root also raises the yield stress, although by only a small factor in the elastic range (probably less than 2).

If, in addition to these effects, the temperature is sufficiently low, the yield stress may become greater than the fracture stress and a perfectly brittle cleavage fracture result, with no measurable plastic deformation. Such a fracture is typical of members having sharp cracks, tested under impact loading at low temperatures.

Notch effect, however, has a more important aspect. It often produces brittle fractures under ordinary temperatures and under static loading with moderate stress-raisers. The combined effect of strain rate, triaxiality, and temperature may not be sufficient to increase the yield stress above the cleavage fracture stress with the result that *yielding takes place* at the root of the notch. After yielding begins, plastic constraint takes the place of elastic constraint and may raise the yield stress by a factor of as much as 3. However, large amounts of local yielding are necessary to produce this high value. During this initial yielding plastic constraint is materially augmented by strain-hardening. If the combined effect raises the yield stress above the fracture stress, a crack will form in the yielded material. The immediate result of crack formation is a sharp local increase in strain rate, which further increases the yield stress, and brittle fracture continues with a crack running through the material at a high rate. The controlling factor in producing brittle fracture is now the strain rate, which can become extremely high at the tip of a fast-moving crack.*

Notch effect thus presents a varied pattern of behavior, in which tri-

---

* Felbeck, D. K., and Orowan, E., "Experiments on Brittle Fracture of Steel Plates," *Welding Journal Research Supplement*, November 1955, p. 5.

axiality, strain rate, and temperature all play roles whose relative importance varies with the material and also changes during fracture.

7.9 NOTCH SENSITIVITY

The tendency of some normally ductile materials to behave in a brittle manner in the presence of notches is called *notch sensitivity*. This property depends on the response of the material to changes in strain rate, triaxiality, and temperature. Some materials, notably carbon steels and plastics, are highly notch-sensitive; others, like the face-centered cubic metals, are not. Materials that are normally brittle are usually not considered notch-sensitive, although their strength is seriously impaired by the stress concentration at a notch.

The effect of notch sensitivity can be visualized in terms of the ductile-brittle transition curve of Fig. 7.15. A curve of this kind can be used to evaluate the notch sensitivity of a given material. Most commonly used is the curve of *fracture energy* vs *temperature* because fracture energy is easily measured and temperature is easily controlled. In contrast, no method has been devised for controlling the variation of triaxiality, and control of high strain rates is far from simple. Experiments with these two variables are therefore still limited to specialized research.

The fracture energy-vs-temperature transition curve is obtained from the *notched-bar impact test* (Art. 7.11). In this test the triaxiality is fixed at an arbitrary high value, which is held constant by using a standard notch in all specimens. The strain rate is held at some high value by using impact or high-velocity loading. The high overall strain rate, when multiplied by the stress concentration factor of the notch, produces local strain rates of the order of 1000 (in./in.)/sec at the root of the notch. Brittle fracture is thus encouraged, and a definite value of fracture energy is assured.

Fracture energy is measured in foot-pounds and is called the *impact value*. It is also a measure of *toughness* in accordance with the definition (Art. 3.12) as the overall capacity of a material to absorb energy. However, it will in general differ from the *static* toughness in simple tension because of the difference in the static and dynamic stress-strain diagrams and the effect of the notch.

Notch sensitivity is measured partly by the sharpness of the transition in the fracture energy-vs-temperature curve. The sharper the transition, the more notch-sensitive the material. If no transition appears, the material is not notch-sensitive.

Another important factor is the location of the transition range. A material that has a transition near the operating temperature is naturally

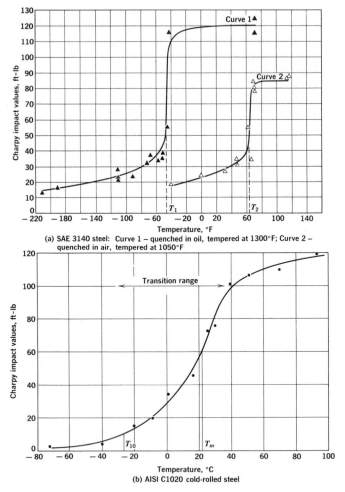

(a) SAE 3140 steel: Curve 1 – quenched in oil, tempered at 1300°F; Curve 2 – quenched in air, tempered at 1050°F

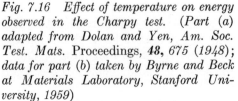

(b) AISI C1020 cold-rolled steel

Fig. 7.16 Effect of temperature on energy observed in the Charpy test. (Part (a) adapted from Dolan and Yen, Am. Soc. Test. Mats. Proceedings, 48, 675 (1948); data for part (b) taken by Byrne and Beck at Materials Laboratory, Stanford University, 1959)

more notch-sensitive at that temperature than one in which the transition is far removed from the operating temperature. It may also be found that whereas no transition is observed within the range of temperatures tested, there is one above or below that range.

Still another factor is the actual fracture energy. A brittle material, for example, may have no transition but will be uniformly low in impact value or notch toughness. A face-centered cubic metal, on the other hand, may have a uniformly high notch toughness. If a transition appears, but the drop in impact value is relatively small, the notch sensitivity is correspondingly small.

The ductile-brittle transition is defined by either a range of temperatures or a single *transition temperature*. In Fig. 7.16a the transition is so abrupt that a single temperature, T, defines it. The more gradual transition in Fig. 7.16b can be specified by a range or a single arbitrarily defined temperature. For example, T_{10} is the temperature corresponding to the 10-ft-lb impact value; T_m is that at the midpoint between the high and low energy values.

A variety of other criteria have been used to define ductile-brittle transition. For example, the per cent *shear* appearing in the fracture surface, or the lateral *contraction* at the root of the notch, have been used in place of the fracture energy. Tests of different types have also been widely used: explosive bulge tests designed to produce brittle fracture; or slow-bend tests with very sharp notches. Unfortunately no correlation is possible between the transition temperatures found by all these different methods. There is even some disagreement between the results of the two standard tests, Charpy and Izod (Art. 7.11). Finally there is no direct correlation between the results of the standard tests and performance in service. For these reasons no quantitative measures of notch sensitivity can be obtained. It will be observed that all the measures that have been given are only *relative*.

The high notch sensitivity of low-carbon steel can be traced directly to its unusually large response to changes in strain rate. As brought out in Art. 7.5, this large response has the same cause as its discontinuous yielding. Whereas materials like copper and aluminum, which yield continuously, can have their yield stresses increased by only 20 or 30 per cent, steel can have its yield stress raised by 300 per cent. The composition, manufacture, and treatment of steel all have important effects on its notch sensitivity. Alloying elements such as nickel improve notch toughness and lower the transition temperature; likewise more complete deoxidation during manufacture. Treatments that produce finer grain structure also have the same beneficial effect.

Generally speaking body-centered cubic metals are most notch-sensitive, while those having face-centered cubic structures are least notch-sensitive. The complete reason for this difference is not clear, but this factor is often utilized in designing for conditions under which notch brittleness is likely to be a problem.

Most plastics are notch-sensitive in varying degrees because of the marked effect of strain rate on their properties (Art. 7.3).

The impact value from the notched-bar impact test is used, without variation in temperature, as a comparison test. If, for example, a certain type of steel has been found to have good notch toughness in service and its impact value is known, other similar steels can be assumed to have good notch toughness if they have the same impact value. This criterion is often used as an acceptance test; the material is accepted or rejected on the basis of its impact value along with other properties.

EXPERIMENTAL METHODS

7.10   GENERAL

In the investigation of dynamic and thermal effects the principal variables that must be controlled are rate of loading and temperature.

Rate of Loading

It is often necessary to control rate of loading in conventional static testing because of the sensitivity of certain materials to it. Testing machines are sometimes equipped with electronic controls which automatically hold constant either the loading rate ($\dot{P}$), rate of crosshead motion, or strain rate, $\dot{\epsilon}$ (Art. 3.17). Sometimes a "pacing" device is attached to the machine to provide a constant rate which can be followed by the operator in controlling the machine. An example is the pacing disk, which can be set to various constant rates of loading ($\dot{P}$); the operator adjusts the controls until the load-indicating hand keeps pace with the disk. In the absence of such controls a stop watch may be used to time the motion of the indicating hand on the strainometer or the loading dial. Some skill is required, but it can be done within the usual limits of accuracy specified in the ASTM *Standards*.

For dynamic experiments in which rates higher than say 0.1 (in./in.)/sec are required, special equipment is needed. A great variety of such machines have been built, and only one general type will be described here. In this type the load is applied to the stationary specimen by a rapidly moving mass, such as a rotating flywheel or a swinging pendulum. A heavy mass is used so that the energy delivered to the specimen will be a small fraction of the kinetic energy of the moving mass. If this fraction is sufficiently small, the moving mass will retain most of its velocity during the deformation, which will, as a result, take place at a nearly constant strain rate. This same principle of operation characterizes all the various flywheel machines used to measure the behavior of materials at different strain rates.*

Figure 7.17 illustrates a rotating-flywheel machine such as that used by M. Manjoine and A. Nadai.† In this machine the specimen is held in

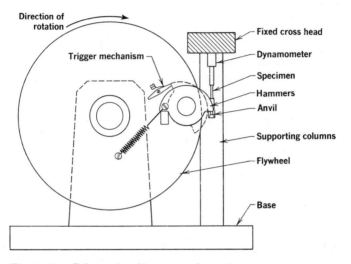

Fig. 7.17 Schematic diagram of a flywheel machine for tension tests at high strain rates. (Adapted from Manjoine and Nadai, Am. Soc. Test. Mats. Proceedings **40,** *827 (1940))*

a vertical position, supported at its upper end by a dynamometer for measuring the load during the test. On its lower end is an anvil in the form of a yoke or inverted T. The hammers mounted on each side of the flywheel can be moved from a retracted position (dotted lines) to a position in which they strike the ends of the inverted-T anvil. They are in the

---

* Mann, H. C., "High-Velocity Tension-Impact Tests," *Proceedings* Am. Soc. Test. Mats. **36,** 85–109 (1936); Manjoine, M., and Nadai, A., "High-Speed Tension Tests at Elevated Temperatures," *Proceedings* Am. Soc. Test. Mats. **40,** 822–839 (1940); Duwez, P. E., and Clark, D. S., "An Experimental Study of the Propagation of Plastic Deformation under Conditions of Longitudinal Impact," *Proceedings* Am. Soc. Test. Mats. **47,** 502–532 (1947); Work, Clyde E., and Dolan, Thomas J., *The Influence of Temperature and Rate of Strain on the Properties of Metals in Torsion,* University of Illinois Bulletin, Vol. 51, No. 24, November 1953, University of Illinois, Urbana, Illinois.

† Manjoine, M., and Nadai, A., "High-Speed Tension Tests at Elevated Temperatures," *Proceedings* Am. Soc. Test. Mats. **40,** 822 (1940).

retracted position while the flywheel is brought up to speed, and through an externally controlled trigger mechanism they are snapped into the striking position.   Striking speeds as great as 1000 in./sec are used.   For specimens having 1-in. gage lengths this top speed corresponds to a strain rate of 1000 (in./in.)/sec.

The dynamometer can be any sort of elastic load-measuring device: for example, a rod equipped with electric resistance-wire strain gages calibrated to read in terms of load.   One problem is keeping the natural period of oscillations of the dynamometer small enough.   If, for example, this period is 0.0005 sec and the test lasts 0.0005 sec, the single natural oscillation that will occur can seriously distort the values of the observed load.   The dynamometer must be as stiff and lightweight as possible to keep the natural frequency high.

Strain can be measured either by recording the distance moved by the lower end of the specimen or by electric resistance-wire strain gages attached to the reduced section of the specimen.

A number of variations have been used in other flywheel machines. The Mann, or Watertown, machine also uses a retractable hammer on the flywheel, but the specimen is supported on a heavy pendulum which is deflected through an angle when the specimen is broken, thus indicating the energy of fracture.   With this machine velocities as high as 1000 ft/sec (12,000 (in./in.)/sec in a 1-in. specimen) have been reached.   A machine used at the California Institute of Technology utilizes fixed hammers on the flywheel and a movable yoke which can be quickly inserted between the hammers and the head of the specimen as the flywheel rotates.

The pendulum machine is much more restricted in its capacity than the flywheel machine.   The pendulum swings freely under its own weight and consequently is limited in its velocity by the height from which it can fall. In the standard machine the maximum striking velocity is 17 ft/sec.   For a 1-in. tension specimen this corresponds to a strain rate of 204 (in./in.)/sec. While it is, of course, possible to obtain higher velocities by constructing larger machines, it is more practical to go to a flywheel machine.

The principal application of the pendulum machine is in the standard notched-bar impact test.   In this test the exact speed with which the specimen is deformed is not particularly important.   The test is usually made at one of two standard striking velocities.   During breaking of the specimen the velocity of deformation may decrease by a large percentage. Consequently this machine is not well-adapted to experiments in which speed of loading is the important variable, although with some modifications it may be used in a limited way.   The standard pendulum machine will be described in Art. 7.11.

Temperature

Control of temperature in the laboratory naturally involves two distinct ranges: that above room temperature, commonly called the elevated-temperature range; and that below room temperature, the low-temperature range.

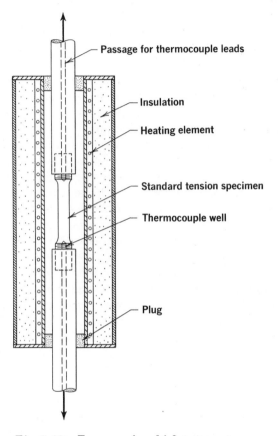

Fig. 7.18   Furnace for high-temperature tension tests.

To provide elevated temperatures various heating devices are used. High-temperature cabinets or furnaces are used for both short- and long-time tests. They are commonly of tubular form to fit over specimens in universal testing machines, fatigue machines, and others (Fig. 7.18). They are lined with refractory insulating materials and heated by conventional electrical-resistance heating elements. Temperatures as high as 2000°F are more-or-less standard, but higher temperatures are available.

The inside dimensions of the furnace must be as small as possible, leaving just enough room for the shackles and extensometer,* perhaps $2\frac{1}{2}$ inches in diameter. Means must be provided to equalize the temperature over the length of the specimen; one way is to divide the heating element into segments which can be controlled individually. Temperature uniformity should be maintained within at least $\pm5°$F and may be held to closer limits (perhaps 1 or 2°F).* A control panel is used to hold the temperature nearly constant during the test. Thermocouples measure the temperature, through suitable potentiometers or millivoltmeter equipment, and transmit the information to the control panel.

Other devices for heating specimens to high temperatures include induction coils surrounding the specimen, radiant heaters, and resistance heaters. Radiant heating units can be assembled around a specimen and produce temperatures as high as 3000°F with good uniformity. Testing times must often be limited to less than one minute because of damage to heating lamps by longer operation. Radiant heaters are especially useful in studying thermal stresses in structures. Resistance heating utilizes the resistance of the specimen itself to produce the heat. Large amounts of current are required, as in radiant heaters, and special shackles must be used in both cases.

Specimens for short-time elevated temperature tests of metals are similar to those for the standard tension test except that the ends are somewhat elongated and each contains a thermocouple well.* Shackles must be carefully made to minimize eccentricity and withstand the high temperatures. Long rods or cables are used to carry the load from the testing machine heads to the specimen inside the furnace. They also aid in reducing eccentricity through their great bending flexibility.

Extensometers in tension tests are usually equipped with long extension arms which are attached to the specimen and transmit its elongation outside the furnace, where it is measured by some conventional means. Thus only the arms and attachments on the specimen are exposed to the heat of the furnace. Extensometers of this type can be made sensitive to 0.0001 in./in. of strain. For tests where this accuracy is not essential the extensometer can be made to measure the displacement between the shackles, which project from the furnace. This method is usually satisfactory for determining yield stress but not modulus of elasticity.

Procedure in short-time elevated-temperature tests is much the same as in room-temperature tests except for the time needed for reaching thermal equilibrium (at least 1 hour) before the test is begun* (Art. 3.17).

A distinctly different type of high-temperature test is that for measuring

---

* ASTM E21.

the flow properties of thermoplastic molding materials.* A standard sample, in the form of a small cylinder, is heated by steam and extruded by a standard force through a standard orifice. The flow temperature is prescribed as that at which the material is extruded exactly 1.0 inch through the orifice. The test is primarily useful for control and identification purposes and not for determining actual physical properties.

Low-temperature experiments are often carried out in specially constructed controlled-temperature cabinets, which either fit around the specimen in the machine or enclose the entire machine. The cabinet is thoroughly insulated and cooled by dry ice (CO_2) and forced-air circulation. Controlled temperatures as low as that of dry ice, about $-109°F$ ($-78°C$) are possible. Heaters are usually included also, to provide controlled temperatures as high as a few hundred degrees. One such cabinet provides temperatures to $+200°F$. Specifications for cabinets are given in ASTM D1197.

Temperatures may also be lowered by immersing the specimen in a liquid bath at the required temperature. Sometimes a container is used which can fit into the machine and surround the specimen with the coolant during the test. Specially designed equipment is almost always required. Sometimes the specimen is immersed in the coolant for a specified time before the test, removed, and tested quickly before its temperature can change appreciably.

The cooling liquid is usually acetone or alcohol, cooled by dry ice to $-109°F$. A range of temperatures can be obtained by adding separate small quantities of dry ice to reach each desired temperature; the temperature is maintained at the various levels by the insulating qualities of the container. For temperatures lower than $-109°F$ a variety of liquids may be used, cooled by liquid nitrogen ($-319°F$) or liquid hydrogen ($-423°F$).

Liquid thermometers are available to $-100°F$. Thermocouples are used to measure lower temperatures.

Time is an important factor in all low-temperature tests. As a rule 15 minutes should be allowed for specimens to come to the temperature of the bath after immersion. When specimens are removed from the bath, experiments show that the temperature begins to rise rapidly after about 5 seconds.

7.11 NOTCHED-BAR IMPACT TESTS

The standard test for notch sensitivity is the *notched-bar impact test*. As pointed out in Art. 7.9, this test is designed to combine into a single

---

* ASTM D569.

standard test the three principal factors involved in notch sensitivity: triaxiality, strain rate, and temperature.   Impact, by itself, is a relatively minor factor.   The notch, on the other hand, is of major importance since it creates both triaxiality and stress concentration and, through the latter, increases the strain rate many fold.   Use of the term *impact testing* for this type of experiment is therefore misleading.   The name *notched-bar impact test* clearly distinguishes it from the simple impact tests to study the effects of high strain rates only.

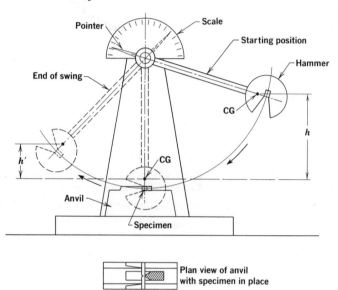

Fig. 7.19   Pendulum impact machine.

The standard notched-bar impact testing machine is of the pendulum type (Fig. 7.19).   The specimen is held in an anvil and is broken by a single blow of the pendulum or hammer, which falls from a fixed starting point.

The pendulum may weigh as much as 50 or 60 lb and is usually lifted to its starting point by hand.   In this position it has a potential energy equal to Wh, where h is the height of the center of gravity above its lowest point. Upon release, and during its downward swing, the energy of the pendulum is transformed from potential to kinetic.   At the bottom of its swing, where it strikes the specimen, its kinetic energy is equal to Wh.   A certain portion of this kinetic energy goes into breaking the specimen.   The remainder carries the pendulum through the lowest point and is then transformed back into potential energy Wh' by the time the pendulum comes to rest. The energy delivered to the specimen is $Wh - Wh'$, the impact value.

The values of h and h' are indicated by a pointer moving on a scale.   The scale is usually calibrated to read directly in ft-lb.

Clearly the initial energy, Wh, must be greater than that required to break the specimen.   For specimens of different toughness, different values of Wh can be obtained by varying both W and h.   Two values of h are usually available on standard machines, determined by the positions of two fixed starting catches.   Two or more weights are also provided to give four or more possible combinations of W and h.   A separate scale must be calibrated for each combination.

The pendulum must be carefully constructed with the striking edge at its center of percussion to minimize vibrations.   If c is the distance from the pivot to the center of gravity, the center of percussion is a distance below the center of gravity equal to i_G^2/c, where i_G is the radius of gyration about the center of gravity.   Since most of the mass of the pendulum is concentrated around the striking edge, i_G is small compared with c and the two points are close to each other (Fig. 7.19).

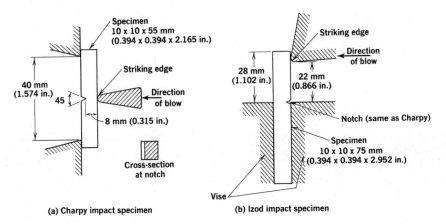

(a) Charpy impact specimen   (b) Izod impact specimen

Fig. 7.20   Standard impact specimens.

The standard specimen is in the form of a *beam*, loaded in bending by the force of impact.   The notch is on the tension side.   Two main types are used: a simply supported beam loaded at the midpoint (Charpy), and a cantilever beam loaded near its end (Izod).   Figure 7.20 gives the dimensions of both types, including the standard notches, and the means of supporting the specimens in the machine.   Certain details of the machine, namely the striking edge and the anvil, must be changed to accommodate the specimen used.   The machine in Fig. 7.19 is arranged for Charpy specimens.   Most machines are constructed so that both types can be used with only minor adjustments.

Perhaps the most important single factor to be controlled is the size and shape of the notch (notch geometry). The standard notch has sides forming a 45° angle and a root rounded to a 0.010-in. radius. Standard milling cutters can be obtained for milling this notch and should be checked frequently for wear. Two other notches are also in common use: the keyhole notch and the U-notch. Exact specifications are to be found in ASTM E23.

The Charpy specimen has two advantages over the Izod. It is easier to place in the machine, an important consideration in low-temperature tests when the test must be performed within a few seconds after removing the specimen from the low-temperature bath. It is also free from compressive stresses around the notch, which are produced in the Izod specimen by the vise; when we consider the complexity of the stress distribution introduced by the notch itself, however, this factor does not seem too important.

Not quite all the energy lost by the pendulum during the impact test goes into fracture; a small amount is lost in friction and air resistance. Corrections can be made when necessary, according to instructions provided in ASTM E23. Other small amounts of energy are lost in vibrations of the testing machine and setting the broken parts of the specimen in motion. These losses are usually neglected.

Step by step, the test consists in (1) checking the machine for alignment, operation of the indicator, friction, and operation of the release mechanism; (2) observing room temperature; (3) setting the pointer to the proper starting point; (4) placing the specimen in the machine; (5) raising the pendulum to its starting point; (6) making certain that everything and everyone is clear of the machine and releasing the pendulum; and (7) observing the impact value on the dial. Detailed instructions are given in the ASTM *Standards* and in manufacturers' booklets.

When the notched-bar impact test is used to compare notch sensitivities of materials, the significant information is simply a tabulation of comparative impact values. If the test is used to detect changes in metallurgy or previous treatment, the impact values are compared with standard acceptance values. In no instance can the impact values be converted into energy figures for use directly in engineering design.

Impact tests at varying temperatures are among the easiest to make because of the rapidity of the test. The simplest procedure is to use an insulated container (for example, a wide-mouthed vacuum jar) and a temperature bath in which the specimens are immersed for about 15 minutes prior to the test. If Charpy specimens are used, it is a matter of only 3 or 4 seconds to remove them from the bath by means of a pair of tongs, place them in position in the machine, and release the pendulum. For safety the entire operation should be done by one man so that there will be no danger of the pendulum being released prematurely. A second man should make sure that the pendulum is not released accidentally while the first is placing the specimen.

An alternative method is to enclose the entire machine in a controlled-temperature cabinet. This eliminates the need for hurrying the test.

The results of controlled-temperature tests are presented in the form of a curve where impact value is the ordinate and temperature the abscissa. If the material being tested has a ductile-brittle transition in the range of temperatures used, the curve will be similar to those in Fig. 7.16.

The notched-bar impact test serves a definite purpose so long as it is used in strictly standardized form.   If different standards are used, results can be compared only with those of other tests using the *same standards*.   Any deviations of individual tests from the standards render those tests worthless.   Finally the student should always remember that the notched-bar impact test does *not* simulate shock loading in service and cannot be correlated with other mechanical tests.

BIBLIOGRAPHY

Freudenthal, Alfred M., *The Inelastic Behavior of Engineering Materials and Structures*, John Wiley & Sons, Inc., New York, 1950, Chs. 3, 4, 5; Zener, Clarence, *Elasticity and Anelasticity of Metals*, The University of Chicago Press, Chicago, Illinois, 1948; Zwikker, C., *Physical Properties of Solid Materials*, Interscience Publishers, Inc., New York, 1954, Ch. VII; Alfrey, Turner, Jr., *Mechanical Behavior of High Polymers*, Vol. VI (Monographs on High Polymers) Interscience Publishers, Inc., New York, 1948.
    For the student who wishes to pursue further the subjects of elastic after-effects, internal friction, viscous flow, and short-time thermal effects.

Parker, Earl R., *Brittle Behavior of Engineering Structures*, John Wiley & Sons, Inc., New York, 1957.
    For a thorough discussion of the brittle failure of ductile materials.

Davis, Harmer E., Troxell, George E., and Wiskocil, Clement T., *The Testing and Inspection of Engineering Materials*, 2nd ed. (McGraw-Hill Civil Engineering Series) McGraw-Hill Book Company, Inc., New York, Toronto, London, 1955, Ch. 7.
    Discusses experimental methods.

PROBLEMS

7.1 A tungsten carbide tension specimen is loaded at the rate of 1000 lb/min
(a) If the specimen is 0.250 in. in diameter, calculate the strain rate, in
(in./in.)/sec $(E = 78 \times 10^6$ psi).   (b) What should be the loading rate in

lb/min for a molded nylon specimen 0.300 in. in diameter ($E = 410{,}000$ psi) to give the same strain rate (assuming linear elasticity)?

7.2   The molded nylon specimen of Problem 7.1 is loaded at the rate of 240,000 lb/min.   What is the strain rate, $\dot{\epsilon}$, in (in./in.)/sec?

7.3   The following data were observed in a tension test of gray cast iron and define an elastic hysteresis loop:

LOADING		UNLOADING	
STRESS, ksi	STRAIN, μin./in.	STRESS, ksi	STRAIN, μin./in.
0	0	12	910
4	200	8	580
8	490	4	265
12	810	0	0
16	1200		

Plot the hysteresis loop and compute the specific damping capacity (areas may be determined by counting squares).

7.4   Plot the data given in Problem 3.10 and compute the specific damping capacity.

7.5   The hysteresis loop for a certain steel at a maximum stress of 25,000 psi is 2μin./in. wide at its midpoint.   Estimate the specific damping capacity of the steel.

7.6   What are the units of the coefficient of viscosity for tension, ϕ, in the English system?

7.7   The following data were observed in a tension test of polyethylene, at a constant stress of 1400 psi:

TIME, sec	ELONGATION, in.	TIME, sec	ELONGATION, in.
90	0.400	356	1.34
170	0.700	480	1.78
262	1.020	540	1.96

(a) The gage length is 2 in.   Convert the elongation to conventional strain and plot.   Determine the coefficient of viscosity for tension, ϕ, assuming that Eq. 7.1b holds.   (b) Approximate this material by a Maxwell model, using $E = 25{,}000$ psi, and determine its relaxation time, τ.

7.8   A tension specimen of nylon is observed to elongate at a steady rate of 1.12×10^{-6} (in./in.)/sec under a stress of 2000 psi.   (a) Assuming that Eq. 7.1b holds, compute the coefficient of viscosity for tension, ϕ.   (b) If this material is represented by a Maxwell model, determine its constants and relaxation time, τ ($E = 374{,}000$ psi).

7.9 Give the approximate temperature, in °F, at which high-temperature behavior may be expected to begin in the following metals:

	MELTING POINT, °F
Columbium	4379
Nickel	2620
Silver	1761
Zinc	756
White metal	475

7.10 Define notch effect.

7.11 Define notch sensitivity.

7.12 Give three possible definitions of a ductile-brittle transition temperature.

7.13 The hammer of a pendulum impact machine weighs 64.2 lb.   The starting height, h, is 43.0 in., and, after breaking the specimen, the pendulum swings to a final height $h' = 35.3$ in.   (a) What is the impact value of the specimen? (b) Compute the striking velocity.   (c) If a tension impact specimen having a reduced section 1.5 in. long is used, what is the strain rate in the specimen, in (in./in.)/sec?   (Neglect all losses.)

7.14 Describe the type of loading used in the Charpy impact test; in the Izod impact test.

7.15 For what purposes are notched-bar impact tests performed?

CHAPTER 8

CREEP

In many applications materials are required to sustain steady loads for long periods of time, e.g., in the blades of a turbine rotor, plastic mountings for parts of electrical devices, timber beams in the roof of a building, filaments in vacuum tubes, steel cables and concrete in a prestressed concrete beam, and lead sheaths on telephone cables. Under such conditions the material may continue to deform until its usefulness is seriously impaired. Such time-dependent deformations may be almost imperceptible, but over the lifetime of a structure they can grow large and even result in final fracture without any increase in load.

Under short-time loading, as in the conventional tension test, there is an initial deformation that increases simultaneously with the load, as shown in the static stress-strain diagram. If, under any conditions, deformation continues when the load is held constant, this *additional deformation* is known as *creep*. ASTM defines creep as "the time-dependent part of the strain resulting from stress." *

Because of its close connection with high temperatures in important applications, creep is usually thought of as an elevated-temperature effect; however, this is true only if elevated temperatures are defined relative to the melting point. Lead and plastics, for example, exhibit significant creep at room temperatures, and in asphalt and tar creep may be found at

---

* ASTM E6.

temperatures far below room temperature. In a few materials, such as concrete and wood, temperature is not an important factor although it may contribute indirectly.*

Recent developments in the analysis of creep are mainly in the field of heat-resistant alloys used in such applications as gas turbines and steam power plants. Since present-day design leads to continually increasing operating temperatures, the situation in this field is critical. Technological advances in this direction depend as much on developments in materials as on any other single factor.

MECHANISMS OF CREEP

8.1 FUNDAMENTAL COMPONENTS

In the study of creep the usual procedure is to apply a *constant stress* or a *constant load* to a member and measure the strain as it varies with time. Figure 8.1 is a creep curve plotted from such observations. The strain

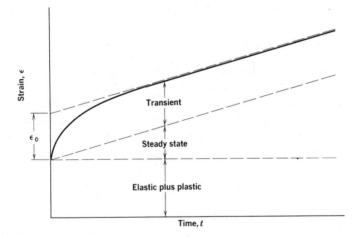

Fig. 8.1   Creep curve, showing basic components.

represented by the ordinates can be associated with three distinct types of mechanism. These components may be visualized by dividing the strain into three parts, as indicated in Fig. 8.1. The first, *elastic strain*—plus plastic strain if the stress is high enough—is the ordinary strain given

---

* Lorman, William R., "The Theory of Concrete Creep," *Proceedings* Am. Soc. Test. Mats. **40**, 1082 (1940).

by the stress-strain diagram and occurs almost instantaneously when the stress is applied.   Thermal expansion may also be included in this component if it is significant.   This component is sometimes omitted from the creep curve.   The other two components—*transient creep strain* and *steady-state creep strain*—make up the total strain traceable to creep.

The principal characteristic of transient creep is its decreasing rate. Deformation is rapid at first but gradually becomes slower and slower as it approaches some fixed value.   Steady-state creep, on the other hand, continues to increase, and under constant stress it does so at a constant rate throughout deformation.   Thus it is identical with viscous flow and is usually referred to as *viscous creep*.

Both components are temperature-dependent through the Arrhenius equation (Eq. 2.4).   However, viscous creep is much more so and is usually insignificant at temperatures lower than 35 to 50 per cent of the absolute melting point of the material (Art. 7.5).   Transient creep is observed at all temperatures, even near absolute zero.   Hence it is sometimes referred to as *cold creep*, and viscous creep as *hot creep*.

Since the two components may be considered as basically different phenomena, they will be discussed separately.

8.2   TRANSIENT CREEP

A number of mechanisms are involved in transient creep; their importance varies with the material and the magnitude of the stress.

The elastic aftereffect (Art. 7.2) always forms a part of transient creep. In crystalline materials it is so small compared with other creep deformations as to be practically insignificant.   In amorphous materials, however, it often contributes a major part, as, for example, the configurational response (uncoiling of molecules) in polymers.   At stresses within the elastic range elastic aftereffect necessarily constitutes almost the entire transient creep for any material.

In crystalline materials another mechanism operates at stresses in the plastic range.   Transient creep consists of small additional amounts of yielding, produced by thermal activation.   Application of stress is accompanied by the initial plastic strain, which ceases as soon as the stress is just balanced by strain-hardening.   Thereafter the impulses of thermal energy continue to cause further small increments of strain.   Each increment, however, causes a further small increase in strain-hardening.   Consequently each increment becomes a little more difficult and further increments less and less frequent.   Thus transient creep gradually approaches a maximum.   This mechanism also operates at stresses in the upper elastic range, where thermal activation can sometimes induce localized yielding at scattered points.

In amorphous materials which do not strain-harden transient creep is entirely an elastic aftereffect phenomenon.

Creep of concrete is a complex process that is not yet fully understood. Under ordinary compressive stresses it consists largely of transient creep; that is, the strain approaches a final value after some period of time. Several mechanisms are involved. The most important seems to be the flow of adsorbed water out of the cement gel as a result of external pressure. Other mechanisms include the closure of internal voids, plastic or viscous flow in the hardened cement paste, and plastic deformation of the aggregates. Creep has been observed at stresses as low as one per cent of the ultimate strength.

8.3 VISCOUS CREEP

Viscous flow is the natural form of inelastic deformation in thermoplastic or amorphous polymers (Art. 3.7). The chain molecules slip past each other, constantly breaking and re-forming their bonds, but there is no strain-hardening. Consequently almost the entire deformation can be classified as creep and is often plotted in the form of a creep curve: strain as a function of time. The amount of this type of deformation varies with temperature and stress. At small stresses and low temperatures it is almost nonexistent, while at temperatures above the flow temperature or for large stresses it becomes very large. Use is made of viscous flow in extrusion and molding operations.

In crystalline materials that strain-harden viscous flow takes place when the strain-hardening effect is just balanced by the softening effect of heat. Each increment of plastic strain is accompanied by an increase in yield stress, which in turn is gradually lowered by thermal softening so that more plastic strain occurs, and the cycle is repeated continuously. The primary mechanism by which deformation takes place is slip, as in normal plastic yielding. Softening occurs largely through an annealing process, in which the atoms of the crystal migrate or diffuse to positions of lower energy, aided by the high thermal energy (Arts. 2.7 and 7.6). One effect of this diffusion is that dislocations are made more mobile and can detour around obstacles, given a little time. Diffusion seems to take place more easily along highly distorted (high-energy) boundaries than through the crystals themselves.[*] Thus a fine-grained metal, which has more such boundaries than a coarse-grained metal, is subject to more diffusion, and consequently more creep at high temperatures.

A secondary process in viscous creep of polycrystalline materials is flow of the grains themselves, as semirigid bodies. It is called *grain-boundary*

---

[*] Parker, Earl R., "Modern Concepts of Flow and Fracture" (1957 Edward de Mille Campbell Memorial Lecture) *Transactions* Am. Soc. Metals **50,** 89 (1958).

shearing and results in rotation of the grains during the creep process. It ordinarily contributes only a small part of the total creep strain,* but is important in fracture produced by creep.

At high temperatures viscous creep occurs at stresses below the short-time yield stress for that temperature, i.e., at stresses which could cause only elastic deformations if applied for short times. This is evidence that yield stress is much more rate-dependent at higher temperatures. The high thermal energy can induce motion of dislocations under lower stresses if given sufficient time.

Viscous creep in such amorphous materials as glass, tar, and sealing wax is like the viscous flow of liquids. In fact, these materials are often thought of as supercooled liquids because of their disordered structure of atoms or small molecules. The mechanism of flow consists of rearrange-

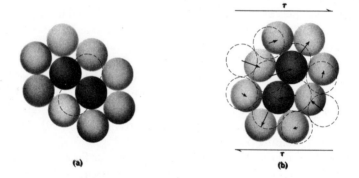

(a)   (b)

*Fig. 8.2   Mobile group of molecules, show-
ing distortion under shear stress. (Ex-
tracted from paper by Orowan, entitled
"Creep in Metallic and Non-metallic
Materials," published in the* Proceedings
of the First U. S. National Congress of
Applied Mechanics, *with permission of
the publisher, The American Society of
Mechanical Engineers)*

ments within many small groups of atoms or molecules. Figure 8.2 shows such a group, which can be distorted simply by movement of the two central molecules, as suggested by Orowan. If these molecules move to the positions shown by the dotted circles in Fig. 8.2a, the entire group will be distorted as in Fig. 8.2b. This distortion amounts to a high local shearing strain. The controlling factors are thermal activation and shear-

---

* Parker, *ibid.*, p. 88.

ing stress. Without stress, thermal activation may be expected to cause random shifts of this kind throughout the material. The net result is zero overall distortion. Under a shearing stress, however, as shown in Fig. 8.2b, the shifts are predominantly in the direction of the shearing stress, and an overall strain results. If the temperature is high enough, the groups continually rearrange themselves, and more mobile groups like that in Fig. 8.2 are constantly formed. Thus strain continues, and the material undergoes viscous flow.

8.4 CREEP FRACTURE

Because of the reduction in cross-section that always accompanies elongation, viscous creep in tension inevitably ends in fracture if allowed to continue long enough. Fracture may, however, take place in several ways.

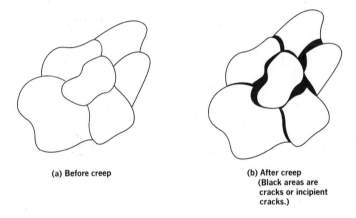

        (a) Before creep   (b) After creep
                                                    (Black areas are
                                                    cracks or incipient
                                                    cracks.)

Fig. 8.3   Grain-boundary shear.

At high stresses and moderate temperatures, involving comparatively short times, fracture is usually the same as in simple tension. If the material is ductile, fracture follows a large plastic elongation and the formation of a neck—a ductile fracture.

At higher temperatures or under longer times ductile metals begin to lose their ability to strain-harden. This behavior is sometimes referred to as *thermal action.** When it occurs, more elongation is required to counteract the effects of thermal softening, and the rate of elongation increases.

---

* Bailey, R. W., "A Critical Examination of Procedures Used in Britain and the United States to Determine Creep Stresses for the Design of Power Plant for Long Life at High Temperatures," *J. App. Mech.* **21**, No. 4, 309 (1954) (Am. Soc. Mech. Engrs. *Transactions* **76** (1954)).

Fracture may then take place following a more nearly uniform elongation, without formation of a neck.   If the elongation is large, the fracture is still ductile.

On the other hand, at high temperatures or after long periods of loading, metals sometimes fracture with very little plastic elongation.   Under these conditions grain-boundary shearing becomes important.   The movement of whole grains relative to each other causes cracks to open between them because of their irregular shape (Fig. 8.3).   When one crack becomes large

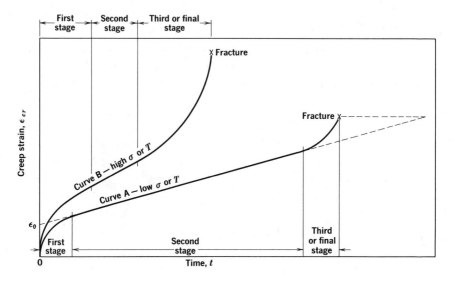

Fig. 8.4   Schematic creep curves, showing the three stages of creep.

enough, or several cracks join to form a larger crack, it spreads slowly across the member until fracture takes place.   At low stresses acting for long times deformation is sometimes almost negligible, and fracture tends to be brittle in character.

Here, then, is still another way in which normally ductile materials may be transformed into a brittle state.   As seen from examples discussed in other chapters, this situation is potentially dangerous.

CREEP PROPERTIES

8.5   ANALYSIS OF CREEP CURVES

The behavior just described is represented by creep curves like those of Fig. 8.4, in which creep strain is plotted against time for constant load and temperature. In this particular illustration the instantaneous strain (elastic and plastic) is omitted so that the strain shown is entirely that resulting from creep.

The total time until fracture is divided into three stages. Division is on a phenomenological basis as contrasted with the division into components on a mechanism basis, as discussed in the preceding articles. The first stage is the time during which most of the transient creep takes place. The strain rate, $\dot{\epsilon}_{cr}$, starts at the initial rate of the elastic and plastic strain, which is comparatively high, but rapidly decreases toward a constant value. This decelerating creep is called *primary creep*. When the transient creep has reached a substantially constant value, the strain continues to increase at a more-or-less constant *creep rate*, $\dot{\epsilon}_{cr}$, under the action of the viscous component. This second stage is called *secondary creep* (Fig. 8.4). In the third stage the creep rate increases again, before final fracture; this portion is called *tertiary creep*.

All three stages do not always appear. If fracture is brittle, without appreciable reduction in cross-section, the third stage may be missing entirely. Curve *B* in Fig. 8.4 represents creep under either a higher stress or a higher temperature than for curve *A*. The second stage is much less important in curve *B*, and for still higher stresses or temperatures it may disappear entirely. If the stress or temperature is low enough, the second stage becomes horizontal (zero viscous creep) and extends indefinitely.

The curves of Fig. 8.4 might be termed "normal" creep curves. High temperatures can also have other effects not ordinarily included in creep effects. In metals these include transformation to different crystal structures (such as the transformation of ferrite to austenite in steel), recrystallization, and grain growth. In plastics, wood, and ceramics, high temperatures may induce chemical changes and even disintegration. These other effects result in distortion of the creep curves from their normal shape.

Creep is more difficult to analyze than other mechanical behavior because it involves prediction of long-time behavior from short-time test results. Creep behavior extends throughout the service life of the member, which is usually measured in thousands of hours. Service lives of 10,000, 100,000,* and even 350,000 hours are not uncommon. The last figure represents the 40-year life of a steam power plant. In investigations of new materials or new conditions (e.g., temperature or stress), on the other hand, much shorter times must be used if the information obtained is to be used in design. Creep tests of this kind are usually limited to 1000 hours (6 weeks) or less. Thus extrapolations to service lives more than ten times the duration of the test are sometimes necessary.

A theoretical understanding is therefore even more desirable in creep

---

* 10,000 hours = 14 months; 100,000 hours = 11.4 years.

than in other types of mechanical behavior. An adequate theory has, however, been very slow in developing, largely because theory must be founded on data from experimental investigations covering the full length of time with which the theory is concerned. It is only recently that such experimental data have become available.

Meanwhile analysis of creep has progressed largely along empirical lines. The limited data available have been used to develop relations between variables simply on the basis of obtaining the best fit to the data. These relations are naturally improved by larger amounts of diversified data. Furthermore, as theory is developed, it is used as a guide in suggesting possible relations to be tried. The study of creep is complicated by the fact that four variables are involved: creep strain, time, stress, and temperature. In this analysis we shall consider the creep-time curve as the primary variation and study the effects of stress and temperature on it. It will be assumed that for the most part there are no structural and chemical changes and the curve has the characteristics of that in Fig. 8.4. Theoretical and empirical relations will be used as needed.

As in other thermal processes, the basic theory is built around the Arrhenius equation (Eq. 2.4),

$$\Phi = Ae^{-\frac{E_a}{kT}},$$

the terms of which are defined in Art. 2.7. Since creep is not a simple thermodynamic rate process, however, this equation cannot be applied without modification. If the rate, Φ, is thought of as the creep rate, $\dot{\epsilon}_{cr}$, it is possible that "constants" A and E_a vary with temperature and stress as well as with other factors. Numerous expressions have been proposed for E_a and A, but none have been completely verified.

Primary Creep

In the first stage the creep rate diminishes from some large value toward a constant value. This decrease is mainly caused by an increase in the activation energy, E_a, required or a decrease in the available atomic mechanisms which can be activated. For a given stress the variation of creep rate with time may be expressed by the empirical equation,

$$\dot{\epsilon}_{cr} = C_1 t^{-n}, \tag{8.1}$$

where C_1 is a constant and n has values between 0 and 1.* For $n = \frac{2}{3}$, this expression can be integrated to give Andrade's law of transient creep,†

---

* Cottrell, A. H., "The Time Laws of Creep," *J. Mech. Phys. Solids* **1**, 53–63 (1952).
  † Andrade, E. M. da C., "The Flow in Metals under Large Constant Stresses," *Proc. Roy. Soc.*, Series A, **90**, 329–342 (1914).

$$\epsilon_{cr} = C_2 t^{\frac{1}{3}}, \tag{8.1a}$$

in which C_2 is another constant. This equation applies to metals as well as some plastics.

Certain materials, such as rubber and glass, appear to follow a logarithmic creep law, corresponding to $n = 1$. Since $\log t$ becomes infinite at $t = 0$, we replace t by $t + t_1$ where t_1 is an arbitrary time, and Eq. 8.1 becomes $\dot{\epsilon}_{cr} = C_1/(t + t_1)$; note that the creep rate at $t = 0$ is C_1/t_1. Integration now gives $\epsilon_{cr} = C_1 \log_e (t + t_1) + C_3$. At $t = 0$, we have $\epsilon_{cr} = 0$, from which $C_3 = -C_1 \log_e t_1$, and the equation becomes

$$\epsilon_{cr} = C_1 \log_e \left(\frac{t}{t_1} + 1 \right)$$

or
$$\tag{8.1b}$$
$$\epsilon_{cr} = \frac{C_1}{M} \log_{10} \left(\frac{t}{t_1} + 1 \right),$$

where $M = \log_{10} e$.

An alternative representation of logarithmic creep is

$$\epsilon_{cr} = K \log t + \epsilon_1 \quad (t > 0), \tag{8.1c}$$

where K is an arbitrary constant and ϵ_1 represents the creep strain at $t = 1$ (unit of time). This equation is obtained by integrating Eq. 8.1 directly, for $n = 1$, and has the disadvantage that the curve representing it does not pass through the origin. However, it has the distinct advantage that its constants are easier to determine from experimental data than those of Eq. 8.1b. If the creep strain is plotted against $\log t$, constants K and ϵ_1 in Eq. 8.1c are found from the slope and intercept, respectively, of the resulting line (Figs. 8.25 and 8.26). Equation 8.1b cannot be plotted as a straight line unless the value of t_1 is known.

For $n = 0$, we have the limiting case of viscous creep at a constant rate, which will be discussed separately.

Timoshenko uses a different empirical expression for transient creep rate,*

$$\dot{\epsilon}_{cr} = C_4 e^{-\alpha t}, \tag{8.2}$$

in which C_4 and α are constants. From this equation we have, by integration,

$$\epsilon_{cr} = C_5(1 - e^{-\alpha t}) \tag{8.2a}$$

(for the starting condition $\epsilon_{cr} = 0$ when $t = 0$).

Concrete creep is represented either by a logarithmic law like Eq. 8.1b or a hyperbolic law†

---

* Timoshenko, S., *Strength of Materials—Part II—Advanced Theory and Problems*, 3rd ed., D. Van Nostrand Company, Inc., Princeton, New Jersey, 1956, p. 523.

† Lorman, William R., "The Theory of Concrete Creep," *Proceedings* Am. Soc. Test. Mats. **40**, 1082 (1940).

$$\epsilon_{cr} = \frac{C_6 t}{n + t}. \tag{8.3}$$

Curves representing four of the above equations are shown in Fig. 8.5.

In these equations the values of the constants n, α, C_1, C_2, etc., may be expected to change with stress and temperature. Just how they change is not usually known. As a matter of fact, comparatively little is known

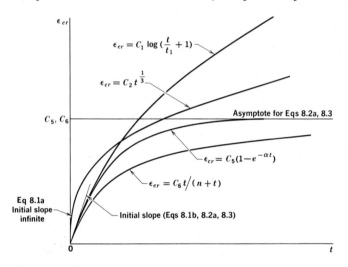

Fig. 8.5 *Comparison of curves representing Eqs. 8.1a, 8.1b, 8.2a, and 8.3 for transient creep.*

about transient creep. It has not been studied as extensively as viscous creep because it is not ordinarily a critical factor in design. A problem in which transient creep is of considerable importance is *stress relaxation* (Art. 8.8).

Secondary Creep

By the end of the first stage the transient creep rate is practically zero and creep becomes almost entirely viscous. If we assume that transient creep is actually complete, the equation of the second stage becomes

$$\epsilon_{cr} = \epsilon_0 + v_0 t, \tag{8.4}$$

where ϵ_0 is the creep intercept (Fig. 8.4) and v_0 is the viscous creep rate. Since it is measured by the minimum slope of the creep-time curve, v_0 is called the *minimum creep rate*. It is commonly expressed in units of (in./in.)/hr, or simply (hr)$^{-1}$.

The viscous creep rate can also be expected to be closely related to the Arrhenius equation. The equation

$$v_0 = Ae^{-\frac{E_a}{kT}} \tag{8.5}$$

does provide a fairly good fit to available data relating v_0 and T, especially for pure metals. However, the values used for the "constants" A or E_a or both may depend on stress and other variables, including the temper-

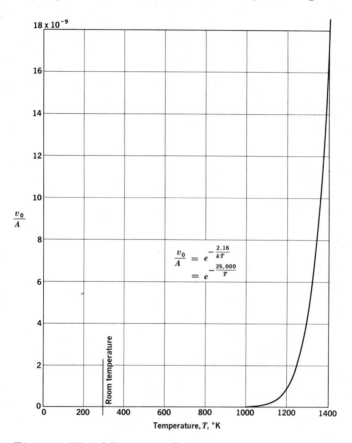

$$\frac{v_0}{A} = e^{-\frac{2.16}{kT}}$$
$$= e^{-\frac{25,000}{T}}$$

Fig. 8.6 Plot of Eq. 8.5 for $E_a = 2.16$ *ev.*

ature. For example, the activation energy, E_a, is frequently found to have two or more distinct values, each of which applies to a certain temperature range. The curve represented by Eq. 8.5 is illustrated in Fig. 8.6.

The minimum creep rate increases with increasing stress. The variation is most commonly expressed by the empirical equation

$$v_0 = B\sigma^n \quad (n > 1), \tag{8.6}$$

where B and n are constants.   Some theoretical support for this equation has developed in a theory proposed by Weertman.[*]   According to this theory, which is based on the mechanism described in Art. 8.3 for metals, the creep rate is given by

$$v_0 = C\sigma^m e^{-\frac{E}{kT}}. \tag{8.7}$$

Where m is a constant.   If we assume that E_a is essentially constant, this equation reduces to Eq. 8.6 for a constant temperature.   Figure 8.7 illustrates the variation represented by Eq. 8.6.

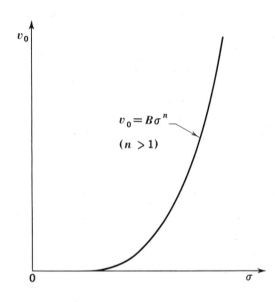

$$v_0 = B\sigma^n$$

$$(n > 1)$$

Fig. 8.7 Variation of creep rate with stress as represented by Eq. 8.6.

The agreement between Eqs. 8.5 and 8.6 and experimental results can be studied by means of suitable logarithmic plots.   The logarithmic forms of the two equations are

$$\log_{10} v_0 = \log_{10} A - M\frac{E_a}{kT}, \tag{8.5a}$$

where $M = \log_{10} e = 0.4343$, and

$$\log_{10} v_0 = \log_{10} B + n \log_{10} \sigma. \tag{8.6a}$$

Thus if $\log_{10} v_0$ is plotted against $1/T$ for constant stress and against $\log_{10} \sigma$ for constant temperature, two straight lines should result.   (Note that T

[*] Parker, Earl R., "Modern Concepts of Flow and Fracture" (1957 Edward de Mille Campbell Memorial Lecture) *Transactions* Am. Soc. Metals **50**, 84 (1958).

is absolute temperature.)   Figures 8.8a and b are two such plots of experimental data, showing the degree of linearity obtained.   Observe that two or more lines are sometimes used to fit the points, suggesting that the constants may have different values in different ranges.

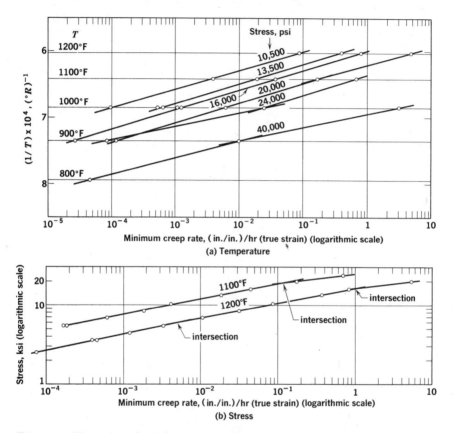

Fig. 8.8   *Variation of minimum creep rate with temperature and stress.   (Creep data from Randall, Am. Soc. Test. Mats. Proceedings **57**, 854–876 (1957))*

The constants for Eqs. 8.5a and 8.6a can be determined by measurements from the graph.   The constant $0.434\, E_a/k$ is given by the average slope in Fig. 8.8a, and constant A is given by the intercept at $1/T = 0$.   Likewise the constant n is given by the average slope in Fig. 8.8b, and B by the intercept at $\sigma = 1$.

The creep intercept, ϵ_0, represents the maximum value of transient strain

(Figs. 8.1 and 8.4). Its value therefore depends on both stress and temperature. Its variation with stress may be taken as

$$\epsilon_0 = D\sigma^m, \tag{8.8}$$

where D and m are constants to be determined experimentally for each temperature, in the same manner as B and n in Eq. 8.6. Figure 8.9 shows

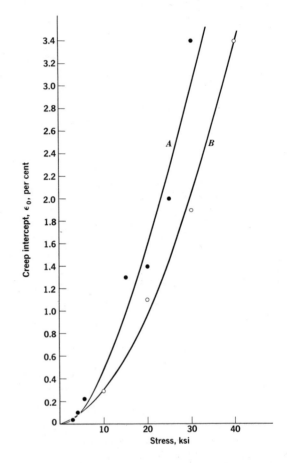

*Fig. 8.9 Variation of ϵ_0 with stress for two ferritic steels (A, 8% Cr; B, 5% Cr). (Adapted from Dulis and Smith, Am. Soc. Test. Mats. Proceedings **53**, 640 (1953))*

the variation of ϵ_0 with stress obtained experimentally.* For very long times and low stresses the transient creep may be negligible compared with total viscous creep, and Eq. 8.4 can be written in the simpler form

$$\epsilon_{cr} = v_0 t. \tag{8.4a}$$

---

*The creep intercept sometimes increases to a maximum at some stress, after which it decreases.

This equation is a satisfactory approximation when the second stage lasts for thousands of hours while the first and third stages last only a few hours, or perhaps only minutes. The minimum creep rate, v_0, becomes the only variable necessary to describe creep behavior.

EXAMPLE 8.1

Determine the activation energy in cal/mole for creep of carbon-silicon steel at 10,500 psi in tension.

Solution: The line labelled 10,500 in Fig. 8.8a represents experimental data obtained for this steel. From it we read the following sets of data:

$$\text{At } T_1 = 1000°F, v_{01} = 1.05 \times 10^{-4} \text{ (in./in.)/hr}$$
$$\text{At } T_2 = 1200°F, v_{02} = 9.4 \times 10^{-2} \text{ (in./in.)/hr.}$$

To obtain E_a in cal/mole we must express T in °K and substitute $R = 1.987$ (cal/°K)/mole for k in Eqs. 8.5 and 8.5a. Thus $T_1 = 810.8$°K and $T_2 = 921.9$°K; by substituting in Eq. 8.5a we obtain the simultaneous equations

$$(0.02119 - 4) = \log_{10} A - (0.0012333)(0.434\, E_a/R)$$
$$(0.97313 - 2) = \log_{10} A - (0.0010847)(0.434\, E_a/R),$$

from which $E_a = 90{,}900$ cal/mole.

From the same equations we can obtain $A = 3.32 \times 10^{20}$. Substituting these constants into Eq. 8.5, we have

$$v_0 = 3.32 \times 10^{20}\, e^{-\frac{45{,}700}{T}},$$

where T is in °K and v_0 is in (in./in.)/hr. Equation 8.5a, a more useful form, becomes

$$\log_{10} v_0 = 20.5207 - 19{,}865/T.$$

Note that to obtain slide-rule accuracy—3 significant figures—in A and E_a it was necessary to use 4 or 5 figures in some steps of the solution.

Tertiary Creep

The third or final stage of creep is when the rate increases just before fracture. There are two principal causes of this increase. If creep takes place under a constant tensile load, the decrease in cross-sectional area makes the true stress increase. Increased stress is accompanied by an increased creep rate (Eq. 8.6). The increase is not usually appreciable until a neck forms, and then the rate increases rapidly, producing tertiary creep. This type of tertiary creep could be entirely prevented by holding the stress constant instead of the load. In principle this is done by decreasing the load in direct proportion to the reduction in area. The result is that the second stage continues right up to fracture, as indicated by the dashed extension of curve *A* in Fig. 8.4.   (Actually this experimental procedure is very difficult.)

The other cause of tertiary creep in metals is *thermal action*, as described in Art. 8.4.   Creep strain accelerates because of a reduction in the ability of a metal to strain-harden.

No particular effort has been made to establish the fundamentals of tertiary creep and to analyze the phenomena using available mathematical techniques.

8.6   CREEP PROPERTIES OF METALS

The most important properties used directly in design for creep are *creep strength* and *creep-rupture strength*.   ASTM defines these as the highest stresses that a material can stand for a specified length of time without excessive deformation, or rupture, respectively.*   The creep strength is also called the *creep limit*.   The creep rupture strength is often referred to as the *stress-rupture strength*, or simply *rupture strength*.   Since these properties vary with temperature, a constant temperature is assumed, and must be specified.   For example, the creep strength required for a steam turbine blade may be that stress which will produce just 0.20 per cent creep in 100,000 hours at 1500°F.

The stress referred to in the foregoing definitions is usually the *initial* stress.   If a *constant load* is involved, in tension, the final true stress will be somewhat greater than this initial stress.   The time of interest in determining the creep or rupture strength is the service life, measured in thousands of hours (also sometimes in years).   The deformation allowed is expressed as total strain—the instantaneous strain plus the creep strain—and is measured in per cent.

The amount of deformation considered excessive depends on the application.   In a jet turbine only a very small strain is permitted because of the close tolerances involved (perhaps 0.01 per cent in 2000 hrs).   In a pressure vessel, on the other hand, 2 per cent creep strain may not be excessive. A plastic aerosol bottle, for example, may creep as much as 4 per cent in one year.

We shall now examine several methods for predicting design stresses for metals.

Two Methods for Predicting Creep Strength

Creep strength is determined experimentally in several ways.   One of the simplest is to test several specimens simultaneously, at the expected

---

* ASTM E6, Sections 49, 50.

operating temperature, but each under a different stress. If the length of time required to produce the *allowable strain* is measured for each specimen, a curve of stress vs time can be plotted (Fig. 8.10).

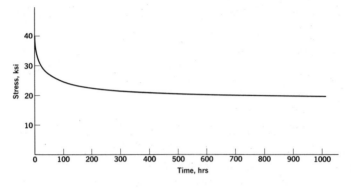

Fig. 8.10   Stress for 1 per cent creep for a stainless steel at 1200°F.

Tests of this kind are usually limited to 1000 hours (occasional tests are carried to 10,000 hours). From the results creep strengths may be tabulated on the basis of a specified amount of creep strain for various temperatures. Table 8.1 lists creep strengths for 1 per cent extension in 1000 hours, at three temperatures, for Type 302 stainless steel; room temperature yield strength is used for comparison.

Table 8.1   Creep Strength of Type 302 Stainless Steel (austenitic)

Yield strength (0.2% offset) (room temp)	40,000 psi
Creep strength (1% extension in 1000 hrs)	
1000°F	18,000 psi
1250°F	4,000 psi
1500°F	1,000 psi

When testing times or available data are limited to 1000 hours, the creep properties used in design for longer times must be based on extrapolation. The obvious thing would be to extend the curve of Fig. 8.10 to the required time. Since it is usually easier to extend a curve if it is linear, an attempt is made to plot the data in such a way that it will be linear or nearly so. For data of this kind it is often found that the points fall near a straight line when log stress is plotted against log time. Figure 8.11 shows a typical family of such curves. It can be seen that linearity is only approximate, and extrapolations should therefore be limited to short times.

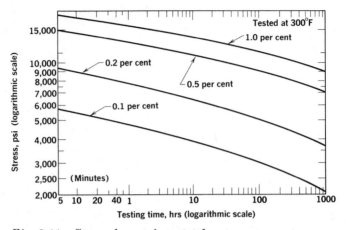

Fig. 8.11   *Stress for various total extensions of ZK51A-T5 magnesium alloy at 300°F. (Adapted from Nelson, Am. Soc. Test. Mats.* Proceedings **54**, 1088 (1954)).

It should be pointed out that the use of a logarithmic time scale in a graph like Fig. 8.11 is apt to be badly misleading.   Extrapolation by only one cycle beyond the test time gives the appearance of being a short extrapolation, whereas it actually extends the time to *ten times the longest*

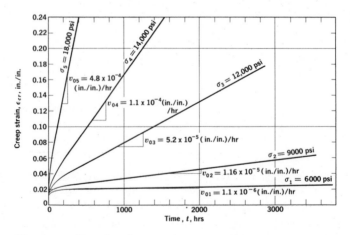

Fig. 8.12   *Family of creep-time curves for a metal like zirconium at five different stresses, all at the same temperature, showing minimum creep rates.*

test time. The effects of thermal action and structural changes in the
material can lead to disastrous errors in such long extrapolations.

Another method which has some foundation in theory is based on the
creep rate and Eq. 8.4a. If Eq. 8.4a is assumed to hold, the allowable
strain, ϵ_1, and the service life, t_1, can be combined to give an allowable minimum creep rate $v_0 = \epsilon_1/t_1$. A curve of v_0 as a function of stress can be
obtained from a series of creep-time tests at the expected operating temperature. Each test is made at a different stress and is continued until
the minimum creep rate appears to be well established. Figure 8.12 shows
a family of creep-time curves for several stresses, at constant temperature.
In each curve the smallest slope is taken as a measure of v_0 and is plotted
against the corresponding stress. To obtain a linear plot Eq. 8.6a is used,
and log σ is plotted against log v_0 as illustrated in Fig. 8.13.

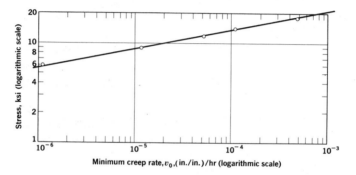

Fig. 8.13   *Variation of minimum creep
rate with stress, from data of Fig. 8.12.*

In using such a curve we divide the total allowable strain, ϵ_1, by the
service life, t_1, as above to give an allowable v_0. Entering the graph with
this value of v_0, we find the *creep strength* as the corresponding stress. If
the service life is shorter than the length of the tests used to construct the
graph, no extrapolation is involved. There is, however, some approximation in that Eq. 8.4a includes neither the instantaneous strain nor the
transient strain, ϵ_0, whereas ϵ_1 includes both. Since neither the instantaneous strain nor the transient strain can be known until the allowable stress
is found, they cannot be subtracted from ϵ_1. Errors from this source are
not serious for times of 1000 hours or more.

Extrapolations to longer times by use of this method are based on the
linearity of the second stage of the creep-time curve. For long times this
linearity may be seriously affected by structural changes in the material

and by thermal action. Consequently such extrapolations should be limited to comparatively short times.*

Predicting Creep-Rupture Strength

The stress required to produce rupture after a given time is found in a manner almost identical to the first method outlined for determining creep strength. Several specimens are tested simultaneously, at the expected

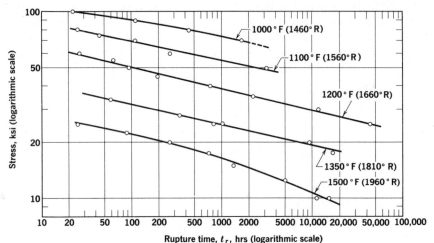

Fig. 8.14   Creep-rupture curves for S590 high-temperature ferrous alloy (20% Cr, 20% Ni, 20% Co).   (Data from Goldhoff, Materials in Design Engineering 49, No. 4, 93–97 (1959))

operating temperature, each under a different stress. The length of time before rupture is noted for each specimen and plotted against the corresponding stress. An approximately linear diagram may be obtained by plotting either σ or log σ against log t. However, long-time test data usually show a definite downward curvature in either type of plot. Figure 8.14 is a log-log plot of creep-rupture data for a high-temperature ferrous alloy (Table 8.2).

---

* It is common practice to assume, on the basis of Eq. 8.4a, that the total strain after $n \times 1000$ hours is n times that after 1000 hours. The method is then extended to any length of time. This practice is justifiable only when low creep rates are involved, and when considerable supplementary information is also available. See ASTM E139, par. 11(c).

Table 8.2   **Creep-Rupture Data for Alloy Steel**
S590ᵃ (20% Cr, 20% Ni, 20% Co)

TEMPERATURE, °F	STRESS, ksi	RUPTURE TIME, t_r, hrs
1000	70	1,677
	80	433
	90	109
	100	22
1100	50	3,149
	60	264
	70	109
	75	44
	80	25
1200	25	43,978
	30	11,937
	35	2,243
	40	756
	45	192
	50	93
	55	63
	60	26
1350	17.5	16,964
	20	9,529
	25	809
	25	1,028
	28	342
	34	59
1500	10	15,335
	10	11,257
	12.5	5,052
	15	1,352
	15	1,356
	17.5	719
	20	267
	22.5	88
	25	25

ᵃ Heat-treated 1 hr at 2275°F, water-quenched, aged 16 hrs at 1400°F, air-cooled; data from Goldhoff, R. M., "Which Method for Extrapolating Stress-Rupture Data?" *Materials in Design Engrg.* **49**, No. 4, 93 (1959).

The creep-rupture strength for a given service life may be found from such a graph by interpolation.   Working stresses are then decided upon by applying a factor of safety, n (Art. 3.12).

If the service life is longer than any of the testing times used to construct the graph, it becomes necessary to extrapolate.   Because of the downward curvature mentioned above, such extrapolations should be limited to comparatively short times.*

EXAMPLE 8.2

Determine a working stress for S590 alloy steel at 1050°F for a service life of 1000 hrs, using Fig. 8.14 and a factor of safety of 2.5.

Solution: From the curves for 1000°F and 1100°F we obtain creep-rupture strengths of 74 and 55 ksi, respectively. If we use a linear interpolation between these values, the creep-rupture strength for 1050°F is 64,500 psi, from which

$$\sigma_w = \frac{64,500}{2.5} = 25,800 \text{ psi.}$$

Parameter Methods

Since none of the three methods described so far has been found to be generally acceptable for extrapolation to long times, it is imperative that new methods be developed for this purpose.

Several new methods have been proposed since 1950. All have in common the central idea that creep can be accelerated by increasing the temperature of testing (Eqs. 8.5 and 8.7). An important advantage is that thermal action is increased. Creep can also be accelerated by increasing the stress, as in the first and third methods described above. Increasing the stress, however, does not affect thermal action. By increasing the temperature, and thereby the rate at which thermal action proceeds, the total thermal action in a short-time test can be brought closer to that occurring during the service life. The result is a more reliable basis for extrapolation.

In the new methods, therefore, the total allowable deformation, or rupture, is enforced within the time of the test by using a temperature higher than the operating temperature. The time required at the higher temperature is then converted to the corresponding time at the operating temperature by means of *time-temperature parameters*, as described below.

The new methods are usually called *parameter methods*. They have been developed on both theoretical and empirical grounds. The theoretical derivations are based on modifications of the Arrhenius equation, and will be discussed first.

Assuming that creep is a process governed by the Arrhenius equation,

---

* By common practice the creep-rupture curves are extrapolated to service lives 10 or more times the length of the test period. This practice can be very dangerous and should be followed only when related supplementary test data are available and with the guidance of a generous amount of experience with creep behavior. See ASTM E139, pars. 11(d) and (e).

as expressed by Eq. 8.5, the *time* required to produce a given strain, or rupture, can be expressed as

$$t = Ge^{\frac{E_a}{kT}}, \tag{8.9}$$

where E_a, k, and T have the same meanings as in Eq. 8.5, and G is a constant related to A. (If the process is creep to rupture, time t becomes t_r.)

Taking common logarithms of both sides of Eq. 8.9, we have

$$\log_{10} t = \log_{10} G + M \frac{E_a}{kT}, \tag{8.9a}$$

where $M = \log_{10} e = 0.4343$. If we assume that E_a and G are functions of the stress only, this equation is linear in $\log_{10} t$ and $1/T$ for any given

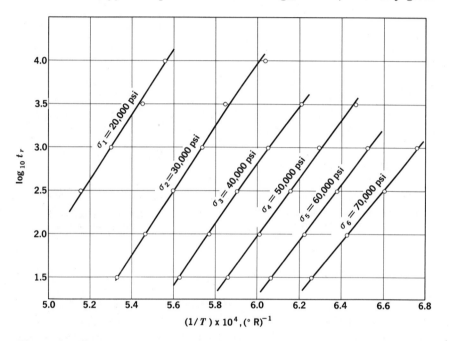

Fig. 8.15   *Curves of constant stress, from Fig. 8.14. (Data from Goldhoff, Materials in Design Engineering* **49**, *No. 4, 93–97 (1959)).*

stress. Figure 8.15 shows the family of curves obtained by plotting $\log_{10} t_r$ against $1/T$ for several different stresses for the high-temperature alloy, S590, derived from the data of Fig. 8.14. The curves are all approximately linear. For any given line, Eq. 8.9a is of the form

$$y = b + mx, \tag{8.9b}$$

where $b = \log_{10} G$ and $m = ME_a/k$. Consequently G is related to the intercept and E_a to the slope of the line. The characteristics of such a family of lines (Fig. 8.15) are therefore determined from the manner in which E_a and G vary with stress. Three possibilities suggest themselves:

If G is constant and only E_a varies with stress, the lines will have a common intercept on the y- or $\log_{10} t$-axis. Figure 8.16a illustrates a family of this type.

If E_a is constant while G varies with stress, a family of parallel lines results, which has a slope equal to ME_a/k. Figure 8.16b illustrates a family of this type.

If both G and E_a vary with stress, the lines may neither be parallel nor converge at a common point.

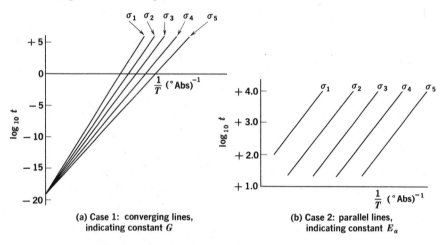

(a) Case 1: converging lines, indicating constant G

(b) Case 2: parallel lines, indicating constant E_a

Fig. 8.16   Constant stress lines of the type shown in Fig. 8.15.

The *Larson-Miller* parameter method[*] is based on the first possibility. By studying large amounts of experimental data for creep rupture, Larson and Miller concluded that the lines representing Eq. 8.9a converge at a common point on the $\log_{10} t$-axis. This evidence indicates that E_a varies with stress while G does not. Consequently $\log_{10} G$ is considered to be constant. If we take $\log_{10} G = -C$ and $ME_a/k = m$ (a function of σ), Eq. 8.9a takes the form

$$\log_{10} t + C = m\left(\frac{1}{T}\right). \tag{8.9c}$$

The value of C can be determined for any material from a plot like Fig.

[*] Larson, F. R., and Miller, James, "A Time-Temperature Relationship for Rupture and Creep Stresses," ASME *Transactions* **74**, 765–771 (1952).

8.16a. For several different high-temperature ferrous alloys C has been found to range between 15 and 30 (for the alloy in Fig. 8.15, $C = 17.5$).

Since m is a function of σ, Eq. 8.9c can be written

$$T \,(\log_{10} t + C) = m, \qquad (8.9d)$$

or

$$P_1 = f_1(\sigma), \qquad (8.10)$$

where $P_1 = T \,(\log_{10} t + C)$ is the Larson-Miller parameter and $m = f_1(\sigma) = ME_a/k$. Thus, if P_1 is evaluated for a variety of pairs of values of t and T and plotted against the corresponding observed stresses, a single curve results for any given material. Such a curve is called a *master curve*, and

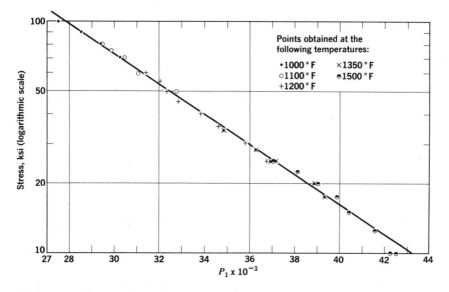

Points obtained at the following temperatures:

• 1000 °F   × 1350 °F
∘ 1100 °F   ● 1500 °F
+ 1200 °F

*Fig. 8.17   Master curve for S590 alloy (Fig. 8.14), based on the Larson-Miller parameter, $P_1 = T(\log_{10} t + 17.5)$. (Data from Goldhoff, Materials in Design Engineering **49**, No. 4, 93–97 (1959))*

is illustrated in Fig. 8.17 for the data from Fig. 8.15. Here C is obtained by extrapolating the lines to the $\log_{10} t$-axis and using their average intercept (Fig. 8.16a).

Parameter P_1 has the same value for an infinite variety of combinations of t and T, ranging from the short times and high temperatures representing test conditions to the longer times and lower temperatures representing service conditions. The part of the master curve that was constructed from test results can therefore be used to obtain design stresses for long service.

As an example, for a service life of 100,000 hours at 1040°F (1500°R) the value of P_1 is $1500(5 + 17.5) = 33,750$. The same value is obtained in a 1000-hour creep-rupture test at 1186°F (1646°R). Obviously the two give the same point on the master curve: 41,000 psi.

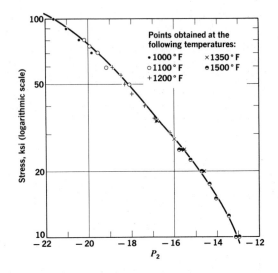

Fig. 8.18 Master curve for S590 alloy (Fig. 8.14), based on the Sherby-Dorn parameter, $P_2 = (log_{10}t - 33,630/T)$. (Data from Goldhoff, Materials in Design Engineering 49, No. 4, 93–97 (1959))

A single average value of C is often used for several different high-temperature alloys. This procedure makes it possible to use the same scale for P_1 for all the master curves so that they can be plotted on the same graph. If the actual value of C for each alloy is close to this average value, such a procedure may be justified by the smaller amount of work involved and the direct comparisons possible between alloys. The most commonly used average value is $C = 20$. It has been demonstrated, however, that considerably more accurate results are obtained when the correct value of C is used for each material.

Another method based on Eq. 8.9 is that originated by Sherby and Dorn.* Experimental evidence obtained by these investigators indicates that E_a is essentially constant for a given material and that G varies with stress. This situation falls into the second category, where the lines representing $\log t$ vs $1/T$ are parallel. If we replace ME_a/k by α, and set $\log_{10} G = \phi$ (a function of σ), Eq. 8.9a can be written

---

*Sherby, Oleg D., and Dorn, John E., "Creep Correlations in Alpha Solid Solutions of Aluminum," *J. Metals*, AIMME, **4**, 959–964 (1952).

$$\log_{10} t - \frac{\alpha}{T} = \phi. \tag{8.9e}$$

This equation states that

$$P_2 = f_2(\sigma), \tag{8.11}$$

where $P_2 = \left(\log_{10} t - \dfrac{\alpha}{T}\right)$ is the parameter and $f_2(\sigma) = \phi$. The constant α, is determined for a given material from the common slope of a plot such as Fig. 8.16b. Figure 8.18 is a master curve representing Eq. 8.11 for the data from Fig. 8.15; the value of α is taken as the average slope of the lines in Fig. 8.15 (33,630).

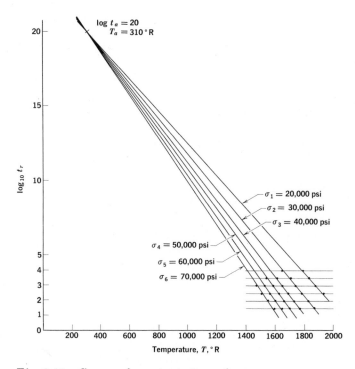

Fig. 8.19 *Curves of constant stress, from Fig. 8.14. (Data from Goldhoff,* Materials in Design Engineering **49***, No. 4, 93–97 (1959))*

If we use the same example as before—a service life of 100,000 hours at 1040°F (1500°R)—$P_2 = -17.42$. For a 1000-hour creep-rupture test the same value can be obtained using $T = 1187$°F (1647°R). The stress taken from the master curve is 41,000 psi, as in the Larson-Miller method.

One promising new method, that of Manson and Haferd,* has been developed on an entirely empirical basis. These investigators observed that plots of $\log_{10} t_r$ vs $1/T$ (Fig. 8.15) are not perfectly linear. They therefore tried other methods of plotting t_r against T and found that $\log_{10} t_r$ vs T gave the greatest linearity. Furthermore, for the same mate-

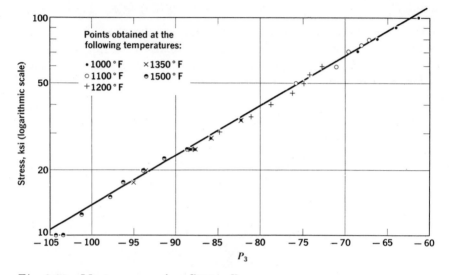

Fig. 8.20   Master curve for S590 alloy (Fig. 8.14), based on the Manson-Haferd linear parameter, $P_3 = (T - 310)/(\log_{10}t_r - 20)$. (Data from Goldhoff, Materials in Design Engineering **49**, No. 4, 93–97 (1959))

rial and different stresses, these lines converged to a common point on the graph. A family of lines of this kind can be represented by the equation

$$T - T_a = S\,(\log_{10} t - \log_{10} t_a),\tag{8.12}$$

where S is the slope—a function of the stress—and T_a and $\log_{10} t_a$ are the coordinates of the converging point. Figure 8.19 shows the data of Fig. 8.15 plotted according to this new equation. From this plot $T_a = 310°R$, and $\log_{10} t_a = 20$.

From these observations Manson and Haferd proposed the following parameter:

* Manson, S. S., and Haferd, A. M., *A Linear Time-Temperature Relation for Extrapolation of Creep and Stress-Rupture Data*, National Advisory Committee for Aeronautics Technical Note 2890, Washington, March 1953.

$$P_3 = \frac{T - T_a}{\log_{10} t - \log_{10} t_a}. \tag{8.12a}$$

According to Eq. 8.12, $P_3 = S$, which is a function of stress. Thus

$$P_3 = f_3(\sigma) \tag{8.13}$$

as in the previous methods. Figure 8.20 is the Manson-Haferd *master curve* for the same S590 alloy. The parameter P_3 is usually called the *linear parameter* because it is based on a linear relation between $\log_{10} t$ and T for a given stress.

If we again use the same example—life of 100,000 hours at 1040°F (1500°R)—the value of P_3 is -79.33. The same value is obtained in a 1000-hour creep-rupture test if $T = 1199$°F (1659°R).

The stress given in Fig. 8.20 is 40,800 psi, compared with 41,000 psi from both the Larson-Miller and Sherby-Dorn curves. In a statistical analysis of the data for the above alloy, the Manson-Haferd linear parameter has been found to give consistently more accurate predictions than the other two methods.[*] However, the Manson-Haferd method poses some disadvantage in determination of the constants $\log_{10} t_a$ and T_a. Because of long extrapolations of nearly parallel lines representing $\log t$ vs T, the exact location of the point of convergence is uncertain; different investigators may decide on different values for the coordinates of the point, giving somewhat different parameters for the same material. However, if a large enough number of specimens is tested, the error from this source appears to be small.

These methods may also be used for predicting creep strength, where t is the time for a permissible strain. Since the time involved is less than the rupture time, tertiary creep is usually not included. Consequently some differences in the performances of the three methods may be expected as compared with their performance in predicting creep-rupture strengths. Insufficient data are available for a thorough comparison of the methods for this purpose.

Several limitations must be kept in mind in using any of the parameter methods to predict creep properties. First, the fact that neither of the methods of plotting t against T yields perfectly straight lines casts some doubt on the complete validity of any of the methods. Certainly the different methods do give conflicting results. However, actual errors are smaller than those of the older methods where long-time extrapolations are necessary.

A more serious limitation in many instances is the necessity of using testing temperatures higher than the operating temperature. If the op-

---

[*] Goldhoff, R. M., "Which Method for Extrapolating Stress-Rupture Data?" *Materials in Design Engrg.* **49**, No. 4, 93 (1959).

erating temperature is high—e.g., near a transformation range—it may be impossible to exceed it without introducing effects other than simple creep. In such instances parameter values corresponding to long times cannot be obtained by use of higher temperatures, and it becomes necessary to extrapolate the master curve itself.   Such extrapolations are usually considered to be not much better than those of the older methods when the same lengths of time are involved.

8.7   CREEP PROPERTIES OF NONMETALS

Plastics

Creep behavior varies widely from one polymer to another as well as with different conditions of loading, temperature, etc.   Figures 8.21, 8.22,

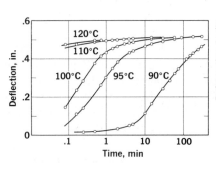

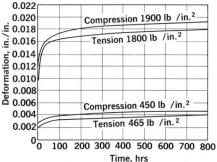

Fig. 8.21   Deflection of Bakelite beams in bending under constant load as a function of time (curves after Leaderman, data of Hetényi). These curves indicate that under proper conditions a phenolic resin can exhibit viscoelastic properties. (Adapted from Leaderman, Elastic and Creep Properties of Filamentous Materials and Other High Polymers, published 1943 by the Textile Foundation, courtesy Textile Research Institute, Princeton, N. J.)

Fig. 8.22   Total deformation vs time for 66 nylon. (Adapted from Technical Data on Plastics, 1957, published by the Manufacturing Chemists' Association, Inc., Washington, D. C.)

and 8.23 are creep curves for three different polymers.   Note that creep of the thermosetting polymer Bakelite seems to approach a maximum value after a short time.   This maximum is independent of the testing temperature. The curves for the thermoplastics nylon and polymethyl methacrylate, on the other hand, appear to increase steadily. No general treatment is possible under the limitations of this text.

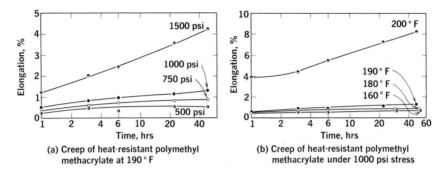

(a) Creep of heat-resistant polymethyl methacrylate at 190 ° F

(b) Creep of heat-resistant polymethyl methacrylate under 1000 psi stress

Fig. 8.23 Creep curves for an acrylic plastic. (Adapted from McCrackin and Bersch, Society of Plastics Engineers Journal **15**, *No. 9, 2 (1959))*

ASTM has standardized creep tests and properties for plastics to some extent.* *Creep strength* is defined as "the maximum stress which may be applied continuously for a specified time without causing fracture" (this

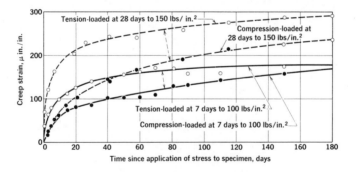

Fig. 8.24 Creep of plain concrete. (Adapted from Davis, Davis, and Brown, Am. Soc. Test. Mats. Proceedings **37**, *Part II, 323 (1937))*

definition corresponds to what is referred to as creep rupture strength for metals). The definition and measurement of "instantaneous strain" in

---

* ASTM D674.

plastics present some problems because the transient creep is relatively large. The strain after a given small increment of time (such as 1 minute) is frequently used to represent the instantaneous strain because it is more easily reproducible.

Concrete

Figures 8.24 and 8.25 are typical creep curves for concrete. In Fig. 8.24 the strain approaches a constant value after a number of years. This type of creep is represented by Eq. 8.3,

$$\epsilon_{cr} = \frac{C_6 t}{n + t}$$

(compare Fig. 8.5). The asymptotic value of creep strain, ϵ_f, is given by the constant C_6 and is often found to vary in direct proportion to the stress: $\epsilon_f = C_6 = m\sigma$, where m is called the *creep coefficient* and σ is the constant stress used in the creep test. A value of m can be determined by estimating ϵ_f from the curve and using $m = \epsilon_f/\sigma$. The creep-time constant, n, is simply the time at which the creep strain is half its asymptotic value.

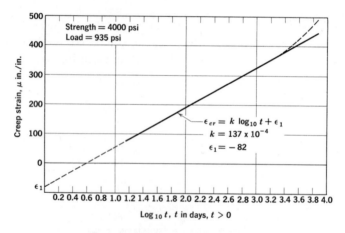

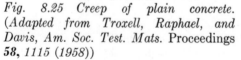

Fig. 8.25 Creep of plain concrete. (Adapted from Troxell, Raphael, and Davis, Am. Soc. Test. Mats. Proceedings 58, 1115 (1958))

In Fig. 8.25 the strain continues to increase indefinitely, at an ever-decreasing rate. This type of creep can be represented by Eq. 8.1c,

$$\epsilon_{cr} = K \log t + \epsilon_1 \quad (t > 0).$$

The constant K is also referred to as the *creep coefficient*, although it has different units from those of m. It is found by measuring the slope of a plot of ϵ_{cr} vs log t, as in Fig. 8.25. Such plots are usually not perfectly linear and sometimes have two distinct parts (Fig. 8.26). Each part is then expressed by an equation of the form of Eq. 8.1c.

Design for Creep

A common method by which creep is taken into account in designing with plastics, concrete, and other nonmetallic materials is through the use of an *apparent*, or *effective modulus*, E_{eff}. It is defined as the *ratio of the stress to the total strain* that has developed after a given time. So long as

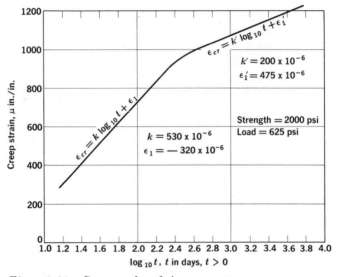

Fig. 8.26 Creep of plain concrete. (*Adapted from Troxell, Raphael, and Davis, Am. Soc. Test. Mats.* Proceedings **58**, 1115 (1958))

the strain continues to increase with time, E_{eff} will decrease, and a curve of E_{eff} vs t can be plotted. Furthermore, if at any given time the strain is assumed to be proportional to the stress, the curve of E_{eff} vs t can be applied to any stress. For example, if the strain is governed by Eq. 8.3 with $C_6 = m\sigma$, we can write

$$E_{eff} = \frac{\sigma}{\dfrac{m\sigma t}{n + t}} = \frac{1}{m}\left(\frac{n}{t} + 1\right) \quad (t > 0),$$

where m and n are constants which depend on the material and the temperature. This is the equation of a hyperbola which approaches a minimum of $1/m$ for large values of t and is independent of the stress. The effective modulus curves of many plastics exhibit these characteristics.

If a creep-time curve is available for a given temperature and stress, E_{eff} can be computed for a number of times and a curve plotted showing E_{eff} as a function of t. Then when the designer wishes to predict the deformation of a part after a specified time *at that temperature*, he can read the value of E_{eff} from the curve at that time and apply the equation $\epsilon = E_{eff}/\sigma$. The student should remember, however, that this method is entirely empirical and gives only approximate values. Predictions for long times are subject to the same risks mentioned in connection with metals (Art. 8.6).

EXAMPLE 8.3

The total strain observed in a nylon resin at room temperature after 100 hrs under a stress of 1800 psi in tension is 0.0168 in./in. (Fig. 8.22). Compute the apparent or effective modulus, E_{eff}, for that time. A part made of this plastic is 6 in. long and can be allowed a total elongation of only 0.05 in. in 100 hours under a load of 150 lbs. Determine the cross-sectional area required.

Solution:

$$E_{eff} = \frac{1800}{0.0168} = 107{,}100 \text{ psi.}$$

The allowable strain is

$$\epsilon = \frac{0.05}{6} = 0.00833 \text{ in./in.,}$$

from which the stress is

$$\sigma = (E_{eff})(\epsilon) = 893 \text{ psi.}$$

The cross-sectional area required is

$$A = \frac{P}{\sigma} = \frac{150}{893} = 0.168 \text{ in.}^2$$

The yield stress for this material is 8600 psi. The working stress, based on the yield stress with a factor of safety of 4, is 2,150 psi. Hence creep is the controlling factor in design.

8.8 STRESS RELAXATION

Bolts and other members which are required to hold two more-or-less rigid parts in tight contact are frequently found to have relaxed considerably after long periods of time as a result of creep. In its simplest form stress relaxation is the time-dependent decrease in stress in a member which is constrained to a certain fixed deformation. Imagine, for example, a bar elongated elastically in tension by a stress σ_i, which produces an initial strain $\epsilon_i = \sigma_i/E$. Under conditions of steady creep at stress σ this bar will tend to elongate at a rate

$$v_0 = B\sigma^n \quad (n > 1). \tag{8.6}$$

If the initial strain, ϵ_i, is maintained constant, the elongation caused by creep is simply subtracted from it, thereby reducing the elastic part of the total strain. The elastic strain at any time is given by

$$\epsilon_{el} = \epsilon_i - \epsilon_{cr}. \tag{8.14}$$

The rate at which the creep strain begins is $v_i = B\sigma_i^n$, but since this strain immediately begins to decrease the elastic strain, the stress is also decreased, and with it the creep rate. Differentiating Eq. 8.14 with respect to time, we have

$$\frac{d\epsilon_{el}}{dt} = -\frac{d\epsilon_{cr}}{dt}. \tag{8.14a}$$

But $\epsilon_{el} = \sigma/E$, where σ is the instantaneous stress, a function of time. Hence

$$\frac{d\epsilon_{el}}{dt} = \frac{1}{E}\frac{d\sigma}{dt}.$$

Also $d\epsilon_{cr}/dt = v_0 = B\sigma^n$, so that Eq. 8.14a becomes

$$\frac{1}{E}\frac{d\sigma}{dt} = -B\sigma^n. \tag{8.15}$$

This is the differential equation for the idealized case of stress relaxation

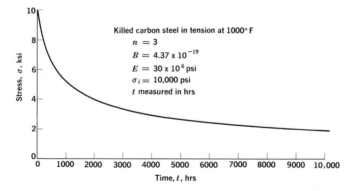

Fig. 8.27   *Stress-relaxation curve.*

if we assume steady creep and a fixed total strain, ϵ_i. Equation 8.15 can be integrated directly as follows:

$$\int \frac{d\sigma}{\sigma^n} = -BE \int dt.$$

$$-\frac{1}{(n-1)\sigma^{n-1}} = -BEt + C.$$

At $t = 0$, $\sigma = \sigma_i$, from which

$$C = -\frac{1}{(n-1)\sigma_i^{n-1}}.$$

The relation between stress and time is therefore

$$\frac{1}{\sigma^{n-1}} = \frac{1}{\sigma_i^{n-1}} + BE(n-1)t. \tag{8.16}$$

This equation is plotted in Fig. 8.27 for typical values of B, E, and n for a starting stress of 10,000 psi.

Equation 8.16 is derived mainly to indicate the principles on which the theory of stress relaxation is based. For accurate predictions a more comprehensive method must be used, in which transient creep and the deformations of the connected parts are considered. Such a method involves solution by step-by-step numerical integration.

Stress relaxation tests have been devised to study this behavior. The load is applied by a screw, through which the strain is automatically controlled as desired (ASTM D674). The change in load is measured by a dynamometer. The result is a graph of stress vs time.

EXAMPLE 8.4

A steel bolt clamping two rigid plates together is held at a temperature of 1000°F. Tests at this temperature give $n = 3.0$ and $v_0 = 2.80 \times 10^{-8}$ (in./in.)/hr at a stress of 4000 psi. If the bolt is initially tightened to a stress of 10,000 lb, determine the stress remaining after 1 year has elapsed.

Solution: The solution described in Art. 8.8 will be used because the plates are assumed to be rigid, and the time is long enough that transient creep effects will be small. Substituting the given values in Eq. 8.6a, we have

$$\log_{10} B = \log_{10} (2.80 \times 10^{-8}) - 3.0 \log_{10} (4000)$$

$$= (0.44716 - 8) - 10.80618,$$

from which

$$B = 4.37 \times 10^{-19}.$$

Equation 8.16 becomes

$$\frac{1}{\sigma^2} = 10^{-8} + (4.37 \times 10^{-19})(30 \times 10^6)(2)t$$

$$= 10^{-8}(1 + 0.00262\,t),$$

or

$$\sigma = \frac{10^4}{\sqrt{1 + 0.00262\,t}} \quad \text{(see Fig. 8.27).}$$

Substituting $t = 8{,}760$ hrs (1 yr), we find

$$\sigma = \frac{10^4}{4.89} = 2{,}050 \text{ psi.}$$

EXPERIMENTAL METHODS

8.9   CREEP TESTS

Creep tests require measurement of four variables: stress, strain, temperature, and time.   Stress is applied by a testing machine which applies either a constant load or a constant stress.   For a constant load all that is required is a dead weight and a system of levers to multiply it to the required load on the specimen.   Some auxiliary equipment is usually necessary to take up the extension of the specimen; otherwise this small extension is also multiplied, and the weights move so far that the lever ratios are changed.   The take-up mechanism automatically adjusts the length of the linkage between the weights and the specimen so that the weights remain approximately in a fixed position as the specimen elongates. Nearly all creep-testing machines are of the constant-load type.

In constant-stress machines the load must be adjusted continuously to conform to the changing cross-sectional area.   Since the creep strain is essentially a plastic strain like that occurring in ordinary simple tension, it is assumed that the volume remains constant.   The cross-sectional area therefore varies inversely with length, as indicated by Eq. 3.17.   For a constant stress, σ_0,

$$P = \sigma_0 A = \sigma_0 \left(\frac{A_0 l_0}{l} \right) = \frac{P_0 l_0}{l},$$

where $P_0 = \sigma_0 A_0$.   So long as the strain is uniform, the length, l, can be taken as the gage length of the specimen and the load need only be made to vary inversely as this length.   Methods that have been used include dead weights having adjustable lever arms and screws controlled by electronic devices.

Eccentricity is a greater problem in creep than in ordinary tension tests. The utmost care must be taken to minimize it.   The use of long loading rods with spherical seats is very helpful.   However, it is good practice to check the alignment before the creep test is started.   This is done by loading the specimen in its elastic range at room temperature and measuring the strain at four points 90° apart around its circumference.   Two extensometers can be used by loading twice and shifting the extensometers 90° between loadings.   The strain readings on opposite sides should not differ by more than 15 per cent.   The tendency of gripping devices to creep during repeated use may gradually increase their eccentricity.   For this reason a check of alignment is advisable before each test.

Specimens for creep tests are usually the same as for conventional tension tests.   Elongated ends having a thermocouple well in each end may be provided.   Shouldered-end ("button-head") specimens are an advantage when oxidation and seizing in the grips cause trouble with threaded ends.

Strain must be measured quite accurately in creep tests.   One method is to use traveling telescopes.   Two telescopes are focused on gage marks on the specimen through windows in the side of the furnace.   Their positions can be adjusted by means of micrometer screws to keep their cross hairs focused on the gage marks.   A variation of this method utilizes a special extensometer (Fig. 8.28).   A platinum alloy wire is spot-welded to the specimen at one end of the gage length, and a platinum alloy tube is spot-welded to the specimen at the other end.   The wire slides inside the tube, and reference marks on both are observed through a single telescope at the middle.   Elongation can be measured on a scale inside the telescope.

Another method of measuring strain is that described in Chapter 7 for short-time elevated-temperature tests.   Extension rods are attached to the specimen at the gage points and carry the elongation of the specimen outside the furnace, where it can be measured by conventional means.   ASTM specifies that elongation should always be measured on opposite sides of the specimen to obtain the average, or center-line strain.*

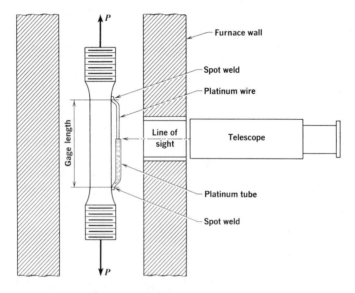

Fig. 8.28   Wire and tube extensometer.

Temperature control is maintained by a furnace like that described in Chapter 7 for short-time elevated-temperature tests.   Basically it is a tubular, electrically heated furnace made to fit around the specimen in the creep-testing machine.   Accurate temperature control is critical.   ASTM specifies that the variation should not exceed ±3°F, either with time or location along the specimen (for temperatures up to 1800°F).*

---

* ASTM E139.

Specimens are sometimes tested in media other than air (vacuum, salt baths, liquid metal). It is known that the particular medium used has some effect on creep properties, although the exact nature of the effect is not completely understood.

BIBLIOGRAPHY

Timoshenko, S., *Strength of Materials—Part II—Advanced Theory and Problems*, 3rd ed., D. Van Nostrand Company, Inc., Princeton, New Jersey, 1956.
Chapter X includes 27 pages (pp. 516–543) on creep and design for creep.

Marin, Joseph, *Engineering Materials—Their Mechanical Properties and Applications*, Prentice-Hall, Inc., Englewood Cliffs, N. J., 1952, Ch. 6.

Keyser, Carl A., *Materials of Engineering—Properties, Fabrication, Uses, and Testing*, Prentice-Hall, Inc., Englewood Cliffs, N. J., 1956, Ch. 5.

The M. W. Kellogg Company, *Design of Piping Systems*, Ch. 1, 2nd ed., John Wiley & Sons, Inc., New York, 1956.

Parker, Earl R., "Modern Concepts of Flow and Fracture" (1957 Edward de Mille Campbell Memorial Lecture) *Transactions* Am. Soc. Metals **50**, 79–91 (1958).
An up-to-date account of creep theories.

Davis, Harmer E., Troxell, George E., and Wiskocil, Clement T., *The Testing and Inspection of Engineering Materials*, 2nd ed. (McGraw-Hill Civil Engineering Series) McGraw-Hill Book Company, Inc., New York, Toronto, London, 1955, Ch. 8; American Society for Testing Materials, *Standards*, 1958, Part 3, pp. 224–236 (E139-58T).
Experimental methods.

PROBLEMS

8.1 The following data were obtained in creep tests of carbon-silicon steel at a constant stress of 16,000 psi.

T, °F	v_0, (in./in.)/hr
900	2.60×10^{-5}
1000	1.27×10^{-3}
1100	4.10×10^{-2}
1200	$8.5 \ \times 10^{-1}$

Plot a graph and show that Eq. 8.5 fits the data. Determine the activation energy for creep, in cal/mole.

8.2   From the results of Problem 8.1 predict the creep rate at 800°F.   At this rate, how much creep would occur in 1 year?

8.3   The following strains were observed in a creep test of high-purity aluminum under constant load (initial stress 1,030 psi) at 547°F:

t, min	ϵ, in./in.	t, min	ϵ, in./in.
0	0	24	0.094
1	0.02	32	.109
2	.029	40	.1225
4	.041	48	.136
8	.057	60	.156
16	.078	72	.176

(a) Construct a graph from the data, on Cartesian coordinates.   (b) Determine from the graph the extent of the primary creep range, the minimum creep rate, and the creep intercept.

8.4   From a series of creep tests on high-purity aluminum, similar to that of Problem 8.3, the following minimum creep rates were obtained:

T, °F	v_0, (in./in.)/min	T, °F	v_0, (in./in.)/min
547	0.00164	639	0.01714
608	.00944	660	.0295
627	.01298	715	.0894

(a) Plot the data in the form $\log_{10} v_0$ vs $1/T$ and fit a straight line to it.   (b) From this line determine the activation energy for creep, in cal/mole.

8.5   A magnesium alloy subjected to a constant stress of 2000 psi is observed to have the following minimum creep rates during secondary creep:

T, °F	v_0, (in./in.)/hr
200	0.00023
280	.0112
350	.185
415	.841

Determine the range of values over which Eq. 8.5 is applicable.   Evaluate the constants for this equation.

8.6   From the line representing 20,000-psi stress (Fig. 8.8a) compute the constants (E_a/k) and A for Eq. 8.5, using only the portion between 900°F and 1100°F.

8.7   From the line representing 1100°F (Fig. 8.8b) compute the constants n and B for Eq. 8.6; use only the part of the line below 20 ksi.

8.8 Repeat Problem 8.7 for 1200°F; use only the part of the line between 7 and 15 ksi.

8.9 The initial clearance between the ends of the blades and the housing of a steam turbine is 0.003 in.   The blades are 8 in. long and their elastic elongation during operation is calculated to be 0.0008 in.   If it is desired to hold the final clearance to a 0.001-in. minimum, what is the maximum per cent creep that can be allowed in the blades?

8.10 In the design of a nuclear reactor a member made of the material of Fig. 8.12 is to be permitted a total of 5 per cent creep in 2500 hrs.   Find the allowable stress, using Fig. 8.13.   From Fig. 8.12, approximately how much error is involved in this stress?

8.11 A member to be used in a supersonic jet aircraft is designed of ZK51A-T5 magnesium alloy.   (a) If the member is subjected to an operating temperature of 300°F for 80 hrs and 0.2 per cent creep is allowed, what is the design stress? (Use Fig. 8.11.)   (b) If the service life is increased to 8000 hrs and the permissible creep to 0.5 per cent, estimate the design stress.   Comment on the reliability of this design stress.

8.12 A member made of S590 alloy steel is designed for a service life of 5000 hrs at 1250°F.   Determine a working stress based on interpolation between the curves of Fig. 8.14 and a factor of safety of 1.5, based on stress.

8.13 The service life of a member which is to be operated at 1325°F is 300,000 hrs. (a) Determine the creep-rupture strength for S590 alloy steel by the Larson-Miller parameter method (Fig. 8.17).   (b) If data for this point on the master curve are obtained in a 1000-hr test, what temperature must be used (°F)?

8.14 Repeat Problem 8.13 and use the Sherby-Dorn parameter method (Fig. 8.18).

8.15 Repeat Problem 8.13 and use the Manson-Haferd linear parameter (Fig. 8.20).

8.16 (a) Construct the curves of Fig. 8.14 directly from the data of Table 8.2. (b) With data measured from these curves, plot a family of curves of log stress vs temperature (°R), in which each curve represents one of the following values of $\log_{10} t_r$: 1.5, 2.0, 2.5, 3.0, 3.5, and 4.0.   (c) From this family of curves, tabulate the corresponding values of $1/T$ and $\log_{10} t_r$ for each of the following stresses: 20, 30, 40, 50, 60, and 70 ksi.   Plot the resulting family of curves of $\log_{10} t_r$ vs $1/T$ (compare Fig. 8.15).   (d) Approximate these curves by straight lines and project them to determine their point of intersection on the $\log_{10} t_r$-axis, which gives the value of C in the Larson-Miller parameter. (e) Determine the average slope of the family of lines and from it find the constant, α, in the Sherby-Dorn parameter.   (f) Compare your results with the results given in the text.   Can you give any explanation for possible differences?

8.17 The following creep strains were obtained in creep tests of plain concrete at 100 psi tension.

TIME AT STRESS, days	CREEP STRAIN, μin./in.	TIME AT STRESS, days	CREEP STRAIN, μin./in.
7	12	60	23.5
14	17.5	90	24.3
28	21	120	24.7
40	22.4		

Plot the points on Cartesian coordinates and fit a curve. Assuming that Eq. 8.3 applies, determine constants m and n (Art. 8.7). (Suggestion: a convenient method of determining m is to plot ϵ_{cr} vs $1/t$ and observe the intercept of this curve at $1/t = 0$.) Construct a curve using Eq. 8.3 and compare it with the actual curve.

8.18 The following experimental data are for an acetal plastic at a constant stress of 1200 psi and a temperature of 160°F.

TIME, hrs	TOTAL STRAIN, in./in.	TIME, hrs	TOTAL STRAIN, in./in.
10	0.0085	400	0.0135
50	.0107	1000	.0148
100	.0121	4000	.0156

(a) Compute the corresponding values of E_{eff} and plot a curve of E_{eff} vs $\log_{10} t$. (b) A member made of this material is designed to carry a load of 200 lb at 160 F. If the member is $\frac{3}{8}$ in. square and 4 in. long, find the elongation to be expected after 5 months of service at 1.6 hrs per day; (c) after 1 year of *continuous* service.

8.19 The following experimental data are for an acrylic plastic at a constant stress of 2500 psi and a temperature of 104°F.

TIME, hrs	TOTAL STRAIN, in./in.	TIME, hrs	TOTAL STRAIN, in./in.
10	0.0083	1000	0.0120
100	.0096	2000	.0132
200	.0102	5000	.0151
500	.0111	10,000	.0160

(a) Compute the corresponding values of E_{eff} and plot a curve of E_{eff} vs $\log_{10} t$. (b) A ring made of this material is 3 in. in diameter and has a cross-section $\frac{1}{8} \times \frac{3}{4}$ in. If the ring carries a hoop tension of 150 lb at 104°F, what is its expected change in diameter after 30 days of continuous service? 150 days? (c) Estimate the probable minimum value of E_{eff} and compute the corresponding expansion of the ring.

8.20 A steel bolt holds two plates together and is subjected to a constant temperature of 1100°F over a period of 5 years.   Tests of the bolt steel indicate that its minimum creep rate is governed by Eq. 8.6, with $n = 5.20$.   At a stress of 6000 psi, $v_0 = 2.8 \times 10^{-5}$ (in./in.)/hr.   Assuming that the plates are perfectly rigid, and using the method of Art. 8.8, determine the initial stress to which the bolt must be tightened if the stress must not drop below 500 psi during the 5 years.

8.21 What variables must be considered when creep of a given material is being investigated experimentally?

8.22 Define transient creep; viscous creep.

8.23 Name five different types of strain that may be involved in creep at high temperatures and high stresses.

8.24 A steel member is designed to operate at 1500°F and 3000 psi for a few minutes at a time, with a limit of 2 per cent total deformation.   What types of strain are important in this application?   Compute the value of each, for comparison.

CHAPTER 9

FATIGUE

Materials subjected to *fluctuating* or *repeated* loads tend to develop a characteristic behavior which differs fundamentally, in certain respects, from their behavior under steady loads. This behavior is called *fatigue* and is distinguished by three main features: loss of strength, loss of ductility, and an increased uncertainty in both strength and service life. All stem from the same source—the *inhomogeneity* of real materials. In Chapter 2 it was pointed out that all materials, even the most perfect crystals, are full of imperfections of many kinds, so that no material is perfectly homogeneous. Under repeated loading the effect of inhomogeneities is strongly emphasized, just as in the fracture of brittle materials (Art. 3.4). Consequently there are striking similarities between fatigue and the behavior of brittle materials.

Fatigue is an important form of behavior in all materials, including such widely different types as metals, plastics, rubber, and concrete. All rotating machine parts are subject to alternating stresses; springs are deflected by varying amounts; aircraft wings are subject to repeated gust loads; rubber tires are deformed repeatedly with each revolution of the wheel. Since metals have always been used for the majority of moving parts, it is natural that fatigue was first encountered in metals. The fact that they are noted for their ductility has made loss of ductility in fatigue a serious problem. Most of the research in this field has therefore been on *metal fatigue.*   Comparatively little attention has been paid to fatigue of brittle materials because they normally exhibit many of the characteristics of fatigue, even under steady loading.   Research has shown, however, that fatigue in brittle materials does result in some loss of strength.   The increased use of plastics for machine parts such as gears and bearings poses new problems in fatigue.   Relatively little work has been done in this field, however, although standard tests have been set up by ASTM.

FATIGUE BEHAVIOR AND ITS INTERPRETATION

The term *fatigue* is quite descriptive and has been in common use among engineers for well over half a century.   Remember, however, that fatigue of *materials* is primarily an effect of the *repetition* of loads and not simply a time effect like creep.*   Note also that fatigue is not a dynamic effect in the ordinary sense of the word.   The rate of application of the load is not usually a factor in fatigue.   If a situation arises in which the load is applied so rapidly as to produce a dynamic effect, this effect is separate and distinct from the effect of mere repetition of the load.   The dynamic effects have been discussed in Chapter 7.

The ASTM *Standards*† contain the following definition of fatigue: "A general term used to describe the behavior of materials under repeated cycles of stress or strain which cause a deterioration of the material that results in a progressive fracture."   Fractures resulting from fatigue are among the most difficult to foresee because conditions producing fatigue are frequently not clearly recognizable.   Fatigue occurs at stresses well within the ordinary elastic range as measured in the static tension test. It sometimes occurs under intermittent loading which at first does not appear to be repeated often enough to cause fatigue.   Like other forms of brittle behavior it is strongly influenced by what may appear to be minor discontinuities in structure.   Because of the difficulty of recognizing fatigue conditions, fatigue failures comprise a large percentage of the failures encountered in engineering.

---

* The term *static fatigue* is sometimes used to designate failure under *steady* stress after long times. Glass, in particular, is known to break unexpectedly following prolonged loading and with no noticeable inelastic deformation.   Apparently air or moisture molecules gradually diffuse to the tips of the microcracks, reducing the surface tension of the glass and allowing the cracks to propagate slowly.   When the microcracks finally reach some critical size, they become self-propagating and fracture takes place.   Other examples of static fatigue include fractures following some slow chemical action.   Sometimes creep is referred to as static fatigue.   Since all forms of the phenomenon involve some inelastic deformation, however small, before fracture, it might be appropriate to classify all forms under the heading of *creep* instead of *fatigue.*

† ASTM D671.

9.1　FATIGUE LOADINGS

　The simplest type of repeated load is an alternating stress like that shown in Fig. 9.1a.　The bending stresses in a rotating axle—one of the first forms of fatigue to be investigated—vary in this way.　The stress amplitude is equal to the maximum stress, and the mean or average stress is zero.

　A member which is deformed alternately on either side of its equilibrium configuration, like the cantilever beam in Fig. 9.2a, is also subject to simple alternating stress.　If, however, the member carries in addition a constant load, such as the weight of a machine (Fig. 9.2b), the variation of stress is as shown in Fig. 9.1b.　Here the alternating stress is superimposed on a

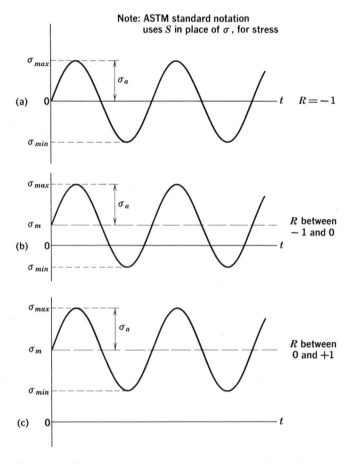

Fig. 9.1　Variations of stress in elementary fatigue loadings.

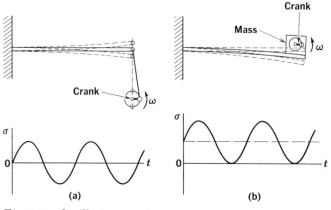

Fig. 9.2   *Oscillating member.*

steady stress resulting from the constant load.   The mean stress is no longer zero but is equal to the steady stress; the maximum stress is equal to the sum of the mean stress and the stress amplitude.

Simple sinusoidal variations of stress like those described above occur in many rotating and reciprocating machine parts.   However, there are numerous other examples of fatigue loading in which the variation is far

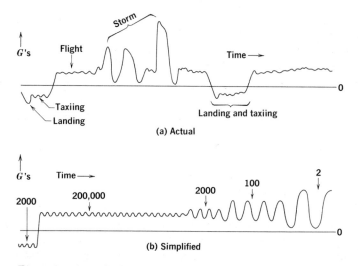

Fig. 9.3   *Actual aircraft loading spectrum and simplified version.* (*Adapted from Sines and Waisman, Eds.,* Metal Fatigue, *McGraw-Hill Book Company, Inc., New York, 1959*)

from regular.   One is in aircraft, where the stress variation during flight is random (Fig. 9.3); others include machines that are operated intermittently, in which natural vibrations of variable amplitudes occur during starting and stopping.

When stress variation is irregular, the actual loading spectrum is of little use in design for fatigue and must be reduced to a simpler form.   The usual procedure is to break up the loading spectrum into several groups of simple oscillations, each group representing the number of actual oscillations having approximately the same amplitude and mean stress.   Figure 9.3 is an actual loading spectrum from aircraft accelerometer records and a simplified version consisting of several groups of sinusoidal oscillations.   The simplified spectrum is assumed to be equivalent to the actual spectrum, and is used in analysis.   In this manner any form of fatigue loading can be represented by simple sinusoidal variations similar to those in Fig. 9.1.

In discussion of fatigue loadings the following notation will be used. The symbols and definitions correspond to those suggested by ASTM* except that stress is designated by σ in accordance with the notation used throughout the remainder of the text.   Long usage has led to the customary use of S for stress when associated with fatigue, as shown in parentheses in the following list.   Several of the symbols used are also illustrated in Fig. 9.1.

Maximum stress, σ_{max} (S_{max}).   The highest algebraic value of stress during a cycle (tensile stress is positive) (Fig. 9.1).

Minimum stress, σ_{min} (S_{min}).   The lowest algebraic value of stress during a cycle (Fig. 9.1).

Mean stress, σ_m (S_m).   The average or steady stress, on which is superimposed the oscillating stress (Fig. 9.1).

Stress amplitude, σ_a (S_a).   The amplitude of the superimposed oscillating stress, $\sigma_{max} - \sigma_m$ (Fig. 9.1).

Range of stress, σ_r (S_r). $\sigma_r = \sigma_{max} - \sigma_{min} = 2\,\sigma_a$.

Stress ratio, R. $R = \dfrac{\sigma_{min}}{\sigma_{max}}$ (Fig. 9.1).

Cycles endured, n.   The number of cycles of stress to which a member is subjected during fatigue loading, without failure.

Fatigue life, N.   The number of cycles required to cause failure of a member under given conditions (e.g., given σ_{max} and σ_m, or given σ_m and σ_a).

---

* *Manual on Fatigue Testing*, ASTM Special Technical Publication No. 91, American Society for Testing Materials, Philadelphia, 1949.   Hereafter this publication will be referred to simply as ASTM STP No. 91.

9.2   MECHANISMS OF FATIGUE

Deterioration resulting from fatigue consists primarily in formation of cracks in the material. Most cracks that are responsible for fatigue failures start at visible discontinuities which act as stress-raisers. These discontinuities include design details such as holes, fillets, or keyways and macroscopic flaws in the material such as inclusions, blowholes, or fabrication cracks. Furthermore, fatigue occurs under all kinds of loadings and

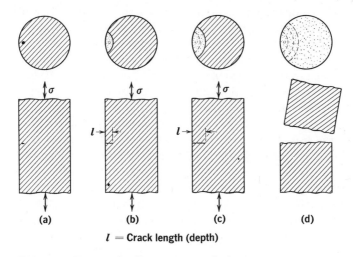

l = Crack length (depth)

Fig. 9.4 Events leading up to fatigue fracture: nucleation (a), crack growth (b) and (c), and fracture (d).

at high and low stresses. When you break a piece of wire by bending it back and forth a few times, you induce a particular form of fatigue involving large plastic strains.

We shall be concerned first with the damage to a material which results *only* from *repetition* of the load. We shall study the effects of *simple alternating tensile and compressive stresses*, in which the *maximum stress is within the elastic range*, on members which are free of visible discontinuities of the types discussed above. This type of fatigue will be referred to as *simple fatigue*. When the mechanisms of simple fatigue are understood, the effects of stress-raisers and plastic strains can be studied by extension of these mechanisms.

The progress of simple fatigue can be traced in a general way. Localized changes in atomic structure begin within the first few cycles at scattered points in the material. These soon develop into submicroscopic cracks which grow, as the cycles of loading continue, through microscopic size and eventually become visible to the eye. Finally, when the cracks have grown to some critical size, the member is so weakened that it breaks. These three stages of fatigue are usually referred to as *nucleation, crack growth,* and *fracture* (Fig. 9.4).

The detailed mechanisms of nucleation and crack growth have been studied extensively only for *metals.* Further discussion will therefore be confined to this class of materials.

Fatigue in metals begins with highly localized yielding. It was pointed out in Art. 3.7 that in polycrystalline metals in simple tension a few crystals will always be so oriented that they will slip easily. As the load is increased these "weak" crystals yield first, but since they are surrounded by elastic material, they do not affect the static stress-strain diagram noticeably. Nevertheless they do yield, and at overall stresses that are nominally within the elastic range of the material.

If the material is loaded only once, the effect is completely insignificant so far as the use of the material is concerned. If the load is repeated, however, each repetition produces additional localized yielding which eventually results in the formation of fatigue cracks in the yielded regions.

The process is as follows. A weak crystal is entirely surrounded by stronger crystals which are so oriented that they remain completely elastic at the highest stress occurring during the repeated loading (Fig. 9.5). As

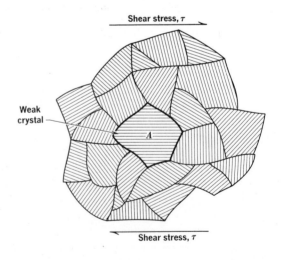

Fig. 9.5   Unfavorably oriented crystal surrounded by favorably oriented crystals; cross-hatching indicates directions of easy slip.

the shear stress, τ, rises to its maximum during the first quarter cycle, the weak crystal (A) yields by a small amount. During yielding the stress in A increases much less rapidly than the overall stress, τ, and thus lags behind as τ increases. Crystal A behaves more-or-less as a single crystal, and its properties are therefore quite different from those of the aggregate.

In the next half-cycle τ decreases to zero and reverses, rising to a maximum in the opposite direction. During this reversal the deformation in the weak crystal, A, is determined almost entirely by the stiffness of the surrounding elastic material, compared with which crystal A is very small. Consequently the negative deformation accompanying the maximum negative stress is the same as the positive deformation that accompanied the maximum positive stress. The first effect of unloading is simply to allow the atoms in all crystals to return elastically to equilibrium positions. However, since its stress was lower to begin with, crystal A reaches its equilibrium configuration first, before the deformation of the whole has reached zero. As the deformation continues to decrease, crystal A begins to deform in the opposite direction, and is almost ready to yield by the time the overall deformation has reduced to zero. Having, in effect, a head start, crystal A then yields more extensively as the deformation reverses.

This process is repeated with each subsequent half-cycle of deformation. Each time the stress reverses, crystal A yields a little more. And each time it yields, it strain-hardens a little more. Even though slip is in opposite directions during successive cycles, strain-hardening is additive because it simply involves the interaction of dislocations from processes like multiple slip, which are not greatly affected by direction. Furthermore, since crystal A behaves as a single crystal, the Bauschinger effect is small (Art. 4.4).

A mechanical model may be an aid to visualization. Let the weak crystal and the surrounding group of stronger crystals be represented by two bars, A and B (Fig. 9.6). Both bars have the same modulus of elasticity and length, so that at equal elastic deformations both will have the same stress. Bar A, however, has a much smaller cross-section than B and yields at a stress Y_0, while B is always elastic. After A yields, its stress increases much more slowly. The stress-elongation diagrams for the two bars are shown in Fig. 9.6b.

Application of a load, P, which alternates between $+P_1$ and $-P_1$, produces a deformation (the same in both bars) which alternates between $+\delta_1$ and $-\delta_1$, where δ_1 is almost entirely determined by the elastic deformation of bar B. So long as the stress is less than Y_0, the entire system is elastic, and both bars have the same stress. When the stress exceeds Y_0, bar A begins to yield, and its stress increases only slowly. At the maximum elongation, δ_1, the stress in bar A is at A_1 (Fig. 9.6b) while that in B is at B_1.

If the model is unloaded from its maximum elongation, δ_1, the *stress* in bar A follows the line $\overline{A_1 A_2}$ (Fig. 9.6c). When the elongation has decreased to δ_2, the stress in bar A is zero, and at zero elongation bar A has a large compressive stress.   When the deformation reverses, bar A yields at A_3—only a small deformation.   The stress at which it yields $(-Y_1)$ is of the same magnitude as the maximum that it reached in tension at A_1, slightly higher than Y_0.   Yielding now continues in bar A until deformation, $-\delta_1$, is reached.   This pattern of events is repeated in each of the following half-cycles of deformation.   The variation of stress in bar A is shown graphically in Fig. 9.6d for several cycles.   Note that the loops become narrower and narrower as cycling continues.   Note also that the stress in bar A increases with each cycle, and approaches the perfectly elastic stress for elongation δ_1.

This is an idealized and simplified model of the real material, but it does represent approximately what happens during the first stages of fatigue in metals.   It explains why repeated application of a small stress can cause progressive deterioration of a material when the same stress applied statically has no noticeable permanent effect.   A more detailed analysis of the above model has been made by Orowan, who originated the idea.*

In summary, the first effect of fatigue in metals is the formation of highly localized slip bands in the individual crystals during the first few cycles. As cycling continues, new slip bands form, mostly in the same crystals, so that deformation remains highly localized.   Furthermore, as the groups of slip bands grow into striations, the material within them becomes progressively harder because of cumulative strain-hardening.

At some point in the process the material in the striations becomes so hard that it cracks, on a submicroscopic scale.   Just when this happens has not been determined because the first actual evidence of cracking is the appearance of microscopic cracks.   However, it is known to be very early in the cycles of loading.   Microscopic cracks have been observed after only 0.1 per cent of the total number of cycles endured before failure. The submicroscopic cracks begin to form in the same directions as the slip bands.   Individual cracks grow, and groups of cracks are joined until the whole reaches microscopic size.   Figure 9.7 shows such microscopic cracks, magnified 11,000 times in an electron micrograph.

In general fatigue cracks start in the surface of the member, probably because the crystals adjacent to the surface are less restricted by surrounding crystals.   It is thus to be expected that the "weakest" crystals will be found next to the surface.

In metal members consisting of single crystals, and in amorphous solids, the unfavorably oriented weak crystals are replaced by other inhomogeneities which act as weak points.   These include the imperfections listed in Art. 2.11 and some of those listed in Art. 2.9.

---

* Orowan, E., "Theory of the Fatigue of Metals," *Proc. Roy. Soc.* (London), Series A, **171**, 79–105 (1939).

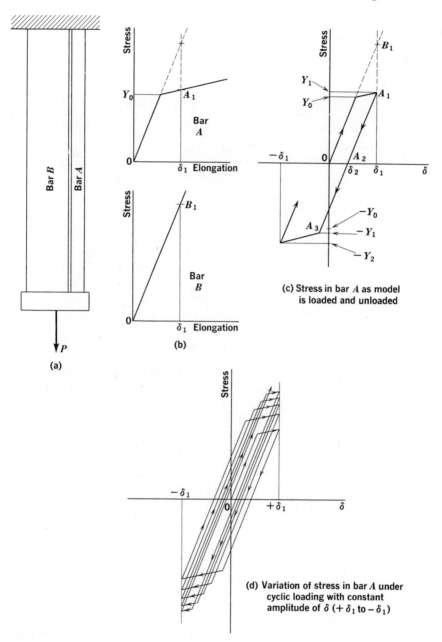

(b)

(a)

(c) Stress in bar A as model
is loaded and unloaded

(d) Variation of stress in bar A under
cyclic loading with constant
amplitude of δ (+ δ₁ to − δ₁)

*Fig. 9.6 Mechanical model, illustrating
progressive strain-hardening in "weak"
crystal under cyclic loading.*

So far we have been concerned with the problem of nucleation—how cracks get started in simple fatigue. This problem has received most of the attention in research on the theory of fatigue.   In some respects, however, the second stage—crack propagation—is of equal or greater impor-

Fig. 9.7   Electron   micrograph   of   alpha brass ($\times$ 11,000). (Courtesy Craig, Am. Soc. Test. Mats. Proceedings **52**, *881 (1952))*

tance.   Some materials of superior strength and toughness seem to permit cracks to grow faster than other materials which are not quite so strong or tough.   This factor provides an indication of the superiority of one material over another in fatigue.   Also, if cracks propagate slowly enough, they can often be detected and remedied before they become large enough to cause failure.

The first microscopic cracks appear in slip bands in certain unfavorably oriented crystals, i.e., crystals whose orientation is such that the slip bands coincide with planes of maximum shear. Hence the microscopic cracks grow in these planes. Since these planes include all planes at 45° to the axis of the member, a number of such planes may be involved. The result is that cracks usually originate in more than one of these planes. The intersection and joining of a number of such cracks produces a zigzag crack in a general direction at right angles to the axis of the member. Growth beyond the crystal of origin to neighboring crystals brings about more changes in direction to accommodate planes of easy slip. However, the general direction is still at right angles to the axis of the member (Fig. 9.4).

As each crack grows it is preceded by a nucleation process similar to that by which it started. Localized slip takes place because of stress concentration at the crack tip, and submicroscopic cracks develop in the slip bands, causing a gradual extension of the crack. A *notch effect* accompanies the crack (Art. 7.8) and increases its tendency to grow in the general direction at right angles to the tensile stress. When the remaining cross-sectional area becomes small enough, final fracture occurs, in which the notch effect is the controlling factor. Failure is thus brittle in nature.

Having traced the process of simple fatigue from beginning to end, we now turn briefly to the more common forms of metal fatigue. As mentioned earlier, a majority of fatigue failures start at visible discontinuities, which act as stress-raisers. In such instances the initial yielding is caused not by an unfavorably oriented crystal but by a local increase in stress resulting from a stress concentration. Nucleation is still highly localized. The weak points are now the small regions affected by the stress concentrations. Once the fatigue cracks start, propagation and fracture are the same as before.

When members are subjected to high maximum stresses, gross yielding of the entire member may take place. Here strain-hardening is general rather than localized. However, the natural inhomogeneity of the material, plus whatever stress-raisers may be present, still produce localized differences in strain-hardening. The end result is much the same as at low stresses: cracks are nucleated at isolated points and propagated through the member. Since general yielding is involved, however, the mechanism is not as highly localized as in simple fatigue. Furthermore, repetition of gross plastic strain in the member causes large amounts of energy to be dissipated in the form of heat and may produce temperature effects in the member. Such effects are especially important in plastics and rubber. Final fracture is more like fracture under static stresses, although there is still evidence of reduced ductility.

Thus we see that in nucleation all forms of fatigue are basically similar. It is only in later stages that differences arise.

9.3 STATISTICAL NATURE OF FATIGUE

The localized nature of fatigue mechanisms has been emphasized. Fatigue cracks start in a few weak points, and the entire process is confined to the vicinity of these points. Material a short distance from the cracks remains elastic throughout. There is a great similarity between fatigue and the fracture of brittle materials. As explained in Art. 3.4, the fracture strength of brittle materials depends on a random distribution of imperfections or weak points; fracture occurs when the stress at one or more of these points reaches the cohesive strength, a highly localized condition. In fatigue, also, fracture depends on a random distribution of weak points. Furthermore, the whole chain of events preceding fatigue fracture depends on a series of random processes and varies widely from one member to another.

Experimental confirmation of these conclusions is plentiful. Table 9.1 presents two typical sets of data on fatigue life. In each instance 48 identical specimens of the same material were subjected to reversed bending to produce alternating tension and compression ($\sigma_m = 0$) at a *uniform maximum stress*. The extent of the variation within the set is illustrated by the ratio of the longest life to the shortest life observed for the same stress: nearly 2 to 1 in the first set, 45 to 1 in the second. Neither of these ratios is particularly unusual. It is quite common to encounter ratios of 10 to 1, and sometimes ratios as high as 100 to 1 are found. Clearly the fatigue life of a material cannot be determined from that of any single specimen. In fact, we would seem quite justified in asking: *Does any material really have a fatigue life for any given stress?*

The answer is that there actually is no single value of fatigue life for the material, even under the most carefully controlled conditions. For most other properties, differences between individually observed values are small enough that an average value, or even a single observation, can be used to represent a particular property. In fatigue, however, as in brittle fracture, the variability, or scatter, of observed values is very great. Consequently neither a single observation nor the average of several can give a measure of fatigue life that can be used with complete assurance. Instead it must be recognized that the fatigue life of a material can only be truly depicted as a *distribution* of values for individual specimens.

Again we are confronted with a question. If there is no definite fatigue life, but only a distribution, how can the engineer design for fatigue? We are used to having property values that we can put our fingers on—values that can be used directly in design, simply by applying a suitable safety factor. Now we are told that we have to deal with distributions of many values.

The answer should be encouraging. Actually, through the use of statis-

Table 9.1   Fatigue Lives[a] for Phosphor Bronze Strip[b] in Reversed Bending (Zero Mean Stress)

| CYCLES TO FAILURE, N | | |
TEST DEFLECTION ±0.420 in.,[c] 10^3 cycles	TEST DEFLECTION ±0.300 in.,[c] 10^3 cycles	RANK
377	1,688	1
381	1,796	2
387	1,800	3
394	2,404	4
401	2,464	5
409	2,466	6
421	2,534	7
433	2,660	8
436	2,717	9
441	2,954	10
444	2,994	11
454	2,999	12
456	3,014	13
458	3,034	14
465	3,295	15
473	3,361	16
475	3,382	17
476	3,382	18
483	3,456	19
487	3,504	20
487	3,547	21
489	4,123	22
489	4,677	23
490	5,568	24
495	5,810	25
499	6,401	26
503	7,104	27
505	7,105	28
506	7,250	29
509	11,212	30
509	11,924	31
516	12,678	32
522	13,542	33
529	14,255	34
531	17,796	35
542	17,912	36
546	17,950	37
556	18,040	38
559	20,634	39
563	25,049	40
575	32,522	41
575	36,921	42
598	50,432	43
599	50,716	44
625	55,525	45
645	62,892	46
708	73,501	47
715	76,074	48

[a] Data taken from Torrey, M. N., and Gohn, G. R., "A Study of Statistical Treatments of Fatigue Data," ASTM *Proceedings* **56**, 1091–1117 (Table III) (1956).

[b] Commercial grade A hard-temper phosphor bronze (5% tin; 0.05% phosphorus). Specimens made to conform to Fig. 10(c) of ASTM STP No. 91; thickness 0.040 in.

[c] Test deflections used correspond to stresses as follows:

Deflection	Stress
±0.300 in.	$\pm31{,}000$ psi
±0.420 in.	$\pm43{,}000$ psi

tical methods, the distribution of values can be used in a much more rational manner than individual values plus a factor of safety. The factor of safety has often been called a "factor of ignorance." One item about which we are usually ignorant is the possible variation of material properties and their distributions; the best we can do is reduce the individual values that we do have by an arbitrary factor. For example, the yield strength of a certain aluminum alloy may be given as $\sigma_y = 70,000$ psi. To obtain a working stress we may divide by a factor of safety, $n_y = 1.5$, to give $\sigma_w = 46,700$ psi (Eq. 3.19). This, we hope, will take care of unavoidable variations in the material, along with unpredictable variations in loading, fabrication, and the like.

With reliable information on the distributions of properties we can do away with part of this factor of ignorance. In its place we can design for a low percentage of failures, or, what is probably more acceptable psychologically, a *high percentage of survivals*. For example, if we know that 99 per cent of all specimens from the above aluminum alloy will be expected to withstand a stress of 60,000 psi without failure, we might use this stress as a point of departure. The safety factor would then need to compensate only for possible variations in the conditions of use, such as fabrication methods and magnitude of applied loads.

Unfortunately such information is not available for most properties. For fatigue, however, the variability is so great that knowledge of this distribution has become a must.

When we speak of the *distribution* of fatigue lives for a material we refer to the fatigue lives of all possible specimens that could be made from that material—the *population*.* This distribution is hypothetical; obviously it is neither possible nor desirable to determine the fatigue lives of all possible specimens of a material. However, an *estimate* of the distribution and its characteristics can be made from samples of the population. A sample consists of a number of specimens (one or more) made from the given material according to some specified plan. It may be thought of as a sort of miniature of the population itself, having similar though not exactly the same characteristics. The larger the sample, the more closely its distribution approximates that of the population. The fatigue lives listed in Table 9.1 are observations made on two samples of fatigue specimens.

By the use of statistical methods we may study the characteristics of distributions in samples and infer from them the characteristics of the distribution in the population.

---

* The specimens must, of course, be prepared and tested in a standard manner.

9.4 STATISTICAL METHODS

Distributions

Distributions such as those of Table 9.1 can be more clearly pictured through the use of various graphical representations. One such representation is the *histogram*. To construct a histogram we first divide the total range of observations into a number of equal intervals and count the number of observations in each interval. In Table 9.2 the range of values

Table 9.2   Frequencies from Table 9.1

CYCLE INTERVAL, 10^3 cycles	FAILURES WITHIN CYCLE INTERVAL	
	FREQUENCY, f	RELATIVE FREQUENCY
371–390	3	0.0625
391–410	3	.0625
411–430	1	.0208
431–450	4	.0833
451–470	4	.0833
471–490	9	.1875
491–510	7	.1458
511–530	3	.0625
531–550	3	.0625
551–570	3	.0625
571–590	2	.0417
591–610	2	.0417
611–630	1	.0208
631–650	1	.0208
651–670	0	.0000
671–690	0	.0000
691–710	1	.0208
711–730	1	.0208
Σ	48	

in column 1 of Table 9.1 is divided into 18 intervals of 20,000 cycles each. The second column gives the resulting *frequencies*, i.e., the number of fatigue lives in each interval.   Next a horizontal axis is laid out, with the intervals shown to a convenient scale.   The histogram is then constructed by erecting on each interval a rectangular strip in which each reading is allotted an equal *area*.   The area of each strip is therefore proportional to the frequency for that interval, and since the intervals are all the same width, their heights are also proportional to the frequencies.   The construction of a *frequency histogram* is illustrated in Fig. 9.8.   The total area in the frequency histogram represents the total number of observations in the sample.

Histograms are often constructed in which the ordinate represents the *relative frequency*, i.e., the *fraction* of the total number of observations occurring in each interval. The third column in Table 9.2 gives the relative frequencies for this example. The same histogram can be used for the relative frequencies. All that needs to be changed is the vertical scale. The total area then represents the sum of all relative frequencies: 1.

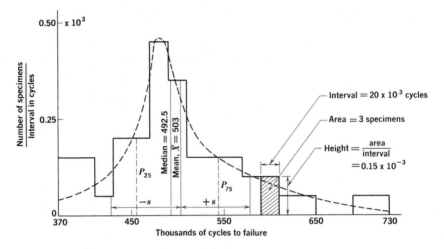

Fig. 9.8   *Frequency histogram of fatigue life from Table 9.2.   (Adapted from Torrey and Gohn, Am. Soc. Test. Mats.* Proceedings *56, 1104 (1956))*

If a larger sample were used to construct the histogram, we could use shorter intervals and the resulting frequencies would give a smoother histogram. As the size of the sample increases, the histogram approaches a smooth curve, called the *theoretical frequency curve* for the population. The dashed curve in Fig. 9.8 might represent the frequency distribution for the population from which this sample was taken.

What the frequency histogram shows most strikingly is that the fatigue lives for a material are clustered around some central value. The relative frequency that fatigue life will be near this value is high, while the relative frequency that it will be far above or below (*extreme values*) is low.

Another form of graphical representation is the *cumulative distribution* (or cumulative percentage) diagram. It shows, for each value of the variable, the fraction (or percentage) of the total number of observations that falls above or below that value. Let us construct a cumulative percentage diagram for the data in Table 9.2. Table 9.3 gives the number of specimens which have fatigue lives longer than a given number of cycles, i.e., the number of survivals, based on the lower side of each cycle interval of Table 9.2. At 731,000 cycles there are no survivals, at 711,000 cycles there is one survival (2.08 per cent), and so on. These percentages are tabulated in column 3 and plotted in Fig. 9.9 to give a polygon. If, as before, the

Table 9.3 Cumulative Frequencies from Table 9.2

LOWER SIDE OF CYCLE INTERVAL, 10^3 cycles	SURVIVALS	
	NUMBER	PERCENTAGE
371	48	100
391	45	93.8
411	42	87.5
431	41	85.5
451	37	77.1
471	33	68.8
491	24	50.0
511	17	35.4
531	14	29.2
551	11	22.9
571	8	16.67
591	6	12.50
611	4	8.33
631	3	6.25
651	2	4.17
671	2	4.17
691	2	4.17
711	1	2.08
731	0	0

number of specimens in the sample is increased, the polygon can be made to approach a smooth curve, which is the theoretical cumulative distribution curve for the population.

Statistics and Parameters

Let us now study the properties of statistical distributions. If we are to use the distributions of fatigue lives of materials for design, we need to know something about these properties. Properties of a sample are measured by *statistics;* properties of the population are called *parameters.* Parameters are not ordinarily measurable but are estimated by statistics.

The first important property is the central value of the distribution. There are several ways of defining the central value, each of which has its own special advantages and applications. Only two are in common use in connection with fatigue: the *arithmetic mean* and the *median.*

The arithmetic mean is defined by

$$\overline{X} = \frac{\sum\limits_{i=1}^{m} X_i}{m}, \tag{9.1}$$

where X_i is the value of one observation (the ith observation), m is the total number of observations in the sample, and $\overline{X}$ is the arithmetic mean,

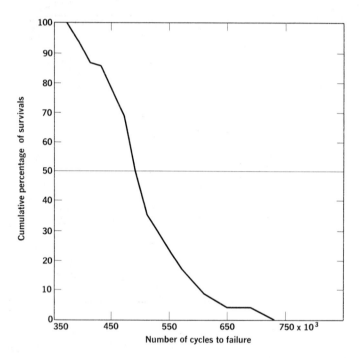

Fig. 9.9   Cumulative percentage diagram from Table 9.3.

or average of the sample.   (Note that n is the more commonly used symbol for the total number of observations, but m is used here to avoid confusion with n as used in Art. 9.1.)   As defined by Eq. 9.1, $\overline{X}$ is termed the *sample average.**   For the data of Table 9.1, column 1, the sample average,

$$\overline{X} = \frac{24,137 \times 10^3}{48} = 503,000 \text{ cycles, provides an estimate of the arithmetic}$$

---

* *A Tentative Guide for Fatigue Testing and the Statistical Analysis of Fatigue Data* (Supplement to *Manual on Fatigue Testing*, STP No. 91), ASTM Special Technical Publication No. 91-A, American Society for Testing Materials, Philadelphia, 1958, p. 3. Hereafter this publication will be referred to simply as ASTM STP No. 91-A.

mean of the population.   Of all the definitions of central value, the arith-metic mean is probably the one most familiar to engineers.

The median is easier to define and easier to calculate.   Its use is recom-mended by ASTM Committee E-9 on Fatigue.*   The *sample median* is simply the middle value of the observations of a sample when they are arranged in order of magnitude, as in Table 9.1.   (If there is an even number of observations, the median is the average of the *two* middle values.) For the data of column 1, then, the sample median is 492,500 cycles.   It provides an estimate of the median of the population.   By definition the median represents the value such that 50 per cent of the observations are above it and 50 per cent below.

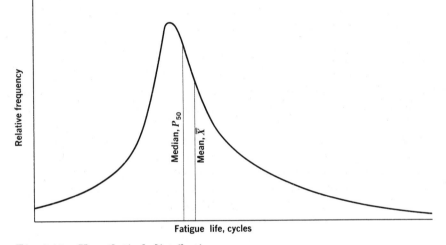

Fig. 9.10   Hypothetical distribution curve for fatigue life.

The arithmetic mean and the median are illustrated graphically in Figs. 9.8 and 9.10, the sample distribution of our example and the hypothetical distribution curve.   Because it represents the 50 per cent point, the median locates a vertical line which divides the area of each diagram into two equal parts (remember that the area under the diagram is proportional to the number of observations).   The arithmetic mean, on the other hand, locates the centroid of the area in accordance with Eq. 9.1.

The second important property of a distribution is its *dispersion*, a measure of the scatter or variability among the possible values.   Most material properties have relatively small dispersions.   It is their large dis-persion that distinguishes fatigue properties and makes statistical analysis essential.   One measure of dispersion is the *standard deviation*, defined by

---

* ASTM STP No. 91-A, p. 3.

$$s = \sqrt{\frac{\Sigma (X_i - \overline{X})^2}{m}}, \tag{9.2}$$

where the symbols under the radical are the same as in Eq. 9.1. According to this equation the standard deviation is the square root of the mean of the squares of the deviations from the sample average—root-mean-square deviation, for short. Its units are the same as those of the observations, X_i. For the data of Table 9.1, column 1, we find the sample standard deviation, $s = 75{,}500$ cycles. The standard deviation determines a range within which a certain percentage of the observations lie. In Fig. 9.8 the vertical lines at a distance s to the right and left of the mean enclose 73 per cent of the observations. The student should compare this with the corresponding figure for the symmetrical Normal distribution given in a later paragraph. The difference results from the asymmetry of the distribution of Fig. 9.8.

A second method of measuring dispersion is the use of *percentiles*. We have already seen an example of a percentile: the median is the 50th percentile, P_{50}. Other percentiles are the values below which the specified percentage of observations falls. For example, P_{25} is the 25th percentile (or *quartile*) and P_{75} the 75th percentile. Since 25 per cent of the observations fall *below* P_{25} and 25 per cent fall *above* P_{75}, it follows that 50 per cent fall between P_{25} and P_{75}. The *range* of the variable between these two points is a measure of the dispersion. Like the median, it is easy to compute. From the two examples in Table 9.1, we find

$$\begin{aligned} \text{Column 1:} \quad & P_{25} = 455{,}000 \text{ cycles} \\ & P_{75} = 544{,}000 \text{ cycles} \\ & \text{Range} = 89{,}000 \text{ cycles} \\ \text{Column 2:} \quad & P_{25} = 3{,}007{,}000 \text{ cycles} \\ & P_{75} = 17{,}931{,}000 \text{ cycles} \\ & \text{Range} = 14{,}924{,}000 \text{ cycles.} \end{aligned}$$

The scatter in column 2 is much greater than in column 1.

If a distribution is symmetrical, the central value will be the same regardless of how it is measured. The distributions illustrated by the diagrams in Figs. 9.8 and 9.10 are noticeably asymmetrical or *skewed*. The type of skewness exhibited, in which the tail is to the right, is called *positive skewness;* the distribution is said to be skewed to the right. Distributions can sometimes be made symmetrical by making a suitable transformation of the variable. For example, if X is replaced by $\log X$, a positively skewed distribution may be made nearly symmetrical.

The Normal Distribution

A particularly useful symmetrical distribution is the *Normal* distribution. (Note that this is the name of the distribution and other distributions are not necessarily *abnormal*.)   Figure 9.11 illustrates the Normal distribution in the form of a relative frequency curve depicting the theoretical distribution of some hypothetical population.   On the basis of the mathematical equation for this curve* it is observed that: the mean and median coincide

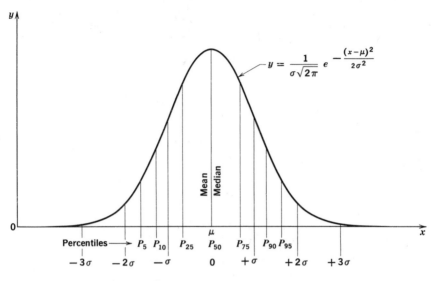

$$y = \frac{1}{\sigma\sqrt{2\pi}}\, e^{-\frac{(x-\mu)^2}{2\sigma^2}}$$

Percentiles → P_5 P_{10} P_{25} P_{50} P_{75} P_{90} P_{95}

-3σ -2σ $-\sigma$ 0 $+\sigma$ $+2\sigma$ $+3\sigma$

Deviation from mean in units of standard deviation, σ

Fig. 9.11   Normal distribution.

at the axis of symmetry, as shown; 68.3 per cent of the population falls between one standard deviation above and one standard deviation below the mean ($\frac{2}{3}$ is often used as a rule of thumb); and the locations of the various percentiles are as shown in Fig. 9.11.   If a sample distribution is approximately symmetrical, or can be made so by a transformation, it may be found to be approximately Normal also.   Then the Normal distribution curve can be used to represent the theoretical distribution curve for the population, and its known characteristics can be useful in making estimates of population parameters from the sample statistics.

The cumulative Normal distribution is shown in Fig. 9.12.   As for sample distributions, the cumulative curve shows the fraction of the popu-

---

* The equation of the Normal curve is

$$y = \frac{1}{\sigma\sqrt{2\pi}}\, e^{-\frac{(x-\mu)^2}{2\sigma^2}}.$$

See Dixon, Wilfrid J., and Massey, Frank J., Jr., *Introduction to Statistical Analysis*, 2nd ed., McGraw-Hill Book Company, Inc., New York, Toronto, London, 1957, p. 48.

lation which falls below each value of the variable.   It also shows the
fraction falling within any given interval, given by the difference between
the ordinates at the ends of the interval.   The curve starts at zero at the
extreme left ($-\infty$) and rises monotonically to 1 at the extreme right ($+\infty$).

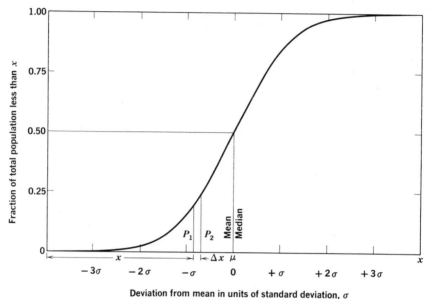

Fig. 9.12   Cumulative Normal distribution.

It crosses the 0.5 line at the median because half the population is below
the median.

Probability

If the theoretical distribution for a population is known—Normal or
otherwise—the *probability* that an observation will fall in any given interval
is given by the theoretical relative frequency for that interval.   The theoretical relative frequency is the fraction of the total population which falls
in the given interval.   It is therefore given by the area of that interval
in the theoretical frequency curve, or by the difference between the ordinates at the ends of the interval in the cumulative distribution curve.   For
example, the probability that any one observation will fall between the
25th and 75th percentiles for the population is one-half; likewise the probability that any one observation will fall below the median is also one-half.

Probability graph paper is designed to facilitate the plotting of cumulative distribution curves for sample observations.   The vertical scale, which

covers the range from 0 to 1, is not linear but is so arranged that the
Normal curve plots as a straight line on the graph.   This adjustment in
scale is illustrated graphically in Fig. 9.13.   In Fig. 9.14 the data from

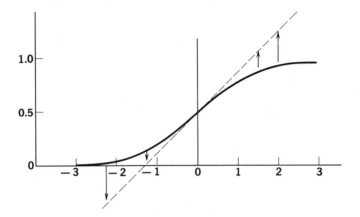

*Fig. 9.13   Adjustment of scale needed to
transform cumulative Normal distribution
curve to a straight line.   Note that the
scale must be expanded vertically by an
increasing amount with increasing distance
above and below the middle of the curve.
Since the curve does not actually reach the
probabilities of 0 and 1.0 except at infinity,
these ordinates are pushed completely off
the scale. (Adapted from Dixon and Massey,*
Introduction to Statistical Analysis, *2nd
ed.,* McGraw-Hill Book Company, Inc.,
New York, 1957)

Table 9.3 are plotted on probability paper.   Although these data are
noticeably skewed, they can be fitted approximately by a straight line.
This graph provides estimates of the median and the various percentage
points, which are given by the intersections of the fitted line with the
corresponding horizontal lines.

9.5   FATIGUE PROPERTIES

Fatigue Life, N.   The total number of cycles required to bring about
final fracture under a given condition of use is the basic fatigue property
in that it is the only one which is directly measurable from experimental
observation.   As measured experimentally fatigue life for a given condition
is a property of the individual specimen.   The fatigue life of the material

is expressed by the distribution of fatigue lives in the population, where the population represents the given material under the given conditions of cyclic loading. We can estimate this distribution by observations of a sample; the larger the sample, the more precise the estimate.

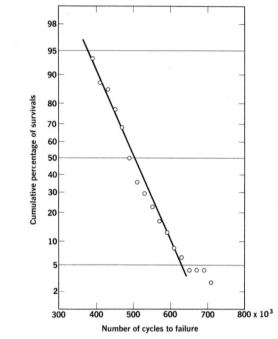

Fig. 9.14   Cumulative distribution of Table 9.2, plotted on probability paper.

Fatigue Life for p Per Cent Survival,[*] N_p. This is the most useful fatigue life for design purposes. It is the fatigue life for which p per cent of the population has a *longer* life; for example, N_{90} is the fatigue life for which 90 per cent will be expected to survive and 10 per cent to fail. Thus N_{90} is the same as the 10th percentile for the population of failures. It can be represented graphically by the corresponding point on the cumulative percentage distribution curve for the population.

The fatigue life for p per cent survival is *estimated* by the corresponding percentile of the sample distribution. For example, in the distributions of Table 9.1, N_{90} is estimated by N for the 5th specimen because 90 per cent (43 specimens) had longer lives. Hence for column 1, $N_{90} = 401,000$ cycles, and for column 2, $N_{90} = 2,464,000$ cycles. The *estimates* are also referred to by the same term: fatigue life for p per cent survival.

---

[*] ASTM STP 91-A, p. 4.

The reliability of the estimate of N_p from a given sample depends on the size of the sample and other statistical considerations. Means for determining the reliability in terms of "confidence intervals" are described by ASTM.*

Median Fatigue Life. Identical with the fatigue life for 50 per cent survival, N_{50}. It is estimated by the middle observation in the sample (or their average if there are two middle observations). In the study of the variation of fatigue life with stress and other factors it will often be convenient to deal with the median fatigue life, but we must remember that it is only a representative property of the distribution at each stress level or other condition.

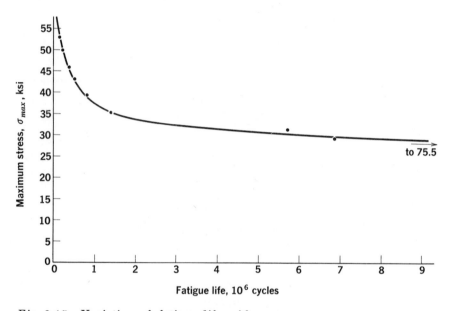

Fig. 9.15 Variation of fatigue life with stress for phosphor bronze strip in reversed bending. (Data from Torrey and Gohn, Am. Soc. Test. Mats. Proceedings 56, 1110 (1956))

The S-N Diagram. Figure 9.15 illustrates the variation of median fatigue life with stress. As in previous examples, stress is assumed to be purely alternating, from tension to compression, with $\sigma_m = 0$. The vertical axis is the maximum stress, σ_{max}, and the horizontal axis is cycles to

---

* ASTM STP 91-A, Section VI.

failure, or fatigue life N.   This diagram is called an *S-N diagram*, where S
stands for stress.   As the stress decreases from some high value, N increases
slowly at first, then more and more rapidly.   There is considerable curvature at all parts of the range, except for very long lives.   It has been found
that if N is plotted on a logarithmic scale, the first part of the curve often
becomes nearly linear.   Figure 9.16 is a typical *S-N diagram* plotted in

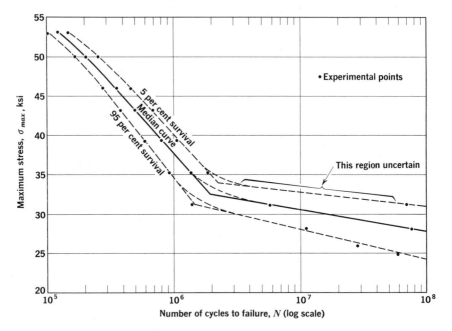

Fig. 9.16 S-N *diagram for phosphor
bronze strip in reversed bending (compare
Table 9.1).   (Data from Torrey and Gohn,
Am. Soc. Test. Mats.* Proceedings *56, 1110
(1956))*

this way; the solid line is the median *S-N* curve (50 per cent survival).
The data in Table 9.1 are included in this curve, which is for hard-temper
phosphor bronze strip.   Note that it is possible to fit most of the points
quite well by two straight intersecting lines.   It is interesting to observe
that in this example the point where the two lines meet is near the proportional limit stress for the material.   This fact seems to indicate that the
variation of N with σ for simple fatigue ($\sigma < \sigma_{pl}$) differs somewhat from
that for higher stresses, where gross yielding is involved.   However, it
should be pointed out that the intersection, if there is one, does not always
come near the proportional limit stress.

The dashed lines in Fig. 9.16 are *S-N* curves for *p* per cent survival, in which the corresponding values of N_p are used for each stress.   A family of curves of this type is referred to as a *P-S-N diagram.*

The upper end of the *S-N* curve is somewhat indefinite.   If ordinary static loading is considered as a fatigue loading of one quarter cycle, then the ultimate strength of the material provides the upper end of the *S-N* curve.   Tests at stresses near the ultimate strength give some indication that the curve bends toward the horizontal near the upper end,* as in Fig.

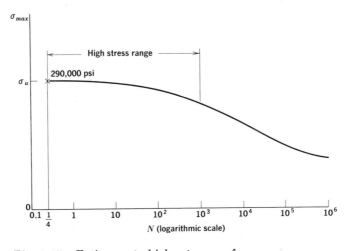

Fig. 9.17   Fatigue at high stresses for high-strength low-alloy steel: AISI4340, 290,000-psi.   (Adapted from Sachs and Scheven, Am. Soc. Test. Mats. Proceedings **57,** *677* (1957))

9.17.   This high stress range, sometimes called *low-cycle fatigue,* is still under investigation.

The lower, or long-life, portion of the curve can sometimes be represented by a straight line (Fig. 9.16) and sometimes by a curve (Fig. 9.17).   Either way the lower portion tends toward the horizontal, and in certain materials actually becomes horizontal for all practical purposes (Fig. 9.18).   When the *S-N* curve approaches a horizontal asymptote, the corresponding stress is called the *fatigue limit,*† σ_e, and the fatigue life at lower stresses is assumed to be infinite.   This indicates that at stresses below σ_e no fatigue

---

* Sachs, George, and Scheven, G., "Relation between Direct-Stress and Bending Fatigue of High-Strength Steels," *Proceedings* Am. Soc. Test. Mats. **57,** 667–681 (1957).
† Formerly called the *endurance limit.*

damage occurs.   Ferrous metals usually have a fatigue limit, whereas non-ferrous metals often do not.

Many attempts have been made to formulate mathematical equations for *S-N* curves.   Equations of some sort are necessary to develop experi-

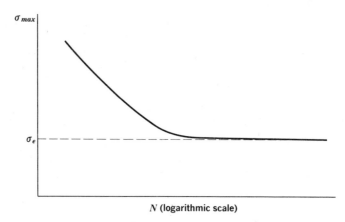

Fig. 9.18   S-N *diagram for a material having a fatigue limit,* σ_e.

mental methods.   One of the most useful equations, suggested by Weibull* on the basis of statistical theory, is of hyperbolic form:

$$(\sigma - \sigma_e)^m N = k \quad \text{(for } \sigma > \sigma_e),\qquad (9.3)$$

where m and k are material constants, σ_e is the fatigue limit, and σ and N are the variables.   This equation is good mainly in the long-life range and implies existence of a fatigue limit.   If we take logarithms of both sides, the equation takes the form

$$m \log (\sigma - \sigma_e) = \log k - \log N,\qquad (9.3a)$$

indicating a linear relation between $\log (\sigma - \sigma_e)$ and $\log N$.

Fatigue Strength, σ_n.   The *S-N* diagram makes it possible to convert from fatigue life, which we can measure, to *fatigue strength*, which is usually more useful in design.   In a general way fatigue strength can be defined as *the stress which a material can withstand repeatedly for N cycles.*   Obviously fatigue strength cannot be measured directly by experimental means because the stress must always be settled upon before starting the test and it would be impossible to preselect a stress for each specimen such

---

* Weibull, W., "Statistical Representation of Fatigue Failures in Solids," *Trans. Royal Inst. of Tech.*, Stockholm, No. 27, 1949 (49 pp.).

that it would fail at just N cycles. Consequently the fatigue strength must be found by interpolation from the S-N curve.

Since fatigue life is defined only by a distribution, it follows that the fatigue strength is defined likewise. There are various definitions of fatigue strength, just as there are various definitions for fatigue life. If fatigue strength is determined from the median curve, it is called the *median fatigue strength at N cycles*, σ_n. It is assumed that at this stress approximately 50 per cent of the population would survive N cycles. A more valuable stress for use in design is the fatigue strength for p per cent survival at N cycles, which may be determined by interpolating in the S-N curve for p per cent survival.

Fatigue Limit, σ_e. A special case of fatigue strength, which may be defined as the limiting value of median fatigue strength as N becomes very large.[*] Here, too, in view of the distribution associated with fatigue limit, it will often be more desirable to use the fatigue limit for p per cent survival. Special methods are usually necessary to obtain the proper estimate of this fatigue limit.[†]

The fatigue limit is highly desirable as a design criterion. Below the fatigue limit it is assumed that the fatigue life is infinite, so that the *number* of cycles is no longer a factor. It should be remembered, however, that the mere existence of cyclic loading may still be expected to cause a certain percentage of failures, depending on which fatigue limit is specified.

Values of σ_e are usually tabulated with other mechanical properties. However, stresses tabulated as "fatigue limits" are sometimes nothing more than fatigue strengths for some high value of N. For example, for aluminum and magnesium alloys the median fatigue strengths for 500 million cycles are sometimes listed as fatigue limits, and for copper- and nickel-base alloys the fatigue strengths for as few as 100 million cycles may be listed in this way.[‡] A duration of 500 million cycles is a common practical limit for fatigue experiments. At the usual cycling rates at least 5 weeks are required to run this many cycles.

The distribution of fatigue limits, or fatigue strengths for N cycles, can be shown by a *response curve* based on observations of per cent survival at a number of stress levels. If plotted on Normal probability paper it can usually be fitted approximately by a straight line. Figure 9.19 illustrates a response curve for a particular type of steel at 10^7 cycles, constructed from the test data of Table 9.4. A total of 51 specimens was tested at five stress levels. The number of specimens surviving 10^7 cycles was observed at each level; this number was then converted to per cent and plotted

---

* ASTM STP 91-A, p. 4.

† ASTM STP 91-A, Section VI.

‡ ASTM STP 91-A, p. 4.

against the corresponding stress in Fig. 9.19. The straight line may be fitted by eye or by use of statistical methods.* This line is the derived response curve and can be used to estimate the fatigue strength for p per cent survival at 10^7 cycles. For example, the median fatigue strength at 10^7 cycles is found from the point where the response curve crosses the 50 per cent survival line: 43.1 ksi. For 90 per cent survival the corresponding fatigue strength is 40.5 ksi.

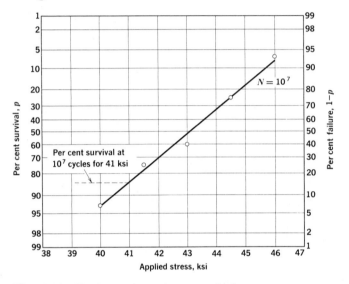

Fig. 9.19   Response curve for a particular type of steel. (Adapted from STP No. 91-A, A Tentative Guide for Fatigue Testing and the Statistical Analysis of Fatigue Data, published by the American Society for Testing Materials, Philadelphia, 1958)

We shall close our study of fatigue properties for alternating tension and compression by examining the nature of their statistical distributions. The distribution of fatigue lives in a group of observations at a given stress level is frequently found to be skewed to the right (Fig. 9.8). If the same set of data is replotted using log N as the variable instead of N, it is found to yield an approximately Normal distribution. Such a distribution is referred to as a *log-Normal distribution*. If it is plotted on the usual *S-N* diagram, where the abscissa is log N, it will be approximately Normal (Fig. 9.20a).

---

* ASTM STP 91-A, Section VI.

Table 9.4   Response Test Data[a]

APPLIED STRESS, ksi	NUMBER OF SPECIMENS TESTED	NUMBER OF SPECIMENS SURVIVING 10⁷ CYCLES	PER CENT SURVIVAL, p
40.0	15	14	93.33
41.5	8	6	75.00
43.0	5	3	60.00
44.5	8	2	25.00
46.0	15	1	6.67

[a] Data from ASTM STP 91-A, Table H, p. 29 (by permission).

Unfortunately very little consistency has been found in fatigue life distributions. At the high-stress end the distribution is often quite close to Normal, but at the low-stress, long-life end it is often impossible to obtain a Normal distribution by any of the usual transformations.

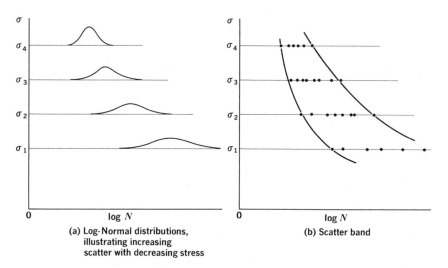

(a) Log-Normal distributions, illustrating increasing scatter with decreasing stress

(b) Scatter band

Fig. 9.20   Schematic S-N diagrams, illustrating distributions of fatigue lives.

In addition to variations in type of distribution there is a variation in the *dispersion* of the distribution. At low stresses the mechanism of failure approaches that of simple fatigue, with its highly random distribution of fatigue lives. As the stress increases and larger plastic deformations are involved, the fatigue process becomes less localized (Art. 9.2) and its statistical character becomes less pronounced. Thus we find that as the stress increases, the amount of scatter usually decreases (Fig. 9.20a). (In this figure it is assumed that all distributions are log-Normal.) A common method of indicating dispersion is by means of a scatter band, as in Fig. 9.20b.   The lines enclosing the band are faired through the end-points of each group of observations.   The width of the scatter band therefore depends on the number of observations in each group.   *The use of S-N curves for p per cent survival is recommended in place of scatter bands.*

The distribution of fatigue strengths is usually close to a Normal distribution, as illustrated by the fact that the response curves usually plot as straight lines on Normal probability paper (Fig. 9.19).   Scatter increases as N increases and is quite large for the fatigue limit.   The following data for 121 specimens of SAE 4340 steel* illustrate the amount of scatter encountered: $\sigma_e = 46{,}270$ psi, with a standard deviation $s = 2900$ psi; if we assume a Normal distribution, the range of stress for 95 per cent of the population is estimated as $\sigma_e \pm 2\,s$, or from 40,470 to 52,070 psi.

FACTORS AFFECTING FATIGUE

9.6 OTHER FORMS OF LOADING

Our study of fatigue has so far been limited to the simplest case: uniaxial stresses alternating between tension and compression, with $\sigma_m = 0$.   We shall now discuss briefly the effects of certain more complex forms of loading: alternating stresses with superposed steady stress (both tension and compression), and torsion (shearing stress).   To provide some uniformity it will be assumed that all properties discussed will be the *median* properties (those for 50 per cent survival).

When an alternating stress is superposed on a steady stress, the specification of the loading must include both parts.   This may be done by specifying σ_m and σ_a, σ_m and σ_{max}, σ_{max} and σ_{min}, σ_{max} and R, etc (Art. 9.1).   Fatigue properties must of course be specified in a similar manner.   For example, if an *S-N* diagram is to be constructed, the vertical axis will be either σ_{max} or σ_a.   A particular *S-N* curve may then be identified by the corresponding value of σ_m, σ_{min}, or R.   Figure 9.21 shows some families of *S-N* curves for various conditions of uniaxial loading.   Fatigue strengths and fatigue limits must be carefully defined, including both quantities indicated on the *S-N* curve in the definitions.

Mean Stress Positive

The simplest variation, for discussion purposes, is that of σ_{an}, the *stress amplitude for a given fatigue life.*   Generally speaking the influence of the

---

* Ransom, J. T., and Mehl, R. F., "The Statistical Nature of the Fatigue Properties of SAE 4340 Steel Forgings," *Symposium on Fatigue—II*, American Society for Testing Materials STP No. 137, 1952, p. 8.

mean stress on σ_{an} is small, provided the yield stress is not exceeded, an indication that the alternating stress amplitude is the main controlling factor in simple fatigue.

As based on experimental observations, the actual variation of σ_{an} appears to be a linear decrease. This is illustrated in Fig. 9.22, where σ_{an}

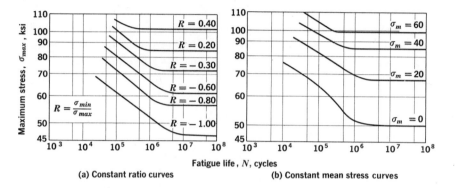

(a) Constant ratio curves   (b) Constant mean stress curves

Fig. 9.21   Families of S-N *curves for different values of stress ratio,* R, *and mean stress,* σ_m. (*Adapted from Grover, Gordon, and Jackson,* Fatigue of Metals and Structures, *report No. NAVAER 00-25-523, published by Battelle Memorial Institute, 1954*)

is plotted against σ_m. In this diagram the maximum stress reaches the yield stress, σ_y, at point Y. Up to that point the variation can be represented by the equation

$$\sigma_{an} = \sigma_n - \lambda\sigma_m, \tag{9.4}$$

where σ_n is the median fatigue strength at N cycles of purely alternating stress and λ is the slope of the line. No connection has been determined between λ and any other properties. All that can be said is that λ is a small slope, such that if the line is extended it intersects the σ_m-axis somewhere *to the right* of point U, which marks the ultimate stress, σ_u. The actual value of λ can only be determined by experiment.

Beyond the yield stress there is a wide variation in the trend of the curve, from an upward slope to a more steeply downward one. In some materials an actual hump has been observed (top curve, Fig. 9.22). Eventually, though, there is always a sharp decrease in stress amplitude, and the curve drops toward U. Since the specimen can be expected to break at a steady stress, σ_u, with no alternating component ($\sigma_{an} = 0$), point U is usually considered the end of the curve.   The shape of the curve at stresses just below σ_u is still very uncertain.

The construction for locating point Y on the curve is of interest.   At this point $\sigma_{max} = \sigma_y$ (the tensile yield stress), and since $\sigma_{max} = \sigma_m + \sigma_{an}$, we have

$$\sigma_{an} = \sigma_y - \sigma_m, \tag{9.5}$$

which is the equation of the 45° line starting at σ_y.   At any point on this line the maximum stress is equal to the yield stress.   Similarly any line parallel to it represents a corresponding constant maximum stress.

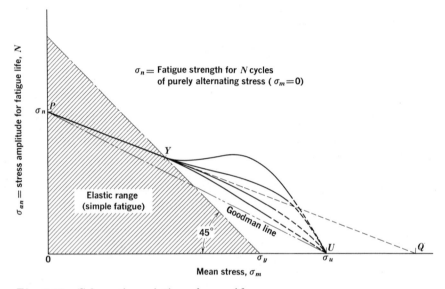

Fig. 9.22   *Schematic variation of* σ_{an} *with* σ_m.

Many empirical equations have been proposed to represent the variation of σ_{an} with σ_m for design purposes.   The most commonly used is the Goodman law,*

$$\sigma_{an} = \sigma_n \left(1 - \frac{\sigma_m}{\sigma_u}\right), \tag{9.6a}$$

where σ_n is the fatigue strength for alternating stress.   This equation represents a straight line variation starting at point P on the σ_{an}-axis and ending at U on the σ_m-axis (Fig. 9.22).   The Goodman law gives values which

---

* Sometimes referred to as the *modified Goodman law* because, as originally proposed, it was found to be of very limited application.   See Gough, H. J., *The Fatigue of Metals*, Ernest Benn Limited, London, 1926, p. 64.

are nearly always conservative and therefore safe to use for design. Only two material constants are required—the ultimate strength in tension and the fatigue strength for purely alternating stress.

Another empirical relation is the Gerber law. Graphically this law is represented by a parabola whose vertex is at P, passing through point U. Its equation is

$$\sigma_{an} = \sigma_n \left(1 - \frac{\sigma_m^2}{\sigma_u^2} \right). \tag{9.6b}$$

As in the Goodman law, this equation is completely defined when two material constants, σ_n and σ_u, are known. The values given by the Gerber law are more nearly average values and are, as a consequence, often on the unsafe side.

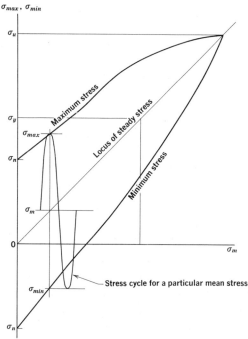

Fig. 9.23 Goodman diagram.

When the Goodman law is too conservative to be economical and the Gerber law is considered too uncertain, the only alternative is to conduct experiments to estimate safe working stresses under the given conditions of loading.

An alternative graphical representation often used by engineers is the Goodman diagram (Fig. 9.23). The horizontal axis is still σ_m, but the vertical axis is the maximum stress, σ_{max}.   The upper curve shows the variation of σ_{max} with σ_m.   To show the range of stress in a more pictorial way, the minimum stress, σ_{min}, is shown on the same diagram.   The Goodman diagram makes it a little easier to visualize yield stress.

Mean Stress Negative

For *small* compressive mean stresses—$|\sigma_m| \ll |\sigma_a|$—the tension part of the cycle is still the most important from the standpoint of fatigue.   As the mean stress decreases (algebraically), the stress amplitude, σ_{an}, in-

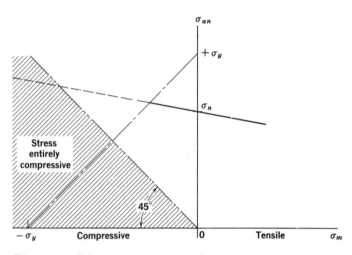

Fig. 9.24   Schematic variation of σ_{an} for negative mean stress.

creases.   Figure 9.24 shows the variation, an extension of the line for small positive mean stress.   Consequently Eq. 9.4 can be used by substituting the value of σ_m with its proper sign.

When the stress is compressive for the entire cycle—repeated compressive stress—the type of failure differs for different materials.   For brittle materials failure is exactly like that in static compression; it occurs on shearing planes at approximately 45° to the axis of loading.   To cause failure in ductile materials, stresses higher than the compressive yield stress are usually required.   Fractures are therefore preceded by considerable distortion.   This type of fatigue fracture is not important from the standpoint of design because compressive plastic deformations are not usually allowed anyway.   Consequently little research has been done in this area.

Torsion of Circular Shafts

Fatigue in torsion is an important factor in the design of coil springs. The wire of which the spring is made may be subjected to many cycles of fluctuating torsion during the life of the spring. Two characteristics of

Fig. 9.25 Fatigue fracture of a helical spring. (Courtesy Hetényi, Ed., Handbook of Experimental Stress Analysis, John Wiley & Sons, Inc., New York, 1950)

torsion are particularly significant in fatigue: the state of stress and its distribution. As shown in Chapter 6, the state of stress is pure shear, in which the maximum shearing stresses act on two well-defined sets of planes —transverse and longitudinal. The distribution is such that the maximum stress occurs in the outer surface of the shaft, whether it is hollow or solid.

The mechanism of crack nucleation and propagation is the same as discussed in Art. 9.2. Because of the two characteristics mentioned above, there is an even greater tendency for cracks to nucleate in the surface, and to be confined to longitudinal and transverse planes. If the material is homogeneous and isotropic, there is an equal tendency for microscopic cracks to form in either direction. After the cracks have grown to some length in the directions of maximum shear, the tensile stress at 45° to the axis takes over, and the cracks continue to propagate in the same manner as cracks in brittle materials. The final crack is therefore helical with a 45° slope. The appearance of such a fracture surface in a spring made of normally ductile materials is evidence of fatigue failure (Fig. 9.25).

Many rods and wires used to make springs are not at all isotropic but have a pronounced directionality. This is because they are cold-drawn, or formed in such a way that the grains are elongated in the direction of the axis. Along with the grains, inclusions and other weaknesses are elongated in the same direction. As a result fatigue cracks are usually nucleated in longitudinal planes of weakness and frequently remain entirely in these planes.

Since it produces a state of pure shear, torsion provides an example of fatigue under combined stresses. It has been shown that nucleation of fatigue cracks in ductile metals is, like yielding, a shearing process. Consequently fatigue failure under combined stresses is related to that under uniaxial stress in the same way that yielding under combined stresses is related to yielding under uniaxial stress. As a first approximation it may be assumed that the critical value of shearing stress for fatigue failure is the same for all states of stress (compare maximum shear stress theory, Art. 6.4). For uniaxial stress the shear corresponding to σ_n (median fatigue strength for N cycles) is $\tau_n = \dfrac{\sigma_n}{2}$. On the basis of this assumption the shearing stress for fatigue failure in pure shear is

$$(\tau_n)_s = \frac{\sigma_n}{2}. \tag{9.7a}$$

Experimental evidence indicates that, as in yielding, the critical value of the shearing stress for fatigue failure varies somewhat with the state of stress. A more accurate criterion is given by the octahedral shear stress theory (Art. 6.4), which states that the octahedral shear stress for fatigue failure is the same for all states of stress. For pure shear, this reduces to

$$(\tau_n)_s = 1.15 \left(\frac{\sigma_n}{2}\right) = 0.58 \, \sigma_n, \tag{9.7b}$$

and shows that the maximum shear stress theory is on the conservative side.

9.7 FATIGUE DAMAGE

The problem of design for a variable loading spectrum has only recently been given the attention it warrants, probably because recent developments in aircraft have elevated fatigue from minor to primary importance.   The increased size of air transports, for example, has resulted in lower maneuvering speeds and a corresponding reduction in maneuver loads.   This, in turn, has led to a relative increase in the importance of gust loads, which by their intermittent nature tend to produce fatigue.   Fatigue is often the controlling factor in design of rotary-wing aircraft.

In Art. 9.1 it was pointed out that a complicated loading spectrum could be replaced by a simplified spectrum consisting of several sets of cycles having different values of σ_m and σ_a (Fig. 9.3).   We have studied the methods used to treat one set of cycles at one pair of values of σ_m and σ_a. Now the question arises as to how these results are affected by prior cycling at other stress levels.

The key to the situation would seem to lie in a thorough understanding of fatigue damage.   Although fatigue damage is qualitatively understood in most respects, quantitative information is still limited.   It is known that fatigue cracks are nucleated during the first few cycles of loading.   Hence practically no phase of the service life is free from damage of some kind.

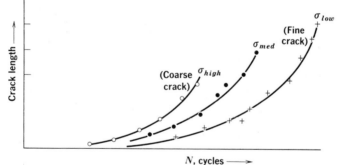

Fig. 9.26   Propagation of fatigue cracks at various constant stresses. (Adapted from Sines and Waisman, Eds., Metal Fatigue, *McGraw-Hill Book Company, Inc., New York, 1959)*

Crack propagation involves many factors.   Cracks are sometimes started but fail to propagate.   An important factor here is the stress gradient.   Cracks start in regions of high stress, and if they grow in directions of decreasing stress, their growth will tend to slow down or even stop.

Evidence is found in the observation that fatigue life in reversed bending is greater than in alternating simple tension and compression.

Cracks also propagate at different speeds in different materials and under different conditions. Experiments have been performed in which crack length was measured as a function of the number of cycles. Figure 9.26 shows some typical curves of crack growth under various stress levels. Each curve ends with fracture at some critical crack length. Note that the critical crack length is greatest for the lower stress levels. Another effect of stress level is its effect on the character of the crack: low stress levels produce fine cracks and high stress levels produce coarse cracks.

The order in which stress levels are applied has important effects on the progress of fatigue damage. For example, it seems logical that a coarse crack started by a previous high stress will not propagate very rapidly under a subsequent low stress. On the other hand, a fine crack left by a previous low stress might propagate very rapidly under a subsequent high stress. At the same time local strain-hardening at the tip of a crack may have important bearing on how it behaves under subsequent higher or lower stresses.

All these variations tend to average out if stress levels are applied in random order. Since many important loading spectra *are* applied in random order, it is reasonable to assume that the variations do average out. It is on this basis that the *cumulative-damage theory* has been developed.

According to this theory each series of stress cycles accounts for a certain fraction of the total damage, and when these fractions add up to unity, failure will occur. The fraction of the total damage done by one series of cycles at a particular stress level is given by the ratio of the number of cycles actually endured at that level to the fatigue life at that level. This ratio is called the *cycle ratio*, $C = n_i/N_i$. The value of N is obtained from the S-N curve for p per cent survival. Expressed mathematically,[*]

$$\sum \frac{n_i}{N_i} = 1. \tag{9.8}$$

As an example, the fatigue lives from the S-N diagram for a certain steel are

$$\sigma_1 = 50,000 \text{ psi}, N_1 = 2,000,000 \text{ cycles}$$
$$\sigma_2 = 55,000 \text{ psi}, N_2 = 500,000 \text{ cycles}$$
$$\sigma_3 = 60,000 \text{ psi}, N_3 = 125,000 \text{ cycles}.$$

Now according to the cumulative damage theory, failure should occur when the values of n satisfy the following equation:

---

[*] Sines, George, and Waisman, J. L., *Metal Fatigue* (University of California Engineering Extension Series) McGraw-Hill Book Company, Inc., 1959, p. 279.

$$\frac{n_1}{N_1} + \frac{n_2}{N_2} + \frac{n_3}{N_3} = 1,$$

or

$$\frac{n_1}{2} + \frac{n_2}{0.5} + \frac{n_3}{0.125} = 10^6,$$

where n_1 is the number of cycles at σ_1, n_2 the number of cycles at σ_2, etc. Obviously if $n_1 = N_1$, we will have $n_2 = n_3 = 0$ (since n can hardly be negative), and similarly for $n_2 = N_2$ or $n_3 = N_3$. Another combination of n's leading to failure is $n_1 = 600{,}000$, $n_2 = 150{,}000$, and $n_3 = 50{,}000$, for which the equation reduces to $(0.3 + 0.3 + 0.4) = 1$. Obviously there is an infinite number of combinations of n's that should lead to failure.

If the loading spectrum is described by saying that a certain *fraction* of the total life, N, is to be at each stress, Eq. 9.8 can be reduced to one unknown, N. If we let k_i be the fraction of N at the stress σ_i, the number of cycles at that stress will be $k_i N$. The total number of cycles is given by $N = \Sigma\, k_i N$, from which $\Sigma\, k_i = 1$. The cycle ratio is now $k_i N / N_i$, and Eq. 9.8 reduces to:

$$\sum \frac{k_i N}{N_i} = N \left(\sum \frac{k_i}{N_i} \right) = 1. \tag{9.8a}$$

In the above example let us suppose we have specified that $k_1 = 0.5$, $k_2 = 0.4$, and $k_3 = 0.1$. To find the fatigue life we substitute these values into Eq. 9.8a to give

$$N \left(\frac{0.5}{2 \times 10^6} + \frac{0.4}{0.5 \times 10^6} + \frac{0.1}{0.125 \times 10^6} \right) = 1,$$

from which $1.85\, N = 10^6$, or $N = 540{,}000$ cycles.

The cumulative damage theory is illustrated graphically in the *S-N* curve of Fig. 9.27. For simplicity, only two stress levels are considered. Cycling is started at σ_1 at point A and continued for n_1 cycles to point B. The cycle ratio is $C_1 = n_1/N_1$. Now the stress is changed to σ_2 and cycling continued for n_2 additional cycles to failure. According to Eq. 9.8

$$\frac{n_1}{N_1} + \frac{n_2}{N_2} = 1,$$

or

$$\frac{n_1}{N_1} = 1 - \frac{n_2}{N_2} = \frac{N_2 - n_2}{N_2}. \tag{9.8b}$$

The ratio $(N_2 - n_2)/N_2$ expresses the fraction of life N_2 that was used up during the first cycling, at σ_1. It is called the *damage ratio*. Equation 9.8b states that the fraction of life used up during the first cycling is equal to the cycle ratio, C_1, which can be applied to any subsequent cycling, regardless of the stress used. Since the *S-N* curve is plotted on a logarithmic scale for N, it follows that the distance $\overline{BE} = \log N_1 - \log n_1 = \log (N_1/n_1)$. According to Eq. 9.8b, this quantity is the same as $\log [N_2/(N_2 - n_2)] = \log N_2 - \log (N_2 - n_2)$. But the distance $\overline{FC}$ represents, to the logarithmic scale, the amount of the fatigue life, N_2, used up during the first loading, and since n_2 cycles remain at this stress, it follows that the amount used up was $N_2 - n_2$; hence $\overline{FC} = \log (N_2 - n_2)$. From the diagram we then see that the distance $\overline{CD} = \log N_2 - \log (N_2 - n_2) = \log (N_1/n_1) = \overline{BE}$. When the stress is changed, therefore, the line representing the process on the graph is always drawn parallel to the S-N curve.

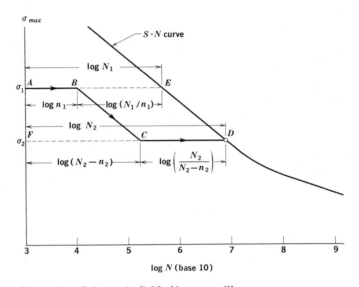

Fig. 9.27   Schematic S-N *diagram, illustrating progress of loading at two stresses.*

In experiments to test the validity of the cumulative damage theory the cycle ratios rarely add up to exactly unity. In fact, sums ranging from 0.5 to 2.5 have been recorded.[*] However, as suggested earlier, much of this variation may be caused by applying all cycles of each stress at one time instead of in a random order. When experimental loads are applied a few cycles at a time, with frequent changes of load, it has been observed that $\Sigma (n_i/N_i)$ tends to give values closer to 1.[†] Thus Eq. 9.8 may be expected to give good results for actual loading spectra. It is recom-

[*] Sines, George, and Waisman, J. L., *Metal Fatigue* (University of California Engineering Extension Series) McGraw-Hill Book Company, Inc., 1959, p. 288.

[†] *Ibid.*, p. 385.

mended that in computing the cycle ratios for Eq. 9.8 the values of N_i be taken from the S-N curve for a high percentage of survival, or from the lowest S-N curve available (for example, the lower boundary of a scatterband). This procedure usually ensures conservative predictions.

When the stress amplitude varies *continuously* rather than in steps, Eq. 9.8 may be replaced by an integral

$$\int \frac{dn}{N} = 1. \tag{9.8c}$$

If the mean stress is constant and σ_a is a known function of n, and if the fatigue life, N, is also a known function of σ_a, the integration can usually be performed and the equation solved.

Suppose, for example, that a purely alternating stress is applied ($\sigma_m = 0$), in which the amplitude increases by a uniform amount, α, with each cycle, starting at the endurance limit, so that

$$\sigma_a = \sigma_e + \alpha n.$$

Let us further assume that the S-N curve is a hyperbola defined by Eq. 9.3:

$$(\sigma_a - \sigma_e)^m N = k.$$

If we use the values of n and N from these two expressions, Eq. 9.8c becomes

$$\int_{\sigma_e}^{\sigma_R} \frac{(\sigma_a - \sigma_e)^m \, d\sigma_a}{k\alpha} = 1, \tag{9.8d}$$

where σ_R is the stress amplitude reached when rupture finally takes place. Carrying out the integration, we have

$$\frac{(\sigma_R - \sigma_e)^{m+1}}{m + 1} = k\alpha,$$

or

$$\sigma_R = \sigma_e + k'\alpha^{\frac{1}{m+1}}$$

$$= \sigma_e + k'\alpha^i \quad \left(i = \frac{1}{m + 1}\right). \tag{9.9}$$

A similar result was obtained by Prot in 1948 in developing his method of fatigue testing using *increasing* rather than constant stress amplitudes. The principal difference was that he assumed a simple hyperbolic relation between σ and N, i.e., $m = 1$ (or $i = \frac{1}{2}$) in Eq. 9.3. His equation corresponding to Eq. 9.9 was therefore of the form*

$$\sigma_R = \sigma_e + k'\sqrt{\alpha}. \tag{9.9a}$$

---

* Prot, E. Marcel, "Fatigue Testing under Progressive Loading; A New Technique for Testing Materials," *Rev. de Metallurgie* **XLV**, No. 12, 481 (1948).

The Prot method and its generalizations will be discussed in more detail in Art. 9.11 on experimental methods.

Recent investigations* have shown that the more general equation, 9.9, fits experimental data better than that used by Prot. The exponent $i = 1/(m + 1)$ has been found to vary from 0.3 to 0.7 for ferrous metals.

9.8   STRESS CONCENTRATIONS

As already pointed out (Art. 9.2), stress concentrations are actually responsible for the majority of fatigue failures occurring in practice. In static loading of ductile materials the peak stress at a notch or other discontinuity normally causes gross yielding in that region, and the load is transferred to other parts of the member. The stress concentration is removed by yielding, and the stress becomes nearly uniform in spite of the notch. Yielding under repeated stresses is restricted to much smaller regions and can do little to equalize the stress distribution. In fatigue, therefore, stress concentrations tend to retain their full effect.

As a first approximation, the elastic stress-concentration factor, K_t, might be used to compute the stress for design purposes. For example, for a small circular hole, like a rivet hole, in a large plate in simple tension, elastic theory† gives $K_t = 3$. In determining the fatigue strength, σ'_n, of a member having a circular hole we would note that the average stress is $\frac{1}{3}$ of the maximum, and therefore $\sigma'_n = \frac{1}{3}\sigma_n$, where σ_n is determined from the S-N diagram. In other words we would take

$$\sigma'_n = \frac{\sigma_n}{K_t}. \tag{9.10a}$$

Values of K_t are available from tables or graphs for various standard discontinuities such as notches, holes, or fillets‡ (Fig. 9.28). For special shapes K_t can be determined by photoelastic experiments.

In general the slight relief given through local yielding and the strengthening effect of the high local strain rate at the root of the notch (Art. 7.8) reduce stress concentrations somewhat from their full elastic values, even in fatigue. The actual effectiveness of a stress concentration is measured by the *fatigue strength reduction factor*,§ K_f. It is defined as the ratio of the fatigue strength of a member *without* any stress concentration (σ_n) to

---

* Corten, H. T., Dimoff, T., and Dolan, T. J., "An Appraisal of the Prot Method of Fatigue Testing," *Proceedings* Am. Soc. Test. Mats. **54**, 875–894 (1954).

† Timoshenko, S., *Strength of Materials—Part II—Advanced Theory and Problems*, 3rd ed., D. Van Nostrand Company, Inc., Princeton, New Jersey, 1956, Ch. VIII.

‡ Peterson, R. E., *Stress Concentration Design Factors*, John Wiley & Sons, Inc., New York, 1953.

§ The term *fatigue notch factor* is also used (ASTM E6-58aT).

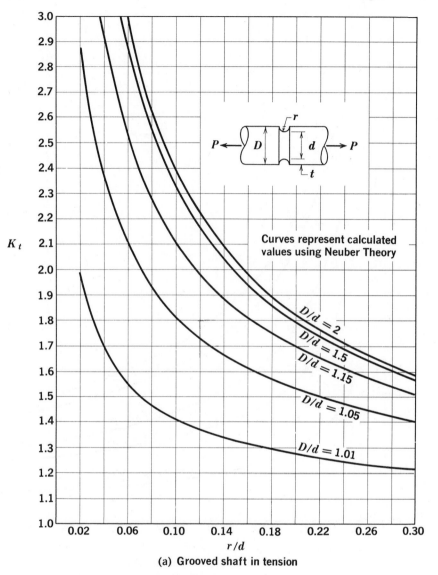

(a) Grooved shaft in tension

Fig. 9.28   Stress concentration factors for grooves, fillets, and holes. (Adapted from Peterson, Stress Concentration Design Factors, *John Wiley & Sons, Inc., New York, 1953)*

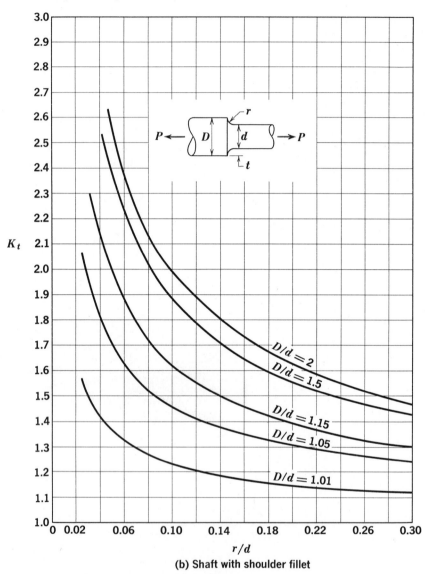

(b) Shaft with shoulder fillet

Fig. 9.28 (Cont.)   Stress concentration factors for grooves, fillets, and holes.   (Adapted from Peterson, Stress Concentration Design Factors, *John Wiley & Sons, Inc., New York, 1953)*

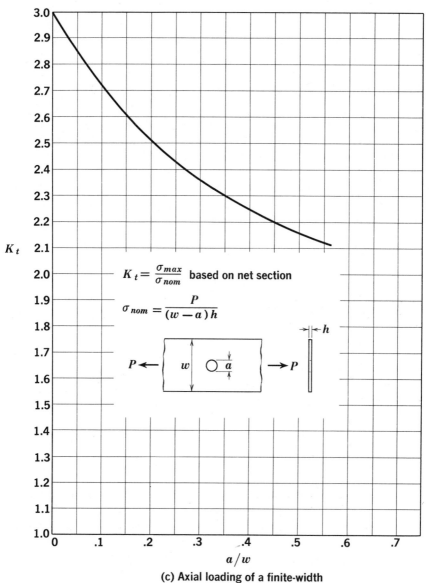

$$K_t = \frac{\sigma_{max}}{\sigma_{nom}} \text{ based on net section}$$

$$\sigma_{nom} = \frac{P}{(w-a)h}$$

(c) Axial loading of a finite-width
plate having a transverse hole

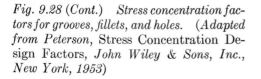

Fig. 9.28 (Cont.)   Stress concentration factors for grooves, fillets, and holes. (Adapted from Peterson, Stress Concentration Design Factors, *John Wiley & Sons, Inc., New York, 1953)*

the fatigue strength of the same member *with* the specified stress concentration (σ_n'),

$$K_f = \frac{\sigma_n}{\sigma_n'}. \tag{9.10b}$$

Commonly determined by experiment, K_f is usually less than K_t. Some variables that are known to influence the value of K_f are the material (type, strength, and previous treatment), the character of the discontinuity (geometric shape, overall size, and critical dimensions), the magnitude of the cyclic stress, and the number of cycles endured. Consequently all these variables should be specified in giving a value for K_f.

The effect of the severity of the discontinuity, as measured by some critical dimension such as the *notch radius, r*, has been studied extensively.

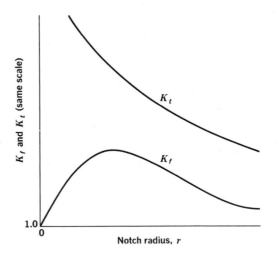

Fig. 9.29 Schematic variation of K_f and K_t with notch radius. (See Grover, Gordon, and Jackson, Fatigue of Metals and Structures, *Report No.* NAVAER 00-25-523, *Battelle Memorial Institute, 1954, for similar curves for a small-diameter hole in a narrow strip.)*

Figure 9.29 shows the general features of the variation of K_f as a function of r for a notch or groove; K_t is also shown for comparison. For a large radius both factors approach unity (no effect); as the radius decreases (sharper and sharper notch), K_t continues to increase toward some large value at $r = 0$. At the same time K_f increases until it reaches a maximum at some small radius and then drops again toward unity at $r = 0$. Thus there appears to be a critical radius at which the reduction in fatigue strength is greatest, and above and below which the effect is less serious. This critical radius is probably related to some characteristic of the material, such as grain size. Neuber* has done considerable work along these

---

* Neuber, H., *Kerbspannungslehre*, Springer-Verlag, Berlin, Vienna (1937); reprinted as a translation, *Theory of Notch Stresses*, J. W. Edwards, Publisher, Inc., Ann Arbor, Mich., 1946, p. 163.

lines.   However, the exact value of the radius for maximum K_f and the exact variations at shorter radii are not completely known.   Consequently it should *not* be assumed that very sharp notches are safe in fatigue.

In the foregoing discussion it has been assumed that fatigue loading is a purely alternating one in which $\sigma_m = 0$.   No standard definition has been devised for K_f in other types of loading.

A convenient factor for studying the effect of stress concentrations is the *fatigue notch sensitivity,*[*] defined as

$$q = \frac{K_f - 1}{K_t - 1}. \tag{9.11}$$

The numerator represents the effectiveness of the notch in fatigue while the denominator represents its effectiveness in a purely elastic situation. If $K_f = 1$, the notch is completely ineffective in fatigue, and the notch sensitivity is zero.   If $K_f = K_t$, the notch is fully effective in fatigue, and the notch sensitivity is unity.   In the rare instances in which $K_f > K_t$, notch sensitivity $q > 1$.

Figure 9.30 illustrates the general variation of q with r for various notches and other discontinuities.   Since K_f approaches unity at $r = 0$, the curves all start at the origin.   For large values of r, K_f approaches K_t and consequently q approaches unity.   Several equations have been proposed to relate q and r from theoretical considerations.   Some are of the form

$$q = \frac{1}{1 + a/r^n}, \tag{9.12}$$

where a is a material constant and n is either $\frac{1}{2}$ or 1.[†]   The value of a varies not only with the type of material but with its tensile strength and heat treatment.   Figure 9.30 also shows some typical trends of q-r curves for various materials and treatments.

When graphs or equations of q vs r are available, the value of K_f can be computed from Eq. 9.11:

$$K_f = q(K_t - 1) + 1. \tag{9.11a}$$

When we know K_f for the given conditions, Eq. 9.10a can be replaced by

$$\sigma_n' = \frac{\sigma_n}{K_f}, \tag{9.10c}$$

from which the fatigue strength, σ_n', of the notched part can be found in terms of the unnotched fatigue strength, σ_n, taken from the *S-N* diagram.

---

[*] *Fatigue notch sensitivity* should not be confused with *notch sensitivity* as discussed in Art. 7.8 since the meanings are different.

[†] Sines, George, and Waisman, J. L., *Metal Fatigue* (University of California Engineering Extension Series) McGraw-Hill Book Company, Inc., 1959, pp. 297–300.

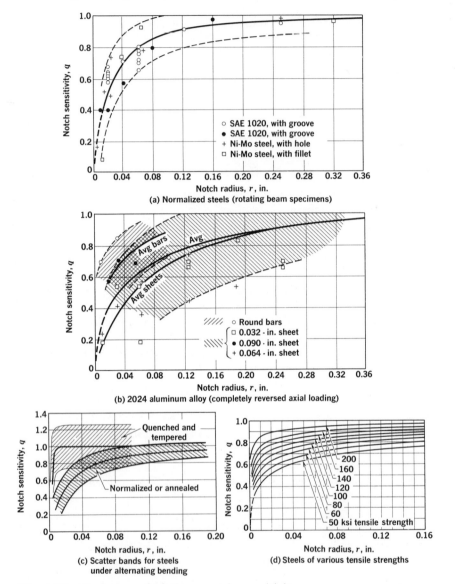

(a) Normalized steels (rotating beam specimens)

(b) 2024 aluminum alloy (completely reversed axial loading)

(c) Scatter bands for steels under alternating bending

(d) Steels of various tensile strengths

Fig. 9.30 Variation of fatigue notch sensitivity with notch radius. (Adapted from Sines and Waisman, Eds., Metal Fatigue, *McGraw-Hill Book Company, Inc., New York, 1959, and* Metals Handbook, *1954 Supplement,* American Society for Metals, Cleveland, p. 101)

The design stress is finally determined from σ_n' by applying a suitable safety factor.

EXAMPLE 9.1

Estimate the fatigue strength for 10^6 cycles in alternating tension for a 1.500-in. diameter shaft having a groove $\frac{1}{4}$ in. deep whose radius is 0.08 in. The shaft is made of 2024-T4 aluminum alloy, whose unnotched fatigue strength is 32,000 psi.

Solution: K_t is determined from Fig. 9.28a. The critical dimensions are $D = 1.500$ in., $d = 1.000$ in., and $r = 0.08$ in. Thus $D/d = 1.5$, $r/d = 0.08$, and we read $K_t = 2.55$.

From Fig. 9.30b we estimate for $r = 0.08$ in., $q = 0.85$.

Using Eq. 9.11a, we obtain

$$K_f = 0.85(2.55 - 1) + 1$$
$$= 2.32,$$

and our estimate of fatigue strength is

$$\sigma_n' = \frac{32,000}{2.32} = 13,800 \text{ psi.}$$

If a factor of safety of 3 is chosen, the working stress becomes 4600 psi.

Since stress concentrations are such an important source of fatigue damage, they should be kept as small as possible. Some changes in section are always necessary in any design. If the change is made by means of a sharp corner (Fig. 9.31a), the stress concentration will be at its worst

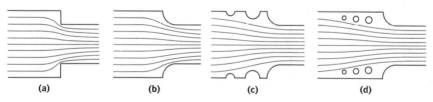

(a)   **(b)**   **(c)**   **(d)**

Fig. 9.31 Methods of relieving stress concentrations at a change in section. Lines represent "flow" of stress.

$(K_t \gg 3)$. By introducing a fillet (Fig. 9.31b) the stress concentration can be made much smaller (perhaps 1.5). A still further reduction can be made by means of relieving grooves or holes, as indicated in Figs. 9.31c and d. The grooves or holes help distribute the stress more evenly in the vicinity of the fillet, as indicated by the "flow" lines of Fig. 9.31.

9.9 OTHER FACTORS

Size

Like strength of brittle materials, fatigue strength shows a distinct dependence on the size of the member, a natural consequence of the statistical nature of fatigue.   In Art. 9.2 it was shown that fatigue fracture depends on a random distribution of "weak points" or imperfections in the material. Hence it is to be expected that a large member, having a larger distribution of weak points than a smaller one, will have more extreme values in its distribution.   The larger member is therefore more likely to have the worst imperfections, and will, on the average, fail at a lower stress than the smaller.   The actual variation with size has not been determined.   Because the weak points that cause fatigue failure are usually in the surface, it is assumed by some investigators that the important factor is *surface area*.   Strong evidence also points to an interrelation between size of specimen and stress gradient.

Regardless of the exact nature of the variation, it is commonly observed that laboratory tests on small specimens usually indicate greater strengths than those obtained in service, when the parts are large.   A great deal of attention has been given to large-scale fatigue testing in recent years. Simulated service tests of actual machine or structural parts, and even of complete machines and structures, are common in many industries.

Rate of Cycling

Loading cycles occur at a great variety of frequencies, and of course it is desirable to make fatigue tests at high frequencies to secure data as rapidly as possible.   Considerable attention has therefore been paid to the effect of cycling rates on fatigue strengths.   Generally speaking fatigue strength increases with increasing rate of cycling, probably because of the increased strain rate accompanying more rapid cycling.   Except for mild steel the increase in fatigue strength is so small within a frequency range of 100–10,000 cpm as to be negligible if temperatures are normal.

However, if hysteresis losses are large, as in materials having high internal friction or under stresses large enough to cause plastic strains, the heating effects of high frequencies may be serious.   Then fatigue strength may be altered drastically with changes in cycling rate, as noted below.

High Temperatures

Temperatures high enough to produce measurable creep have several important effects on fatigue.   First, the variation of fatigue strength with rate of cycling becomes much more pronounced; for example, at 1200°F the fatigue strength of structural steel may be doubled by increasing the cycling rate from 200 to 2500 cpm. Second, the importance of a steady stress component, σ_m, is emphasized. The steady stress naturally tends to cause continuing creep, which is added to the effect of fatigue. Figure 9.32 shows some typical experimental curves relating stress amplitude to mean stress for high temperatures.

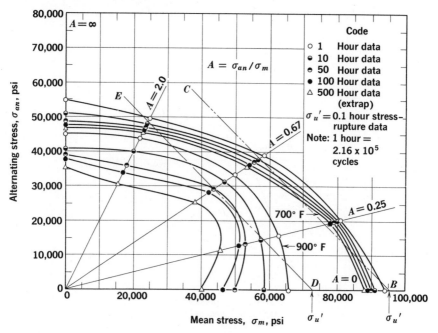

Fig. 9.32 Stress combinations for 1-, 10-, 50-, 100-, and 500-hr rupture times for stainless steel type 403 at 700° and 900°F. (Adapted from STP No. 196, Metals, published by the American Society for Testing Materials, Philadelphia, 1957)

A third effect of high temperatures is to decrease notch sensitivity. The strengthening effect of the high local strain rate at the root of the notch (Art. 9.8) is more pronounced at high temperatures.

An important point to keep in mind is that creep is a *time*-dependent phenomenon, while fatigue depends primarily on the *number* of repetitions of stress.

Surface Effects

It has been observed that most fatigue cracks are nucleated in the surfaces of members. The condition of the surface is therefore of utmost importance.   A rough surface can lower the fatigue strength by as much as 15 or 20 per cent.   The surfaces of all members and specimens to be subjected to fatigue should therefore be carefully finished.   This can be done by slow grinding and polishing operations which will remove scratches and damaged surface material without introducing any new residual

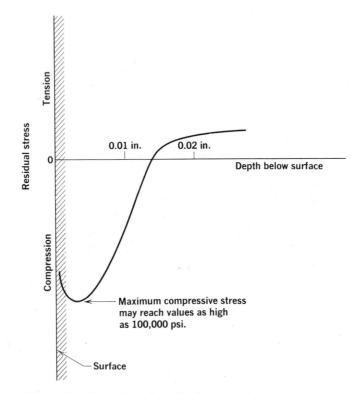

Fig. 9.33   *Variation of residual stresses in shot-peened surface.*

stresses.   It should be pointed out, however, that not all common surface treatments improve fatigue resistance.   Electroplating a surface usually *lowers* its resistance to fatigue.   The explanation is that the metal which is deposited electrically contains microscopic cracks perpendicular to the surface, and these act as countless stress-raisers.   Nevertheless, proper surface treatment can substantially increase the fatigue strengths of members over the strengths of corresponding plain smooth members.

The most common form of surface treatment for fatigue is one that produces compressive residual stresses in the directions parallel to the surface.

One way of doing this is by *peening* the surface. Peening consists in striking the surface with a rounded hammer or ball, which makes a series of overlapping indentations covering the entire surface. When the peening tool is pressed into the surface, the metal flows outward from the indentation in all directions. If a thin sheet were to be peened in this way the flow would be confined to the direction of the surface and the whole sheet would tend to expand in area. In a thicker piece of metal the surface layer is prevented from expanding by the metal below it, and is thus held in *compression* in the direction of the surface. This compressed surface layer acts as a crack-resistant armor around the inner material and greatly reduces the possibility of fatigue. Any tensile stress applied to the member in the direction of the peened surface is now reduced by the amount of the

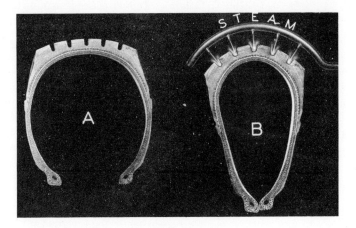

Fig. 9.34   Residual stress produced by heat softening.   (Courtesy J. O. Almen)

residual stress and is just that much less effective in causing fatigue. Compressive stress is, of course, increased by the same amount, but compressive stress is far less effective in causing fatigue than tensile stress. Figure 9.33 shows the variation of residual stress with depth below the surface following peening. The interior of the member is subjected to a small residual tensile stress to preserve equilibrium. Since it is below the surface, and is small, it does not offset the effects of the peening. In some instances fatigue strength may be improved more than 100 per cent by peening.

Various tools are used for peening. Shot peening is one of the most popular techniques. Metallic shot ranging from about 0.007 to 0.175 in. in diameter are propelled against the surface at high velocities (perhaps

200 ft/sec).* Careful control and consideration of the variables involved are necessary to produce uniform results. Shot peening can be used on almost any surface (except an interior surface) and is therefore a versatile method.

Other methods of introducing compressive residual stresses in surfaces are as follows. *Surface rolling* is similar to shot peening except that compression of the surface layer is done by rollers instead of by blows. *Heat softening* is used on rubber tire treads.† The tread is bent as shown at *B* in Fig. 9.34, and the outer surface is heated by steam jets. As the surface softens, it flows and relieves tensile stress. When the tread is released, the stresses in the inner surface spring it back to its normal shape as at *A* in Fig. 9.34. The outer surface of the rubber is now under a residual compression and is less susceptible to fatigue. In *thermal contraction* the material is heated throughout to produce a uniform expansion. The surface is then cooled rapidly and contracts. The warm interior, being softer, yields, and equilibrium is maintained in the whole. When the interior cools, it contracts and introduces a compressive residual stress in the surface. Tempered glass is formed in this way (Art. 12.5).

Tensile residual stresses in the surface are as bad for fatigue as compressive residual stresses are beneficial. Heavy surface grinding should therefore be avoided because it can cause heating of the surface and induce tensile residual stresses (Art. 12.5).

Understressing

In some materials having well-defined fatigue limits it has been observed that application of stress cycles at stresses below the fatigue limit, σ_e, can strengthen the material. If these cycles are applied to some materials in a series of increasing stress levels, starting just below σ_e, with a large number (e.g., 10,000,000) of cycles at each level, these materials have been found to withstand stresses much higher than σ_e without failure. The process of repeated cycling at successively higher levels, by which the fatigue properties of a material may be improved, is called *understressing* or *coaxing*.

The coaxing effect is caused by metallurgical changes which, while they are stimulated by the localized slip in fatigue, require time to produce any noticeable strengthening. *Strain aging* seems to be one of the principal causes. This phenomenon occurs in annealed low- and medium-carbon steels. If mild steel, for example, is strained plastically and allowed to age at room temperature for a few days, it will be found to have a higher

---

* Sines, George, and Waisman, J. L., *Metal Fatigue* (University of California Engineering Extension Series) McGraw-Hill Book Company, Inc., 1959, p. 206.

† *Ibid.*, p. 215.

yield stress than that accounted for by strain-hardening alone. The mechanism involves dislocations and diffusion processes and is explained in texts on metallurgy. Materials which exhibit strain-aging effects are also most susceptible to coaxing.*

Many alloy steels and nonferrous alloys are not affected by coaxing. Experience with particular materials seems to be the best guide by which to judge possible coaxing effects. Much still remains to be learned about the subject.

EXPERIMENTAL METHODS

Experiments with fatigue are of two general types: laboratory tests on simple, easily reproduced specimens, for studying the theory of fatigue and determining fatigue properties of materials; and simulated service tests on components or entire machines and structures. We shall limit our discussion to experiments of the former type.

9.10 FATIGUE TESTING MACHINES

Many different kinds of machines have been developed by investigators in the field of fatigue. The ASTM *Manual on Fatigue Testing* illustrates more than thirty. They may be classified in a variety of ways, but the most important classifications are with respect to type of load, and the manner in which it is applied. The basic types of loading are simple axial loading, bending, torsion, and combinations of these three. Specimens are loaded by applying either a constant maximum load or displacement. In constant-load machines the loading cycle remains the same throughout the experiment; the deflection usually increases as the specimen becomes weaker. In constant-deflection machines a fixed cycle of displacement is imposed on the specimen, and the resulting stress may change as fatigue progresses.

Many of the machines developed for fatigue testing are similar, and only a few have become widely used. Four types will serve to illustrate the general features of machines in common use: rotating-bending machines; repeated-bending machines with constant displacement; mechanical oscillator machines; and resonance machines.

Rotating-Bending Machine

A specimen of circular cross-section is loaded with transverse loads in a fixed plane while being rotated about its axis with respect to this plane.

---

* Sinclair, G. M., "An Investigation of the Coaxing Effect in Fatigue of Metals," *Proceedings* Am. Soc. Test. Mats. **52**, 743–751 (1952).

The transverse loads set up bending stresses in the member. Rotating the member causes the stress at any point on its surface to vary sinusoidally between maximum tensile and maximum compressive stress. This type of loading is called *reversed bending*.

The most popular machine of this type is the R. R. Moore rotating-beam fatigue machine (Fig. 9.35). The specimen is rigidly attached be-

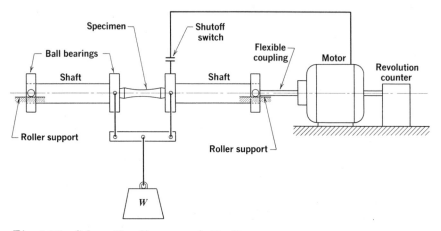

Fig. 9.35   Schematic diagram of R. R. Moore rotating-beam fatigue machine.

tween the ends of two shafts and becomes part of a long beam which is loaded in pure bending (compare Fig. 5.1). The beam is supported and loaded through ball-bearings on the shaft extensions so that it can rotate freely around its axis. Loading is by means of dead weights so that bending takes place in a vertical plane. As the specimen rotates, the topmost fibers are always in compression and the bottom fibers in tension, producing a sinusoidal variation of stress at each point on the surface of the specimen. The specimen is rotated at speeds varying from 3600 to 10,000 rpm by a motor directly connected to one of the shaft extensions. A counter records the number of revolutions (stress cycles), and a switch is provided to shut the machine off automatically when the specimen breaks.

The R. R. Moore machine is a *constant-load* type since the loads are applied by dead weights. It is also classified as *mechanical-loading*, as contrasted with hydraulic or electric.

The fact that rotating-bending machines are relatively simple and inexpensive accounts for their wide use. They are, however, limited in their application since the stress is always completely reversed and the mean stress is always zero. Furthermore, specimens must always be circular in cross-section so that as they rotate they will have a constant section modulus.

A variation of the rotating-bending machine uses a specimen which is mounted and loaded as a cantilever beam instead of a simple beam. In another variation the specimen is held fixed and the plane of loading is rotated about the axis of the specimen. Machines of these types are described in the ASTM *Manual on Fatigue Testing* and in the literature.

Repeated-Bending Machine with Constant Displacement

In machines of this type the specimen is mounted as a stationary beam, and an arm attached to it is driven by a crank or eccentric, which produces a fixed alternating deflection (Fig. 9.36). The specimen may be in the form

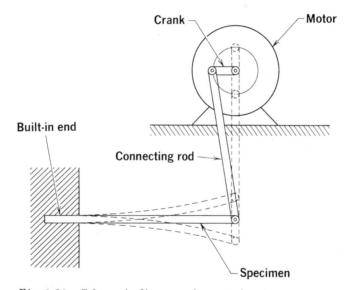

Fig. 9.36   Schematic diagram of repeated-bending machine.

of either a cantilever or a simply supported beam. It can also take a variety of shapes, an advantage over the rotating-bending machine, for which a circular cross-section is always required. Sheet metal and flat and square bars can be tested in repeated-bending machines. The machines themselves are among the simplest to build and are thus widely used. Loading is, of course, mechanical. Adjusting the length of the arm provides a variety of combinations of alternating and steady loads.

An important characteristic of machines that produce constant displacements is the fact that changes take place in the load and stress acting on the specimen during the experiment.   As fatigue progresses, the resistance of the material changes as a result of strain-hardening and formation of cracks.   When a macroscopic crack has formed, the changes may be very complicated: when the crack is in tension it opens up and offers no resistance at all, with the result that the stress in the remaining material is very high; when the crack is in compression during the other half of the cycle, it closes and the material is ï early as strong as before.   The result is a drastic change in the shape of tïe stress cycle.

Mechanical Oscillator

The load is produced by the centrifugal force of a rotating eccentric mass.   The principle of operation is shown in Fig. 9.37.   The specimen is

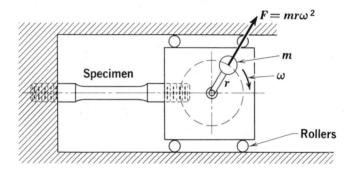

Fig. 9.37   Model illustrating principle employed in fatigue machines of mechanical oscillator type.

mounted on a fixed support, and the load is applied by the small platform which supports the mechanical oscillator—an eccentric rotating mass. The centrifugal force is a rotating force vector, $F = mr\omega^2$, where m is the mass of the rotating body, r is the radius to its center of gravity, and ω is its angular velocity.   The projection of this vector in the direction of motion is a force having a sinusoidal variation.   Thus a load cycle of constant magnitude is applied to the specimen, and the machine can be classified as a constant-load type.

Mechanical oscillators offer the widest variety of possibilities for research.   By applying a *preload* to the specimen, any desired combination of steady and alternating loads can be obtained.   By the use of the proper fixtures the specimen can be loaded in repeated bending, axial loading, torsion, or combination loads.   Figure 9.38 shows a Sonntag universal fatigue machine of this type.

Resonant Machine

Any spring-supported mass has a natural frequency of oscillation given by

$$f = \frac{1}{2\pi}\sqrt{\frac{k}{m}},$$

where k is the spring constant and m is the mass.   If such a system is set

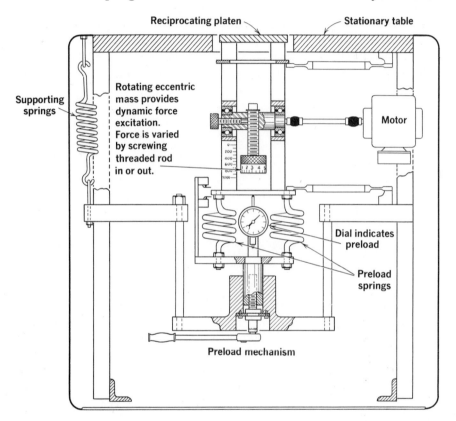

Fig. 9.38 *Schematic diagram of the Sonntag fatigue machine. (Courtesy Baldwin-Lima-Hamilton Corporation, Waltham, Mass.)*

into forced vibrations by a sinusoidal force having the same frequency as the natural frequency of the system, a condition of resonance is established. The amplitude of the oscillations becomes very large and is kept within bounds only by the damping capacity of the system.

A fatigue specimen and the machine to which it is attached constitute a system as described above. The resonant frequency of a small specimen by itself is high because of its large stiffness and small mass. If the machine is included, the resonant frequency is much lower. Springs are sometimes inserted in the system to tune it to a certain frequency. A convenient way to obtain vibratory loading is by means of electromagnets. A large number of different types of magnetic resonant machines have been made. Electronic controls are used to ensure the proper frequency of oscillation. Mechanical and pneumatic loading systems are also used at resonant frequencies. Bending, axial, and torsional loads can be applied. Since the vibrational characteristics of the specimen change with fatigue, the resonant frequency and amplitude change accordingly.

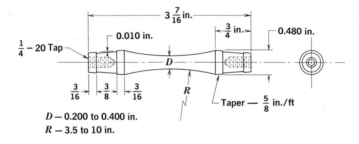

Fig. 9.39   Specimen for R. R. Moore fatigue machine.

This discussion is intended only to give some idea of the general features of fatigue testing machines used in research. Machines designed for testing components or structures have been purposely left out of the discussion.

It is sometimes desired to make experiments at various controlled temperatures. Methods used are similar to those described in Chapters 7 and 8. Rotating-bending machines usually present the greatest difficulties for temperature control, although some special types have been developed for this purpose. Heating coils can be placed around the specimen in the ordinary R. R. Moore machine, but the bearings are so close that high temperatures interfere with their operation. Machines like the mechanical oscillator can easily be equipped with furnaces to fit around the specimen.

9.11   SPECIMENS AND TEST PROCEDURES

Fatigue specimens must be carefully made to avoid stress concentrations, rough surfaces, and tensile residual stresses. A typical example is the R. R. Moore rotating-beam specimen in Fig. 9.39. By use of a constant curvature from end to end, a reduced section is formed without the necessity for fillets, which would introduce undesirable stress concentrations. The ASTM *Manual on Fatigue Testing* contains complete specifications for many standard specimens, together with recommended procedures for their preparation.

There are several methods of planning and conducting fatigue tests, and each has its own particular purpose or advantages. Details of seven methods are contained in the ASTM *Tentative Guide for Fatigue Testing* (STP No. 91-A). So far as the actual operation and observations are concerned, there are two main types of test: those using *constant* and those using *increasing* stress amplitudes. Constant-amplitude tests have been almost universally used up to the present. The first such tests were conducted by Wöhler in 1870 and are often referred to by his name. They are used to obtain data for *S-N* curves ("standard" tests), and response curves (response tests). The test is simple and straightforward. Each specimen is mounted in the testing machine and cycled at a constant stress amplitude until it fails. Most machines are equipped with automatic shutoffs, and the test therefore requires no attention. After failure, the number of cycles is recorded as the fatigue life of that specimen under the given conditions.

Standard Tests

Standard tests at constant stress amplitude are those designed to secure data for *S-N* curves. Although they are not actually standardized by ASTM, they have become accepted through long usage. In this type of test a *group* of specimens is tested to failure at each of several stress levels. To establish the necessary distributions of fatigue lives, each group should consist of at least ten specimens. In general at least four or five stress levels are needed to define the *S-N* curve. If a fatigue limit is to be determined, two or three additional stress levels are required. Since the scatter of test results is greatest at the lower stresses (Art. 9.5), more specimens should be allocated to the low-stress levels and fewer to the high-stress levels for an approximately equal degree of precision. The total number of specimens needed varies from 40 to 80 or more. At the lower stress levels there are always a few specimens whose individual fatigue lives turn out to be greater than the maximum number of cycles that can be run in the time allowed. These specimens (called *runouts*) remain unbroken at the end of the test and contribute little to the experimental data.

For many years it was thought sufficient to test only one specimen at each stress level. From the results of such tests a single *S-N* curve was drawn. When we consider the large scatter in fatigue lives of individual specimens, it seems surprising that any sort of a curve could be fitted to results for single specimens. The explanation is that the probability of values falling within a certain small interval is highest in the center of the distribution and decreases rapidly above and below the center.   Consequently most of the single points fall by chance somewhere near the median, and when a curve is faired in between these points it is usually close to the median *S-N* curve.   However, such a procedure is now considered unacceptable for determining an *S-N* diagram for the study of fatigue behavior and properties.   It provides no information about the *distribution* of fatigue lives or strengths and should only be used to obtain a rough idea of the quality of a material when specimens are difficult to obtain, or when time or testing facilities are limited.

In investigations of cumulative damage under a loading spectrum, it is desirable to *program* the loading cycles so that each constant amplitude is

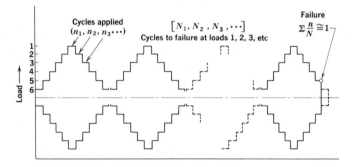

Fig. 9.40 Recommended program. (Adapted from Sines and Waisman, Eds., Metal Fatigue, *McGraw-Hill Book Company, Inc., New York, 1959)*

applied a few cycles at a time, as suggested in Art. 9.7.   Figure 9.40 shows a recommended program in which the loading spectrum is repeated as many times as possible until failure.

Response Tests

Response tests at constant amplitude are specifically designed to yield data for response curves (Art. 9.5).   The data for Table 9.4 were obtained from a Probit type response test.   The statistical considerations involved in selecting stress levels and numbers of specimens in individual groups are beyond the scope of this text, but are quite thoroughly discussed in the ASTM *Tentative Guide for Fatigue Testing.*   Likewise the analysis and interpretation of fatigue life data must be left for more advanced treatments.

Increasing-Amplitude Tests

Tests at increasing stress amplitudes include the newer procedures developed to conserve both time and specimens. A common characteristic is to cycle each specimen at increasing stress levels until it fractures. Hence all specimens contribute to the test data and there are no runouts (specimens which do not fail). Since each specimen is cycled at more than one stress level, the possibility of cumulative damage and coaxing effects must be taken into account. Cumulative damage is minimized when the tests are applied to materials which have definite fatigue limits. For such materials cycling can be started at a stress level below the fatigue limit, and it can be assumed that no fatigue damage will occur until the fatigue limit is reached. If no fatigue limit is known to exist, these methods can sometimes be used to estimate long-life fatigue strengths.* Since the manner of loading is exactly that under which coaxing effects take place, these methods are usually limited to materials which are not sensitive to coaxing (Art. 9.9).

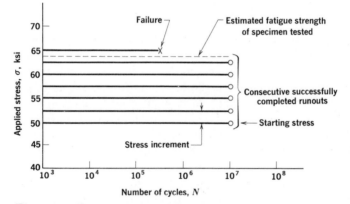

Fig. 9.41   Representation of "step" testing of a single specimen.   (Adapted from STP No. 91-A, A Tentative Guide for Fatigue Testing and the Statistical Analysis of Fatigue Data, *published by the American Society for Testing Materials, Philadelphia, 1958)*

Two main types will be discussed. The first is known as the *step test*, in which each specimen is cycled at a series of stress levels, each higher than the preceding one. The test is started at a stress lower than the

* ASTM STP 91-A, pp. 11, 12.

fatigue limit, perhaps 70 per cent of σ_e.   The prescribed number of cycles, N (say 100,000,000), is applied at this stress, and if the specimen does not break, the stress level is increased by some small amount.   The same number of cycles is again applied, after which the stress is again increased. This process is continued until the specimen breaks.   The fatigue strength of the specimen, for N cycles, is taken as the stress *midway* between the last stress survived and the fracture stress.   The process is illustrated graphically in Fig. 9.41.   Several specimens are tested in this way and the results analyzed statistically to provide an estimate of the median fatigue strength for N cycles.

Step tests have the advantage of requiring only a few specimens.   They have the disadvantage that each specimen must usually be run several times for the full number of cycles; the time involved may be prohibitive.

In the *Prot test* the amplitude is increased *steadily* rather than by steps. It was developed by Marcel Prot* to accelerate fatigue tests and thereby conserve time.   The theory discussed in Art. 9.7 led to the equation

$$\sigma_R = \sigma_e + k'\alpha^i, \tag{9.9}$$

where σ_e, k', and i are all unknown material constants; σ_e is the one to be determined by the test, but one or both the others may also have to be found.   The test variables are α and σ_R.   A number of different values of each are required to complete the test.   As in all fatigue tests there is considerable scatter in the data, in view of which it is recommended that at least 3 rates of loading be used and a total of 20 specimens be tested.†

Standard fatigue testing machines can be used for the Prot test provided some means can be arranged for increasing the load at a predetermined uniform rate.   Any machine using dead weights (e.g., the R. R. Moore machine) can be adapted by replacing the weights with a container into which a stream of water or shot can be poured at a constant rate.

According to theory (Art. 9.7) the alternating stress should be started at the fatigue limit, σ_e, but since it is unknown, the standard procedure is to start at a stress of about 60 to 70 per cent of the estimated fatigue limit stress.   It is assumed that the cycles of stress that take place at stresses below σ_e do not affect the material; consequently the lower limit in the integral of Eq. 9.8d can still be σ_e.

Analysis of the experimental data consists briefly of solving Eq. 9.9 for σ_e. If i were known, this would be simple.   Figure 9.42 illustrates the procedure, using Prot's assumption that $i = \frac{1}{2}$.   If Eq. 9.9 is written $\sigma_R = \sigma_e + k'\sqrt{\alpha}$ and σ_R is plotted against $\sqrt{\alpha}$, a straight line should be obtained.

---

* Prot, E. Marcel, "Fatigue Testing under Progressive Loading; A New Technique for Testing Materials," *Rev. de Metallurgie* **XLV**, No. 12, 481 (1948).
† ASTM STP 91-A, p. 13.

The intercept of this line on the σ_R-axis is the fatigue limit, σ_e. In Fig. 9.42 the average value of σ_R has been plotted for each of three loading rates. A straight line fitted to these points and extended to $\alpha = 0$ gives the value of σ_e.

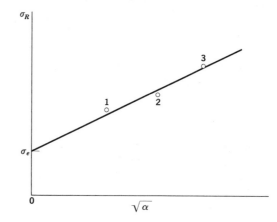

Fig. 9.42 Prot method. Points 1, 2, and 3 are average stresses obtained at loading rates α_1, α_2, and α_3; the straight line averaging these points is extended to $\alpha = 0$ to determine σ_e.

To obtain a better fit to the experimental data i should be left as an unknown. The solution of Eq. 9.9 then becomes more difficult. The method recommended by ASTM is one of trial-and-error.

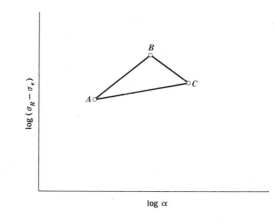

Fig. 9.43 Trial plot of results of Prot test, using a particular trial value of σ_e. Points A, B, and C are averages of several observations at each of three loading rates, α_1, α_2, and α_3. Since A, B, and C are not close to the same line, another trial must be made.

The equation can be written

$$\log (\sigma_R - \sigma_e) = \log k' + i \log \alpha, \qquad (9.9b)$$

which represents a straight line in a log-log plot of $(\sigma_R - \sigma_e)$ vs α. The method consists in selecting trial values of σ_e and making a series of trial plots until one is found in which the points lie on a straight line. As before, the arithmetic means of the observed values of σ_R obtained for each of the three values of α are used. The first value chosen for σ_e should be close to but a little less than the lowest mean failure stress. Using this value in Eq. 9.9b, we can plot points A, B, and C as in Fig. 9.43. The slopes, i, of the lines joining the points are computed and compared. If they differ by more than one or two per cent, a new trial value of σ_e must be selected and the process repeated. The value of σ_e that brings the slopes to within one or two per cent of each other is taken as the fatigue limit.

There is still some uncertainty about the reliability of the Prot test under various conditions. To obtain information for use in design it should be used only by an engineer who has considerable experience in the field of fatigue. Several limitations and precautions are specified by ASTM.* The method is restricted to materials that appear to have a fatigue limit and are not sensitive to coaxing. The rate of increase of stress and the speed of cycling must both be carefully controlled because small variations in either may cause considerable scatter in the observations.

EXAMPLE 9.2

The following data were obtained in a Prot fatigue test:†

MEAN RATE OF INCREASE OF STRESS, α, psi/cycle	MEAN FRACTURE STRESS, σ_R, psi
0.208	92,700
.0592	80,600
.00705	71,800

Determine the fatigue limit by trial-and-error.

Trial 1: Assume $\sigma_e = 70,000$ psi. Substitution in Eq. 9.9b gives three simultaneous equations.

$$4.3560 = \log k' + i(9.3181 - 10) \tag{a}$$
$$4.0253 = \log k' + i(8.7723 - 10) \tag{b}$$
$$3.2553 = \log k' + i(7.8482 - 10) \tag{c}$$

From (a) and (b) we obtain $i = 0.606$, from (b) and (c) $i = 0.833$, and from (c) and (a) $i = 0.749$. Since these values differ by as much as 37 per cent, a new trial is necessary. If we skip intermediate trials, we can go directly to the final one.

Final Trial: Assume $\sigma_e = 67,400$.
Now

$$4.4031 = \log k' + i(9.3181 - 10) \tag{d}$$
$$4.1206 = \log k' + i(8.7723 - 10) \tag{e}$$
$$3.6435 = \log k' + i(7.8482 - 10) \tag{f}$$

---

* ASTM STP 91-A, pp. 12–14.
† ASTM STP 91-A, Table Q, p. 51.

Repeating the above process for (d), (e), and (f), we find $i = 0.518, 0.516$, and 0.517. These values differ by a maximum of 0.4 per cent, indicating that the second trial value of σ_e is the correct one.

Thus $\sigma_e = 67{,}400$ psi. Using the average of the three computed values of $i(= 0.517)$, we can also obtain the value of $k' = 56{,}900$.

BIBLIOGRAPHY

Shanley, Francis Reynolds, *Strength of Materials*, McGraw-Hill Book Company, Inc., New York, Toronto, London, 1957.
 Contains a good condensed discussion of fatigue in Ch. 27, pp. 681–699.

Marin, Joseph, *Engineering Materials—Their Mechanical Properties and Applications*, Prentice-Hall, Inc., Englewood Cliffs, N. J., 1952.
 An elementary treatment of fatigue.

Sines, George, and Waisman, J. L., Eds., *Metal Fatigue* (University of California Engineering Extension Series) McGraw-Hill Book Company, Inc., New York, Toronto, London, 1959; Murray, William M., Ed., *Fatigue and Fracture of Metals*, The Technology Press of the Massachusetts Institute of Technology and John Wiley & Sons, Inc., New York, 1952; Grover, H. J., Gordon, S. A., and Jackson, L. R., *Fatigue of Metals and Structures* (Prepared for the Bureau of Aeronautics, Department of the Navy) NAVAER 00-25-534, U. S. Govt. Printing Office, 1945.
 More complete discussions of all phases of fatigue.

Manual on Fatigue Testing, ASTM Special Technical Publication No. 91, American Society for Testing Materials, Philadelphia, 1949; *A Tentative Guide for Fatigue Testing and the Statistical Analysis of Fatigue Data* (Supplement to STP No. 91), ASTM Special Technical Publication No. 91-A, American Society for Testing Materials, Philadelphia, 1958.
 Experimental methods and statistical treatments.

PROBLEMS

9.1 What type of fatigue is involved when a piece of sheet metal is broken by bending it back and forth on itself a few times?

9.2 What are the three stages of fatigue?

9.3 Plot a frequency histogram for the data in column 2 of Table 9.1. Use 20 intervals of 4×10^6 cycles each. Estimate the median fatigue life, N_{50}, and the fatigue lives for 10 and 90 per cent survival, and indicate their locations on the histogram.

9.4 Determine the sample average (arithmetic mean) and sample standard deviation for the data in column 2 of Table 9.1.

9.5 Construct a cumulative percentage diagram of survivals for the data in column 2 of Table 9.1 (use Cartesian coordinates) (see Table 9.3 and Fig. 9.9).

9.6 (a) Make a table of $\log_{10} N$ from the data in column 2 of Table 9.1. (b) From this table construct a frequency histogram, using intervals of 0.100. (c) Determine the median and the 10th and 90th percentiles, and indicate their locations on the histogram.

9.7 From the data of Problem 9.6 construct a cumulative percentage diagram of survivals, using Normal probability paper (compare Fig. 9.14). From this diagram estimate the values of N_{10}, N_{50}, and N_{90}. (NOTE: This is an example of a distribution that fits neither the Normal nor the log-Normal distribution very well.)

9.8 Determine the sample average (arithmetic mean) and sample standard deviation for the data of Problem 9.6.

9.9 The results of 40 fatigue tests of an aluminum alloy at each of five stress levels are

APPLIED STRESS, σ, psi	PER CENT SURVIVAL, p, AT 10^6 CYCLES
24,000	97.5
25,000	85.0
26,000	57.5
27,000	37.5
28,000	10.0

(a) Plot a response curve on Normal probability paper (see Fig. 9.19).
(b) Determine from the response curve the median fatigue strength and fatigue strength for 95 per cent survival at 10^6 cycles.

9.10 From the curve for $R = -1.00$ (Fig. 9.21a) estimate the values of the constants σ_e, k, and m in Eq. 9.3 (or 9.3a).

9.11 (a) Estimate the fatigue limits for the constant mean stress curves of Fig. 9.21b. Compute the corresponding values of σ_a, and using these as σ_{an}, plot a graph of σ_{an} vs σ_m. (b) From this graph estimate the values of the constants in Eq. 9.4. (c) If the yield stress for this material is 80,000 psi, draw the line represented by Eq. 9.5 and locate point Y.

9.12 Develop an equation relating σ_a and σ_m for constant stress ratio R. What are the limiting values of R for positive mean stress?

9.13 Prove that the 45° line starting at the origin (Fig. 9.24) delineates the region of the graph in which the stress is entirely compressive.

9.14 The loading spectrum on an aircraft part is defined by the number of cycles at each stress occurring in 100,000 cycles, as tabulated below. The fatigue life for 90 per cent survival is also tabulated for each stress.

STRESS, ksi	FREQUENCY OF OCCURRENCE IN 10^5 CYCLES	FATIGUE LIFE, N_{90}, cycles
45	5,000	70,000
33	10,000	600,000
26	30,000	3,000,000
23	55,000	40,000,000

Determine the expected fatigue life of the part on the basis of the *cumulative damage theory*.

9.15 Estimate the fatigue strength for 10^5 cycles in alternating tension for a 2-in. diameter steel shaft reduced to 1.74-in. diameter with a $\frac{1}{8}$-in. radius shoulder fillet (see Fig. 9.28b). The steel has a tensile strength of 60 ksi and an unnotched fatigue strength of 38 ksi (use Fig. 9.30d).

9.16 Estimate the safe load for an indefinite number of cycles in alternating tension for a mild steel strap of rectangular cross-section $\frac{1}{4}$ in. thick by 2 in. wide with a $\frac{3}{8}$-in. diameter hole in the center. Use a fatigue limit of 25,000 psi, and Figs. 9.28c and 9.30a.

9.17 Describe three methods by which the surface of a member may be improved to increase its fatigue life.

9.18 Name three basic types of loading, in addition to simple axial loading, available in fatigue machines.

9.19 Name four types of fatigue testing machines in common use. Which normally use constant load, which constant displacement, and which can use either?

9.20 In view of the variation in the amount of scatter found in fatigue tests at high and low stresses, should more specimens be tested at high or low stresses?

9.21 Plot the data used in Example 9.2 in the form suggested by Prot (compare Fig. 9.42). Determine the fatigue limit from this graph and compare with that obtained in Example 9.2.

9.22 The following data were obtained in a Prot fatigue test of AISI 2340 steel.

MEAN RATE OF INCREASE OF STRESS, α, psi/cycle	MEAN FRACTURE STRESS, σ_R, psi
0.250	107,000
.0320	83,000
.0010	71,000

Determine the fatigue limit by trial and error. Suggestion: make the first trials graphically, using log-log paper and starting with the assumption that $\sigma_e = 65,000$ psi; make final check analytically.

CHAPTER 10

HARDNESS

The term *hardness*, when used as a technological property of materials, is primarily associated with the *surface*. Mineralogists were the first to be concerned with technological hardness because of its close connection with the resistance of precious stones to surface scratching and wear (abrasion). With the development of metal alloys that could be hardened for high abrasion resistance the concept of hardness, still with a surface connotation, was carried over to metals.

The hardness of a surface is, of course, a direct result of the interatomic forces acting in the surface material. There is, therefore, a direct connection between hardness and other mechanical properties of this surface material. In many bodies the surface material differs considerably from that of the bulk, as in surface-hardened steel. If, on the other hand, the material is uniform in composition and structure, the surface constitutes a layer only a few atoms thick and may lose much of its importance in technological hardness. In the usual means of measuring technological hardness (Art. 10.2) any such thin surface layer is penetrated and what is actually measured is the hardness of the bulk of the material. Hence, in view of the connection between hardness and other mechanical properties, the hardness measured on the surface may serve as an indication of overall strength.

As soon as it was discovered that hardness measurements could be used as criteria of strength, their importance to metallurgists and engineers grew rapidly. Hardness measurements are among the easiest to make and are extensively used for a variety of purposes.   That hardness is primarily a surface property should not be lost sight of, though.   All hardness measurements are made on or close to the surface as contrasted with other measurements of mechanical strength, which are made on the bulk of the material.

TECHNOLOGICAL HARDNESS

An appropriate definition of technological hardness is *the resistance of a material to permanent deformation of its surface.*   This deformation may be in the form of scratching, mechanical wear, indentation, or cutting. By including cutting we extend the definition to include machinability.

10.1 HARDNESS AND STRUCTURE

The relation between hardness and atomic structure can be illustrated by reference to the Mohs hardness scale, the first generally used hardness scale, originated by a German mineralogist, Friedrich Mohs, in 1832.   It consists of a series of numbers from 0 to 10, in order of increasing hardness. Diamond, the hardest known material, is assigned the hardness number $H_M = 10$.   Talc, one of the softest minerals, is assigned the number $H_M = 1$.   The other integers, 2 through 9, are assigned to other natural minerals of corresponding relative hardness.   All other materials can be specified by intermediate numbers: for example, tungsten carbide, 9.7; mica, 3.5; polystyrene, 2.3.   Hardness for the Mohs scale is determined by surface scratching; a material which will scratch another is assigned a higher Mohs hardness number.   Table 10.1 lists the minerals representing the ten steps of the scale, together with their crystal structures.*

Table 10.1   Hardness and Structure

MOHS HARDNESS NUMBER, H_M	MINERAL	FORMULA	CRYSTAL STRUCTURE
1.	Talc	$3MgO.4SiO_2.H_2O$	Layer
2.	Gypsum	$CaSO_4.2H_2O$	Layer
3.	Calcite	$CaCO_3$	Layer
4.	Fluorite	CaF_2	Ionic
5.	Apatite	$CaF_2.3Ca_3P_2O_8$	Ionic
6.	Feldspar	$K_2O.Al_2O_3.6SiO_2$	Mixed ionic-covalent
7.	Quartz	SiO_2	Mixed ionic-covalent
8.	Topaz	$(AlF)_2SiO_4$	Mixed ionic-covalent
9.	Corundum	Al_2O_3	Covalent
10.	Diamond	C	Covalent

---

* Zwikker, C., *Physical Properties of Solid Materials*, Interscience Publishers, Inc., New York, 1954, p. 28.

Talc is formed of "sheet molecules"; although the bonds within the individual sheets are covalent, the sheets themselves are held together only by van der Waals forces (Art. 2.9). Since the sheets can be easily pulled apart, the structure is soft. The gypsum and calcite structures are ionic, but because the crystals are in the form of layers, they are not as hard as the ionic structures of fluorite and apatite. The covalent bonding of feldspar, quartz, and topaz produces much greater hardness, and the purely covalent bonding of corundum and diamond (Art. 2.9) makes them hardest of all.

Metallic structures are usually near the lower end of the Mohs scale, although some alloys and metallic compounds can be treated to produce very high hardness. For example, some alloy steels can be hardened to approximately 7 Mohs. Many steels and other hard metals are in the range of 4 to 5 Mohs. Annealed alloys and most pure metals, however, have hardnesses well below 4 Mohs. Soft lead lies so far below 1 Mohs that it can hardly be included in the scale (Fig. 10.3).

For most engineering applications the Mohs scale is not quantitative enough to distinguish clearly between materials, particularly metals, of similar hardness. Moreover, the measurement of hardness by scratching is difficult to standardize and interpret. Consequently new scales, based on other methods of measuring hardness, have been developed.

10.2 HARDNESS MEASUREMENTS

One way in which a surface may be deformed is by *indentation*. A permanent deformation is produced by pressing an indenter of some kind into the surface. The depth of penetration and the force required are easily measured and provide an indication of hardness (resistance to permanent deformation). The simplicity of the observations has made indentation the most widely used measure of hardness.

Resistance to permanent deformation has been measured for the bulk of a material in terms of the stress-strain diagram (Chapters 3 and 4), or more specifically in terms of the stress required to produce a certain strain (expressed as the secant modulus for a certain strain (Eq. 3.8)):

$$E_{sec} = \frac{\sigma}{\epsilon}.$$

For *simple compression* E_{sec} can be expressed in terms of the load and the instantaneous area of the cross-section, as follows: $\sigma = P/A$; $\epsilon = (l/l_0) - 1$, but A increases with the compression, and for constant volume $l/l_0 = A_0/A$, so that $\epsilon = (A_0/A) - 1$. Therefore

$$E_{sec} = \frac{P}{A\left(\dfrac{A_0}{A} - 1\right)},$$

or

$$E_{sec} = \frac{P}{A_0 - A}.$$

This illustration for simple compression shows that when the area is a geometrical function of the deformation (determined here by *constant volume*), the resistance to permanent deformation can be expressed simply in terms of load and corresponding area. This is how indentation hardness is measured.

Indenters are made in various geometrical shapes: spheres, cones, and pyramids. The area over which the force acts increases with the depth of penetration (Fig. 10.1). Thus the resistance to permanent deformation, or hardness, can be expressed in terms of force and area alone.

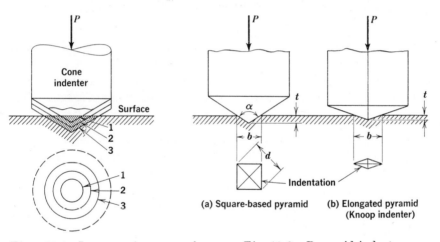

Fig. 10.1 *Increase in area of contact of cone indenter as it penetrates a surface; 1, 2, and 3 are successive positions of the indenter.*

Fig. 10.2 *Pyramid indenters.*

There is, of course, a great difference between deforming a member in simple uniaxial compression and deforming a surface by pressing a ball (or other shape) into it. Around the indentation produced by a ball the stress distribution is exceedingly complex. As the material is forced outward from the indentation, it is subjected to triaxial stresses which vary greatly from the center to the edge of the indentation. Friction between the ball and material adds to the hydrostatic compression component.   In pyramidal indenters the sharp corners produce even more complex conditions. The amount of plastic deformation may reach 30 per cent or more at the tip of the indenter.   And, in addition, the surface of contact is inclined by varying amounts to the direction of the applied force.

In view of these complications an expression corresponding to that for the secant modulus cannot be derived.   Instead an arbitrary expression is used which includes both variables—load and area (or depth of penetration).

Pyramid Hardness

The most versatile hardness measurements make use of diamond points, ground in the shape of a pyramid, as indenters.   Figure 10.2 shows the two principal types.   The indenter is forced into the surface, leaving an impression the size of which is measured by the length of the diagonal, d. The hardness number is then defined as the ratio of the load to the area of the impression,

$$H = \frac{P}{A}.$$ (10.1)

It has been found experimentally that for pyramid indenters the load varies as the square of the diagonal, d.   For a given shape of pyramid, then,

$$P = \lambda d^2,$$ (10.2)

where λ is a constant which depends on the material and the shape of the pyramid.   The area of the impression, A, is also proportional to the square of the diagonal,

$$A = \beta d^2,$$ (10.3)

where β depends on the shape of the pyramid.   Substituting these expressions in Eq. 10.1, we have

$$H = \frac{\lambda d^2}{\beta d^2} = \frac{\lambda}{\beta},$$ (10.1a)

which is independent of both load and size of indentation.   This equation has a very important meaning: within certain limits (see below) *the hardness number for a given shape of pyramid is the same regardless of the load used.* To illustrate, suppose that under a 5-kg load an impression is formed whose diagonal is 0.272 mm; we calculate $H = 125$.   Then a 25-kg load is used, and the impression measures 0.609 mm, which again gives $H = 125$.   At. low loads there is some deviation from this rule, and hardness numbers become somewhat load-dependent.

The independence of hardness number and load makes it possible to use a wide range of loads for different purposes: large loads and correspondingly large indentations for measuring gross or average hardness; small loads for measuring local hardness. In this respect pyramid indenters have an advantage over spherical indenters.

Another advantage of the pyramid indenter is the ease of measuring the square or diamond-shaped impression as compared with a circular impression. The ends of the diagonal are much sharper under the microscope than the opposite sides of a circle. Of course the surfaces of the pyramid must be very accurately ground to ensure a sharp impression. The advantages just described make the pyramid hardness a valuable tool for the research laboratory.

The hardness measured by a square-based pyramid (Fig. 10.2a) is the *Vickers hardness* and is standardized by ASTM under the more general name *diamond pyramid hardness* (DPH) (ASTM E92). The angle between opposite faces of the pyramid is 136°. The area used in Eq. 10.1 is that of the surface of contact between the indenter and the impression. By geometry

$$A = \frac{d^2}{2 \sin \frac{\alpha}{2}}, \tag{10.3a}$$

where $\alpha = 136°$, as noted above. Thus Eq. 10.1 for Vickers hardness is

$$H_V = \frac{P}{d^2} \left(2 \sin \frac{\alpha}{2} \right)$$
$$= (1.8544) \frac{P}{d^2}. \tag{10.1b}$$

The load, P, is measured in kilograms and the diagonal, d, in millimeters.

Figure 10.3 compares the relative positions of a number of materials on the Mohs and Vickers scales. The relation between the two scales is approximately logarithmic.* The highest hardness on the Vickers scale is 2600 for diamond, corresponding to a Mohs value of 10. Soft lead, at about $H_V = 5$, is considerably below the bottom of the Mohs scale.

The elongated pyramid of Fig. 10.2b is the *Knoop indenter*, developed especially for studying microhardness—the hardness of microscopic areas as in individual metal grains. The Knoop hardness is computed from the *projected* area of the impression rather than the area of contact. It is therefore larger than the corresponding Vickers hardness.

Other Hardness Measurements

Indenters in the form of spheres and cones are frequently used. One of the earliest hardness measurements was the *Brinell hardness*, developed in

---

* H_M is approximately proportional to log H_V.

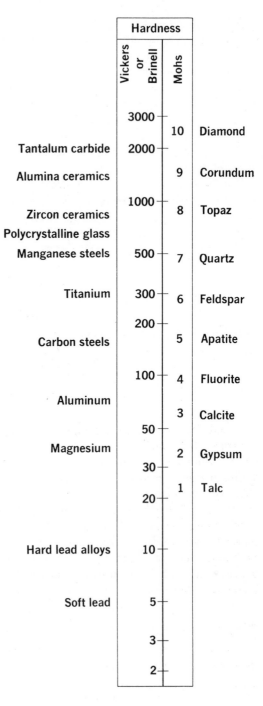

Fig. 10.3 Approximate relative hardnesses of certain metals and ceramics. (Adapted from Zwikker, Physical Properties of Solid Materials, *Pergamon Press, London (1954), p. 261.)*

1900 by J. A. Brinell, using a hardened steel ball. This measurement is still used as a basic standard. The indentation is a circular depression (Fig. 10.4), and the Brinell hardness number is defined by Eq. 10.1,

$$H_B = \frac{P}{A},$$
(10.1c)

where A is the area of contact between the ball and the indentation, as in the Vickers hardness. If the deformation of the ball during the indenta-

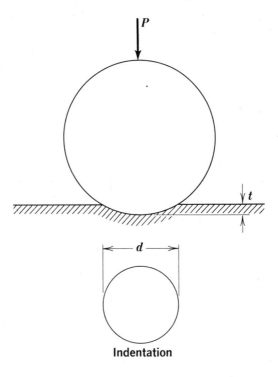

Fig. 10.4 *Ball indenter.*   Indentation

tion is neglected, the surface of contact is a spherical segment whose area is $A = \pi D t$, where D is the diameter of the ball and t the depth of the impression. In terms of the diameter of the impression, the usual measurement, we note that by geometry $t = (D - \sqrt{D^2 - d^2})/2$. Equation 10.1c now takes the form

$$H_B = \frac{2P}{\pi D(D - \sqrt{D^2 - d^2})}.$$
(10.1d)

For spherical indenters the force does not always vary as the square of a linear dimension of the impression, and the exponent in Eq. 10.2 must be replaced by n, which is called *Meyer's index,*[*]

$$P = \lambda d^n; \qquad (10.2a)$$

n varies between 2 for hard materials and 2.5 for soft materials.

If Eq. 10.2a is substituted into Eq. 10.1d, the diameter of the impression does not cancel out. The Brinell hardness number is therefore *dependent on the load used.* For this reason it is necessary to use the same load on all measurements with a given ball if a comparison is desired. This factor restricts the usefulness of the Brinell hardness as a research tool.

The *Rockwell hardness* is measured by use of either a steel *ball* or a *cone-shaped diamond point.* It differs from measurements already discussed in that the *depth* of the impression is measured instead of its diameter. However, since the two are always geometrically related, the hardness measurements are the same in principle. The Rockwell hardness is defined as

$$H_R = h - \frac{t}{0.002}, \qquad (10.4)$$

where h is a constant which depends on the type of penetrator and the *load* used, and t is the depth in millimeters. Each increment of 0.002 mm in depth represents a decrement of one unit in the hardness number. Equation 10.4 applies only over a limited range of values of t.

Mechanism of Indentation

When the indenter is pressed into the surface under a static load, large amounts of plastic deformation take place locally. The material thus deformed flows out in all directions. The region affected extends to a distance approximately three times the radius of the indentation itself. As a result of the principle of constant volume, the surface surrounding the impression bulges slightly to account for the volume displaced from the impression.

Friction between the indenter and the material plays an important part in determining the manner of plastic flow. In some instances the material in contact with the surface of the indenter flows outward rapidly enough to produce a ridge around the impression. In others the material is pulled downward by friction, and the edge of the impression is quite rounded.

Time is an important factor in the whole process. Large amounts of plastic deformation are accompanied by large amounts of *transient creep*, which vary with the material. As described in Art. 8.2, transient creep

---

[*] Zwikker, C., *Physical Properties of Solid Materials*, Interscience Publishers, Inc., New York, 1954, p. 260.

takes place rapidly at first and more slowly as it approaches its maximum. The penetration of the indenter therefore varies with time. With the harder materials the time required to reach very nearly the maximum deformation is short (15 sec for iron and steel). Softer materials may require unreasonably long times, so that it becomes necessary to specify a certain definite time (e.g., 2 min for magnesium alloys).

When viscous creep may take place, as in metals at high temperatures, or in thermoplastics, both the time of application of the load and the rate at which it is applied become important. Because of elastic aftereffects, the material may recover somewhat after removal of the indenter, and the time elapsed before making diameter measurements should be taken into account.

Rebound Hardness

Hardness measurements are sometimes made by dropping a hard object onto the surface and observing the height of rebound. Resistance to permanent deformation is still involved because the surface is always indented by the falling object. Usually a diamond point is used to strike the surface. As it falls its potential energy is transformed into kinetic energy, which is passed on to the surface when it strikes. Part of this energy is stored in the form of elastic strain energy in the surface, and part is dissipated in producing plastic deformation. The amount stored elastically depends on the yield strength of the material *and its stiffness* (Art. 3.2). Thus, in addition to resistance to permanent deformation there is a new factor— stiffness. Still another factor is the damping capacity of the material. Not all the elastic strain energy is recoverable because of internal friction. Consequently the rebound hardness measures a combination of hardness, stiffness, and damping capacity. If comparisons are limited to materials having the same modulus of elasticity, E, the factor of stiffness is eliminated. If, in addition, measurements are restricted to metals of low damping capacity, rebound hardness depends only on the amount of plastic deformation taking place during indentation and becomes virtually an indentation hardness measurement.

10.3 RELATION BETWEEN HARDNESS AND OTHER MECHANICAL PROPERTIES

Because of the highly complex state of stress in an indentation, there is no way of relating hardness measurements to each other or to other mechanical properties *on the basis of theory*. However, in view of their similarities different types of hardness numbers can be related to each other empirically for any given material. Qualitatively, we might also expect some sort of correlation between hardness and other properties involving about the same amount of plastic deformation. It has been noted that in some indentation measurements plastic strains are as high as 30 per cent. In the tension test of a ductile material such strains are encountered in the neck soon after it begins to form. At the yield stress, on the other hand, the usual plastic strain is only about 0.2 per cent. Empirical relations between hardness number and tensile strength are therefore to be expected and have actually been observed for ductile metals; on the other hand no such relations are found for yield stress.

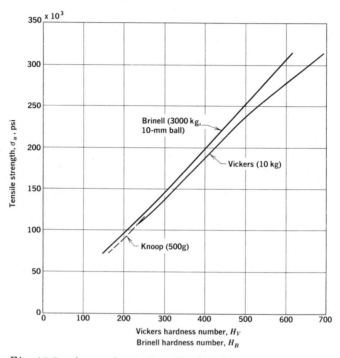

Fig. 10.5 Approximate strength of steel in tension, corresponding to values of Vickers and Brinell hardness numbers (from Wilson Table 52).

Empirical relations between hardness numbers are usually shown in the form of conversion tables for specific materials. Tables for steel, nickel and high-nickel alloys, and cartridge brass are given in ASTM E140. Similar conversion tables including corresponding values of tensile strength are published by various organizations, such as the American Society for Metals in its *Metals Handbook*. Figure 10.5 illustrates graphically the variations for steel.

EXPERIMENTAL METHODS

It has been pointed out that hardness numbers represent the behavior of materials under certain specified conditions. Because of the complexities of stress and deformation it is not usually possible to allow for changes in the conditions. For this reason the hardness numbers from one type of measurement cannot be compared with those from another except empirically. For the same reason the importance of maintaining uniform conditions is even greater than in other mechanical tests.

Since uniformity is so important, it is highly desirable to have special machines designed for hardness tests. Several have been developed which make a test that was already simple almost completely automatic. Hardness tests can often be classed as nondestructive. If the indentations can be made on surfaces that will not be damaged by slight irregularities, hardness tests can be used as a basis for 100 per cent inspection. In view of these advantages, hardness tests are used extensively in industry and research.

10.4 HARDNESS TESTING MACHINES

Some of the machines designed especially for various types of hardness measurement are described briefly.

Diamond-Pyramid Hardness Tester

This machine is designed to apply a predetermined load to a diamond pyramid indenter, forcing it into the surface being tested. Loads may be varied between 1 g and 120 kg, by small increments, although this total range may not be available on any one machine. Machines are usually arranged so that the load is applied smoothly and automatically, by means of dead weights operating through systems of levers and dashpots. The dashpots control the speed of loading. The machine has a table, or anvil, on which the specimen can be placed so that the indenter will be perpendicular to the surface. The dimensions of the resulting impression are measured to within ± 0.0005 mm by a micrometer microscope which is part of the machine.

The foregoing description applies to both the Vickers hardness tester, which uses a square-based pyramid, and the Tukon microhardness tester, which uses the Knoop indenter.

Brinell Hardness Tester

This machine forces a hardened steel ball into the surface under a predetermined load supplied by dead weights and hydraulic pressure. Three

standard loads are used: 3000, 1500, and 500 kg.   Other loads are not
ordinarily used because of the lack of comparison between Brinell hardness
numbers as found using different loads.   The standard ball is 10 mm in
diameter and is made of hardened steel; special carbide balls are available
for measuring high hardnesses.   When the impression has been made, its
diameter is measured to within ±0.02 mm by a detached micrometer
microscope.

Rockwell Hardness Tester

Since this machine is designed to indicate the depth of penetration,
certain differences in its construction are necessary.   The specified load is
still applied to the indenter by dead weights acting through levers and
dashpots, but it is applied in two stages.   In the first stage a small load
pushes the indenter tightly against the surface, holding the specimen
securely in place and incidentally producing a small preliminary indentation.   This is called the *minor* load and is the same for all Rockwell tests—
10 kg.   The indentation caused by the minor load acts as a zero point from
which the depth of the final indentation is measured.   The final indentation is produced by the addition of a larger second load.   The final load,
which is the sum of the minor load and the added load, is called the *major*
load.   The major load can be set at one of three values—60, 100, or 150 kg.
Other loads are not ordinarily used, for the same reason as in the Brinell
test.   The indenter is either a steel ball or a diamond cone (actually a cone
having a spherical tip).

A variety of scales of hardness are made available by using different combinations of weight and indenter.   The most common are the *B* scale, used
for such materials as soft steels and aluminum alloys, and the *C* scale, for
hard steels, titanium, and the like.   For the *B* scale a $\frac{1}{16}$-in. ball is used
with a 100-kg major load.   For the *C* scale the diamond cone (called a
brale) is used with a 150-kg major load.   Thirteen other scales are listed
by ASTM E18 for other special purposes.

The Rockwell machine is so constructed that it automatically indicates
the depth of penetration on a dial, which is calibrated to read directly in
Rockwell hardness numbers, based on Eq. 10.4.

Shore Scleroscope

This machine measures rebound hardness.   A $\frac{1}{12}$-oz hammer having a
rounded diamond tip is dropped from a height of 10 inches to strike the
surface of the specimen.   Special means are provided to ensure that the
hammer strikes the surface at right angles and that no energy is lost during
the fall or the rebound.   The hardness number is determined by the height
of the rebound, which may be read either by direct observation of the

hammer itself, or from a dial which indicates the height in terms of an arbitrary scale.

10.5 HARDNESS TESTS

Test Procedures

In most tests there is a choice of loads, and in some a choice of indenters. The first step is to select the proper combination on the basis of the type of material and its expected hardness.

The machines used for hardness tests are largely automatic. Nevertheless several precautions must be observed. For example, the perpendicularity of the load line to the surface of the specimen should be checked. Care must also be taken that the load is applied and released smoothly. The location of indentations is another important consideration. Since the area of plastic deformation extends to nearly 3 times the radius from the center of the indentation, adjacent indentations should be kept 3 diameters apart, center-to-center. Indentations should also be kept a corresponding distance from the edge of the specimen.

In static indentation tests the application of the load must be carefully timed in view of the transient creep. Detailed instructions are given for each type of test in manufacturers' booklets and the appropriate ASTM *Standards*.

Interpretation of Results

Observations in hardness tests are either the size of the indentation in millimeters or a hardness number indicated on a dial. When the diameter of the spherical indentation or the diagonal of a pyramidal one is obtained, the corresponding hardness number can be computed from the appropriate formula (since the load used in the test is known). More common practice, however, is to use conversion tables. Tables for Brinell hardness numbers (BHN) are given in ASTM E10 and for diamond pyramid hardness (DPH) in ASTM E92. Rockwell and scleroscope hardness numbers are indicated directly on the machine, and no conversion is necessary. Rockwell numbers must include the scale used, e.g., $B63$, $C35$. The number by itself is meaningless.

The condition of the surface is of great importance in interpreting hardness results. The surface is frequently harder than the interior material, producing a hardness gradient. If the surface is clean and flat, as in a cleavage surface of a crystal, the surface layer is of atomic dimensions and any gradient will be so small that the hardness readings will not be affected. In most materials, however, and especially in metals, fabrication of the part develops surface layers of various thicknesses in which the hardness gradient may be important.   The cold work caused by machining, for example, can produce a harder layer a few thousandths of an inch thick. Case-hardening a surface may produce a layer 0.01 inch thick, and sometimes as thick as 0.05 inch.

If the penetration of the indenter is small compared with the thickness of the surface layer, or if the gradient is not steep, the hardness number can be taken as an indication of the hardness of the very surface of the material.   In diamond pyramid hardness tests the depth can be kept very small by selecting the proper load.   The Rockwell machine is available in a special form, called a *superficial tester*, in which small loads can be used. The scleroscope indentation is also very small.   In all three the depth of the indentation can be of the order of 0.001 inch to provide a good indication of *surface* hardness.

If the penetration of the indenter is deep compared with the thickness of the surface layer, the hardness number indicates the hardness of the inner material.   The indentation of the Brinell test varies from 0.01 to 0.04 in., making it a good indication of inner hardness except for case-hardened surfaces, which are often too thick.

If the penetration of the indenter is nearly the same as the thickness of the surface layer, or if there is a steep gradient, the hardness number will be affected by the gradient and will not be a reliable indication of the hardness of either the surface or inner material.   Such numbers can only be useful for comparison of pieces having similar gradients, and then the load must always be specified.   Different types of hardness number measured on the same material do not always agree with the standard conversion table for that material.   Such disagreement can usually be traced to the presence of a thin surface layer, perhaps a result of machining or grinding.

BIBLIOGRAPHY

Davis, Harmer E., Troxell, George E., and Wiskocil, Clement T., *The Testing and Inspection of Engineering Materials*, 2nd ed. (McGraw-Hill Civil Engineering Series) McGraw-Hill Book Company, Inc., New York, Toronto, London, 1955, Ch. 6; Liddicoat, R. T., and Potts, Philip O., *Laboratory Manual of Materials Testing*, The Macmillan Company, New York, 1952, Ch. 2.
 Additional information on hardness testing methods and apparatus.

Freudenthal, Alfred M., *The Inelastic Behavior of Engineering Materials and Structures*, John Wiley & Sons, Inc., New York, 1950, Ch. 18.
 Interesting comments and suggestions on interpretation of hardness.

PROBLEMS

10.1 Define technological hardness.

10.2 What condition must be fulfilled if hardness is to be expressed as a function of load and area alone?

10.3 A Vickers hardness test made on a certain steel with a load of 30 kg produces an impression whose diagonal measures 0.654 mm. Compute the Vickers hardness number and determine the load that should be used if the hardness of an area 0.050 mm in diameter, in the same piece of steel, is to be measured. Estimate the ultimate strength of the steel.

10.4 List all the methods discussed in this chapter for measuring hardness, and give their principal characteristics.

10.5 Which method of measuring hardness will be affected most by compressible material, such as dust, between the specimen and the anvil on which it rests? Why?

10.6 Will the presence of oil on the surface of a specimen cause the observed indentation hardness to deviate from its true value, and if so in which direction?

10.7 Discuss the effects on the observed hardness numbers of making an indentation (a) too close to the edge of the specimen; (b) too close to another indentation.

10.8 Discuss the effect on the observed hardness of using too thin a specimen.

10.9 What is the purpose of the dashpots used in indentation hardness testing machines?

10.10 What is the purpose of the minor load used in the Rockwell hardness tester?

10.11 What is wrong with the hardness number Rockwell 50?

10.12 A rebound hardness test is made on a thermoplastic having a pronounced elastic aftereffect. Will the indicated hardness be higher or lower than that measured by static indentation?

10.13 Give an explanation for the observation that hardness indicated by the Shore scleroscope is often higher than that indicated by the Brinell machine.

PART THREE

PHYSICAL
BEHAVIOR

CHAPTER 11

ELECTRICAL AND MAGNETIC PROPERTIES

Some of the most impressive advances in our understanding and use of materials have been made in the field of electronics. The development of a workable theory by which many electrical and magnetic phenomena can be analyzed quantitatively has led to such new applications as the transistor, with its potentialities for miniaturization and low power requirements, the fine-particle permanent magnet, and ferrites. These new applications are in addition to the many existing applications of materials in electrical engineering, such as conductor materials, iron for transformer cores, magnetomechanical transducers, piezoelectric crystals, ferroelectric memory devices, insulating materials, and glass for vacuum tubes.

In our study of the electrical and magnetic behavior of materials we shall rely on relatively simple physical concepts to explain the various phenomena. For example, many aspects of conduction in metals are adequately explained by the free-electron "gas" concept. In this way the student can get a feel for the effects of various factors on the electrical and magnetic properties of materials without becoming deeply involved in the more profound aspects of solid state theory.   It should be recognized, however, that the free-electron gas is only a model, with definite limitations.

CONDUCTION

11.1   CONDUCTION IN METALS

Electrical currents are conducted through solids primarily by means of free electrons.   In metal crystals, which are the best conductors, the valence electrons are not bound to the individual atoms, but are free to form an electron "gas" surrounding the ions of the metal (Art. 2.2).   Because of thermal energy, these electrons are in constant motion throughout the crystal, at velocities of the order of 10^8 cm/sec.   At the same time the ions are oscillating about their equilibrium positions (Art. 2.7).   As a result, there are continual collisions between the electrons and ions, and each electron travels only a short distance between collisions.   Like that of molecules in a gas, the motion of the electrons is random and averages the same in all directions.

The average distance traveled by an electron between collisions is called its *mean free path*, λ.   The length of the mean free path depends to a great extent on the magnitude of the thermal oscillations of the ions, which in turn depends on the absolute temperature, T.   Thus we can say that λ is a function of T, decreasing as T increases.   In addition to the interference of the oscillating ions, there is interference caused by imperfections in the metal.   These include imperfections in the crystal structure, such as dislocations, impurities, and others mentioned in Art. 2.9, plus grain boundaries in polycrystals.   This interference is almost entirely independent of temperature.   Furthermore it is approximately in proportion to the number and extent of the imperfections, and is therefore structure-*in*sensitive.   The length of the mean free path has been calculated for various metals and is found to range from a few atomic distances to several thousand.

When an electric potential is applied to a conductor, a field is set up within it.   The *field strength* is equal to the change in potential, or voltage, per unit length: $\varepsilon = -\upsilon/l$.   It represents the force exerted per unit charge on any charge carrier under the influence of the field.   Thus the force on each free electron in the conductor is $\mathbf{f} = -e\varepsilon$ where $-e$ is the electron charge.*   As is indicated by the minus sign, force $\mathbf{f}$ is in the direc-

---

* $\mathbf{f}$ and ε are vector quantities, as are $\mathbf{a}$ and $\mathbf{v}$, below.   Their magnitudes are expressed as f, ε, a, and v, respectively.

tion opposite the field.   The electrons are all given an acceleration in that direction according to Newton's law,

$$\mathbf{a} = \frac{\mathbf{f}}{m} = -\frac{e\mathcal{E}}{m},$$ (11.1)

where m is the electron mass.

If the electrons were perfectly free of interference they would continue to accelerate as long as the field was applied.   Because of their limited motion, however, their actual increase in velocity is small and depends on the length of the mean free path.   To illustrate, imagine an electron moving with an initial velocity $\mathbf{v}_0$ (Fig. 11.1).   During its time of flight, t, the

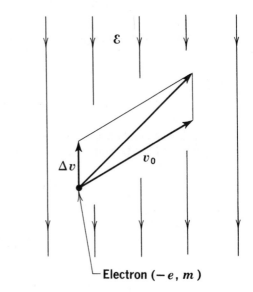

Fig. 11.1   Electron moving in an electric field, $\mathcal{E}$.

Electron $(-e, m)$

electric field imparts to it a constant acceleration, $\mathbf{a}$.   The increment of velocity is represented by $\Delta\mathbf{v} = \mathbf{a}t$.   The time of flight is given by $t = \lambda/v_{av}$, or, to a good approximation, $t = \lambda/v_0$, and v_0 can be thought of as the average magnitude of the velocity of the electrons in their random motion. (v_0 is approximately constant, varying only slightly with temperature.) Hence the increment of velocity given to the average electron is

$$\Delta\mathbf{v} = \frac{\mathbf{a}\lambda}{v_0}$$ (11.2a)

in the direction shown.   Thus the electrons drift in that direction with an average net velocity

$$\mathbf{v} = \frac{\Delta\mathbf{v}}{2} = \frac{\mathbf{a}\lambda}{2\,v_0}.$$ (11.2b)

Substituting the value of **a** from Eq. 11.1, we have

$$\mathbf{v} = -\frac{\mathcal{E}e\lambda}{2\ mv_0}. \tag{11.2c}$$

The magnitude of current flowing through the conductor can now be calculated. If there are n conduction electrons per unit volume, moving with the average velocity, v, the charge flowing through a unit area per unit time is nev. This is the current density, J; the total current is $I = JA$, where A is the area of the cross-section of the conductor. Substituting the magnitude of v from Eq. 11.2c and remembering that $\mathcal{E} = -\mathcal{V}/l$, we have

$$I = \frac{n\mathcal{V}e^2\lambda A}{2\ mv_0 l}. \tag{11.3a}$$

This equation expresses Ohm's law

$$I = G\mathcal{V}, \tag{11.3b}$$

or

$$I = \sigma\frac{A}{l}\,\mathcal{V}, \tag{11.3c}$$

where G is the *conductance* and σ the *conductivity* of the material. Comparing Eqs. 11.3a, b, and c, we find that

$$\sigma = G\frac{l}{A} \tag{11.4a}$$

and

$$\sigma = \frac{ne^2\lambda}{2\ mv_0}. \tag{11.4b}$$

Since the resistance, R, and the resistivity, ρ, are the reciprocals of G and σ, respectively, we can also write

$$\rho = R\frac{A}{l} \tag{11.5a}$$

and

$$\rho = \frac{2\ mv_0}{ne^2\lambda}. \tag{11.5b}$$

The electron charge and mass are, of course, constant, and the average velocity magnitude, v_0, can be assumed to be approximately constant. Hence from Eq. 11.4b we conclude that the conductivity of a metal is directly proportional to (1) the number of free electrons, n, per unit volume, and (2) the length of the mean free path, λ. Since λ is a function of temperature, decreasing as T increases, it follows that σ varies in the same manner. It has been observed that for a large number of metals σ is inversely proportional to T over a useful range, indicating that λ also varies inversely with T in that range.   It is usually more convenient to deal with the resistivity, ρ, which, being the reciprocal of σ, varies linearly with T over the same range (Fig. 11.2).

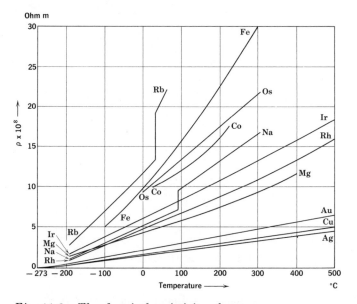

Fig. 11.2   The electrical resistivity of metals is proportional to the absolute temperature. (Adapted from Zwikker, Physical Properties of Solid Materials, *Pergamon Press, London (1954) pp. 247, 249)*

The resistivity is made up of two parts: the temperature-dependent part, ρ_T, caused by thermal agitation of the ions; and the residual resistivity, ρ_0, which is caused by imperfections and is independent of temperature.

$$\rho = \rho_0 + \rho_T. \tag{11.6a}$$

The variation of ρ with temperature is shown in Fig. 11.3.   At absolute zero we have $\rho_T = 0$, and ρ_0 represents the total resistivity.   As the temperature rises, ρ_T begins to be significant and is found to be proportional to a power of T.*   Since ρ_0 is usually quite small, ρ_T soon becomes predominant and at some higher temperature ρ_T becomes a linear function of T and ρ_0 is practically insignificant.   The dividing line between high and low temperatures can be specified in terms of a characteristic temperature, Θ_D, which will be defined in Art. 12.1 since it is fundamentally a specific heat

---

* T^5 at very low temperatures.

parameter. At still higher temperatures there are other factors which tend to produce nonlinearity. The total range over which ρ is a linear function of T varies widely from material to material (Fig. 11.2). The transition metals have nonlinear variations at most temperatures, as shown for iron.

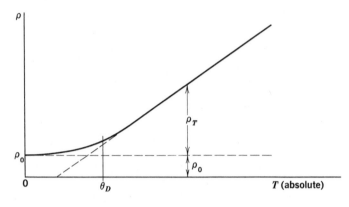

Fig. 11.3   Schematic variation of resistivity, ρ, with absolute temperature, T.

At temperatures for which ρ is a linear function of T it is customary to write

$$\rho = \rho_r + C(T - T_r), \qquad (11.6b)$$

where T_r is any arbitrarily chosen reference temperature, ρ_r is the corresponding resistivity, and C is a constant. The units of ρ can be derived from Eq. 11.5a:

$$\rho = R\frac{A}{l} = \left[\text{ohms}\,\frac{(\text{length})^2}{\text{length}}\right] = [\text{ohms} \times \text{length}].$$

The most commonly used units, found in most tables, are *ohm-cm*. We can also think of ρ as the resistance of a unit cube for which $A = l = 1$.

To specify the variation of ρ with temperature, a *temperature coefficient of resistance*, α, is usually used. It is defined by

$$\alpha\rho_r = C. \qquad (11.7)$$

Substituting in Eq. 11.6b, we have

$$\rho = \rho_r + \alpha\rho_r(T - T_r). \qquad (11.6c)$$

The units of α are reciprocal degrees (deg^{-1}) as shown by solving this equation for α:

$$\alpha = \frac{\rho - \rho_r}{\rho_r} \cdot \frac{1}{T - T_r}. \qquad (11.8)$$

Thus the value of α depends on the values selected for ρ_r and T_r and is independent of the units chosen for ρ; T_r is usually taken as 20°C.

Table 11.1 gives values of ρ and α for a few representative metals, at 20°C. Also listed are conductivities, σ, in mhos (reciprocal ohms) per cm (Eq. 11.4a), and conductivity-density ratios. The last is often a determining factor when weight is at a premium. Note that although both copper and silver have higher conductivities, aluminum has a higher conductivity-density ratio because of its lighter weight.

Table 11.1   Electrical Properties of a Few Representative Metals at 20°C

METAL	RESISTIVITY, ρ, ohm-cm	TEMPERATURE COEFFICIENT OF RESISTANCE, α, per °C	CONDUCTIVITY, σ, mhos/cm	CONDUCTIVITY-DENSITY RATIO
Copper	1.67×10^{-6}	3.92×10^{-3}	0.599×10^6	66.9×10^3
Silver	1.62×10^{-6}	4.1×10^{-3}	0.627×10^6	58.9×10^3
Aluminum	2.65×10^{-6}	4.3×10^{-3}	0.378×10^6	139.8×10^3
Aluminum alloys (annealed)	$2.93\text{–}5.94 \times 10^{-6}$	—	$0.344\text{–}0.168 \times 10^6$	—
Magnesium	4.33×10^{-6}	4.2×10^{-3}	0.231×10^6	132.7×10^3
Magnesium alloys	$5\text{–}14.5 \times 10^{-6}$	—	$0.2\text{–}0.069 \times 10^6$	—
Low-carbon steels	14.3×10^{-6}	4×10^{-3}	0.070×10^6	—
Titanium	55×10^{-6}	3.3×10^{-3}	0.0182×10^6	2.8×10^3
Manganin[a]	48×10^{-6}	0.01×10^{-3}	0.0208×10^6	—
Nichrome[b]	112×10^{-6}	0.16×10^{-3}	0.00893×10^6	—

[a] 4 Ni, 12 Mn, 84 Cu.
[b] 60 Ni, 15 Cr, 25 Fe.

EXAMPLE 11.1

What is the conductance of a copper wire 0.008 in. in diameter and 30 ft long at 68°F? at 800°F?

Solution: From Table 11.1, for 20°C, which is equivalent to 68°F, $\sigma = 0.599 \times 10^6$ mhos/cm. From Eq. 11.4a, $G = \sigma A/l$, in which $A = 50.3 \times 10^{-6}$ in.², and $l = 360$ in. To change σ to mhos/in. we multiply by 2.54 cm/in. Thus

$$G = (0.599 \times 10^6)(2.54)\left(\frac{50.3 \times 10^{-6}}{360}\right)$$

$$= 0.213 \text{ mhos at } 68°F.$$

From Table 11.1, $\rho = 1.67 \times 10^{-6}$ ohm-cm, and $\alpha = 3.92 \times 10^{-3}$ per °C. To convert °F to °C we use $°C = \frac{5}{9}(°F - 32) = \frac{5}{9}(768) = 427°C$. Using Eq. 11.6c, we have

$$\rho = 1.67 \times 10^{-6}(1 + 3.92 \times 10^{-3} \times 407)$$

$$= 4.33 \times 10^{-6} \text{ ohm} = \text{cm}$$

or

$$\sigma = 0.231 \times 10^6 \text{ mhos/cm,}$$

from which $G = 0.0822$ mhos at 800°F.

From Fig. 11.2, which shows the curve for copper as essentially linear to 500°C, we conclude that Eq. 11.6c is sufficiently accurate.

Mechanical Effects

Volume changes associated with hydrostatic pressure, tensile stress, or other forms of mechanical loading produce changes in resistance that are of particular interest in connection with electromechanical transducers. Such resistance changes can be traced to two sources: dimensional changes and resistivity changes.

The effect of dimensional changes on resistance can be studied by the method of Art. 3.17 (effects of small errors) since the changes are small. From Eq. 11.5a we can write

$$R = \rho \frac{l}{A}.$$

Applying Eq. 3.27b, we have

$$\frac{dR}{R} = \frac{d\rho}{\rho} + \frac{dl}{l} - \frac{dA}{A}, \tag{11.9}$$

which shows how the relative change in resistance is related to the relative changes in resistivity and physical dimensions. However, the resistivity itself is also affected by changes in the physical dimensions, as will now be shown.

From Eq. 11.5b, using the above procedure, we have

$$\frac{d\rho}{\rho} = \frac{dv_0}{v_0} - \frac{d\lambda}{\lambda} - \frac{dn}{n} \tag{11.10}$$

(since m and e are constants). It is through the number of conducting electrons per unit volume, n, that the resistivity is affected by the physical dimensions. If N_0 is the total number of conducting electrons in the conductor, the volume of which is $V = Al$, then

$$n = \frac{N_0}{Al}, \tag{11.11}$$

and using Eq. 3.27b again,

$$\frac{dn}{n} = \frac{dN_0}{N_0} - \frac{dA}{A} - \frac{dl}{l}, \tag{11.12}$$

so that Eq. 11.10 becomes

$$\frac{d\rho}{\rho} = \frac{dv_0}{v_0} - \frac{d\lambda}{\lambda} - \frac{dN_0}{N_0} + \frac{dA}{A} + \frac{dl}{l}.$$

Thus the total relative change in resistivity can be divided into two parts: a change in what may be called the intrinsic resistivity, ρ_i, associated with changes in the average electron velocity, v_0, the mean free path, λ, the total number of conducting electrons, N_0, and perhaps other factors; and a change in physical dimensions A and l. Hence we can write

$$\frac{d\rho}{\rho} = \frac{d\rho_i}{\rho_i} + \frac{dA}{A} + \frac{dl}{l}. \tag{11.13}$$

Equation 11.9 now reduces to

$$\frac{dR}{R} = \frac{d\rho_i}{\rho_i} + 2\frac{dl}{l}, \tag{11.14}$$

in which the first term on the right represents possible changes in intrinsic resistivity and the second is all that remains of the effect of changes in physical dimensions. The fact that the change in cross-sectional area cancels out is easily explained by noting that for a given total number of conducting electrons, an increase in cross-sectional area A has no net effect on the number of such electrons available to conduct current through it. An increase in length, on the other hand, not only increases the distance to be traveled by the electrons but also decreases the number of electrons per unit length; thus the double effect of a change in length.

Since $dl/l = \epsilon_x$, the strain in the direction of current flow, Eq. 11.14 can be written

$$\frac{dR}{R} = \frac{d\rho_i}{\rho_i} + 2\,\epsilon_x. \tag{11.14a}$$

Over a considerable range of strains it has been found experimentally that dR/R varies linearly with ϵ_x, an indication that if it varies at all, ρ_i varies linearly with ϵ_x. Thus we can write

$$\frac{dR}{R} = K_s\epsilon_x, \tag{11.15}$$

where K_s is a constant. Comparison with Eq. 3.25 reveals that K_s corresponds to the gage factor for an electric strain gage.

Table 11.2 Gage Factors of Wires of Different Compositions[a]

MATERIAL	APPROXIMATE COMPOSITION	AVERAGE K_s
Advance	55 Cu, 45 Ni	2.1
Nichrome	75 Ni, 12 Fe, 11 Cr, 2 Mn	2.5
Constantan	60 Cu, 40 Ni	1.8
Isoelastic	36 Ni, 8 Cr 50 Fe, Mn, Si, Mo	3.54
Manganin	9–18 Mn, $1\frac{1}{2}$–4 Ni, Remainder Cu	0.5
Nickel		−12

[a] Hetényi, M., Ed. *Handbook of Experimental Stress Analysis*, John Wiley & Sons, Inc., New York, 1950, pp. 172–173 (by permission).

For most metals K_s is close to 2, indicating that $d\rho_i/\rho_i \approx 0$.   For several metals and alloys, however, it deviates considerably from 2 (Table 11.2). In these metals $d\rho_i/\rho_i$ varies with the strain for various reasons.   Isoelastic wire has a high positive gage factor (Table 11.2) and is used in strain gages for measuring dynamic strains where its high output is useful.   From Eq. 11.15 $dR/R = 3.54\ \epsilon_x$, and substituting in Eq. 11.14a, we find

$$\frac{d\rho_i}{\rho_i} = \frac{dR}{R} - 2\ \epsilon_x = 1.54\ \epsilon_x,$$

an indication that there is an increase in resistivity with increasing volume over and above that resulting from the dimensional changes alone.   The transition metal, nickel, at the other extreme, has a very large *negative* gage factor.   Using Eqs. 11.15 and 11.14a as above, we find

$$\frac{d\rho_i}{\rho_i} = -14\ \epsilon_x,$$

which indicates a great *decrease* in resistivity with increasing volume.   It probably indicates that the number of conducting electrons, N_0, increases as the volume increases.   A possible source of these additional electrons is the incomplete $3d$ inner shell in nickel.   Much remains to be learned about the actual mechanisms of intrinsic resistivity changes.

11.2   SEMICONDUCTORS AND INSULATORS

Nonmetallic crystals are held together by ionic and covalent bonds, and the valence electrons are much more closely associated with their own atoms than in the metallic bond.   Hence the concept of a free electron gas, available to conduct electricity, which is used with metals, is no longer applicable.   These materials are therefore insulators in varying degree.   A good insulator may have a resistivity as high as 10^{16} ohm-cm—22 orders of magnitude higher than for metals, whose resistivities are of the order of 10^{-6} ohm-cm.   In an ideal insulator *all* valence electrons are occupied in bond formation and *none* are available for conduction.   Thanks to thermal agitation and imperfections in real materials, a few electrons are always free to conduct electricity.   Assuming that Eq. 11.4b defines conductivity for all materials, we can obtain a rough idea of the ratio between the number of conducting electrons in an insulator and that in a metal.   Since the variation of v_0 and λ from one material to another is relatively small, it follows from Eq. 11.4b that

$$\frac{n_{\text{ins}}}{n_{\text{met}}} \approx \frac{\sigma_{\text{ins}}}{\sigma_{\text{met}}} = \frac{\rho_{\text{met}}}{\rho_{\text{ins}}} \approx 10^{-22}.$$

Thus for every 10^{22} conducting electrons in a metal there is only one in an

insulator.   The effect of an increase in temperature is to release more and
more conducting electrons.   In view of the extremely small number to
start with, this effect far outweighs the decrease in the mean free path, so
important in metals.   As a result the conductivity of insulators *increases*
with temperature.

Some nonmetallic elements have an electron structure which allows far
more valence electrons to be made available by thermal energy than in
the majority of insulators.   These elements are known as *semiconductors*.
They are insulators at absolute zero but develop significant conductivities
at room temperature.   Elements classed as semiconductors include carbon,
silicon, germanium, and gray tin in column IVA of the periodic table and
selenium and tellurium in column VIA.

Semiconduction produced by thermal energy alone is called *intrinsic
semiconduction*.   Since relatively few electrons are free at any instant (of
the order of one out of 10^{12} in silicon at room temperature), the conductivity
is small (Table 11.3); however, it increases exponentially with temperature.

When an electron is broken free of its bond, it becomes mobile and can
migrate through the crystal like an electron in a metal.   At the same time,
of course, the place that it formerly occupied becomes vacant and is referred to as a *hole*.   Like the electron, the hole can also migrate.   This
comes about when a nearby electron jumps from its place into the hole,
thereby creating a new hole.   The mobile hole behaves just about like an
electron having a positive charge and can conduct electricity as well as an
electron.

Impurity atoms can have a marked effect on the conductivity of semiconducting materials.   The basic crystal structure in silicon and germanium, for example, is a diamond structure in which all four valence electrons
are used to form bonding pairs (Art. 2.9) just as in the carbon atoms of
diamond.   If impurity atoms having different numbers of valence electrons
are substituted for some of the original atoms in the structure, there will
be a local excess or deficiency of electrons in the covalent bonds.   An element in column VA of the periodic table, such as phosphorus or arsenic,
has 5 valence electrons.   Each atom of one of these elements substituted
for one of the silicon or germanium atoms will therefore provide one extra
electron not needed for bonding.   These electrons are available for conduction.   On the other hand, an element in column IIIA of the periodic
table, such as boron or aluminum, has only 3 valence electrons.   When an
atom of this kind replaces one of the regular atoms in the structure, it
is short one electron and a hole is created which is available for conduction.
Conduction resulting from electrons or holes provided by impurity atoms
is called *extrinsic semiconduction*.   An element that provides extra electrons is called a *donor*, and a semiconductor having such an impurity is

called an *n-type* (for the negative charges on the electrons).   An element that lacks electrons is called an *acceptor*, and the corresponding semiconductor is a *p-type* (for the positive charges of the holes).

The effect of impurity atoms is far out of proportion to their number relative to the number of original atoms.   The reason is that the impurity atoms contribute practically 100 per cent to the conductivity whereas the original atoms contributed only an extremely small fraction of their electrons.   The relative increase in conductivity is therefore much larger than the proportion of impurity atoms added.   For example, the addition of only one part in 10^8 of an impurity can increase the conductivity by a factor of 7.*   Semiconduction is therefore a good example of a structure-sensitive property.

This brief introduction to the subject of semiconductors is intended only to present a simplified general picture.   Further development of the theory requires an understanding of the band theory of solids.†   Some of the most important principles are those governing the behavior of junctions between different types of semiconductors.   The properties of these junctions are responsible for many of the devices, such as rectifiers and transistors, which represent important applications of semiconductors.   They are discussed at length in textbooks on semiconductors.   The list of semiconducting materials includes other elements and a variety of compounds, such as cuprous oxide, Cu_2O; silicon carbide, SiC; lead sulfide (galena), PbS; and zinc oxide, ZnO.

Table 11.3   Comparative Resistivities

TYPE OF MATERIAL	RESISTIVITY, ohm-cm
Metals	10^{-5} to 10^{-6}
Semiconductors	
Extrinsic	10^{-2}
Intrinsic	10 to 10^5
Insulators	10^{15}

Table 11.3 compares the resistivities at room temperature of conductors, semiconductors, and insulators.   Note that they are separated by wide gaps so that they are easily distinguished one from another.

---

* Von Hippel, Arthur R., et al., *Molecular Science and Molecular Engineering*, The Technology Press of Massachusetts Institute of Technology and John Wiley & Sons, Inc., New York, 1959, p. 410.

† Sinnott, Maurice J., *The Solid State for Engineers*, John Wiley & Sons, Inc., New York, 1958.

MAGNETISM

11.3 PARAMAGNETISM AND DIAMAGNETISM

Passage of an electric current through a wire produces a magnetic field around the wire. If the wire is wound into a coil, the magnetic field is concentrated inside of the coil and is expressed by

$$H = \frac{4 \pi n I}{10},\tag{11.16}$$

where n is the number of turns in the coil per centimeter, I is the current in amperes, and H is the *magnetizing force** in oersteds. As a result of the magnetic field there is a *magnetic flux density*,† B, measured in lines of force per square centimeter or gausses.

If the coil is empty (except for the surrounding air), the flux density is numerically equal to the magnetizing force ($B = H$) when they are measured in the specified units (cgs electromagnetic units). If a solid material is placed within the coil, the flux density is altered by its presence and no longer equals H. It is this *interaction between magnetic fields and solid materials* that we are concerned with in this discussion.

Magnetism is dipolar, i.e., characterized by having two opposite poles— north and south. The strength of a magnetic dipole is measured by the product of the pole strength, p, and the distance between the poles, d; it is called the *magnetic moment*, $\mathbf{m} = p\mathbf{d}$. One source of magnetic moment in an atom is the orbital motion of its electrons. Each electron revolving around the nucleus constitutes a circulating electric charge, or current, and thus produces a small magnetic field. In addition, each electron, spinning on its own axis (Art. 2.1), can be conceived as a circulating charge and also produces a small magnetic field.

In the atoms of most materials the electron orbits are more or less random so that all or nearly all the moments cancel each other. Likewise, in most atoms all or nearly all the spin moments are paired and contribute nothing to the net moment. The weak moments remaining in some atoms are normally prevented from lining up by thermal agitation. As a result most materials, in the absence of a magnetic field, have no magnetism.

The application of a magnetic field to such materials has two effects. The first is an induced change in the orbital motion of the electrons. The electron orbits in each atom tend to be reoriented so that their magnetic moments *oppose* the applied field. As a result the flux density is reduced

---

* Also called the *magnetic field strength*.

† Also called the *magnetic induction*.

slightly from that of air.   The induced changes in moment are linear, and consequently B remains proportional to H but is slightly smaller.   This effect is common to all materials and is called *diamagnetism*.   If it is the only effect of a magnetic field on a given material, the material is said to be *diamagnetic*.   Organic materials and the rare gases are examples of diamagnetic materials.

The second effect of a magnetic field occurs in materials whose orbital and spin moments do not entirely cancel.   In such materials the individual atoms act as permanent magnets and are reoriented by the field so that their moments *add to* the field.   This behavior increases the flux density slightly and is referred to as *paramagnetism*.   Materials in which this effect outweighs the induced diamagnetism are called *paramagnetic* materials. The alignment of atomic dipoles is a linear function of the field strength, so that B is still proportional to H but is slightly larger.

The incomplete electron shells are the sources of unbalanced magnetic moments in atoms.   The valence shells of some materials contain as many as 3 unpaired electrons whose spin moments can contribute to the atomic dipole.   However, since the valence electrons are largely occupied in forming atomic bonds, their magnetic effect is not likely to be large.   The most important source of magnetic moments is the incomplete inner shells of the transition elements and rare earths.   The electrons in these shells tend to have their spins aligned in the same direction until the shells are half filled and consequently can develop significant net moments.   In addition there are sometimes unbalanced orbital moments in these incomplete inner shells. Hence the transition metals are often strongly paramagnetic.

Both diamagnetism and paramagnetism can be expressed by the equation

$$B = \mu H, \tag{11.17}$$

where μ is the *permeability* of the material.   For diamagnetism $\mu < 1$, and for paramagnetism $\mu > 1$.   This equation can also be expressed as

$$B = H(1 + 4\pi\chi), \tag{11.18}$$

where the second term in parentheses represents the change in flux density caused by the material in the magnetic field.   The dimensionless constant χ is called the *susceptibility* of the material; it is of the order of -10^{-6} for diamagnetic materials, zero for air, $+10^{-6}$ for most paramagnetic materials ($+10^{-2}$ for some transition metals).   Figure 11.4 shows the three variations of B with H.   The spread of the three lines is greatly exaggerated to illustrate the differences.

For most engineering purposes both dia- and paramagnetic materials can be assumed to be magnetically inert.   An understanding of their behavior is, however, desirable as a preliminary to the study of the more important ferromagnetic materials.

11.4 FERROMAGNETISM

In certain materials whose atoms have permanent magnetic moments additional forces tend to align the atoms parallel to each other even in the absence of an external field and against the effects of thermal agitation. This behavior results in spontaneous magnetization of small regions in the material, called *domains*. Materials which have this characteristic are called *ferromagnetic*.

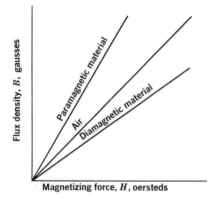

	3*d* Electrons		4*s* Electrons
	No.	Spin directions	
Sc	1	↑	2
Ti	2	↑ ↑	2
V	3	↑ ↑ ↑	2
Cr	5	↑ ↑ ↑ ↑ ↑	1
Mn	5	↑ ↑ ↑ ↑ ↑	2
Fe	6	↑ ↑ ↑ ↑ ↑ ↓	2
Co	7	↑ ↑ ↑ ↑ ↑ ↓ ↓	2
Ni	8	↑ ↑ ↑ ↑ ↑ ↓ ↓ ↓	2

Fig. 11.4 Variation of B *with* H, *illustrating difference between dia- and paramagnetic materials, schematically.*

Fig. 11.5 Spin directions of the 3d *electrons in the manganide transition metals.*

The source of the permanent magnetic moments in ferromagnetic materials is almost entirely electron spin. In the manganide transition metals the electrons in the 3*d* shells align themselves as shown in Fig. 11.5. The result is strong paramagnetism. Iron, cobalt, and nickel, all ferromagnetic, are to be found in this group. The other ferromagnetic element, gadolinium, is one of the rare earths.

The forces which produce spontaneous alignment in the ferromagnetic elements are the *exchange forces*, the result of the exchange interaction of quantum theory.* These forces are a function of the ratio of the *atomic spacing in the metal crystal* to the *diameter of the 3d shell*. For a positive

---

*Von Hippel, Arthur R., et al., *Molecular Science and Molecular Engineering*, The Technology Press of Massachusetts Institute of Technology and John Wiley & Sons, Inc., New York, 1959, p. 315.

exchange interaction this ratio must be within certain narrow limits (just over 3).   The ferromagnetic elements are the only elements for which the exchange interaction energy is positive.   For other transition elements the exchange forces actually prevent the magnetic moments from lining up. Thus, although elements like vanadium and chromium appear, from Fig. 11.5, to be good candidates for ferromagnetism, they are prevented by their negative exchange interaction.   Even iron in its austenitic form (face-centered cubic γ-iron) is nonmagnetic because of the change in atomic spacing on transformation from ferrite (body-centered cubic α-iron).

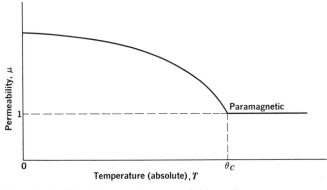

Fig. 11.6 Variation of permeability of iron with absolute temperature, under constant magnetizing force.

A number of alloys and compounds also have ferromagnetic properties. One group includes alloys of iron, cobalt, and nickel, such as silicon iron, cobalt steel, and Alnico.   Another group includes, surprisingly enough, alloys and compounds based on manganese, a nonferromagnetic element. Being adjacent to iron in the transition group, manganese can apparently be easily transformed to a ferromagnetic form when alloyed with such elements as copper and aluminum.   A third group includes the oldest of the ferromagnetic materials, magnetite.   This group has been augmented since 1945 by the *ferrites*, which are essentially ceramics and consequently have very high resistivities, a useful property in high-frequency applications.

The effect of temperature on ferromagnetism is very important.   As the temperature increases, thermal energy tends more and more to break the spontaneous alignment of the atoms.   At a critical temperature called the *Curie temperature*, Θ_c, the exchange forces are completely overcome, and the ferromagnetism disappears.   Figure 11.6 illustrates this effect. At temperatures above Θ_c the material behaves simply as a paramagnetic material.   Table 11.4 gives the Curie points for the four ferromagnetic elements.

Table 11.4   Curie Temperatures

ELEMENT	θ_c, °C
Fe	780
Co	1125
Ni	365
Gd	16

The discussion which follows deals only with behavior below the Curie point.

In a single crystal of ferromagnetic material the atoms tend to line up with their magnetic poles all pointing in the same direction.   In a crystal like that in Figure 11.7a this situation tends to create a bar magnet with

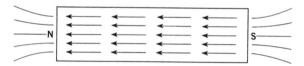

(a) Unstable

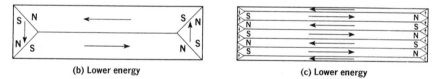

(b) Lower energy   **(c) Lower energy**

Fig. 11.7   Single ferromagnetic crystal, illustrating subdivision into domains.

a north pole at one end and a south pole at the other.   However, this is not a desirable situation so far as magnetic energy is concerned because the return path for the lines of flux is outside the material.   The external field has a high magnetostatic energy associated with it.   Figure 11.7b shows an arrangement of lower energy, in which the bar is divided into four *domains* which form a closed magnetic circuit.   The magnetostatic energy of each domain varies with its volume—the third power of a linear dimension.   There is, however, a new source of energy in the domain walls.   This energy varies with surface area—the second power of a linear dimension.   If the crystal subdivides into several domains, as in Fig. 11.7c, the volume energy of each domain is lowered but its surface energy is increased.* The net effect is still a decrease of energy, and so long as this continues to be so, the crystal will subdivide into smaller and smaller domains. When the point is reached, however, where the decrease in volume energy is just balanced by the increase in surface energy, no further subdivision takes place. The dimensions of the domains vary between 10^{-2} and 10^{-5} cm.

In a given crystal there are certain directions in which the orientation of atoms is easiest. In body-centered cubic crystals the directions of easiest magnetization are those coinciding with the cube edges [100]; for face-centered cubic crystals they are the cube diagonals [111]. There are also directions of difficult magnetization: [111] for body-centered cubic and [100] for face-centered cubic crystals. This fact is further evidence of the anisotropy of crystal structures. The energy of magnetization is affected by this anisotropy. The *anisotropy energy* is lowest when the domains are lined up with the axes of easy magnetization. Since there are several of these axes, the domains have considerable freedom of orientation.

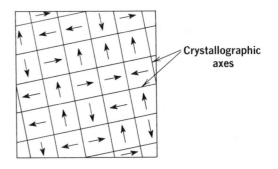

Crystallographic axes

Fig. 11.8 Two-dimensional crystal, illustrating random orientation of domains.

In the absence of an external field the domains are oriented in some combination of directions such that the net magnetization of the whole is zero. Figure 11.8 shows a hypothetical two-dimensional random arrangement of domains in a part of a cubic crystal. When a magnetic field is applied, the domains shift their orientation toward the direction of the field. This can be done in two ways: by rotation of atoms in the domains away from their directions of easy magnetization toward the direction of the field (Fig. 11.9a), or by expansion of the domains that are already oriented nearest the direction of the field (Fig. 11.9b). Both mechanisms require

---

* Like the grain boundaries in a polycrystalline metal, the domain walls are regions of distortion because the direction of magnetization must change across the thickness of the wall. Hence the walls of a domain have a higher energy than its interior. (See Kittel, C., *Introduction to Solid State Physics*, 2nd ed., John Wiley & Sons, Inc., New York, 1956, pp. 419, 432.)

energy.   The boundary motion in the second process is largely irreversible, so that energy is dissipated during this process.

As a consequence of this mechanism of magnetization, the variation of B

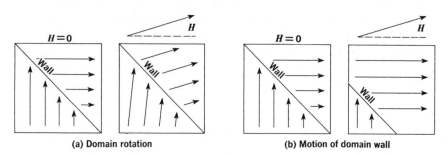

| (a) Domain rotation | (b) Motion of domain wall |

Fig. 11.9   Effect of magnetic field on domain orientation.   (From Bozorth, Ferromagnetism, *Copyright 1951, D. Van Nostrand Company, Inc., Princeton, N.J.)*

with H is nonlinear (Fig. 11.10).   Equation 11.17 is still used, although μ is no longer constant but varies with H from a relatively low initial value, μ_0, to a maximum, μ_m (Fig. 11.10).   Thus μ is analogous to the secant modulus of elasticity (or its reciprocal).   Figure 11.11 shows the variation

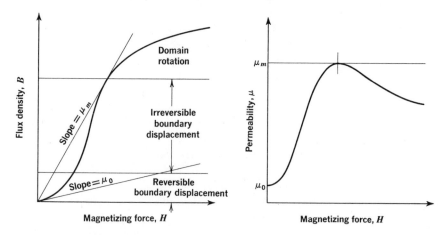

Fig. 11.10   Nonlinear magnetization curve for ferromagnetic material.   (From Bozorth, Ferromagnetism, *Copyright 1951, D. Van Nostrand Company, Inc., Princeton, N. J.)*

Fig. 11.11   Permeability corresponding to magnetization curve of Fig. 11.10.   (From Bozorth, Ferromagnetism, *Copyright 1951, D. Van Nostrand Company, Inc., Princeton, N. J.)*

of μ with H, based on Fig. 11.10; μ can be as high as 100,000 or even higher. Compared with this value the permeability of paramagnetic materials is indeed insignificant.

As the field strength increases, the domains become progressively more closely aligned to the direction of the field. When alignment is complete, the crystal is *saturated*. Any further increase in H causes only a linear increase in B such as would occur if the material were replaced with air. It should be noted that each domain taken by itself is always in a saturated condition.

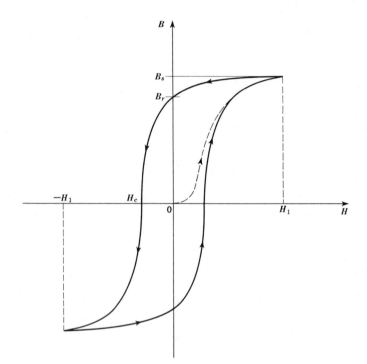

Fig. 11.12 *Hysteresis loop produced by reducing field strength from* $+H_1$ *to* $-H_1$, *followed by increase to* $+H_1$ *again. Dashed line shows original magnetization curve.*

When the field strength is reduced from a high value, the domains do not reorient themselves to any appreciable extent, and the material remains magnetized, having a high *residual induction*, B_r (Fig. 11.12). To reduce the induction to zero a negative magnetizing force, H_c, is required. This demagnetizing force is called the *coercive force.* During a complete cycle of magnetizing force the domains are forced to go through irreversible changes in each direction, and as a result, energy is dissipated in proportion to the area of the hysteresis loop. The situation is analogous to the elastic aftereffect, in which a mechanical hysteresis loop is generated (Art. 7.2).

The motion of domain walls during magnetization or demagnetization may be greatly interfered with by imperfections in the crystal structure. This interference has a direct bearing on the magnitudes of the permeability, coercive force, and hysteresis loss. These properties are therefore *structure-sensitive.*

Because it determines the width of the hysteresis loop, the coercive force, H_c, is closely associated with the amount of hysteresis loss. A material having a low coercive force has low hysteresis and is called *magnetically soft.* A material having a high coercive force is called *magnetically hard.*

Some factors having marked effects on the structure-sensitive properties are chemical composition, crystal structure, impurities, previous plastic strains, and temperature. Cold-forming operations, like rolling or drawing, multiply the imperfections in a metal, reducing its permeability and making it magnetically as well as mechanically harder. Relief of internal stresses by annealing usually improves the permeability and makes the material softer, both magnetically and mechanically. Impurities have the same general effect as internal stresses. Increasing the percentage of carbon in mild steel from 0.02 to 0.2 can decrease the permeability by a factor of $\frac{1}{2}$.

Hard magnetic materials make good permanent magnets because of the high coercive force required to demagnetize them. Soft magnetic materials are useful where hysteresis losses in alternating current applications are to be kept to a minimum.

Structure-*in*sensitive properties include the saturation induction, B_s (Fig. 11.12), and the Curie temperature. These are intrinsic properties depending on the unbalanced electron spins and the exchange interaction. They are not unduly affected by imperfections and change only slowly with chemical composition.

A particularly intriguing application of the theory of magnetic domains is in the improvement of permanent magnets. The reasons for formation of domains were discussed earlier, and it was pointed out that there is an optimum domain size for minimum energy. Similarly there is an optimum particle size in which, for minimum energy, only a single domain can exist. For iron this optimum size is about 300 Å.* A larger particle will sub-

---

* Goldman, J. E., Ed., *The Science of Engineering Materials*, John Wiley & Sons, Inc., New York, 1957, p. 321.

divide into more than one domain; in a smaller one the influence of thermal agitation becomes too great for stability.

Being a single domain, and at the same time a single crystal, such a particle will naturally have its axis of spontaneous magnetization in one of the easy directions (e.g., [100] for iron). If a magnetic field is applied in a different direction and the particle is held fixed, the only way that the magnetic axis can change is by rotation (there are no domain walls to move). Because it must rotate through the direction of hard magnetization, considerable energy is required. The necessary field strength is the coercive force for the particle. Thus the coercive force for a particle should be much higher than for a large piece of the same material. Values 500 times as great have been observed.

Permanent magnets made of compacted powder offer the possibility of great improvement over those made of a single piece. The full potentialities have yet to be realized.

11.5 MAGNETOMECHANICAL EFFECTS

The spontaneous magnetization of a domain in a ferromagnetic crystal is accompanied by an elongation or contraction in the direction of magnetization, called *magnetostriction*. It is associated with the inherent anisotropy of the crystal structure and the fact that the preferred directions of magnetization are always in definite crystallographic directions.

The effect on a crystal or polycrystal containing many domains can be studied by considering first the effect on a single domain. Imagine a small sphere of a magnetic material in a completely demagnetized state at a temperature above the Curie point. The sphere is cooled, and at the Curie temperature it becomes spontaneously magnetized as a single domain in some preferred direction. Because of this spontaneous magnetization the diameter of the sphere increases slightly in the direction of magnetization. If we call the new length l_s, the unit increase in length, or strain* is

$$\lambda_s = \frac{l_s - d}{d}, \tag{11.19}$$

where d is the original diameter (Fig. 11.13). If we assume that the volume remains constant, there is also a transverse contraction,

$$\lambda_t = -\frac{\lambda_s}{2} \tag{11.20}$$

(Art. 3.9). Thus the sphere becomes a prolate spheroid having a major axis l_s and two equal minor axes l_t (the very slight variation of dimensions in different directions relative to the crystal axes is neglected). The di-

---

* The symbol λ is used for strain resulting from magnetostriction.

ameter of the spheroid in any direction making an angle θ with the major axis can be approximated by

$$l = l_t + (l_s - l_t) \cos^2 \theta,$$

or

$$l = A + B \cos^2 \theta. \tag{11.21}$$

This expression is a good approximation because $(l_s - l_t)$ or B is always small compared with l_t or A.

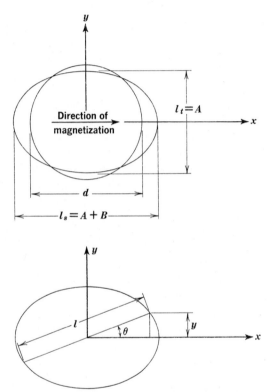

Fig. 11.13   Elongation of a spherical domain with positive magnetostriction.

The average biameter is equal to d since the volume remains constant. To fulfill this condition we must have

$$d^3 = l_s(l_t)^2$$

$$= (A + B)A^2$$

$$= A^3 \left(1 + \frac{B}{A}\right),$$

but since $B/A \ll 1$,

$$d \approx A \left(1 + \frac{B}{3A}\right) = A + \frac{B}{3}. \tag{11.22}$$

This result also follows from the fact that the average value of $\cos^2 \theta$ for a sphere is $\frac{1}{3}$ (it may be recalled that $\cos \theta = 1/\sqrt{3}$ defines the octahedral direction). The strain in any direction can now be calculated from

$$\lambda = \frac{l - d}{d}. \tag{11.23}$$

Using Eq. 11.19, we have

$$\frac{\lambda}{\lambda_s} = \frac{l - d}{l_s - d} = \frac{A + B \cos^2 \theta - \left(A + \dfrac{B}{3}\right)}{A + B - \left(A + \dfrac{B}{3}\right)},$$

which reduces to

$$\lambda = \tfrac{3}{2} \lambda_s (\cos^2 \theta - \tfrac{1}{3}). \tag{11.24}$$

The student should check the value of λ for $\theta = 0$ and $\pi/2$, and for the octahedral direction.

In a demagnetized material having many domains they may be considered to be oriented at random. If we choose any fixed direction in the material, the strain in this direction owing to each domain is given by Eq. 11.24. For the whole assemblage of domains the average strain is found by substituting $(\cos^2 \theta)_{av} = \frac{1}{3}$, giving $\lambda_{av} = 0$.

When the material is saturated, on the other hand, all domains are oriented in the direction of the magnetization. If we choose this direction, we have $\theta = 0$ for all domains, and from Eq. 11.24 the overall strain is λ_s. Thus the expansion in the direction of magnetization is the same at saturation for a single domain or for an assemblage of domains. This expansion, λ_s, is called the *saturation magnetostriction*. It is positive in some materials and negative in others. A negative value of λ_s means that the small spherical domain of which we spoke *contracts* in the direction of magnetization instead of expanding, becoming an oblate spheroid having one short axis, l_s, and two equal longer axes, l_t. Equation 11.20 still holds for constant volume.

Magnetostriction is fundamentally a result of crystal anisotropy. Any elastic deformation, whether expansion or contraction, causes an increase in strain energy. However, in magnetostriction the deformation also causes a decrease in *anisotropy energy* which more than offsets the increase in strain energy.

The saturation magnetostriction strain is very small. Of the ferromagnetic elements, nickel has the highest magnitude: $\lambda_s = -40 \times 10^{-6}$. In iron the magnetostriction is positive at low field strengths, but barely reaches 5 or 10 microinches per inch. At high values of H it reverses and becomes negative, with $\lambda_s = -8 \times 10^{-6}$. Of the ferromagnetic alloys, low-nickel Permalloy (e.g., 45 per cent nickel) has one of the highest positive magnetostrictions ,approximately 25×10^{-6}. One of the ferrites, cobalt ferrite crystal, has been found to have an unusually high positive magnetostriction, more than 800×10^{-6} in the direction of the crystal axis.* Figure 11.14 gives magnetostriction curves for some common materials.

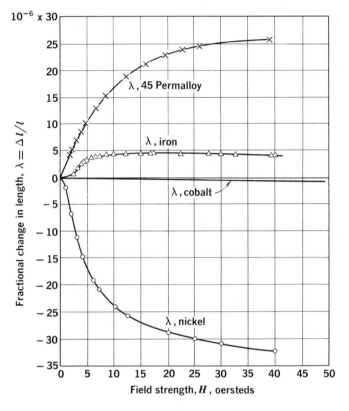

Fig. 11.14   Magnetostriction of some common materials, showing expansion or contraction. (From Bozorth, Ferromagnetism, *Copyright 1951, D. Van Nostrand Company, Inc., Princeton, N. J.)*

Saturation magnetostriction, λ_s, is a structure-*in*sensitive property. Magnetostriction is an important engineering property. In transducers it transforms electrical into mechanical energy, in underwater sonar gear, for example. It can also cause damage by setting up serious vibrations in the magnetic parts of electrical machinery.

* Goldman, J. E., Ed., *The Science of Engineering Materials,* John Wiley & Sons, Inc., New York, 1957, pp. 311, 312

Mechanical deformation of magnetic domains has other important consequences.   When a ferromagnetic material is strained, the domains tend to realign themselves into positions of lower energy.   The permeability of

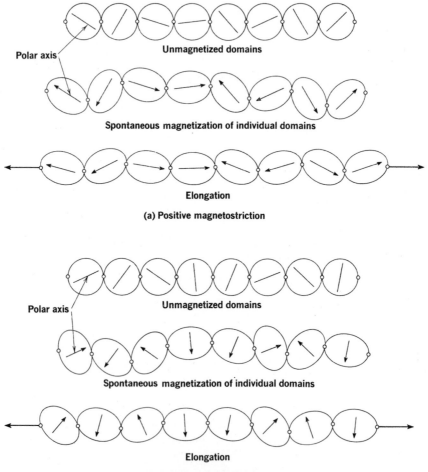

(a) Positive magnetostriction

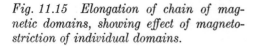

(b) Negative magnetostriction

Fig. 11.15   Elongation of chain of magnetic domains, showing effect of magnetostriction of individual domains.

the material is thereby changed, and it becomes easier or more difficult to magnetize; and at the same time the realignment of domains uses up energy. Realignment of the domains under strain can be illustrated qualitatively by the two series of links in Fig. 11.15.   Each link represents a domain, lengthened or shortened by its spontaneous magnetization (positive or negative magnetostriction). When either series is strained longitudinally, the links rotate into positions more nearly parallel to the direction of strain.

One consequence of the realignment of domains is that the material *deforms more easily* than if no domains were present. When a stress is applied, the total strain is made up of two parts,

$$\epsilon = \epsilon_e + \epsilon_m,$$ (11.25)

where ϵ_e is the ordinary elastic strain and ϵ_m the magnetic strain caused by reorientation of the domains. Figure 11.16 shows the relation between

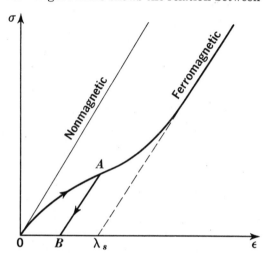

Fig. 11.16 Stress-strain relation for ferromagnetic material compared with that for a nonmagnetic material of equal stiffness.

stress and strain in the elastic range for a ferromagnetic material. The stress-strain diagram is nonlinear, and the effective modulus of elasticity (secant modulus, E_{sec}) is reduced.* Note that deformation is always made easier, regardless of the sign of the magnetostriction, as illustrated by Fig. 11.15.

As mentioned in Art. 11.4, realignment of magnetic domains is largely an irreversible process, involving dissipation of energy. During unloading the strain tends to decrease in an ordinary elastic way, as from A to B in Fig. 11.16. Thus a mechanical hysteresis loop is generated (Art. 7.2), an important source of internal friction and damping. The more easily the domains rotate during loading, the greater will be the energy dissipated. Thus soft magnetic materials have greater damping capacity than hard ones. If a high magnetic field is applied, so that the domains are immobilized, the damping can nearly be made to disappear.

---

* Bozorth, Richard M., *Ferromagnetism*, D. Van Nostrand Company, Inc., Princeton, New Jersey, 1951, p. 684.

The realignment of domains under strain does not alter the net magnetism in the crystal because the actual distribution of polarities is still random (Fig. 11.17b and c).   The permeability of the crystal is affected, however.   In materials having positive magnetostriction realignment puts the domains in a better position to be polarized (Fig. 11.17d), and the

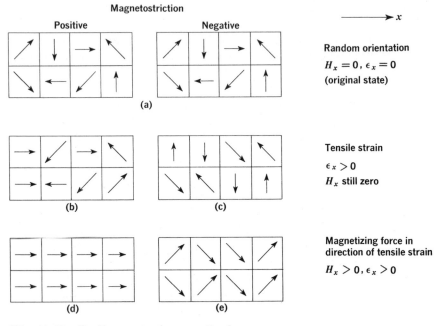

Fig. 11.17   *Realignment of magnetic domains under tensile strain and magnetizing force.   (Adapted from Bozorth,* Ferromagnetism, *Copyright 1951, D. Van Nostrand Company, Inc., Princeton, N. J.)*

permeability is *increased.*   In materials having negative magnetostriction realignment of the domains makes them more difficult to polarize (Fig. 11.17e), and the permeability is *decreased.*   Figure 11.17 illustrates the effect of tensile strain; the effect of compressive strain is just the reverse, and can be seen by interchanging the two columns.   Figure 11.18 shows the change in permeability of Permalloy under stress.

The effect of an applied stress on magnetostriction can be deduced from Fig. 11.15.   If the chain at (a) is partly straightened by a tensile stress, there is less possibility of expanding it further by applying a magnetic field.   Hence a tensile stress usually *decreases* the magnetostriction if λ is positive, and conversely, a tensile stress *increases* the magnetostriction if λ is negative.   Compressive stress has the opposite effect.

Many other factors are involved in magnetomechanical behavior.   The

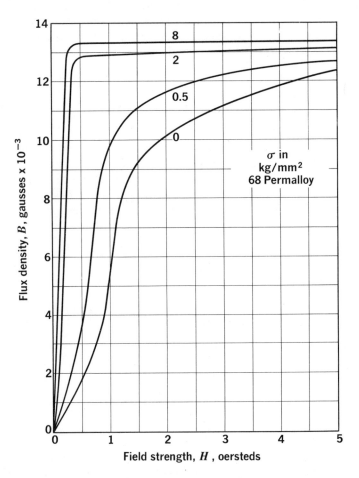

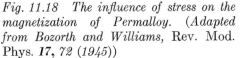

Fig. 11.18   *The influence of stress on the magnetization of Permalloy.* (*Adapted from Bozorth and Williams,* Rev. Mod. Phys. **17,** *72* (*1945*))

graphs of Figs. 11.14 and 11.18 are for polycrystalline materials and are assumed to be independent of direction of magnetization.   In single crystals the magnetostriction varies considerably, depending on the direction of magnetization with respect to the crystal axes.*   Preferred orientation, as in cold-rolled metal, can have effects similar to those in single crystals.

It has also been assumed that strains are within the elastic range.   The effect of strains in the plastic range is a subject in itself.†

Because of thermal agitation in the crystal structure, magnetostriction usually decreases in magnitude at higher temperatures; the domains are hindered in their reorientation by the fact that the atoms are in constant motion.

11.6   FERRITES

It was mentioned in Art. 11.4 that in some materials the exchange interaction energy prevents the magnetic moments from lining up.   Although each ion in the crystal structure has a magnetic moment resulting from unbalanced electron spins, the moments in neighboring ions point in opposite directions (Fig. 11.19).   Such a situation is called *antiferromagnetism.*

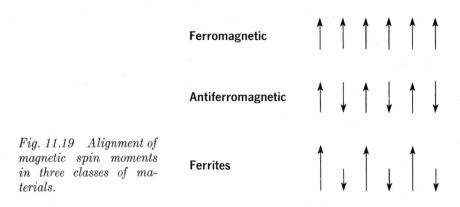

Fig. 11.19   Alignment of magnetic spin moments in three classes of materials.

In some materials having a characteristic crystal structure the ions are so arranged that although the magnetic moments point in opposite directions, those in one direction are larger than those in the other (Fig. 11.19). This is a form of antiferromagnetism, but it produces typical ferromagnetic properties, although on a smaller scale than in ferromagnetic materials. It is the type of magnetism found in the *ferrites.*

Ferrites are oxides similar to magnetite, $FeO \cdot Fe_2O_3$.   Their crystal

---

* Bozorth, Richard M., *Ferromagnetism*, D. Van Nostrand Company, Inc., Princeton, New Jersey, 1951, pp. 645–649.

† *Ibid.*, p. 596.

structure is cubic and corresponds to that of the mineral spinel ($MgAl_2O_4$).*
They are manufactured in the form of a ceramic, usually polycrystalline.
Their magnetic permeability is small compared with ferromagnetic materials: a typical value is $\mu_{max} = 10,000$.   For Permalloys $\mu_{max} = 100,000$ is
common.

The great advantage of the ferrites is their *high resistivity;* commercial
ferrites can have resistivities as high as 10^9 ohm-cm.   Eddy currents resulting from alternating fields are therefore reduced to a minimum, and the
range of application of these magnetic materials is extended to high frequencies—even to microwaves.

Other materials similar to the ferrites are also in use, such as magnetic
garnets and perovskites.   Developments in the field of microwave applications of magnetic materials are continuing at a steady pace.

DIELECTRICS

11.7   DIELECTRIC PROPERTIES

Polarization

A material placed in an electric field, as between the plates of a condenser,
interacts with the field through the displacement of charged particles

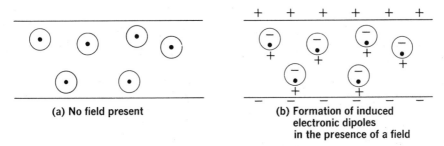

(a) No field present

(b) Formation of induced
electronic dipoles
in the presence of a field

Fig. 11.20   Electronic polarization.

within the material.   If the material is a conductor, some of the free electrons simply move to the side nearest the positive electrode until they
completely counteract the applied field.   Thus no field is left within the
material.   The shift occurs almost instantaneously, bringing about equilibrium.

* Von Hippel, Arthur R., et al., *Molecular Science and Molecular Engineering*, The
Technology Press of Massachusetts Institute of Technology and John Wiley & Sons,
Inc., New York, 1959, p. 317.

In a nonconducting material, or *dielectric*, electrons can only be displaced locally because they are bound to the individual atoms.   This local displacement, however, is sufficient to *polarize* the material.   In each atom the negative electron cloud is displaced relative to the positive nucleus, creating a small *induced dipole* whose negative pole is toward the positive side of the field (Fig. 11.20).   All dielectrics are subject to such *electronic* polarization.

Another form of *induced* polarization occurs in materials containing ions. In an ionic crystal, for example, the negative ions are attracted toward the positive side of the field and *vice versa* (Fig. 11.21).   The net result is that

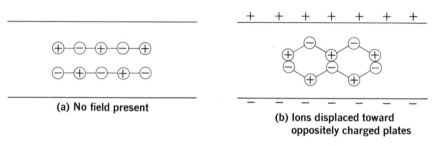

(a) No field present

(b) Ions displaced toward oppositely charged plates

Fig. 11.21   Ionic polarization.

the centers of positive and negative charge are displaced relatively and the material becomes polarized.

Polarization also takes place in certain materials by alignment of *permanent dipoles*.   Some molecules contain permanent charges which produce dipole moments in the individual molecules (Art. 2.6).   Many of the polymers are also of this type (polar polymers), and glass is still another material that contains permanent dipoles.   The *dipole moment* of a single pair of charges is

$$\mu = Q\mathbf{d},\qquad(11.26)$$

where Q is the magnitude of one of the charges and $\mathbf{d}$ is the distance between them.   The analogy between this and the magnetic dipole moment (Art. 11.3) should be noted.   In an electric field, ε (Art. 11.1), the force acting on each charge of the dipole produces a torque tending to align it with the direction of the field.   If θ is the angle between the axis of the dipole and the field (Fig. 11.22), the torque is

$$T = \mu \varepsilon \sin \theta.^*\qquad(11.27)$$

---

* The dipole moment, μ, is a vector pointing toward the positive charge of the dipole, and ε is also a vector.   The torque is therefore the vector product $T = \mu \times \varepsilon$ and is represented by the moment vector T in Fig. 11.22.

The resulting alignment, illustrated in Fig. 11.23, is sometimes referred to as *orientation polarization,* as distinguished from induced polarization.

Permanent dipole moments are in general much larger than induced dipole moments and therefore have a greater polarizing effect when fully oriented. Complete orientation is not usually possible at ordinary temperatures because of the randomizing effect of thermal agitation. Induced dipoles, on the other hand, are relatively unaffected by thermal agitation. Induced polarization is therefore just as important as orientation polarization except at low temperatures or high field strengths, under which the permanent dipoles can be fully aligned (Fig. 11.23).

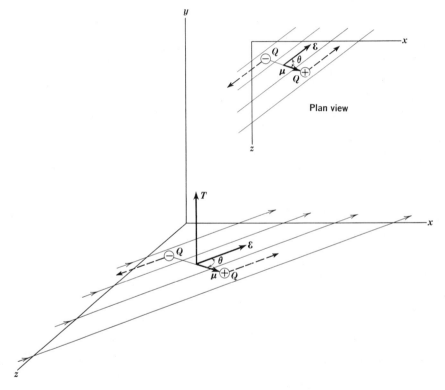

Fig. 11.22 Torque exerted by an electric field on a dipole.

The effect of polarization of the dielectric, when it is placed between two electrodes, is to increase the storage capacity of the electrodes (Fig. 11.24). This phenomenon can be visualized by imagining the formation of dipole chains during polarization (Fig. 11.25). A certain fraction of the charge on the electrodes is neutralized by the charge on the ends of the dipole

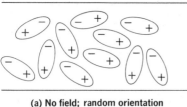

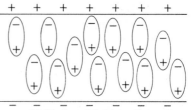

(a) No field; random orientation
of dipoles

(b) Dipoles rotated into alignment
with field

Fig. 11.23   Dipole polarization.

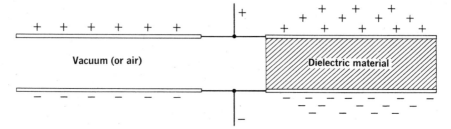

Vacuum (or air)

Dielectric material

*Fig. 11.24   Effect of dielectric polarization
on storage capacity of electrodes.*

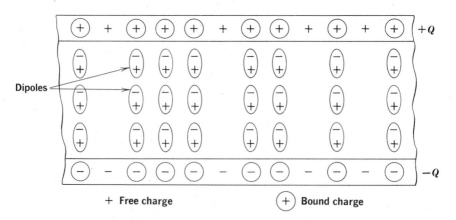

Dipoles

$+Q$

$-Q$

+ Free charge   (+) Bound charge

*Fig. 11.25   Neutralization of charges on
electrodes by dielectric polarization.*

chains. The neutralized charges can then be replaced by additional
charges from the external field (Fig. 11.24).

The *fraction* of the total charge that is neutralized by polarization is a
characteristic of the dielectric material. The ratio of the *total charge, Q,*

to the *free charge, Q'* (i.e., that part which is *not* neutralized by polarization (Fig. 11.25)) is called the *relative dielectric constant* or *permittivity, κ*.   Thus

$$\kappa = \frac{Q}{Q'}. \tag{11.28}$$

Since Q' is always a fraction of Q, κ is always greater than unity, and for most materials exceeds 2. In other words Q' is nearly always less than $\frac{1}{2} Q$, an indication that the polarized dielectric neutralizes at least half the charge. Rubber, for example, may have a dielectric constant of 3, and that of glass varies from 4 to 10. The dielectric constant for air is 1.0006 and is usually taken as unity (i.e., the same as a vacuum). Plastic foams have dielectric constants intermediate between those of air and solids (1.06 to 1.49).

The relative dielectric constant is usually measured in terms of the increased storage capacity of a pair of electrodes (e.g., a condenser). For a given condenser in a vacuum the capacitance is defined by

$$C_0 = \frac{Q}{\upsilon}, \tag{11.29}$$

where Q is the charge and υ the applied voltage. When a dielectric is inserted between the plates of the condenser, Eq. 11.29 gives the *free charge,*

$$Q' = C_0\upsilon. \tag{11.29a}$$

Since the total charge on the condenser, with the dielectric in place, is κ times the free charge, it follows that

$$Q = \kappa Q' = \kappa C_0 \upsilon. \tag{11.29b}$$

But the total charge is also given by

$$Q = C\upsilon, \tag{11.29c}$$

where C is the capacitance of the condenser with the dielectric. We see that the capacitance is increased by the dielectric to

$$C = \kappa C_0. \tag{11.30}$$

We can therefore define the relative dielectric constant as the ratio of the capacity of a condenser with the dielectric to that of the same condenser without the dielectric:

$$\kappa = \frac{C}{C_0}. \tag{11.31}$$

It is clear from both definitions (Eqs. 11.28 and 11.31) that κ is a dimensionless constant.

The discussion above is based on static conditions, analogous to static conditions in mechanical loading (Chapter 3). A dielectric subjected to a steady field, $\mathcal{E}$, is very much like a material subjected to a steady mechanical force, F. In either instance the material has time to adjust itself to the imposed condition and reach equilibrium. The adjustment of a material to a force is a displacement of atoms and molecules from their equilibrium positions, resulting in an overall deformation of the solid. The adjustment of a dielectric to an electric field is a displacement of induced and permanent dipoles, resulting in overall polarization of the material.

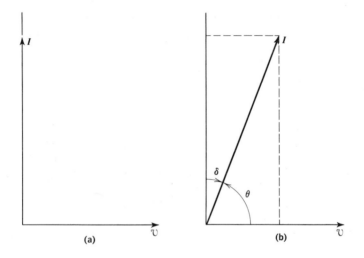

Fig. 11.26 *Phase shift of current with respect to voltage, caused by the presence of a dielectric.*

In an ideal material the displacements take place instantaneously upon application of the force or field and disappear instantaneously upon its removal. In real materials the atoms and molecules cannot always respond instantaneously to a force, and the elastic aftereffect is produced. Under an alternating force, energy is dissipated by mechanical hysteresis arising from the elastic aftereffect (Art. 7.2). Similarly the displacement of electric dipoles takes time. Polarization by ions and permanent dipoles takes longest because it involves mechanical displacement of relatively large particles. Electronic polarization has a much faster response because it involves only the electron clouds in the individual atoms. The result of the delay in polarization is twofold: the polarization may not be as complete at high frequencies, resulting in a decreased dielectric constant; and energy is dissipated by electrical hysteresis arising from the time delay.

In most materials the variation of the dielectric constant with frequency is not great because different mechanisms of polarization are effective at different frequencies. Materials in which polarization is primarily a result of orientation of permanent dipoles are likely to be affected to the greatest extent. The dielectric constant of nylon, a polar polymer, for example, may drop from 8 at 60 cps to 4 at 10^6 cps. Tables commonly give values of κ for several frequencies.

Dissipation of energy by a dielectric is measured in various ways. If an alternating voltage is applied to a condenser in a vacuum, the current is just 90° out of phase with the voltage (Fig. 11.26a), and no energy is lost. When a dielectric is inserted between the plates, the delay in polarization causes a phase shift of the resulting current (Fig. 11.26b). The phase shift angle, δ, is called the *loss angle* and its tangent the *loss tangent*. The power lost in the dielectric is computed as

$$P = \mathcal{V}I \cos \theta, \tag{11.32}$$

where $\mathcal{V}$ and I are the magnitudes of the voltage and current and $\cos \theta$ is termed the *power factor*.

For most materials the power factor is very small—a few per cent or less. Consequently the three measures of energy dissipation—δ, $\tan \delta$, and $\cos \theta$ ($= \sin \delta$)—are all approximately the same. Tables sometimes contain one and sometimes another. Since the values often vary somewhat with frequency, the frequency must be specified, and tables usually give values at several frequencies. The actual magnitude of the dielectric power factor may vary from low values such as 0.0005 for glass and polystyrene to high values of perhaps 0.20 for molded nylon and certain phenolics.

Both loss of power and the heat through which it is dissipated are usually undesirable factors. High permittivity, high power factor, and high frequency combine to produce the worst situation. For high-frequency applications it is therefore necessary to have the lowest possible permittivity and power factor. Polystyrene and polyethylene have exceptionally low power factors (less than 0.0005) which are practically independent of frequency, plus low dielectric constants (2.3–2.7).* The development of these materials helped make possible television and radar.

Other factors affecting dielectric losses include impurities, moisture content in porous materials, and density. No general rules are available for these factors, but graphs showing typical variations are sometimes available from manufacturers.

---

* Miner, Douglas F., and Seastone, John B., *Handbook of Engineering Materials*, 1st ed. (Wiley Engineering Handbook Series) John Wiley & Sons, Inc., New York, 1955, pp. 3–189.

Dielectric Strength

If the voltage imposed across a dielectric is large enough, it may cause a breakdown of the material as an insulator. This voltage, per unit thickness of material, is called the *dielectric strength*, and is commonly measured in volts per mil. Dielectric failure involves several factors—surface discharge, thermal and chemical deterioration, and electronic breakdown or *cascading*. Resistance to electronic breakdown is the *intrinsic* dielectric strength of the material. The other factors involve influences other than the electric field itself.

Intrinsic breakdown is associated with imperfections of the kinds listed in Art. 2.9. When the potential becomes high enough, a few electrons are broken loose at points where their bonds are strained by the presence of imperfections. Upon being freed these electrons are accelerated rapidly through the material. Each electron strikes other electrons and dislodges them also, creating more free electrons to be accelerated. The process thus multiplies rapidly, and soon a cataclysmic flow of electrons takes place, resulting in complete loss of insulating capacity.

Thus dielectric strength is seen to be a structure-sensitive property. It is also sensitive to structural anisotropy, being different in different directions for many materials. The *actual* thickness of the material affects the breakdown potential per unit thickness (dielectric strength). Thicker materials usually possess lower dielectric strengths than thinner materials. The situation is analogous to that of brittle strength, in which larger specimens have lower ultimate strengths than smaller ones. The basic cause is the same—the dependence of the property on imperfections in the material. Tabulated dielectric strengths should include the thickness for which they were measured.

11.8   FERROELECTRICS

A few materials have special crystal structures which permit *spontaneous polarization*. They are called *ferro*electrics because their spontaneous polarization is analogous to the spontaneous magnetization of *ferro*magnetic materials. There is no connection between ferroelectrics and ferrous metals.

Spontaneous polarization is the result of permanent dipoles being switched from one position of stable equilibrium to another by application of an electric field. The "perovskite" structure of barium titanate ($BaTiO_3$) is perhaps the most commonly cited example (Fig. 11.27). Under proper conditions the positive titanium ion at the center of the cube in (a) can occupy either of the positions shown in (b). In either instance the unit cell is given a polar axis and becomes a permanent dipole. The titanium ion can also occupy similar positions in the other two principal directions, making possible six directions for the polar axis,* all at equal energy.

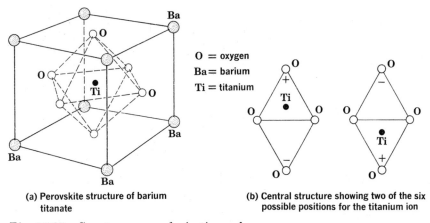

O = oxygen
Ba = barium
Ti = titanium

(a) Perovskite structure of barium titanate

(b) Central structure showing two of the six possible positions for the titanium ion

Fig. 11.27 Spontaneous polarization of barium titanate.

One of the conditions for spontaneous polarization is proper temperature range. Like ferromagnetic materials, ferroelectrics have a *Curie temperature*: at temperatures higher than the Curie point thermal agitation prevents spontaneous alignment of dipoles, while at lower temperatures the material becomes ferroelectric. Barium titanate has one of the highest Curie temperatures: 260°F±. For Rochelle salt, the first recognized ferroelectric, the Curie point is close to room temperature, while in other ferroelectrics it can be much lower than room temperature.

When the temperature of a ferroelectric is lowered through its Curie point, polarization begins at scattered points throughout the material. If no field is present, the orientation at these points is random. As polarization spreads from these nuclei, however, *domains* are formed in which the directions of polarization are the same as those of the nuclei. The result is a network of randomly oriented domains analogous to those in unmagnetized ferromagnetic materials.* Ferroelectric domains do not have the freedom of orientation that ferromagnetic domains have. In barium titanate, for example, it has been pointed out that there is a choice of six directions for the polar axis; in other materials there may be even fewer directions to choose from. Nevertheless, because there *is* a possibility of

* Von Hippel, Arthur R., *Dielectrics and Waves*, John Wiley & Sons, Inc., New York, 1954, p. 211.

more than one direction, the domains form in such a way that the net polarization is zero.

Application of an electric field to a ferroelectric in which the domains have random orientation tends to align the domains in much the same manner as a magnetic field aligns magnetic domains. Those oriented in the direction nearest the direction of the field grow by movement of domain walls, and other domains have their polar axes rotated by a simultaneous rotation of the dipoles in the domains. This motion takes energy, and consequently polarization is not reversible. We observe a hysteresis loop analogous to that of ferromagnetism. If the dielectric flux density, D (or magnetic flux density, B), is plotted against the electric field strength, ε (or magnetic field strength, H), it is found that: the variation is not linear; a saturation value of polarization (or magnetization) is reached when all the domains are aligned; when the field strength is reduced, the flux density does not become zero but retains a residual value even when the field is zero; a negative field, or coercive force, is required to reduce the polarization (or magnetization) to zero; and a complete cycle of the electric (or magnetic) field strength results in a hysteresis loop (Fig. 11.28).

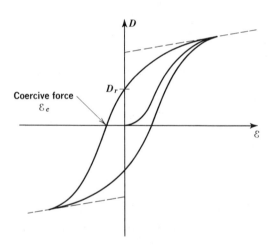

Fig. 11.28   Hysteresis loop for a ferroelectric material.

Like the permeability, μ, the permittivity, κ, is indicated by the secant of the hysteresis curve at any point and is no longer constant. Because of the complete polarization approached at saturation, the permittivity can reach extremely high values in ferroelectrics. For barium titanate the relative permittivity can be in the neighborhood of 10,000.*

---

* Zwikker, C., *Physical Properties of Solid Materials*, Interscience Publishers, Inc., New York, 1954, p. 215.

11.9 ELECTROMECHANICAL EFFECTS

Electrostriction is a mechanical deformation which always accompanies polarization in dielectrics.   The fact that the electron clouds are displaced relative to their nuclei (electronic polarization) produces a small expansion in the direction of the applied field.   This expansion varies with the square of the field strength, ε, and is the same whether the field is positive or negative.   Its magnitude is ordinarily very small.   There is no inverse effect because mechanical deformation simply displaces each atom as a whole and does not distort its electrical charge—thus no polarization results.

Ferroelectric crystals exhibit a special kind of electromechanical effect associated with the presence of permanent dipoles in the crystal structure. The mass realignment of permanent dipoles in domains causes relatively large deformations in the crystal.   The strain is directly proportional to the applied field instead of to its square.   Of equal or greater importance is the inverse effect: *distortion of a ferroelectric crystal causes it to be polarized.* The permanent dipoles are reoriented under strain to create a polar axis in one direction or the other.

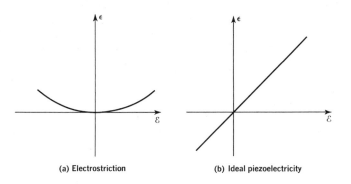

(a) Electrostriction   (b) Ideal piezoelectricity

Fig. 11.29   Schematic   representation   of strain, ϵ, vs field strength, ε.

The combination of electro $\rightarrow$ mechanical and mechano $\rightarrow$ electrical actions is called *piezoelectric* effect.*   All ferroelectric materials have piezoelectric properties.

Certain other crystals are also piezoelectric because of their permanent dipoles, although they are not spontaneously polarized like the ferroelectrics.   The basic requirement is that the crystal structure have no center

---

* "Pressure-electric."

of symmetry.   Many crystals fulfill this requirement.   Quartz is one of the commonest examples (Fig. 2.15).

The relation between strain and field strength in piezoelectricity is approximately linear.   Furthermore, when the field is reversed in direction, the strain is also reversed in direction, and *vice versa*.   Figure 11.29 shows the variation of strain with field strength for both electrostriction and ideal piezoelectricity.   The magnitude of the piezoelectric effect is illustrated by potassium dihydrogen phosphate (KH_2PO_4, commonly called KDP).   This material is also ferroelectric.   When polarized to saturation it has a strain of approximately 3000×10^{-6}, compared with a saturation magnetostriction of 40×10^{-6} for nickel.   Other common piezoelectrics include ammonium dihydrogen phosphate (ADP), Rochelle salt, and tourmaline.

Piezoelectric properties, being directly related to the crystal structure, are highly anisotropic.   The strains caused by potentials (or potentials caused by strains) in different directions vary in a most complex manner, depending on the way the crystal has been cut in making the particular piece in question.   The whole subject is much too involved to discuss in this text.

Piezoelectrics are invaluable as electromechanical transducers, where their large response makes them often more efficient than transducers using magnetism.   Some of their uses are: electric filters; pressure measuring devices for high pressures; phonograph pickups; underwater sound equipment for both sending and picking up sound waves; ultrasonic vibrators for producing frequencies up to 500,000 kilocycles per second.

BIBLIOGRAPHY

Shortley, George, and Williams, Dudley, *Elements of Physics*, Prentice-Hall, Inc., Englewood Cliffs, N. J., 1953.
>   Chapters 27, 28, 30, and 31 provide a good review of the fundamental relations between electrical and magnetic quantities.

Fitzgerald, A. E., and Higginbotham, David E., *Basic Electrical Engineering* 2nd ed., McGraw-Hill Book Co., Inc., New York, 1957.
>   Covers the basic laws for both electrical and magnetic circuits.   For the student.

Sinnott, Maurice J., *The Solid State for Engineers*, John Wiley & Sons, Inc., New York, 1958.
>   For the student who wishes to go deeper into certain areas of electrical and magnetic behavior.

Bozorth, Richard M., *Ferromagnetism*, D. Van Nostrand Company, Inc., Princeton, N. J., 1951; Von Hippel, Arthur R., et al., *Molecular Science and Molecular Engineering*, The Technology Press of the Massachusetts Institute of Technology and John Wiley & Sons, Inc., New York, 1959; Von Hippel, Arthur R., *Dielectrics and Waves*, John Wiley & Sons, Inc., New York, 1954; Dekker, Adrianus J., *Solid State Physics*, Prentice-Hall, Inc., Englewood Cliffs, N. J., 1957; Zwikker, C., *Physical Properties of Solid Materials*, Interscience Publishers, Inc., New York, 1954.

For the inquiring or advanced student.

PROBLEMS

11.1 (a) Determine the resistance at 20°C of a flat magnesium wire 0.006 in. thick, 0.08 in. wide, and 50 in. long. (b) Compute the resistance of the same wire at 400°C, using Eq. 11.6c. Is this equation likely to be inaccurate at this temperature?

11.2 Find the resistance of a titanium wire 0.001 in. in diameter and 4 in. long, at 350°F; at −200°F.

11.3 (a) Using data from Table 11.1, compute the slopes of the lines in Fig. 11.2 for copper, silver, and magnesium. Compute the corresponding slopes for aluminum, manganin, and nichrome. (b) Construct a graph similar to Fig. 11.2, showing the lines for all six metals for the temperature range 0 to 200°C.

11.4 What factors influence the mean free path of an electron in a metal? Explain the influence of each factor.

11.5 A copper wire 10 cm long, having a resistance of 0.1 ohm, is subjected to a potential difference of 1 volt between its ends. Estimate the magnitude of the drift velocity, v, of the electrons in the conductor. Assume that for copper $v_0 = 1.6 \times 10^8$ cm/sec and $\lambda = 3 \times 10^{-6}$ cm. HINT: 1 volt/cm = 10^3(g × cm)/(coul × sec²).

11.6 A manganin wire 0.1 mm in diameter and 8 cm long is used to measure the pressure in a test chamber. Assuming the bulk modulus to be $K = 20 \times 10^6$ psi, what change of resistance will be produced by a hydrostatic pressure of 1 million psi?

11.7 Does the resistance of a long circular rod change under torsion? Explain your answer.

11.8 A 1-mil diameter nickel wire 15 in. long is cemented onto a steel bar with paper between for insulation. The initial resistance of the wire is 94.400 ohms. When the steel bar is loaded in tension, the wire is strained by the same amount as the bar, as indicated by a suitable strain gage. At a strain of 350 μin./in. the resistance is observed to be 94.035 ohms. What is the gage factor of the nickel wire? Compute the relative change in intrinsic resistivity at this strain.

11.9 The variation of resistivity with temperature in conductors is opposite to that in semiconductors. Explain this difference. How can the difference be expressed in terms of the temperature coefficient of resistance, α, for each class of material?

11.10 Explain the mechanisms of electronic conduction in (a) intrinsic semiconductors; (b) n-type and p-type impurity semiconductors.

11.11 What are the identifying characteristics of ferromagnetic materials?

11.12 Explain why the ferromagnetic domains subdivide until they reach a certain minimum size.

11.13 If a piece of soft iron is cooled through its Curie temperature in the complete absence of a magnetic field, will it exhibit any overall magnetism? Does your answer depend in any way on the physical dimensions of the piece?

11.14 What form of domain reorientation dissipates the most energy? What part of the magnetization curve is produced by this effect?

11.15 Explain the meaning of *residual induction;* of *coercive force.*

11.16 Sketch comparative magnetization curves for magnetically hard and soft materials.

11.17 Which ferromagnetic properties are structure-sensitive and which structure-insensitive?

11.18 What effect, if any, does the sense ($+$ or $-$) of magnetization in a given direction have on whether a material with negative magnetostriction expands or contracts in that direction?

11.19 What effect, if any, does increasing temperature have on magnetostriction?

11.20 What effect, if any, does the sign of magnetostriction have on the stress-strain curve of a ferromagnetic material?

11.21 Explain the effect of increasing frequency on the dielectric constant, for each of the three types of polarization.

11.22 The dielectric constant of a polar polyvinyl chloride at 60 cps is 6.8. Would the dielectric constant at 10^6 cps be more likely to be 10, 6.9, or 4.9?

11.23 The dielectric strength of an acrylic plastic is 500 volts per mil for a thickness of 125 mils. Is the breakdown voltage for 500 mils thickness likely to be equal to, greater than, or less than 250,000 volts?

11.24 Explain the origin of the term *ferroelectric.*

CHAPTER 12

THERMAL
PROPERTIES

In this chapter we shall study the response of solid materials to thermal changes—the addition or subtraction of heat, the raising or lowering of temperature. We have already considered the effects of temperature on the *mechanical behavior* of materials (Chapters 7 and 8). Here we are concerned with the *thermal behavior* of solids, which is important in such applications as thermodynamics, heat transfer, melting, thermal stresses, and thermal shock.

The concepts of specific heat, thermal conductivity, thermal expansion, and the melting point have been introduced in elementary courses in chemistry and physics; emphasis was largely on gases, whose atoms and molecules have greater freedom of motion than those in solids. In gases there is assumed to be no interaction between molecules except in the form of collisions. The only interatomic forces are those which hold the atoms of each molecule together. The molecules themselves are so widely separated that the forces between them are zero to all intents and purposes. According to the kinetic theory of gases thermal energy consists entirely of the kinetic energy associated with the large translational displacements of the gas molecules.

In liquids and solids, on the other hand, the atoms and molecules are condensed to the point where the forces between them are significant, holding them at definite equilibrium spacings.   Individual molecules are no longer able to wander off on long free flights as in gases.   In liquids the molecules are still capable of considerable freedom of motion in mobile groups.   In solids the atoms and molecules are tied down to definite positions.   In both liquids and solids the total energy content is divided about equally between potential and kinetic energy.   The potential energy is that part which produces structure or order.   The kinetic energy is that associated with the motion of the particles.

The kinetic energy of a solid takes the form of vibrations of atoms and molecules about their equilibrium positions (Art. 2.7).   Motion is violent at high thermal energies but is limited to a very small space (except, of course, when an activation of some kind takes place and a particle is released to seek a new equilibrium position).   Since the atoms are so restricted in their motion, the electrons also tend to play a part in thermal behavior, as they do in electrical behavior.

With these concepts in mind, we shall now discuss thermal properties of solids.

12.1 SPECIFIC HEAT

When heat is added to a solid, it increases the energy content: a certain part of the energy goes into thermal vibrations (kinetic energy) and appears as a rise in temperature; the remainder goes into thermal expansion (potential energy) unless some structural change—crystal transformation, vaporization, or melting—or a chemical change occurs.

If we assume that no structural or chemical changes are involved, the *specific heat capacity* (or *specific heat*) of a solid is defined by

$$c = \frac{1}{m}\frac{dE}{dT},\tag{12.1}$$

where m is the mass, E the total energy content, and T the temperature. If m is taken as one unit of mass and the increment of temperature as one degree, it reduces to the more common definition: $c = \Delta E$, the quantity of heat that must be added to a unit mass of the solid to raise its temperature by one degree.

Specific heat capacity is measured in several systems of units.   In engineering applications the most commonly used units are (Btu/lb)/°F, and in the metric system, (cal/g)/°K (or °C).   The *specific heat* of a material is sometimes defined as the ratio of its heat capacity to that of water, measured in the same units.   Defined in this way it is dimensionless. Since the specific heat of water is *unity* when measured in either engineering or metric units, the specific heat of any given material has the same *numerical* value whether measured as a dimensionless ratio or in either of the above systems.   For this reason specific heat values are tabulated in all three systems interchangeably.   This type of specific heat, based on a fixed mass (lb or g), is designated by c.

Physicists and chemists frequently use the *mole* as the unit of mass to replace the gram in the metric system.   The mole is defined as the quantity of the material which contains a fixed number of molecules, Avogadro's number, $N = 6.0238 \times 10^{23}$ (Art. 2.7).   The weight of a mole of a substance is its formula weight in grams (the sum of the atomic weights of the atoms in a molecule of the substance).   The specific heat capacity per mole is called the *molar heat* and is designated by C in (cal/mole)/°K.*   In these units the specific heat of water is, of course, no longer unity.

The specific heat capacity of a substance varies with the conditions under which it is measured.   If the substance is allowed to expand as heat is added, the work done against atmospheric pressure will divert some of the heat energy from the process of raising the temperature.   Under these conditions the specific heat will be higher than if the volume is held constant. It is conventional to use c_p for the specific heat at *constant pressure* when volume expansion is permitted and c_v for the specific heat at *constant volume* when the pressure increases enough to hold the volume constant.   The corresponding molar heats are C_p and C_v.   The difference between C_p and C_v is

$$C_p - C_v = TVK(3\,\alpha)^2, \tag{12.2}$$

where T is the temperature, V the molar volume of the substance, K the bulk modulus, and α the coefficient of linear expansion (Art. 12.2).

In solids and liquids the expansion with heating is very small, and α is in the neighborhood of 10^{-5}.   The difference between C_p and C_v is therefore so small as to be negligible except at very high temperatures.   We shall thus assume that $C_p \approx C_v$ and therefore $c_p \approx c_v$ also.

The variation of specific heat from one element to another is shown to a first approximation by the classical kinetic theory of heat (Art. 2.7), which states that each atom in a solid has, on the average, an energy $3\,kT$, and the total energy content of a mole is $E = 3\,RT$.   Using Eq. 12.1 we find, for the molar heat,

$$C_v = 3\,R \approx 6 \text{ (cal/mole)/°K.} \tag{12.3a}$$

This equation is known as the *Dulong-Petit rule*.

That most elements follow this rule quite closely at room temperature or above is borne out by the observation that for most elements the product

---

* The molar heat may be obtained from the specific heat per gram by multiplying the latter by the molecular weight since

$$\left[\frac{\text{cal}}{\text{mole} \times \text{°K}}\right] = \left[\frac{\text{cal}}{\text{g} \times \text{°K}}\right]\left[\frac{\text{g}}{\text{mole}}\right].$$

of the specific heat, c_v, and the molecular weight is very nearly 6 (Table 12.1).   Consequently an approximate value of c_v can be obtained from the formula

$$c_v \approx \frac{6}{\text{mol wt in g}}. \tag{12.3b}$$

(Note that for monatomic elements the molecular weight is equal to the atomic weight.)

Observe (Table 12.1) that the molar heat of beryllium is low, as is that of certain other elements.   The major defect of the Dulong-Petit rule is its failure to account for variations of the specific heat with temperature. Figure 12.1 shows the actual variation of atomic heat (molar heat) for

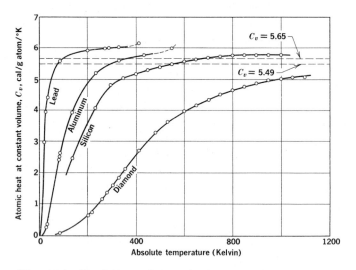

Fig. 12.1 *Variation of atomic heat at constant volume with temperature.   (Richt-myer, Kennard, and Lauritsen,* Introduction to Modern Physics, *5th ed., McGraw-Hill Book Company, Inc., New York, 1955, p. 410)*

several elements.   Although at relatively high temperatures it approaches the Dulong-Petit value of 6 for all the elements shown, there is a sharp drop at low temperatures.   Furthermore these drops take place at different temperature ranges for different materials.   The reason for this behavior is that on the atomic scale energy is always quantized, i.e., it can be absorbed or emitted only in integral multiples of energy units or quanta (Art. 2.1).   At high temperatures the energy is great enough that the steps

Table 12.1   **Specific Heats at Room Temperature**

SOLID	SPECIFIC HEAT, c_v, (cal/g)/°K	MOLAR WEIGHT,[a] g/mole	MOLAR HEAT, C_v, (cal/mole)/°K
Lead	0.030	207.21	6.22
Nickel	.112	58.69	6.57
Magnesium	.248	24.32	6.03
Aluminum	.217	26.98	5.85
Beryllium	.425	9.013	3.83

[a] Equivalent to the atomic weight for elements.

between quanta are insignificant and the classical theory applies. As the temperature decreases, a point is reached below which the quantum effect can no longer be ignored. Just where this point is on the temperature scale varies from material to material, and depends on the accuracy with which the specific heat is to be measured.

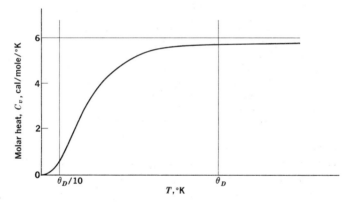

Fig. 12.2   *Heat capacity of a solid according to the Debye equation (Eq. 12.4).*

The Debye theory for specific heat is based on quantum principles and accounts for variations with temperature for simple solids. A *characteristic temperature*, also known as the *Debye temperature*, Θ_D, can be determined for each material; it is the temperature at which C_v is significantly less than 6 (cal/mole)/°K. According to this theory the specific heat is given by

$$C_v = 3R \times 3\left(\frac{T}{\Theta_D}\right)^3 \int_0^{\frac{\Theta_D}{T}} \frac{e^x x^4}{(e^x - 1)^2}\, dx. \qquad (12.4)*$$

---

* Dekker, Adrianus J., *Solid State Physics*, Prentice-Hall, Inc., Englewood Cliffs, N. J., 1957, p. 43.

Figure 12.2 shows the shape of the curve represented by this equation. By suitable choice of Θ_D the curve can be adjusted to fit data for different solids to a good approximation, thus determining Θ_D. At relatively high temperatures (roughly speaking those greater than Θ_D) this expression for C_v approaches the Dulong-Petit value, $3R$. At low temperatures the expression reduces to

$$C_v \approx 3R\left(\frac{4}{5}\pi^4\right)\left(\frac{T}{\Theta_D}\right)^3$$

$$\approx 465\left(\frac{T}{\Theta_D}\right)^3,$$

(12.4a)

indicating a cubic variation with temperature. Equation 12.4a applies at temperatures lower than $\Theta_D/10$. Table 12.2 gives Debye temperatures for some representative elements.

Table 12.2   Approximate Values of the Debye Characteristic Temperature

ELEMENT	Θ_D, °K	Θ_D, °F
Lead	88	−302
Nickel	375	+215
Aluminum	390	+242
Silicon	658	+725
Diamond	1860	+2888

The effect of variations in Θ_D on the C_v vs T curve may be seen in Fig. 12.1. Materials having high Debye temperatures show much greater variation in C_v in the neighborhood of room temperature (approximately 300°K), as illustrated for diamond.

The Debye temperature is usually thought of as an adjustable parameter which is set at any value necessary to make Eq. 12.4 fit the experimental data. Hence it does not represent a temperature at which any particular phenomenon takes place.

In this theory the contribution of electrons to specific heat is neglected, a satisfactory approximation for most materials at ordinary temperatures because the vibrational energy of the atoms and molecules is affected so much more strongly by temperature changes than that of the electrons. At low temperatures, however, atomic vibrations may become small enough that the electronic contribution becomes significant; at high temperatures, too, the electronic energies may become large enough to be significant. In the transition metals the electronic contribution is large even at room temperature because of the partly filled d-shells in their electron structure. As a result these metals have abnormally large specific heats.

Table 12.3   Representative Specific Heats, in (cal/g)/°C or (Btu/lb)/°F at 20°C

Metals		Ceramics		Polymers	
Lithium	0.79	Glass	0.17	Polyethylene	0.55
Iron	.107	Alumina	.2	Nylon	.40
Uranium	.028	Zirconium oxide	.11	Acrylics	.35

Table 12.3 gives typical specific heats for several solids—molecular as well as crystalline—at room temperature. When the specific heat of a solid is known, it is possible to compute the change in temperature caused by the addition of a certain amount of heat. For small temperature changes, or for constant specific heat (at $T \gg \Theta_D$), Eq. 12.1 becomes

$$\Delta T = \frac{Q}{mc}, \tag{12.5}$$

where $Q = \Delta E$ is the heat added. For large temperature changes, during which the specific heat varies, it may be necessary to use numerical integration based on

$$Q = m \sum c \cdot \Delta T. \tag{12.5a}$$

The *heat capacity per unit volume* is found by multiplying the specific heat capacity per unit mass by the density (mass per unit volume): ρc.

12.2   THERMAL EXPANSION

The physical dimensions of a crystal are determined by the spacing of its atoms. Since the atoms are in constant random motion, the effective spacing is the *average* spacing of each pair of atoms. At any instant, for every pair at greater than average separation there is always another at less than average separation. Thus the maximum spacing of atoms during thermal vibrations is of no more consequence than the minimum spacing in determining the overall dimensions of the crystal.

If the atoms always vibrated symmetrically about their equilibrium positions, their average spacing would be constant and *there would be no thermal expansion.* Such a situation could only exist for a potential energy curve symmetrical about a vertical line through its minimum (equilibrium) point, as in the hypothetical curve of Fig. 12.3. If the energy variation followed this pattern, an increase in thermal energy from level 1 to level 2 would simply increase the amplitude from a_1 to a_2; the average spacing would remain r_0 at all times.

The *actual* energy curve for atoms of a solid is of the form shown in

Fig. 2.5, repeated at a different scale in Fig. 12.4.   This curve is represented by Eq. 2.2,

$$U(r) = -\frac{a}{r^m} + \frac{b}{r^n},$$

and is *not* symmetrical about the vertical line at r_0.   Owing to the asymmetry of the energy curve the average spacing, $\bar{r}$, *increases as the energy level increases.*   The so-called equilibrium spacing, r_0, applies only to the limiting case of perfectly stationary atoms.   So long as there are any thermal oscillations, the average spacing will be greater than r_0.   When the thermal energy increases from level 1 to level 2, for example, the amplitude increases from a_1 to a_2, and at the same time the average spacing increases from $\bar{r}_1$ to $\bar{r}_2$.

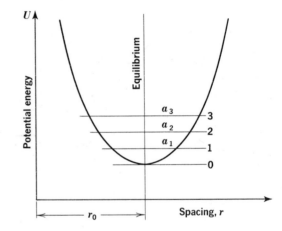

Fig. 12.3 Hypothetical energy curve without thermal expansion (symmetrical).

The coefficient of thermal expansion may be defined as the rate of change of length with respect to temperature, per unit length,

$$\alpha = \frac{1}{l}\frac{dl}{dT}, \tag{12.6}$$

or since $dl/l = d\epsilon$, where ϵ is the strain,

$$\alpha = \frac{d\epsilon}{dT}. \tag{12.6a}$$

Zwikker[*] presents some interesting relations associated with thermal expansion.   The strain in Eq. 12.6a can be referred to the equilibrium spacing, r_0: thus the average strain in the spacing of two atoms is

---

[*] Zwikker, C., *Physical Properties of Solid Materials*, Interscience Publishers, Inc., New York, 1954, pp. 154–156.

$$\bar{\epsilon} = \frac{\bar{r} - r_0}{r_0}, \tag{12.7}$$

while the maximum and minimum strains are

$$\epsilon_p = \frac{r_p - r_0}{r_0} \quad \text{and} \quad \epsilon_q = \frac{r_q - r_0}{r_0}. \tag{12.7a}$$

If we approximate the oscillation by a sinusoidal one, the average amplitude of strain is

$$\epsilon_a = \frac{|\epsilon_p| + |\epsilon_q|}{2}. \tag{12.8}$$

It can then be shown that

$$\bar{\epsilon} = \frac{m + n + 3}{4} \epsilon_a^2, \tag{12.9}$$

where m and n are the exponents of Eq. 2.2. The thermal energy is, of course, kinetic energy, but at the extreme positions of any two atoms it is

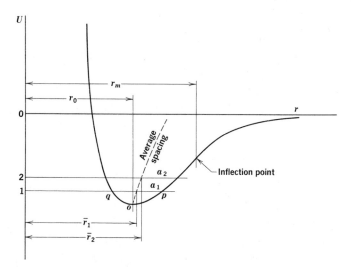

Fig. 12.4   *Actual form of energy curve,
showing that average spacing increases as
energy level rises.*

momentarily transformed to potential energy, which is proportional to ϵ_a^2. We can therefore replace Eq. 12.9 by

$$\bar{\epsilon} \propto E, \tag{12.10}$$

which states that the average strain is proportional to the thermal energy, E. Using Eqs. 12.6a and 12.2, we now discover that

$$\alpha \propto \frac{dE}{dT} \propto C_v. \tag{12.11}$$

Hence the coefficient of thermal expansion turns out to be proportional to the specific heat. Figure 12.5 illustrates that α and C_v vary with tem-

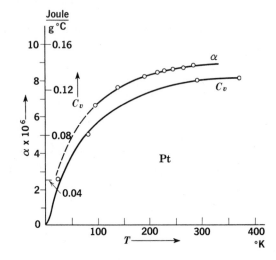

Fig. 12.5 Expansion coefficient and specific heat as a function of temperature for platinum. (Adapted from Zwikker, Physical Properties of Solid Materials, Pergamon Press, London (1954) p. 155

perature in the same way. The actual equation represented by Eq. 12.11, as derived by Grüneisen, is

$$\alpha = \frac{1}{3} \frac{C_v}{KV} \frac{m+n+3}{6}, \tag{12.12}$$

where K is the bulk modulus and V the molar volume. The constant $(m + n + 3)/6$ is known as Grüneisen's constant, γ. It can be found experimentally by measuring α, C_v, and K. The experimentally determined value can then be used as a check on the assumed values of m and n (Art. 2.2). As a general rule γ is observed to vary between 1 and 3; hence the sum $(m + n)$ must vary between 3 and 15. Remembering that m is usually 1 for primary bonds, and $n > m$, we obtain a fairly good idea of the variation of n between materials. As an example, for body-centered cubic crystals, γ is found to vary from 1.17 to 1.75. Hence $(m + n)$ varies from 4 to 7.5, and n probably varies from 3 to 6.

Most materials behave in approximately the same way as crystals with regard to thermal expansion. There are variations in magnitude from material to material. For atomic crystals these variations are expressed by Eq. 12.12. For such solids C_v and V are fairly constant, so that α varies inversely with K and directly with $(m + n)$. Covalent and ionic crystals have much higher values of K than metallic crystals, and somewhat higher values of n (Art. 2.2). The net result is that α is lower for covalent and ionic crystals than for metallic crystals.

Molecular solids, although they may not fit this theory very well, nevertheless have high thermal expansions which can be associated with their low bulk moduli (high compressibility). There are exceptions to this rule: e.g., in some polymers the entropy of the system plays a dominant part and may result in a *negative* coefficient of expansion.

Owing to their natural anisotropy crystals tend to have different thermal expansions in different directions. This is not true of cubic crystals, however, which are isotropic in this respect.

The expansion of a solid in its linear dimensions causes an increase in volume as well. The volume coefficient of thermal expansion is called α_v, and it can be shown on the basis of Eq. 6.30a that for an isotropic solid

$$\alpha_v = 3\,\alpha. \tag{12.13}$$

Thus α is sometimes called the coefficient of linear expansion to distinguish it from α_v.

Since α is proportional to C_v, it follows that α is approximately constant for most materials at temperatures above the Debye temperature. For constant α, Eq. 12.6a can be written as

$$\alpha = \frac{\Delta\epsilon}{\Delta T}, \tag{12.6b}$$

from which the units of α are $\deg^{-1}$ because ϵ is dimensionless. This equation can be used to compute the thermal strains in a solid resulting from a temperature rise: $\Delta\epsilon = \alpha\Delta T$.

Thermal expansion gives rise to internal stresses if expansion is hindered in any way. When two different materials are to be joined permanently, as in the electrical connections to an incandescent lamp or a vacuum tube, it is important that they have nearly the same values of α if there is to be no danger of failure from cracking. The same precaution applies to enamel coatings on metal. Thermal stresses are discussed in detail in Art. 12.5.

12.3 THE MELTING POINT

As heat is added to a solid, its thermal energy increases until the atoms (or molecules) on the surface begin to break away from their equilibrium positions. The amplitude of thermal vibrations at which this takes place is associated with the interatomic spacing at which the bonding force is maximum, for if the atoms can be separated to that point, no further increase in force is required to separate them farther. This spacing, r_m, is indicated on the force curve in Fig. 12.4, and it is seen that it corresponds to the spacing at the inflection point in the energy curve. This fact follows from Eq. 2.3b, which shows that if $dF(r)/dr = 0$, $d^2U(r)/dr^2$ must be zero also. Thus there is a definite amplitude and consequently a definite melting temperature for each type of atom, i.e., each element.

As more heat is added, after melting begins, it is all used in activating more particles of the solid. The particles thus activated collide with neighboring particles, transmitting their energy to them. The structure is thereby gradually transformed from a solid, having definite equilibrium positions, to a liquid, having only short-range order in the form of "flow groups" of particles. During this process no further rise in temperature occurs, and the two phases—solid and liquid—exist at the same temperature.

The temperature at which melting begins depends on the amount of thermal energy required, which in turn depends on the characteristics of the interatomic and intermolecular bonds. Thus materials having stronger bonds tend to have higher melting points. This restriction places materials in order of decreasing melting points as follows: covalent, ionic, metallic, molecular. The abruptness of melting depends on the uniformity of size of particles and the degree of order in their arrangement. Atomic crystals have the most sharply defined melting points, while amorphous solids like polymers have a greater tendency toward local breakdown and gradual melting. Furthermore, the solidification of atomic crystals is just the reverse of melting, whereas the solidification of polymeric materials may not be. In the process of melting polymeric materials, some or all of the macromolecules may be broken into smaller molecules which do not necessarily recombine upon solidification. In fact, there may be irreversible chemical changes in these materials, so that melting is more a disintegration process which changes the nature of the material. The melting points of plastics seldom exceed 700°F.

Since both melting temperature and thermal expansion depend on the bonds between the atoms or molecules of a solid, it is not surprising that they are found to be related. Solids can be divided into classes, and for each class there is a characteristic amount of thermal expansion at which melting begins. Thus for a given class

$$\alpha T_m = \text{Constant.} \tag{12.14}$$

Any two materials of a given class that have the same coefficient of expansion will therefore have approximately the same melting point. Three main classes of materials are known:[*] metals and ionic compounds, for which $\alpha T_m \approx 0.02$; certain salts, for which $\alpha T_m \approx 0.03$; and covalent-bonded oxides and glasses, for which $\alpha T_m \approx 0.007$. We conclude that if we are looking for a coating material to be melted onto another material, and if both must have the same thermal expansion, the coating will have

[*] Zwikker, C., *Physical Properties of Solid Materials*, Interscience Publishers, Inc., New York, 1954, p. 159.

to be of a different class than the base material. Some typical melting points are listed in Table 7.1.

12.4   THERMAL CONDUCTIVITY

Heat is transmitted through solids by two distinct mechanisms: elastic vibrations of atoms and molecules, and transfer of energy by free electrons. The former occurs in all materials, but the latter is a much more effective

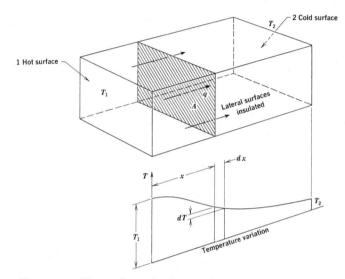

Fig. 12.6   *Thermal conductivity, showing thermal gradient and direction of heat flow, q.*

process when it can be utilized. It accounts for the high conductivity of metals, which have a plentiful supply of free electrons. Because insulators must rely entirely on the vibrations of atoms and molecules they have lower conductivities.

Electronic Conductivity

Electronic thermal conduction is analogous to electrical conduction. Instead of an electrical field, or potential gradient, a *thermal gradient* provides the driving force. Instead of an electric current, in charge per unit time, there is a heat flow, q, in *quantity of heat per unit time* (e.g., cal/sec). The heat flow through an area, A, perpendicular to the direction of flow, is directly proportional to the area and the thermal gradient:

$$q = -k_t A \frac{dT}{dx}, \tag{12.15}$$

where k_t is the *thermal conductivity* and x the distance in the direction of flow. (The minus sign is necessary because heat flows in the direction of a negative thermal gradient—"downhill".) The quantities in Eq. 12.15 are illustrated in Fig. 12.6.

The *mechanism* of electronic thermal conduction is also much like that of electrical conduction (Art. 11.1). The electrons in the electron "gas" are in constant random motion caused by thermal energy. When the temperature at surface 1 (Fig. 12.6) is raised, the electrons in that region are given a somewhat higher energy as they move away from the surface. The result is a net velocity from the hot surface toward the cold surface, 2. As the electrons move through the solid, they collide with other particles and transmit their energy—the heat—through the solid. It is because of the high velocity to which the electrons can be accelerated—more than 100 times that of elastic waves—that the electronic thermal conduction is so much greater than atomic or molecular conduction.

The effect of a change in overall temperature on electronic thermal conductivity differs in an important respect from its effect on electrical conductivity. If the overall temperature increases (the gradient dT/dx remaining the same), the interference of the ions with the progress of the electrons increases. This interference causes the mean free path to decrease in direct proportion to the increase in temperature, as in electrical conductivity (Art. 11.1). However, at the same time, the *heat capacity of the electron gas increases* in direct proportion to the temperature.[*] This means that the electrons are capable of having their energy increased by a larger amount for a given increment of temperature than at lower temperatures. The two effects just cancel each other, with the result that electronic thermal conductivity is almost *independent of temperature*. Analytically electronic thermal conductivity can be expressed by an equation similar to Eq. 11.4b for electrical conductivity

$$k_t = \frac{\pi^2}{3} \left(\frac{k}{e}\right)^2 T \frac{ne^2\lambda}{2\,mv_0}, \tag{12.16}$$

where k is Boltzmann's constant, T the absolute temperature, and the other factors are the same as in Eq. 11.4b. Remember that the mean free path, λ, is approximately inversely proportional to T, so that the product, λT, is constant, and k_t becomes independent of T. Dividing Eq. 12.16 by Eq. 11.4b, we obtain

---

[*] Zwikker, C., *Physical Properties of Solid Materials*, Interscience Publishers, Inc., New York, 1954, pp. 246, 247.

$$\frac{k_t}{\sigma} = \frac{\pi^2}{3}\left(\frac{k}{e}\right)^2 T,$$ (12.17)

where $(\pi k)^2/3\, e^2$ is known as the Wiedemann-Franz ratio. Thus the thermal conductivity, k_t, and the electrical conductivity, σ, vary in the same way from one material to another. This fact often provides a convenient means of estimating thermal conductivity when the electrical conductivity is known.

The units of thermal conductivity can be derived from Eq. 12.15 as follows:

$$k_t = \frac{q}{A}\frac{\Delta x}{\Delta T}.$$

In engineering units this expression becomes

$$\left[\frac{\text{Btu} \times \text{ft}}{\text{hr} \times \text{ft}^2 \times {}^\circ\text{F}}\right],$$

and in metric units

$$\left[\frac{\text{cal} \times \text{cm}}{\text{sec} \times \text{cm}^2 \times {}^\circ\text{K}}\right].$$

Since the Wiedemann-Franz constant is equal to $k_t/\sigma T$, Eq. 12.17 can be written in terms of metric units as

$$\frac{k_t}{\sigma T} = 5.85 \times 10^{-9}\left[\frac{\text{cal} \times \text{ohm}}{\text{sec} \times ({}^\circ\text{K})^2}\right].$$

Atomic and Molecular Conductivity

In nonmetals there are practically no free electrons for thermal conduction. Consequently the only mechanism available is elastic vibration of the atoms and molecules, which is a slower mechanism than electronic conduction. Thus the thermal conductivity of nonmetals is much lower than that of metals.

When the surface of a nonmetallic solid is heated (Fig. 12.6), thermal agitation is increased among the atoms or molecules at the hot surface. This agitation is transmitted through the solid by means of the bonds between neighboring particles, in the form of elastic waves. Because of the nonlinearity of the bonds, however, these waves are anharmonic and their energy is dissipated through interference with one another as they pass through the crystal.

The progress of an elastic thermal wave through a crystal is similar to that of a gas molecule through a gas. In the same way that the gas molecule is deflected by collisions with other gas molecules, the elastic thermal wave is deflected by "collisions" with other waves. This similarity has led to the use of a *phonon* to represent the particle characteristics of a thermal wave. The solid is replaced by a hypothetical "phonon gas," in which the phonons are in constant random motion.   At a heated surface the motion is increased so that collisions with other phonons occur at an increased rate, and thus the heat is transmitted to other parts of the phonon gas.

The thermal conductivity of a gas can be expressed by*

$$k_t = \tfrac{1}{3}\, cv\lambda, \qquad\qquad (12.18)$$

where c is the heat capacity, v the average particle velocity, and λ the mean free path.   This equation can also be used to express the conductivity of a phonon gas, and through it that of the corresponding solid.   Here c is the heat capacity of the phonons, v is their velocity (the velocity of sound), and λ their mean free path.   By suitably choosing these constants a satisfactory representation can be obtained for the thermal conductivity of a nonmetallic solid.

For temperatures well above the Debye temperature, the only variable in Eq. 12.18 is λ.   In crystalline materials the mean free path varies inversely as the temperature, as in electronic conduction.   Hence the thermal conductivity of nonmetallic crystals also varies inversely with temperature,

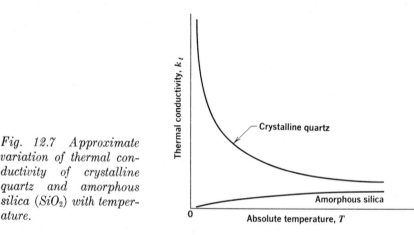

Fig. 12.7 Approximate variation of thermal conductivity of crystalline quartz and amorphous silica (SiO_2) with temperature.

as shown in Fig. 12.7 for quartz.   In amorphous materials like glass, an increase in temperature apparently tends to increase the order of the structure slightly, thereby providing a net increase in the mean free path.†   Hence the thermal conductivity of such materials *increases* slightly with rising temperature, as shown for amorphous silica (Fig. 12.7).   The same illustration shows the great effect of structural order on thermal conduc-

---

* Jeans, J. H., *The Dynamical Theory of Gases*, 4th ed., Dover Publications, Inc., New York, 1954, Ch. XII.

† Sinnott, Maurice J., *The Solid State for Engineers*, John Wiley & Sons, Inc., New York, 1958, p. 310.

tivity—that of the crystalline quartz being much greater than that of the amorphous silica.

There are many interesting variations in thermal conductivity. At low temperatures, for example, λ may become longer than the dimensions of the body, and k_t is different for bodies of different sizes. The presence of pores, impurities, and other defects tends to shorten the mean free path and thereby decrease the conductivity.

Conductivity in crystals is different in different directions because of the anisotropy of crystal structures. In polycrystalline and amorphous materials, however, conductivity is substantially isotropic. Values of thermal conductivity vary all the way from 0.0001 to 1.00 (cal $\times$ cm)/(sec $\times$ cm^2 $\times$ °C) for the two basic mechanisms. Those for metals vary from 0.02 to 1.00, for ceramics from 0.002 to 0.1, and for plastics from 0.0001 to 0.002. Those for molecular materials are the lowest because of the difficulty in transferring energy from one molecule to another. The process is similar to diffusion and is very slow. By introducing voids, as in plastic foams, k_t can be made even smaller. Table 12.4 gives a few representative values in both sets of units.

Table 12.4   Representative Thermal
Conductivities

MATERIAL	(Btu/hr)/ft^2 °F/ft	(cal/sec)/cm^2 °K/cm
Silver	242	1.001
Aluminum	128	0.53
Iron	42	.174
Zirconium carbide	11.9	.049
Titanium alloys	5.2	.021
Glasses	0.6	.0025
Silicone plastics	.53	.0022
Acrylics	.125	.0005
Foamed polystyrene	.025	.0001

12.5 THERMAL STRESSES

When thermal expansion is restrained, serious thermal stresses can develop within the material. Restraint may take one of two forms: external bodies connected to the one in question, or nonuniform expansion of the body itself. Examples of the first type are found in welded structures, railroad rails, and shrink fits. Problems involving this type of restraint can usually be handled by the methods of elementary mechanics of materials.*

---

* Timoshenko, S., *Strength of Materials—Part I—Elementary Theory and Problems*, 3rd ed., D. Van Nostrand Company, Inc., Princeton, New Jersey, 1955, Ch. I.

The second type of restraint results from variations in *composition* or *temperature* within the body.   An example of a body having variable composition is the bimetallic strip used in thermostatic controls; it is made of two materials selected for their *different* coefficients of expansion and welded together (Fig. 12.8).*   If we assume a uniform change in tempera-

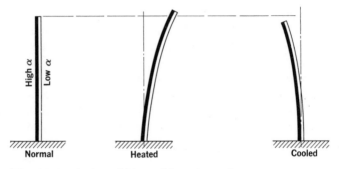

Fig. 12.8   Action of bimetallic strip under temperature changes.

ture, the expansion or contraction of each part can be calculated; the difference determines the deflection of the strip, which can be estimated from elementary theory.   If the strip is restrained from deflecting, the internal stresses can also be estimated.

Another example of a body having variable composition sometimes occurs in the refractory brick used to line a furnace.   If slag penetrates the brick during use, or if there are structural changes in the brick because of the high operating temperatures, the coefficient of expansion of the surface layer may differ from that of the inside of the brick.   This variation contributes to *spalling* (discussed later).

Variations in temperature occurring as thermal gradients caused by local heating are an important factor in a multitude of applications.   Some examples are welded joints, rocket skins, parts of internal combustion engines, furnace linings, and massive concrete structures (subject to internal heating during the chemical reaction of hydration of the cement).

The magnitude of the stress developed by a temperature gradient is affected by both the temperature and the steepness of its variation.   The determining factors are the heat capacity per unit volume, ρc (Art. 12.1), and the thermal conductivity, k_t.   When heat is applied locally, for example to a small area on the surface of a solid, two things happen: the solid

---

* Miner, Douglas F., and Seastone, John B., *Handbook of Engineering Materials*, 1st ed. (Wiley Engineering Handbook Series) John Wiley & Sons, Inc., New York, 1955, pp. 2–490.

absorbs heat locally at a rate depending on its heat capacity; and the heat is conducted away at a rate depending on its conductivity.   Thus a high heat capacity, with its attendant high local heating, tends to produce high thermal gradients.   At the same time, a high conductivity carries the heat away to other parts of the solid at a high rate and tends to reduce the thermal gradients.   These opposing effects are combined in the *thermal diffusivity*, $k_t/\rho c$.

A high diffusivity is desirable in that it tends to *reduce* the thermal gradients caused by local heating, thereby reducing the local stresses.   Obviously a low k_t, by itself, does not necessarily mean a low diffusivity. Lightweight insulating materials may have diffusivities as high as more dense materials.   Metals, with their high conductivities, always have high diffusivities.   Since k_t varies with temperature, diffusivity does likewise. This fact should be kept in mind when diffusivity is used in problems of heat transfer.

The action of a temperature gradient in a solid involves two distinct stages, the establishment of the gradient and its removal.   The reaction of the material to the resulting stresses depends, of course, on its ductility and on whether the stresses are repeated.

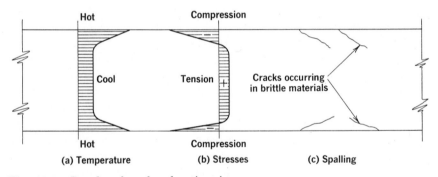

Fig. 12.9   Results of surface heating in a flat slab.

When the surfaces of a material are heated, temperature gradients are set up (Fig. 12.9).   Because the surface layer is prevented from expanding fully by restraint of the interior, and the interior is stretched somewhat by the surface layer, internal stresses are developed.   The material at the surface is put into compression in the direction of the surface.   If the material is ductile and the stress high enough, it will yield and relieve the stress.   Because of the high temperature, yielding will take place at lower stresses than usual, and the stress distribution will be reduced practically to zero.   If the material is brittle, it may fail by compression in the surface.

Such a failure takes place as a shearing failure on 45° planes (compare Art. 4.3) and is called *spalling* (Fig. 12.9c).

The reverse effect can be obtained by cooling a uniformly heated body on its surface.   Here the surface material is prevented from contracting at once and is put in tension (Fig. 12.10).   If the tensile stress is high

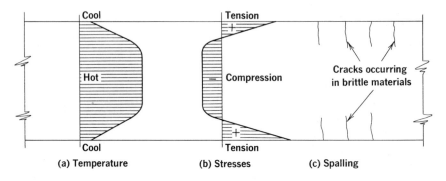

(a) Temperature   (b) Stresses   (c) Spalling

Fig. 12.10   Results of surface cooling in a flat slab.

enough, it, too, can cause yielding in a ductile material or cracking in a brittle material.   In the latter, because of the tension in the surface, the cracks will occur at right angles to the surface instead of at 45°.

The rule illustrated by these two examples is that in *increasing thermal gradients the hot region is in compression* while *the cooler region is in tension*.

Once a thermal gradient is established and internal stresses have been relieved by yielding, the next question is the effect of its removal.   Removal may take the form of cooling the previously heated surface (Fig. 12.9) or of heating the member throughout to the same temperature as the surface.   The two other possibilities are the final cooling of the interior of the heated member (Fig. 12.10) or the reheating of its surfaces.

If the stresses have been reduced to zero while the gradient was in effect, any part that is cooled will be put in tension, and any part that is heated will be put in compression, as before.   Thus if we cool the surface of the member in Fig. 12.9, or heat its interior, the surface will be put in tension. Likewise, cooling the interior or reheating the surface of the member in Fig. 12.10, will put its surface in compression.

The following rule can now be stated: *In nonuniform heating or cooling with yielding, the part that cools last is always put in tension*, and *the part that heats last is always put in compression*.   In the manufacture of tempered glass the surface of the hot sheet of glass is cooled rapidly by air jets. It is first put in tension by its contraction, and flows to relieve the stresses. When the interior cools, the surface is put in compression, which helps prevent the formation of microcracks, so harmful to the strength of glass.

When the surface layer cools last (Fig. 12.9), resulting in tension in the surface, a very dangerous condition exists for possible fatigue loading. This situation commonly develops following heavy grinding operations which cause surface heating. The resulting surface tension can seriously reduce the fatigue strength of the part.

Thermal fatigue is a term which describes the mechanical effect of repeated thermal stresses caused by repeated heating and cooling. Since thermal stresses can be very large, involving considerable plastic flow, fatigue failures can occur after relatively few cycles (low-cycle fatigue, Art. 9.5). The effect of the high part of the temperature cycle on the strength of the material is also an important factor in reducing its life under thermal fatigue.

Thermal shock is the effect of a *sudden* change of temperature on a material. Thermal diffusivity is an important factor here, too, for if the heat can be dissipated rapidly enough, the effects of the shock are greatly reduced. Other controlling factors are the coefficient of thermal expansion, α, the modulus of elasticity, E, the mechanical strength, σ_u, and Poisson's ratio, μ. A thermal shock parameter is a variable which combines the effects of all these factors to indicate the capacity of a given material to absorb thermal shocks. The original parameter was suggested by Schott and Winkelmann in 1894. It is

$$P = \frac{\sigma_u}{E\alpha} \sqrt{\frac{k_t}{\rho c}}. \tag{12.19}$$

Other parameters have been suggested from time to time, but this one remains the most widely accepted. The quantity $\sigma_u/E\alpha$ appears to be the most important factor in shock resistance and is incorporated in all the proposed parameters. A material having a low strength can still have a high P if E is low enough, as in plastics.

Closely related to thermal shock is spalling, of importance in ceramic materials. As noted previously, spalling is the cracking of brittle materials caused by thermal stresses in the surface. When a brittle body is heated, compressive failures on 45° shearing planes cause splitting off of corners and edges and flaking of the surface. Cooling causes tensile cracks at right angles to the surface. Resistance to spalling is indicated by the thermal shock parameter.

A great deal of work needs to be done in the field of thermal shock. Tables frequently list the resistances of refractories simply as "good" or "poor." Some arbitrary quantitative measures are used, but they lack any theoretical basis. Glass, for example, is tested by plunging specimens into cold water after heating in an oven. For a plate of given size and thickness, the thermal shock resistance is given as the *temperature dif-*

ferential (in °C), between the oven and the cold water, that the specimen will stand without cracking. Spalling resistance of bricks is sometimes given in terms of the number of quenches that can be withstood, or the average loss of weight after quenching.

BIBLIOGRAPHY

Shortley, George, and Williams, Dudley, *Elements of Physics*, Prentice-Hall, Inc., Englewood Cliffs, New Jersey, 1953.
  Part II, Heat, provides review of fundamental laws and definitions.

Sinnott, Maurice J., *The Solid State for Engineers*, John Wiley & Sons, Inc., New York, 1958.
  For the student.

Dekker, Adrianus J., *Solid State Physics*, Prentice-Hall, Inc., Englewood Cliffs, New Jersey, 1957; Zwikker, C., *Physical Properties of Solid Materials*, Interscience Publishers, Inc., New York, 1954; Goldman, J. E., Ed., *The Science of Engineering Materials*, John Wiley & Sons, Inc., New York, 1957.
  For advanced study.

PROBLEMS

12.1 Check the validity of Eq. 12.3a for the following elements, whose specific heat capacities, c, are given in parentheses: antimony (0.049), boron (0.309), cobalt (0.099), silicon (0.162), cesium (0.052), thorium (0.034), uranium (0.0275). Atomic weights are given in Table 2.1.

12.2 Determine the percentage difference between C_p and C_v for aluminum at 20°C. Use $K = 0.75 \times 10^9$ g/cm^2, and $\alpha = 23.9 \times 10^{-6}$/°K. (HINT: the molar volume, V, is found by dividing the atomic weight in g by the density in g/cm^3, giving cm^3/mole; also 1 g $\times$ cm $= 2.34 \times 10^{-5}$ cal.)

12.3 (a) Explain briefly the significance of the Debye characteristic temperature. (b) Does the fact that Table 12.2 shows Θ_D for silicon to be 725°F offer any explanation for the value found for C_v in Problem 12.1?

12.4 What property other than specific heat involves the Debye characteristic temperature?

12.5 To what temperature will 5000 Btu heat 250 lb of aluminum, starting at 70°F? What temperature would result if the aluminum were replaced by the same weight of water?

12.6 The melting points of iron and lead are 1536 and 327°C, respectively. Their coefficients of thermal expansion are 11.7×10^{-6} and 29.0×10^{-6}/°C, respectively. Does this illustrate a general relation between T_m and α? Explain any qualifications that must be made.

12.7 What are the different types of thermal conductivity in materials? How does each vary with temperature?

12.8 How do pores in such materials as plastic foams affect the thermal conductivity? Explain the mechanism.

12.9 (a) A flat slab of a brittle refractory is heated uniformly to a high temperature. By means of circulating pipes the interior of the slab is suddenly cooled. In what directions would you expect spalling cracks to form in the surface? (b) If the slab in part (a) is uniformly cool and a hot liquid is circulated through its interior, in what directions would spalling cracks form?

12.10 If a member that will be subjected to repeated loading is heated and cooled nonuniformly during fabrication (by heat treatments, machining, forging), what precautions should be taken about the order of final heating or cooling of the surface and interior of the member?

12.11 What factors are involved in design for thermal shock? Which are the most important factors?

CHAPTER 13

CORROSION
AND
RADIATION

The effects of both corrosion and radiation are primarily *damaging* to materials, although the internal changes brought about by radiation can sometimes be beneficial, as in the cross-linking of polyethylene.

Corrosion has been an important problem for centuries, but with the rapidly multiplying uses of metals, the increasing occurrence of corrosive environments, and the depletion of supplies of ore, it has become much more serious in recent years. Radiation, on the other hand, has only lately come into importance as a materials problem. The use of controlled nuclear reactors and particle accelerators always involves the irradiation of materials, with results that should be understood by the designer.

Hence corrosion and radiation play a part in the general study of materials, and it is from this point of view that we discuss them. The field is exceedingly complex and not completely understood. It is the purpose here to outline the mechanisms in the light of present theory and discuss ways of reducing damage to materials from these sources. Much detailed information is to be found in the bibliography references at the end of this chapter.

CORROSION

According to the following definition, approved by the American Co-ordinating Committee on Corrosion, corrosion is limited to *metals* and involves some kind of *chemical reaction*.

> *Corrosion.* Destruction of a metal by chemical or electrochemical reaction with its environment.[*]

There are other forms of degradation of materials, such as the attack of organic materials by solvents, or the dissolving of glass by sodium hydroxide. These are important subjects in certain areas, but they do not come under the general heading of corrosion as understood in engineering and hence will not be considered here.

A closely related topic is *erosion*, the wearing away of surface material by mechanical means. It will be treated only for those situations in which the *combined* action of erosion and corrosion produces serious effects, as in fretting corrosion and cavitation.

Corrosion as a chemical reaction is a characteristic of metals that goes along with the freedom of their valence electrons. It is this very freedom which produces the metallic bond and allows electronic conduction to take place. Hence the property which makes metals so useful also accounts for their main weakness.

Being loosely bound to their atoms, the electrons in metals are easily removed in chemical reactions. In the presence of nonmetals such as oxygen, sulfur, or chlorine, with their incomplete valence shells, there is almost always a tendency for metals to form a compound. Stated another way, the free energy of such compounds is almost always lower than that of the metal in the metallic state. Consequently only the most inactive or noble metals, like gold and platinum, are found in the metallic state. The rest are always in the form of ores, in which the compounds are bonded by covalent or ionic bonds. The constant tendency of refined metals to return to this natural state accounts for corrosion.

The rate at which corrosion reactions take place is governed largely by the relative activity or passivity of the metal, which in turn depends on many factors. As already mentioned a few metals, e.g., gold and platinum, are found only in the metallic state because they are truly inert. Other metals, because of their electron structure, have an inherent tendency to

---

[*] Uhlig, Herbert H., *The Corrosion Handbook*, John Wiley & Sons, Inc., New York, 1948, p. xxvii.

be passive.   Still others are frequently made passive by the products of corrosion itself.

Some of the products of corrosion are usually deposited on the corroded surface and interfere to some degree with the further progress of corrosion. The degree of interference is extremely variable, however.   Under certain conditions a tightly adhering, impenetrable film of only a few Angstroms thickness is formed at once, effectively stopping further corrosion.   Under other conditions the corrosion products are loose and porous.   In corrosion by liquids the products may be precipitated at some distance from the surface being corroded.   Thus the *progress* of corrosion is primarily a surface phenomenon, although the reactions involved *at the start* depend on the electron structure of the atoms in the bulk of the material.

Almost all corrosion involves electrochemical action of some kind.   We shall, however, consider corrosion of a metal by a *liquid* and corrosion of a metal by a *gas* as separate topics because each has its own special characteristics.   Both involve the loss of electrons by the metal atoms—known as *oxidation*—and gain of electrons by other atoms—*reduction.*

13.1   CORROSION OF A METAL BY A LIQUID; GALVANIC CELLS

Because of the constant thermal agitation of the ions in a metal there is always a tendency for some of the surface ions to escape into the surrounding medium.   The presence of ions and molecules of a liquid at the metal surface causes significant numbers of the metal ions to escape or dissolve in the liquid.   The loss of positive ions leaves the metal with a slight negative charge.   Thus the metal ions are attracted back to the metal, and an equilibrium is reached in which as many ions return as leave. The negative charge on the metal is known as the *solution potential.*   The reaction can be expressed as

$$\text{Metal} \rightleftarrows \text{Metal ion} + \text{Electron.} \qquad (13.1)$$

If two different metals are placed in contact with a liquid, they will dissolve at different rates and set up different potentials.   The same will be true if two pieces of the same metal are immersed in different liquids.   In the first instance the difference is a result of differences in the ease with which metals part with their valence electrons.   In the second, it is a result of differences in ion concentration in the two liquids.   The dissolving of metal ions is significant only in *electrolytic* solutions, i.e., those containing ions.

The relative ease with which metals lose their valence electrons is shown by the electromotive force series (Table 13.1).   Those at the beginning of the list are more prone to dissolve in electrolytes because it is easier for the ions to break away from their valence electrons.   They therefore acquire larger negative charges than those farther on in the list.   The metals at the end of the list are the inactive *noble* metals, which are difficult to separate from their valence electrons.

Table 13.1   Electromotive Force Series

METAL	METAL
(anodic)	
Lithium	Cobalt
Potassium	Nickel
Calcium	Tin
Sodium	Lead
Magnesium	Hydrogen
Beryllium	Bismuth
Aluminum	Copper
Manganese	Mercury
Zinc	Silver
Chromium	Palladium
Gallium	Platinum
Iron	Gold
Cadmium	(cathodic)
Indium	
Thallium	

Figure 13.1 shows, alternatively, two dissimilar metals in the same electrolyte, or two similar metals in different electrolytes (with a barrier at the

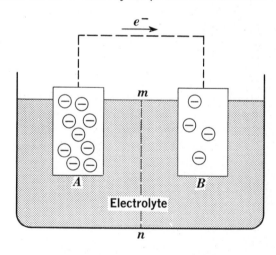

Fig. 13.1 Galvanic cell. Case 1: A *and* B *dissimilar metals in the same electrolyte; Case 2:* A *and* B *similar metals in different electrolytes, with a porous barrier at* mn.

dashed line *mn*). In either situation conditions are such that more metal goes into solution at *A* than at *B*, leaving a larger negative charge at *A* than at *B*. Metals *A* and *B* are electrodes, and their potentials are referred to as *electrode potentials*. The combination of electrodes and electrolytes is called a *galvanic cell*. Electrode A, with its larger negative potential, is the *anode,* and B, with its less negative (or more positive) potential, is the *cathode*. The metal used for A must be nearer the beginning of the electromotive force series (Table 13.1) than that used for B, and is said to be *anodic* with respect to B. Some suitable combinations are:

Anode	Cathode
Zinc	Iron
Iron	Tin
Nickel	Silver

If a conductor is connected between the electrodes, as shown by the dashed line, electrons will flow *toward the cathode* and upset the equilibrium at each electrode. At the anode some of the excess electrons are removed, permitting more metal atoms to be oxidized and go into solution. At the cathode more electrons are added, lowering the number of metal ions escaping and permitting positive ions from the electrolyte to be reduced. Accompanying the flow of electrons from anode to cathode is a flow of ions in the liquid (electrolytic conduction):* positive ions flow from anode to cathode, and negative ions from cathode to anode. The specific ions and their rate of flow depend on the particular metals and electrolytes involved. In certain combinations some of the ions traveling through the electrolyte will react with each other and precipitate a reaction product at a point between the electrodes.

The important point in this discussion is that when the galvanic cell is shorted, the anode is made to dissolve or *corrode* continuously. This mechanism is the source of nearly all corrosion of metals by liquids.

13.2   GALVANIC CELLS INVOLVED IN CORROSION

Metals in contact with electrolytes form galvanic cells in many unexpected ways. The most obvious situation would probably be two dissimilar metals, connected and immersed in the same solution. Let us look at some easily recognized examples. Domestic water pipes in which copper and iron are used together in contact with the electrolyte tap water, which contains many ionic impurities. Or ships' propeller shafts made of steel and running in bronze bearings; sea water makes an excellent electrolyte because of the dissolved salts.

Somewhat less apparent, but of the same type, are these examples.

Galvanized iron in drainage structures: so long as it remains intact, the layer of zinc provides mechanical protection and prevents an electrolyte from

---

* It should be noted that the flow of ions requires that if there is a barrier such as *mn* in Fig. 13.1, it must be a porous one that will simply prevent free circulation and mixing of the electrolytes.

reaching the iron; when the iron is cut to expose the edge, or scratched on its surface, a galvanic cell is set up.   The zinc, being anodic to the iron, is dissolved instead of the iron.   A coating of tin on iron has just the opposite effect (iron is anodic to tin), and its protection is purely mechanical.

Iron covered with brittle mill scale, which is cathodic with respect to the iron: breaks in the mill scale are common, allowing water to reach the iron underneath (Fig. 13.2), which becomes the anode.   The anode is so small that very concentrated action takes place, resulting in serious pitting.

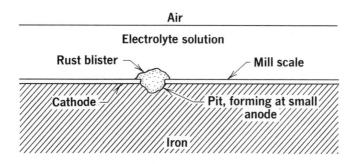

Fig. 13.2   Pitting at break in mill scale. (Reprinted with permission from Uhlig, The Corrosion Handbook, *John Wiley & Sons, Inc., New York, 1948)*

Minute differences from point to point in the surface of a single piece of metal, which may include differences in composition of individual metal grains, different crystal orientation, and the grain boundaries themselves.   The last-named is especially important because it accounts for grain-boundary corrosion.   Being at a higher energy level than the atoms within the grains, those in the grain boundaries tend to dissolve more easily so that these areas become anodic.   They are therefore eaten away more rapidly by corrosion.   This fact accounts for their visibility following etching for micrographic study.   It should be pointed out, however, that the tendency for any metals to be anodic depends on the electrolyte.   In some electrolytes there may be no grain-boundary corrosion.

Another way in which corrosion can take place when only one metal is involved is through differences in the electrolyte.   A single electrolyte can vary from one location to another by having different *concentrations of ions*. Generally speaking, at the place where the concentration is lowest the metal becomes anodic, forming a galvanic cell.   This type of galvanic cell is called a *concentration cell*.   It occurs in places where the electrolyte is flowing past discontinuities.   Ions tend to concentrate in corners and holes, and the difference in concentration produces corrosion.

13.3   CORROSION REACTIONS AND PRODUCTS

A simple reaction that illustrates the process of corrosion is observed when copper is immersed in a solution of mercurous nitrate. Since copper comes before mercury in the electromotive series, copper ions are dissolved and mercury atoms deposited on the surface of the copper. The two processes can be written

$$Cu \rightarrow Cu^{++} + 2\ e^{-} \qquad (13.2a)$$

$$2\ e^{-} + Hg_2^{++} \rightarrow 2\ Hg. \qquad (13.2b)$$

The first equation represents the change from metallic copper to copper ions in solution, leaving two electrons behind. The second represents the change from mercury ions in solution to metallic mercury through the gain of two electrons. The mercury ions in solution are displaced by the copper ions because copper comes before mercury in the electromotive series. The copper is oxidized and the mercury reduced. The latter reaction takes place at the metal surface, where the mercury ions come in contact with the excess electrons. Mercury is therefore deposited on the copper surface in a thin film.

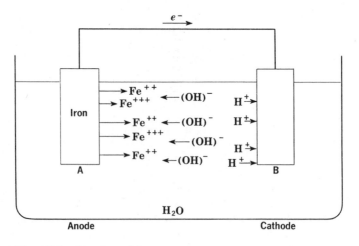

Fig. 13.3   Rusting of iron.

A more common reaction, and one of great concern to engineers, is the rusting of iron (Fig. 13.3): electrode A represents any anodic area of an iron surface, while electrode B is any cathode connected to the iron—perhaps a piece of tin or copper, mill scale, or even another part of the same iron surface. The electrolyte is ordinary water containing dissolved oxygen and salts.

At the anode two reactions may take place:

$$Fe \rightarrow Fe^{++} + 2\,e^- \qquad (13.3a)$$

$$Fe \rightarrow Fe^{+++} + 3\,e^-. \qquad (13.3b)$$

The excess electrons at the anode flow through the conductor to the cathode, where they react with hydrogen ions in the electrolyte. The hydrogen ions are thus deposited at the surface of the cathode as gaseous hydrogen. The reaction is

$$2\,e^- + 2\,H^+ \rightarrow H_2. \qquad (13.4a)$$

The presence of gaseous hydrogen (H_2) molecules on the cathode surface interferes with other hydrogen ions reaching it to be reduced, and the whole process becomes slower as more hydrogen accumulates. This behavior is an example of the protection offered by a film of reaction products.

The hydrogen gas film is removed by two processes: when enough molecules have accumulated to form a bubble, it breaks free and floats to the surface; and if O_2 molecules are available, a reaction takes place of the form

$$2\,e^- + 2\,H^+ + \tfrac{1}{2}\,O_2 \rightarrow H_2O. \qquad (13.4b)$$

In ordinary water the first process is very slow, whereas when normal amounts of dissolved oxygen are present, the second process is rapid and predominates. In acids hydrogen is released rapidly enough to bubble away easily and the first process predominates.

The reactions that take place in the electrolyte are very complex. The positive metal ions move toward the cathode and the negative (OH^-) ions toward the anode. Between the electrodes the ions react with each other to form $Fe(OH)_2$, $Fe(OH)_3$, and FeO. Under various conditions the corrosion products are formed *between* the electrodes or at the cathode. If they are formed between the electrodes, no protection is offered, and corrosion goes on without interference. If they form at the cathode, a more-or-less protective layer will be produced.

Oxygen plays a very important part in corrosion. It is instrumental in removing the hydrogen at the cathode and produces other important compounds which stimulate the action of the cathode. The corrosion rate often depends on the rate at which oxygen diffuses through the solution to the cathode. Variations in oxygen concentration produce concentration cell action more frequently than variations in ion concentration. An example is the corrosion at a water surface: when a bar of iron is immersed in water, there will be a higher oxygen concentration near the surface. The part at the water line therefore becomes cathodic, and the lower part becomes anodic, with resulting "water-line corrosion."

13.4   CORROSION OF A METAL BY A GAS

In the reaction between a metal and a gas the molecules of gas are adsorbed on the surface of the metal and react with the surface atoms of metal to form the corrosion products.   The reaction is usually of the form

$$\text{Metal} + \text{Nonmetal} \rightarrow \text{Oxide or Salt.} \tag{13.5}$$

Examples are

$$4\,\text{Fe} + 3\,\text{O}_2 \rightarrow 2\,\text{Fe}_2\text{O}_3 \tag{13.5a}$$

$$2\,\text{Na} + \text{Cl}_2 \rightarrow 2\,\text{NaCl.} \tag{13.5b}$$

In more active combinations, like solid sodium in chlorine gas, or aluminum in air, the reaction takes place rapidly on the clean metal surface.   Other combinations, like iron in dry air, require high temperatures to produce a significant reaction.

The corrosion products always form a layer or film on the metal surface. If the volume of the corrosion product is *greater* than that of the metal consumed in the reaction, the layer must be compressed to fit the surface on which it is formed.   The result is a nonporous, protective shield over the metal surface.   If, on the other hand, the volume of the corrosion product is *less* than that of the metal consumed, the layer must expand to cover the surface.   Here the result is a porous covering which offers little or no protection against further corrosion.   Which situation applies is determined by comparing the specific or molar volume of the corrosion product with that of the metal.   Molar volume can be expressed as M/ρ cm^3/mole, where M is the molecular weight and ρ the density.   Thus if

$$\frac{M_c}{\rho_c} > \frac{M_m}{\rho_m}, \tag{13.6}$$

where the subscript c stands for corrosion product and m for metal, a protective film will be favored.   Most metals satisfy this equation, and their corrosion is therefore largely dependent on the characteristics of the protective layer.   In the alkali metals and alkali earths the spacing of the atoms in the metal is much greater than that in the corresponding ionic compounds, and Eq. 13.6 is not satisfied.

EXAMPLE 13.1

Compare the specific volumes of calcium and its corrosion product (CaO), and discuss the possibility of a protective film being formed.

Solution: From Table 2.1, the molecular weights of Ca and CaO are 40.08 and 56.08, respectively.   The corresponding densities are 1.55 and 3.39 g/cm^3. The specific volumes are

$$\frac{M_m}{\rho_m} = 25.9 \text{ cm}^3/\text{mole and } \frac{M_c}{\rho_c} = 16.6 \text{ cm}^3/\text{mole,}$$

and Eq. 13.6 is far from satisfied.   Thus a protective film will not be formed, and corrosion will follow the linear law (Eq. 13.7).

When the corrosion layer is porous, allowing the gas to remain in direct contact with the metal, the chemical reaction at the metal surface proceeds at a constant rate. This is an example of direct chemical attack in which electrochemical action is not important. The rate of corrosion can be measured in terms of film thickness, x, or weight increase per unit area, w. Using the former, we have, for a constant rate, C_1 (Fig. 13.4),

$$x = C_1 t. \tag{13.7}$$

When a nonporous, adhering layer is formed, corrosion can proceed only by diffusion, an electrolytic action in which the corrosion film behaves as a

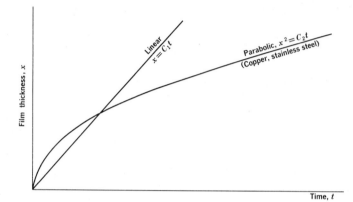

Fig. 13.4 *Growth of protective films with time. Linear: porous films; parabolic: nonporous, adherent films.*

galvanic cell. As shown in Fig. 13.5, the metal-film interface acts as the anode, at which electrons are liberated, and the gas-film interface acts as the cathode, at which the electrons are received. The film plays the part of an external circuit in conducting electrons from anode to cathode, and of an internal circuit in conducting the ions. As in any electric cell, the ions move in both directions—positive metal ions toward the cathode, negative gas ions toward the anode. The gas ions, however, are much larger than the metal ions, partly because they have *more* electrons than normal, while the metal ions have had their outer electrons removed. As a result the diffusion of gas ions is much slower—in fact, almost negligible. The reaction is therefore predominantly at the gas-film interface or outer surface of the film.

The rate of growth of the film can be calculated in terms of the current flow and the increase of resistance with thickness. The amount of material added to the outer surface per unit time depends on the current of electrons and metal ions flowing toward the surface. Thus

$$\frac{dx}{dt} = CI,$$ (13.8)

where x is the film thickness, t the time, I the current, and C a constant. From Ohm's law we have

$$I = \frac{E}{R},$$ (13.9)

where E is the electromotive force associated with the reaction at the film

Fig. 13.5 Diffusion of ions and electrons through the oxide film during oxidation of copper. The metal ions, being smaller, diffuse more rapidly than the gas ions. Hence the outer surface becomes positively charged (cathodic) and attracts electrons, which flow outward through the film. The reaction $Cu^{++} + O^{--} \rightarrow CuO$ takes place mainly at the outer surface. (Adapted from Uhlig, The Corrosion Handbook, John Wiley & Sons, Inc., New York, 1948)

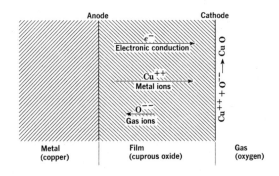

surface and R is the resistance of the film. But R is proportional to the thickness, x,

$$R = \rho \frac{x}{A},$$ (13.10)

where ρ is the resistivity and A the area of the film. Substitution in Eq. 13.8 gives

$$\frac{dx}{dt} = \frac{CEA}{\rho x},$$ (13.11)

where x and t are the only variables. Integrating, we have

$$x^2 = C_2 t,$$ (13.12)

the parabolic equation for film growth (Fig. 13.4). Copper and stainless steel are examples of materials which follow this equation. It has been possible to predict successfully the value of the parabolic rate constant, C_2, through the use of this theory.

There are many examples in which corrosion follows a logarithmic rather than a parabolic law. The equation can be written

$$x = C_3 \log\left(\frac{t}{t_1} + 1\right)$$ (13.13)

(Fig. 13.6). Iron and nickel are sometimes found to fit this law,[*] which is identical with the logarithmic creep law (Eq. 8.1b).

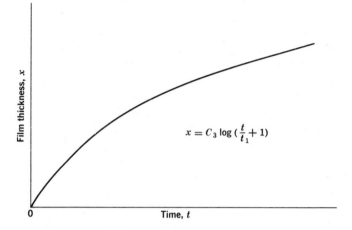

Fig. 13.6 *Logarithmic law of protective film growth;* t_1 *is an arbitrary time, selected to fit the given data.*

Since diffusion is such an important factor in metal-gas corrosion, it follows that the variation of corrosion rate with temperature is usually governed by the Arrhenius equation,

$$\Phi = Ae^{-\frac{E_a}{kT}}.$$ (2.4)

Thus the corrosion rate increases rapidly at high temperatures. The oxidation of iron and steel in air is an outstanding example of high-temperature corrosion. The principal reaction is

$$2\,Fe^{++} + O_2^{--} \rightarrow 2\,FeO.$$ (13.14)

The oxide forms a scale, which grows to considerable thickness with prolonged heating. Although the rate of diffusion of oxygen ions toward the

---

[*] Uhlig, Herbert H., *The Corrosion Handbook*, John Wiley & Sons, Inc., New York, 1948, p. 12.

metal is small compared with that of the metal ions outward, at high temperatures enough oxygen reaches the metal to have serious effects. Upon reaching the metal the oxygen ions diffuse into it, preferentially along the grain boundaries where the energy is highest. They react with metal ions to form oxide pockets between the grains. Being brittle, these oxide pockets affect the behavior of the steel adversely.

Many factors complicate the oxidation of metals. For detailed information on oxidation of specific metals in specific environments the student is referred to the *Corrosion Handbook.**

13.5 PASSIVITY

When the elementary processes of corrosion are discussed it is assumed that the surface of the metal is *perfectly clean* at the start and is in this condition when brought into contact with the corrosive medium. Actually, however, metals are almost always in contact with air before being put to use. In some metals this contact with air produces initial surface changes which make the metal *passive*, or much less likely to corrode. Sometimes contact with the corrosive medium itself produces initial surface changes which passivate the metal.

Passivity results from the formation of a protective film over the surface of the metal. The film protects in two principal ways. When it is relatively thick, as is the scale formed on steel in high-temperature oxidation, protection is largely mechanical, similar to that provided by a coat of paint. The protection offered by thin films, of the order of one atom in thickness, is more important because the surface is not noticeably impaired by the film. Films of this type are responsible for the passivity of aluminum and stainless steel.

The mechanism of protection by monatomic or monomolecular films is believed to be an actual alteration of the characteristics of the metal at its surface. Metals in which this type of protection is common are mostly transition metals such as iron, chromium, or nickel. All have incomplete *d* subshells inside the outer, or valence, shells. In the presence of reducing agents, which give up their electrons easily, there is a tendency for the *d* subshells to be filled, and the metal is active. Oxidizing agents, on the other hand, tend to absorb electrons and prevent the filling of the incomplete *d* subshells and thus passivate the metal.

Oxygen is one of the most common passivators of this type. Oxygen atoms are adsorbed on the surface of the metal, absorbing electrons from a corrosive medium and thereby preventing activation of the metal itself. Thus the metal is, in effect, shifted toward the less active, or cathodic,

---

* Uhlig, Herbert H., *The Corrosion Handbook*, John Wiley & Sons, Inc., New York, 1948, p. 12.

end of the electromotive series.   Table 13.2 shows the differences in the positions of several metals and alloys in their active and passive states. Oxides and other oxidizing compounds act as passivators in this sense.

Table 13.2   An Electromotive Force Series of Several Metals and Alloys, Including Active and Passive States

METAL	METAL
(anodic)	
Magnesium	Nickel (passive)
Magnesium alloys	Inconel (passive)
Aluminum	Cr steel (passive)
Aluminum alloy 2017	Type 302 stainless
Carbon steel	steel (passive)
Type 302 stainless	Silver
steel (active)	Graphite
Nickel (active)	(cathodic)
Inconel (active)	
Brass	
Copper	
Titanium	
Monel	

Another outstanding example of this type of passivation is aluminum. Its protective film is probably an oxide and is thick enough to prevent good electrical contact with the surface even though invisible to the eye.

13.6 MECHANICAL EFFECTS

Stress Corrosion

The effect of distortion of a metal under stress is much like the effect of grain boundaries (Art. 13.2) where corrosion is concerned.   If a local disorder is produced, the local energy is increased and the distorted material tends to become more anodic.   The result is a localized decrease in resistance to corrosion.

An example is the localized attack of cold-worked areas, such as sharp bends and punched holes.   Slip bands are heavily distorted regions and may act as paths for internal corrosion across crystals—transcrystalline corrosion.

Another example is *stress corrosion cracking*, in which a metal under constant stress fails in tension after a time.   The first requirement is an environment in which the grain boundaries are sufficiently anodic to the grains.   The second requirement is a steady tensile stress somewhere near the yield stress.   Under these conditions attack begins at grain boundaries, which are at right angles to the direction of the tensile stress.   As it penetrates notches are formed between the grains, and the local stress in the grain boundaries increases.   Corrosion proceeds even more rapidly, and the grains are gradually pulled apart by the tensile stress.   The final result is a fracture with little or no plastic deformation of the metal.

The first requirement mentioned above is fulfilled only by certain specific environments for each metal.*   Furthermore, in the absence of stress, even such an environment usually does not produce serious corrosion.   The stress seems to provide the added distortion necessary to activate the process.   The stress must, however, act at right angles to some possible continuous path for corrosion.   In most polycrystalline metals this condition is satisfied by a stress in almost any direction.   Corrosion is usually intergranular; however, in addition to grain boundaries, slip bands and other distorted regions can act as paths for corrosion, resulting in some transcrystalline corrosion.   Residual stresses are particularly important because they are not always considered in design and their magnitudes are often unknown.

Stress corrosion cracking requires varying amounts of time, depending on the rate of corrosion and the magnitude of the stress.   Times range from a few minutes to years.   The phenomenon has been observed in almost all metals.   Some examples are: *season cracking* in brass exposed to moist atmospheres with traces of ammonia; *caustic embrittlement* of mild steel in steam boilers where small leaks permit high ion concentrations to build up; intergranular cracking in aluminum alloys containing more than 12 per cent zinc or 6 per cent magnesium; transcrystalline cracking in Type 316 stainless steel in acid chlorides.

When stress corrosion is caused by residual stresses, the obvious preventive measure is stress relief by annealing.   When constant external stresses are the cause, however, other means must be used.   The introduction of residual compressive stresses in the surface may be of considerable help.   The methods used are those described for protection against fatigue, including peening, rolling, and heat treatment (Art. 9.9).

Corrosion Fatigue

Pits and other surface irregularities produced by corrosion have the same effect on fatigue as other stress-raisers.   There are, however, certain peculiarities connected with the combination of corrosion and fatigue that should be discussed.   The progress of corrosion depends on *time*, while that of fatigue depends on *number of cycles* of repeated stress.   Hence, like

---

* Uhlig, Herbert H., *The Corrosion Handbook*, John Wiley & Sons, Inc., New York, 1948, pp. 570–574.

high-temperature fatigue, corrosion fatigue is sensitive to changes in rate of cycling. Failure may vary from a primarily corrosive disintegration at zero cycling rate and high corrosion rate to primarily fatigue failure at high cycling rate and low corrosion rate. The rate of corrosion also depends somewhat on the stress. Stress corrosion becomes a factor in increasing the corrosion rate at high stresses. The constant reversal of strain has the effect of breaking any passivating film that may form on the surface. Even when healing is very rapid, if the film is broken at every cycle, it offers much less protection than under other conditions. For this reason the corrosion fatigue strength of stainless steel may be as low as that of plain carbon steels. Finally, with the formation of fatigue cracks at corrosion pits, the intensification of stress at the tip of the crack further increases the corrosion rate. Corrosion products fill the crack, preventing the formation of protective films and exerting a wedging action on the crack.

It is clear that corrosion fatigue involves many new variables and is therefore even more uncertain than ordinary fatigue. About all that can usually be done in designing for it is to *compare* the resistances of several possible materials by means of carefully controlled standard tests. It is rarely possible to analyze and reproduce the actual service conditions in a controlled experiment. The results of the standard tests must therefore be coupled with judgment and experience.

Fretting Corrosion

When two pieces of metal are held in contact and subjected to repeated small sliding motions on each other, there is often considerable damage to the surfaces in contact. Part of the action is a special form of fatigue resulting from mechanical wear and is found in many materials other than metals. For example, a steel ball rubbed on a glass surface produces microscopic cracks in its wake because of the surface tensile stresses following it.*

In metals mechanical wear is accompanied by an increased susceptibility to corrosion. Two factors contribute to this effect: the oscillating sliding under pressure continually removes protective surface films, leaving the surface exposed; and the surface tensile stresses produced tend to encourage stress corrosion. The result is that in heavily loaded parts serious pitting takes place, roughening the surface, destroying dimensional accuracy, and frequently leading to fatigue fractures.

Fretting corrosion occurs most frequently in parts that are intended to

---

* Grover, H. J., Gordon, S. A., and Jackson, L. R., *Fatigue of Metals and Structures* (Prepared for the Bureau of Aeronautics, Department of the Navy) NAVAER 00-25-534, U. S. Govt. Printing Office, 1954, p. 144.

be clamped together so tightly as to prevent relative movement. The elasticity of the parts makes perfect clamping difficult if not actually impractical in many instances. Imagine a bar clamped between two blocks (Fig. 13.7). When the bar is bent downward the tensile stress in the upper

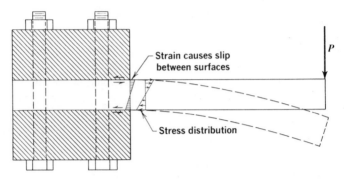

Fig. 13.7   Slipping of surfaces at clamped end of cantilever beam, causing fretting corrosion in repeated bending.

surface is highest adjacent to the clamping block. This stress is transmitted to the material between the blocks and through friction to the block itself. Under ordinary conditions the friction at the edge is insufficient to prevent sliding at this point, and the upper surface of the bar stretches more than the clamping block. The local relative sliding may not be more than a few microinches, but even this amount is enough to cause fretting if the bar is vibrated vertically. A similar situation exists in a ball-bearing race pressed onto a shaft. Other examples are shrunk-fit collars, bolted and riveted joints subject to vibrations, and splined shafts.

Obviously if slipping can be completely prevented, fretting corrosion will be eliminated. Increasing the pressure between the surfaces will sometimes suffice. Another method is to increase the friction by roughening the contact surfaces. The opposite remedy is to lubricate the surfaces, thus reducing friction and at the same time protecting the surfaces from corrosion. Still another possibility is the introduction of compressive residual stresses in the surface.

Cavitation Damage

The flow of fluids around solid bodies often produces rapidly changing pressures under which bubbles or "cavities" form and collapse in swift succession. Cavities collapsing near a solid surface exert a pounding action on the surface like that of many small hammer blows. Since each force is concentrated on a very small area, the pressure reaches many thousand pounds per square inch. The overall effect is similar to that of shot-peening. If the material is brittle, it is cracked and flaked away on the surface. If ductile, it is deformed plastically, with accompanying strain-hardening. The hardened surface may then crack like a brittle material under continued bombardment. The resulting roughening and wearing away of the surface is called *erosion*.

The effect of cavitation is to accelerate corrosion. Constant erosion of the surface removes corrosion products and protective films as they are formed, making it easier for the corrosive environment to reach the actual metal surface. The roughening of the surface caused by corrosion also tends to intensify cavitation.

Examples of cavitation-corrosion damage are found in marine propellers, pumps, and valves, where sea water provides the electrolyte.

If cavitation cannot be eliminated by suitable hydraulic design, it can be resisted by the use of high-strength, corrosion-resistant metals such as Cr-Ni stainless steels.

13.7 PROTECTION AGAINST CORROSION

Corrosion-Resisting Materials

Copper and copper alloys have long been used in applications where the corrosive environment consists of water or salt air. Other metals, such as stainless steel, monel metal, and lead, are used in special environments. Newer metals include titanium and zirconium, which are outstanding in their resistance to chlorine and chlorine compounds as well as certain other media. The high first cost of such metals can be more than compensated by the increased service life and resulting lower annual replacement costs.

Nonmetallic materials are also becoming available in larger numbers as replacements for metals. Plastics in general are highly resistant to many of the corrosive environments which attack metals. The improved strength and durability of these materials makes them useful in many fields: some examples are piping for water systems, marine piping, equipment for chemical plants, and control valves. Refractories like graphite, silicon carbide, and alumina are finding uses where high-temperature corrosion is serious. New methods of fabricating these materials have made possible their use in steam orifices, dampers, pump parts, valves, and liners of various kinds.

Coatings

It is frequently impractical to use the most corrosion-resistant materials because of high cost, lack of strength, or some other limitation. An alternative is the use of protective coatings. Coatings can be classified as those offering purely mechanical protection, separating the electrode from the electrolyte or atmosphere; those offering galvanic protection by being anodic to the base metal; and passivators, which in effect shift the base metal toward the cathodic end of the electromotive series.

The first category includes organic coatings such as paints, asphalt compounds, and grease: inorganic coatings such as fired enamels and concrete (e.g., in reinforced concrete structures); and certain metals such as tin (hot-dipped or electroplated) or noble metals (electroplated). The most important considerations are the porosity of the coating and its flexibility and adhering qualities if any deformations are expected. The latter are especially important if fatigue is involved. Remember that electroplated metals often reduce the fatigue strength of the base metal (Art. 9.9). New plastic coatings have been developed which can be applied easily in the field.* Adhesives are now available which offer the advantage of electrical insulation when dissimilar metals are joined (making it possible to avoid the formation of a galvanic cell).

Of the second category, the most familiar example is the zinc coating on galvanized iron (Art. 13.2). Others are cadmium and aluminum coatings on iron, and pure aluminum on an aluminum alloy base (cladding). At least part of the overall protection results from the fact that the coating is anodic to the base metal. At holes and cut edges the coating becomes the anode and the base metal the cathode, and in electrolytic action the coating metal is deposited on the exposed base metal, adding to its protection. The coating also provides mechanical protection, which is often a major part of the total protection.

Oxidizing agents tend to passivate the surfaces of certain metals by forming a protective film over them (Art. 13.5). Chromate and nitrite ions are among the most important passivators. They are supplied by various chromates and nitrites used either in paints or in the electrolyte. They absorb or share electrons from the surface atoms of the metal and change the galvanic potential of the surface, making it more cathodic. They also offer mechanical protection by forming an outer layer of insoluble oxides. Zinc chromate used as a pigment in paint is a common example. Water diffusing through the paint film carries with it enough chromate ions (CrO_4^{--}) to passivate the base metal.

Various oxide coatings whose protection is largely mechanical are also classified as passivators. An example is "black iron," which is made corrosion-resistant by heating iron in air to form black magnetic iron oxide, Fe_3O_4, which adheres tightly to the iron surface.

---

* Fabian, Robert J., "New Ways to Combat Corrosion," *Materials in Design Engrg.* **50**, No. 3, 97 (1959).

Inhibitors

Instead of applying a coating to the metal surface to slow down corrosion it is sometimes possible to do the same thing by adding certain chemicals to the electrolyte (in corrosion of metals by liquids). Inhibitors act in many different ways. Some, containing chromate or similar ions, act as passivators in changing the activity of the metal surface itself. Others produce nearly insoluble deposits on either the cathode or anode, stifling the electrochemical process.

Cathodic Protection

In corrosion of metals by liquids, galvanic cells are formed in which certain areas become anodes and others cathodes. Electric currents flow from anodic to cathodic areas through the electrolyte. As the currents flow, the metal at the anode is dissolved or corroded. Cathodic protection reverses these currents and thereby makes *cathodic* all the metal to be

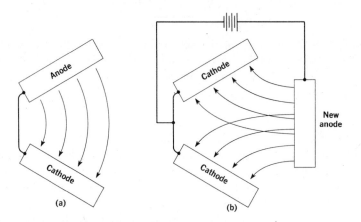

Fig. 13.8 Cathodic protection. At (a) the anode is part of the metal to be protected; at (b) the new anode is at a voltage high enough to change the original anode into a cathode, thereby protecting it from corrosion.

protected. The mechanism is to insert a new anode in the system (Fig. 13.8), the potential of which is adjusted to overcome the potential of the original anodes plus the resistance of the circuit elements (electrolyte, metal parts, connections, etc.). In this way corrosion is concentrated in the new anode, which can be replaced from time to time.

One way of supplying the necessary potential for the new anode is to use a battery or generator as a source of emf (Fig. 13.8). This method is often used to protect pipe lines, with wind-driven generators to produce the emf. The other method is to use a metal close to the anodic end of the

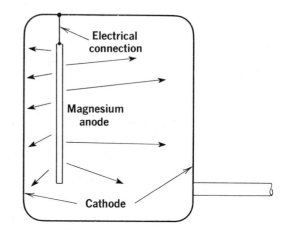

Fig. 13.9   Protection of a water tank by magnesium anode.

electromotive force series for the new anode. This method is used for the protection of water tanks by suspending magnesium anodes in the water, as in Fig. 13.9. Many other applications are made of the principle of cathodic protection.*

Deaeration of Water

Corrosion of iron and steel by water probably accounts for the greatest losses from corrosion. The controlling factor is usually the oxygen normally dissolved in natural waters. This type of corrosion can therefore be considerably reduced by removing the free oxygen—by *deaeration*.

Removal of free oxygen is particularly useful in water that is recirculated, such as boiler feedwater. The water is usually deaerated by spraying in a low-pressure or vacuum chamber; several types of equipment are now available to do this. It is possible to reduce the free oxygen to 0.005 part per million, although 0.03–0.30 ppm is often satisfactory.

RADIATION EFFECTS

Radiation affects the properties of materials in a variety of ways. This variety is as much a result of the diversity of types of radiation encountered

---

* Uhlig, Herbert H., *The Corrosion Handbook*, John Wiley & Sons, Inc., New York, 1948, p. 935.

as of differences between materials. Some radiation effects have been known for many years. For example, when photographic film is exposed to light or other types of electromagnetic radiation, the energy provided by the radiation activates the chemical reaction which produces a photograph. Discoloration of glass after prolonged exposure to light is another radiation effect that has long been known. These examples illustrate that radiation may have either beneficial or damaging results.

With the advent of nuclear reactors and accelerators new forms of radiation, having much higher energies, have become common. Since some information on the effects of this high-energy radiation on materials is vital to the engineering design of reactors, many large-scale experimental investigations have been undertaken at great expense. While the resulting data have been useful, they have not been sufficiently correlated to give a good understanding of the overall subject. Some highly significant radiation effects have been observed, but others appear to be quite minor in their significance.

Some sound basic theory has been developed for the effects of radiation at the atomic level. The connection between these effects and the macroscopic properties of materials is under intensive study.

13.8 TYPES OF RADIATION

Two distinct types of radiation—both produced by nuclear reactions—are of particular interest for their effects on materials: gamma rays and neutrons. Gamma rays are electromagnetic in character and have very short wave lengths and high energies.* Neutron radiation consists of particles whose velocities and energies vary over a wide range. We are primarily concerned with neutron radiation.

The range of neutron energies is from less than 1 ev for *slow neutrons* to approximately 10^6 ev (1 mev) for *fast neutrons*. The low-energy neutrons are called *thermal neutrons* when their speed is of the same magnitude as that of the thermal vibrations of the atoms of the solid.†

The quantity of radiation is measured in terms of *neutron flux density*, the number of neutrons traversing one unit of area per unit of time. If n is the number of neutrons per unit volume and v their average velocity, the neutron flux density is nv and is so abbreviated. For slow neutrons the neutron flux density varies from 10^{11} to 4×10^{14} neutrons per square centimeter per second.‡

---

* Wave lengths are of the order of 10^{-10} cm (about $\frac{1}{100}$ those of X-rays); energies are of the order of 10^5 ev (10 to 100 times the energy of X-rays).

† *Symposium on Radiation Effects on Materials*, Vol. 2, ASTM Special Technical Publication No. 220, American Society for Testing Materials, Philadelphia, 1958, p. 5.

‡ Reinsmith, Gerald, "Nuclear Radiation Effects on Materials," *ASTM Bull.* No. 232, September 1958, p. 37.

The total irradiation exposure is measured in terms of the *integrated neutron flux density, nvt,* where t is the total time involved. Exposures of the order of 10^{18} to 10^{20} neutrons per square centimeter are commonly used in experimental work.

13.9 MECHANISMS OF INTERACTION WITH MATTER

The passage of a neutron through a solid is much like the passage of a molecule through a gas. A neutral particle, it is neither attracted nor repelled by other particles. It can therefore interact with the solid only by means of direct collisions with atomic nuclei. The atomic nucleus, however, is exceedingly small, only 1/100,000 of the total diameter of the atom. Consequently the solid consists largely of open space, and in the absence of attractive forces the neutron is free to travel long distances without interference.

Thus the likelihood of collisions between neutrons and atoms is determined statistically, taking into account the energy of the neutron and the nature of the material being traversed. The probability of a collision is expressed in terms of a quantity called *neutron cross-section.* The larger the cross-section, the greater the probability of interactions between neutrons and the atoms of the solid. Neutron cross-section is measured in *barns*, where

$$1 \text{ barn} = 10^{-24} \text{ cm}^2 \text{ per nucleus.}$$

When a neutron collides with an atomic nucleus, one of two things may occur.[*] The neutron may be absorbed, or it may simply knock the atom out of position. If the neutron is absorbed by the nucleus, the atom is transmuted to produce a new isotope or fission products. While this possibility is of primary importance in the operation and control of the reactor, it is of minor importance in radiation damage to materials. Of greater consequence is the possibility of an impact by which momentum is transferred to the struck atom: the neutron is deflected from its path, its velocity is diminished, and the struck atom either oscillates violently about its original position or is broken loose completely and propelled through the solid (Fig. 13.10).

Following the collision two energetic particles are moving in the solid. The neutron continues on its flight with somewhat lower energy and a new path, on which it may eventually collide with other atoms. The struck atom transmits its energy to the surrounding atoms either by means of its large thermal oscillations or by being knocked on and colliding with the surrounding atoms. These atoms in turn transmit their energies to the next in line, and the disturbance spreads rapidly.

---

[*] *Symposium on Radiation Effects on Materials*, Vol. 2, ASTM Special Technical Publication No. 220, American Society for Testing Materials, Philadelphia, 1958, p. 5.

The overall result is to produce defects in the atomic or molecular structure. Several such defects are recognized. Perhaps the most obvious is
the *vacancy* left by a *knocked-on atom*, which simultaneously becomes an
interstitial atom. If the knocked-on atom, or *knock-on*, has the right
amount of energy, each collision that it makes with another atom causes
further displacements until several thousand atoms have been displaced

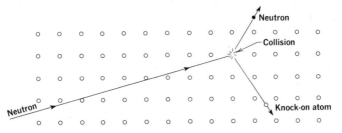

Fig. 13.10 *Two-dimensional representa-*
tion of a neutron collision resulting in a
displaced atom.

in a concentrated region. This causes a third type of defect—a *displacement spike*. Still another type of defect is observed when an atom is hit
just hard enough to make it vibrate without actually being displaced. The
excitation is rapidly transferred to neighboring atoms until a region containing several thousand atoms is heated to a temperature of 1000–2000°K.
The heating lasts only for perhaps 10^{-10} second and is followed by rapid
transfer of heat to adjacent material so that the temperature decreases
drastically. This defect is called a *thermal spike*. Such a spike may be
roughly in the shape of a sphere or of a cylinder having its axes along the
paths of energetic particles. Other defects include impurity atoms produced by nuclear transmutations and the effects of ionization.

Ionization occurs through the removal of electrons from atoms by
charged particles or waves passing through the solid. Whereas neutrons,
having no charge, cannot produce ionization as a primary effect, the
knock-on atoms can become charged simply by leaving some of their electrons behind. Such charged particles can then carry away electrons from
atoms that they pass on their flight. Thus ionization can be produced as a
secondary effect of neutron bombardment. Gamma rays, on the other
hand, can supply energy for displacement of electrons directly, and ionization is a primary effect of gamma irradiation. Figure 13.11 shows several
of the effects produced by energetic neutrons in a two-dimensional lattice.

In metals the effects of ionization are transient because of the availability
of large numbers of free electrons to replace those displaced. Ionization
therefore does not produce permanent radiation effects in metals. Gamma

rays do, however, tend to heat the metal as they pass through and may thus introduce thermal stresses. Long-time irradiation may therefore produce creep, and cyclic irradiation may produce fatigue in the metal.

In nonmetals, whose valence electrons are largely occupied in the formation of bonds, leaving few if any free electrons, ionization can interfere with

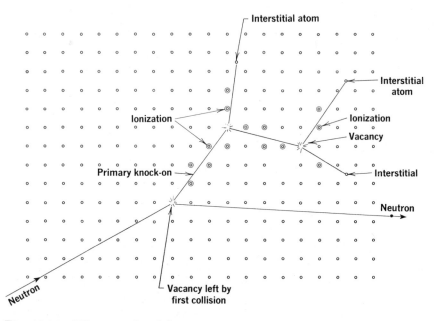

Fig. 13.11 Effects produced by one energetic neutron in a two-dimensional crystal lattice. First atom (primary knock-on) produces ionization of atoms near its path. Collision with second atom is followed by more ionization and a third collision. All three atoms finally come to rest as interstitials, and the neutron proceeds on its way.

interatomic bonds and drastically change the concentrations of free electrons.

Irradiation of polymers by either neutrons or gamma rays produces marked changes in their molecular structure. Two general types of reaction have been recognized: *cleavage* or *scission*, and *cross-linking*. The former breaks down the chain molecules into smaller fragments, and the latter results in a network like that in thermosetting polymers. Both reactions usually occur simultaneously, but one effect predominates over the other, depending on the conditions of reaction.

13.10   EFFECTS ON PROPERTIES

Through the mechanisms just described irradiation changes many of the properties of materials. The distortion of crystal lattices causes volume changes so that the density is altered slightly. The introduction of defects into crystals causes mechanical effects similar to strain-hardening. Changing the concentration of current carriers in semiconductors through ionization produces drastic changes in conductivity. Thermal conductivity is affected by the scattering of phonons by lattice imperfections. Polymer chains are broken to form free radicals or new cross-links with other chains.

Changes in many properties are so small as to be insignificant, while in others the changes are large. Some of the significant effects will be discussed in the following paragraphs.

Metals

Radiation by neutrons usually causes significant *increases in yield strength and tensile strength,* coupled with decreases in ductility. Figures 13.12 and 13.13 show the variations of some of these properties for stainless steels

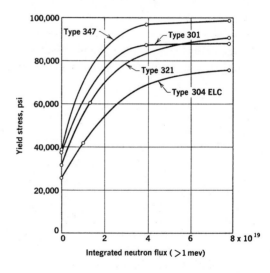

Fig. 13.12 Effect of integrated fast neutron flux on the yield strength (0.2 per cent offset) for types 301, 304 ELC, 321, and 347 austenitic stainless steels irradiated below 200°F. (Adapted from Wilson and Berggren, Am. Soc. Test. Mats. Proceedings **55,** *695 (1955))*

and Type A-212 carbon-silicon steel with variable exposures to neutron flux. Table 13.3 shows some recent observations on miniature specimens of Type A-201 steel. Annealed stainless steel, which normally yields continuously, can be made to yield discontinuously with a definite yield point at a much higher stress.

Such hardening effects can, like strain-hardening, be removed by annealing, which allows vacancies and interstitials to become mobile enough to

**Table 13.3   Mechanical Properties[a] of Irradiated
Specimens of ASTM A-201 Steel[b]**

INTEGRATED NEUTRON FLUX, n/cm^2, above 500 ev	TEMPERATURE AT WHICH IRRADIATED, °F	YIELD STRENGTH, 0.2% OFFSET, psi	ULTIMATE TENSILE STRENGTH, psi	ELONGA-TION, %	NUMBER OF SAMPLES
0		47,600	75,000	31	5
2.3×10^{19}	120–160	76,600	82,200	17	5
4.4×10^{19}	120–160	77,500	82,800	15	2
6.5×10^{19}	120–160	88,500	92,800	13	3
1.2×10^{20}	120–160	94,300	98,000	9.5	3
3.1×10^{19}	425–515	59,800	84,200	16.3	6
7.4×10^{19}	525–700	53,600	82,600	21	5

[a] These strengths are abnormally high because of the particular test conditions involved, but are consistent among themselves. Data taken from Trudeau, "Irradiation of Some Pressure Vessel Steels," Paper No. 196, presented at Third Pacific Area Meeting of the American Society for Testing Materials, San Francisco, October 1959.
[b] Analysis in weight per cent: 0.17 C, 0.55 Mn, 0.020 P, 0.022 S, 0.21 Si, 0.05 Ni, 0.04 Cr, 0.01 Mo, 0.06 Cu, 0.02 V, 0.04 W, 0.04 Al, 0.005 N_2 (as hot-rolled).

recombine, eliminating many of the defects.   Thus if the metal is held at a high temperature while being irradiated (a common situation in a reactor), it can be expected that very little hardening will actually occur.

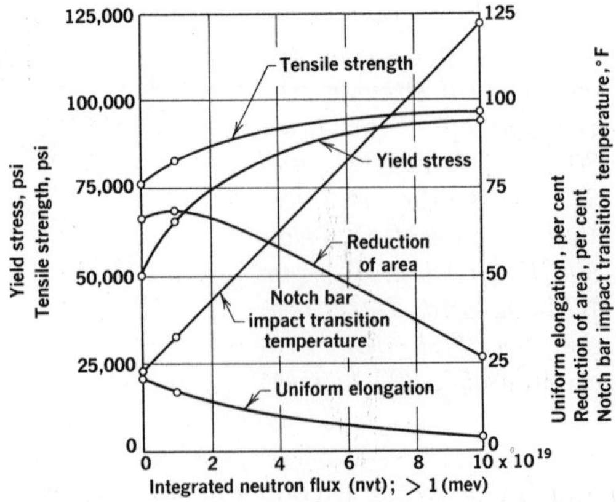

Fig. 13.13 Integrated fast neutron flux dependence of several mechanical properties of A212B carbon-silicon steel. (Adapted from Wilson and Berggren, Am. Soc. Test. Mats. Proceedings 55, 702 (1955))

A most important corollary of radiation hardening in carbon steels is an increased susceptibility to brittle fracture.   Impact tests on irradiated steels indicate that the impact value is decreased and the ductile-brittle

transition temperature is raised. Figure 13.14 is a typical comparison
between irradiated and unirradiated structural steel. Similar results are
obtained with various pressure vessel steels.

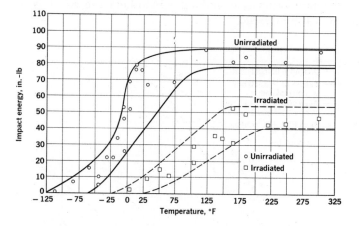

*Fig. 13.14 Impact tests of irradiated
ASTM type A70 steel. (Adapted from
Leeser and Deily,* Symposium on Radiation Effects on Materials, *Vol. I, STP
208, published by the American Society
for Testing Materials, Philadelphia, 1957)*

A disturbing development is the discovery that radiation embrittlement
of steels cannot be depended upon to anneal out at ordinary operating
temperatures. Investigations have shown (Fig. 13.15) that even when
irradiated at 500°F many pressure vessel steels have their impact value
lowered and their transition temperature raised. Stainless steels offer
possibilities for avoiding embrittlement because they are not normally
notch-sensitive. However, even stainless steels may have their impact
resistances lowered by irradiation.* Consequently other metals, like aluminum, titanium, and zirconium, are finding uses in the structural components of reactors.

Electrical resistivity of metals is increased by irradiation. Most of the
change is in the residual resistivity, which is associated with imperfections
(Art. 11.1). It is therefore most noticeable at low temperatures.

---

* Warde, John M., "Materials for Nuclear Power Reactors," *Materials and Methods*
44, No. 2, 128 (1956).

Polymers

Irradiation of polymers destroys their useful properties if continued long enough.   Short periods of irradiation can improve the properties of certain polymers by promoting cross-linking.   In others the effect is always a degradation of the material.

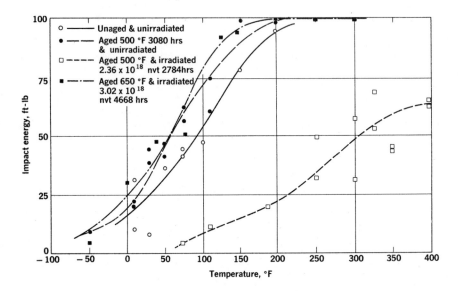

Fig. 13.15 Impact energy transition curves for type HY-65 as received 6-in. plate. (Adapted from Alger and Skupien, Neutron Radiation Embrittlement at 500°F and 650°F of Reactor Pressure Vessel Steels, Report No. WAPD-T-913 of Westinghouse Electric Corporation, 1959)

Among those in which cross-linking predominates are polyethylene, nylon, natural rubber, and polystyrene.*   The stiffness and breaking strength are increased, and viscous flow is decreased, as illustrated for nylon in Fig. 13.16.

Polymers in which degradation predominates include acrylics, cellulose, polyvinyl chloride, and Teflon.   Figure 13.17 shows the effect of irradiation on the stress-strain curves for vinyl chloride acetate polymer.

---

* Reinsmith, Gerald, "Nuclear Radiation Effects on Materials," *ASTM Bull.* No. 232, September 1958, p. 43.

Cross-linking by irradiation as a means of increasing polymerization has certain advantages over chemical means, but it has the decided disadvantage of high cost. This method is used commercially in cross-linking of polyethylene, but less expensive means are also under development.

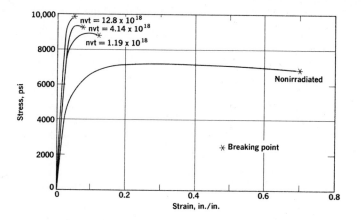

Fig. 13.16 Stress-strain curves for pile-irradiated nylon FM-3003. (Adapted from Sisman and Bopp, Symposium on Radiation Effects on Materials, *Vol. I, STP 208, published by the American Society for Testing Materials, Philadelphia, 1957)*

Radiation in the form of gamma rays and neutrons has about the same effect when energies are equal.

13.11 SELECTION OF MATERIALS

The most likely sources of radiation of concern to the engineer are nuclear power reactors. Figure 13.18 indicates the variety of materials used in their construction.

Factors which must be considered in selecting materials for reactors are:

Mechanical strength, stiffness, and ductility. These properties are most important in structural materials for such applications as pressure vessels, supports, piping, and gaskets. They must also be considered in the materials used for shielding.

Corrosion resistance. Corrosion of structural materials becomes a problem when metals are used in conjunction with liquid coolants at high temperatures and pressures. Control rods must also have good oxidation resistance for high-temperature operation.

Heat transfer.   Heat liberated inside the nuclear fuel must be removed by structural components associated with cooling systems.   Heat generated inside shielding materials by radiation must also be dissipated.

Effects of radiation on properties.   Pressure vessel steels may be embrittled, gaskets may have their elasticity destroyed, and pipe lines may have their corrosion resistance reduced.   Other important changes are also involved, as noted in the previous articles.

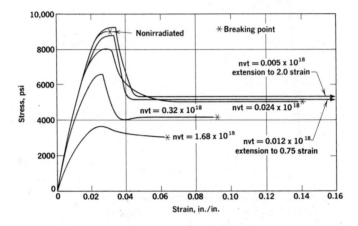

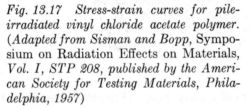

Fig. 13.17   Stress-strain curves for pile-irradiated vinyl chloride acetate polymer. (Adapted from Sisman and Bopp, Sympo-sium on Radiation Effects on Materials, Vol. I, STP 208, *published by the Ameri-can Society for Testing Materials, Phila-delphia, 1957)*

Neutron cross-sections.   Large and small cross-sections are needed for dif-ferent purposes.   Operation of the reactor depends vitally on the cross-sections of the various materials used.

Radioactivity.   Metals which tend to absorb neutrons and thereby become radioactive must be avoided, even in such small amounts as those of alloying elements or impurities.   Hence the need for high purity in reactor metals.

Much useful information on the selection of materials for nuclear reactors is contained in the references listed in the bibliography.

13.12   RESEARCH

Irradiation with energetic particles can be used as a research tool to introduce defects into crystals under controlled conditions.   Thus the study of radiation effects takes on a much broader aspect.   Its importance

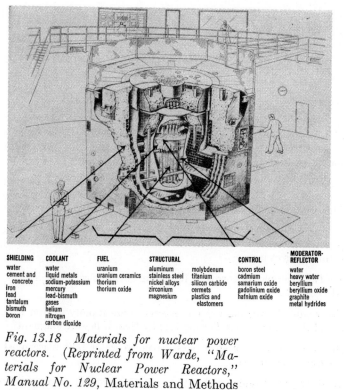

SHIELDING	COOLANT	FUEL	STRUCTURAL		CONTROL	MODERATOR-REFLECTOR
water	water	uranium	aluminum	molybdenum	boron steel	water
cement and concrete	liquid metals	uranium ceramics	stainless steel	titanium	cadmium	heavy water
iron	sodium-potassium	thorium	nickel alloys	silicon carbide	samarium oxide	beryllium
lead	mercury	thorium oxide	zirconium	cermets	gadolinium oxide	beryllium oxide
tantalum	lead-bismuth		magnesium	plastics and elastomers	hafnium oxide	graphite
bismuth	gases					metal hydrides
boron	helium					
	nitrogen					
	carbon dioxide					

Fig. 13.18   Materials for nuclear power reactors.   (Reprinted from Warde, "Materials   for   Nuclear   Power   Reactors," Manual No. 129, Materials and Methods *44, No. 2, 121 (1956))*

in studying the part played by imperfections in solids is at least equal to its importance in evaluating materials used in nuclear reactors.   Basic research in the solid state should be greatly aided by this new tool.

BIBLIOGRAPHY

Corrosion in Action, published by the International Nickel Company, Inc., 67 Wall Street, New York 5, 1955 (under the supervision of F. L. LaQue).

An easy-to-read narrative, profusely illustrated, which covers the basic ideas of corrosion in a clear and graphic manner.   For the student.

Uhlig, Herbert H., *The Corrosion Handbook*, John Wiley & Sons, Inc., New York, 1948.

Probably the most complete source of authoritative information and data on corrosion.

Speller, Frank N., *Corrosion—Causes and Prevention*, 3rd ed., McGraw-Hill Book Company, New York, 1951.

PROBLEMS

13.1 (a) Into what two main classifications can corrosion of metals be divided? (b) What common factor is almost always involved in both types of corrosion?

13.2 (a) Account for the development of a solution potential on a metal immersed in a liquid. (b) What main characteristic is usually required of such a liquid if the solution potential is to be significant?

13.3 (a) Under what conditions would you expect corrosion to take place in a tinned copper wire? Which metal would be corroded? (b) Answer part (a) for tinned sheet iron.

13.4 Give two examples of corrosion involving galvanic cells not described in the text (Art. 13.2).

13.5 Why would the rusting process proceed more rapidly in iron if the water around the cathode were flowing rapidly than if it were stagnant?

13.6 Why does corrosion of steel piles driven in water take place most rapidly near the water surface?

13.7 Investigate the likelihood that the oxidation product of copper, Cu_2O, will form a protective film over the copper (densities: Cu, 8.96 g/cm^3; Cu_2O, 11.81 g/cm^3).

13.8 Repeat Problem 13.7 for the following metals (densities in parentheses): (a) Mg (1.74), MgO (3.65); (b) Ni (8.90), NiO (7.08); (c) Cr (7.14), Cr_2O_3 (10.28).

13.9 Explain the important factors involved in high-temperature oxidation of steel.

13.10 Account for the fact that aluminum, a highly reactive metal, is apparently unaffected by many corrosive environments.

13.11 Give three examples of corrosion associated with mechanical deformation.

13.12 List all the requirements for progress of stress corrosion cracking.

13.13 Explain the factors involved in corrosion fatigue.

13.14 Give an example, other than those given in the text, under which fretting corrosion might occur.

13.15 Explain the factors involved in cavitation corrosion.

13.16 Why does a zinc coating give better protection to steel than a copper coating?

13.17 Describe two ways in which a boiler may be protected from corrosion.

13.18 Explain how neutron bombardment can change the conductivity of a semi-conductor.

13.19 Would you expect any appreciable hardening of a carbon steel subjected to neutron bombardment in a high-temperature region of a nuclear reactor? What can you say about embrittlement under the same conditions?

APPENDIX A

PROPERTY TABLES

Typical Mechanical, Thermal, Electrical, and Physical Properties of Metals, Organic Materials, and Ceramics at Room Temperature

Observed values may differ considerably from the typical values listed in these tables, for the following reasons:

1. In most instances the necessarily brief specification of the material permits more or less variation in the actual composition and previous treatment. Such variations produce corresponding changes in all properties listed.

2. Variations in environment may affect the properties of certain materials, notably the organic materials.

3. Structure-sensitive properties, particularly strengths, are subject to statistical variations. This effect is most pronounced in brittle materials such as ceramics, although it also is seen in ductile materials.

Table A.1 Typical Properties of Metals (subject to variations as noted on p. 517)

Material	Density lb/in.³	Elastic Constants E, 10⁶ psi	Elastic Constants G, 10⁶ psi	Elastic Constants μ	Yield Strength σ_y (or σ_{pl}) ksi	Tensile Strength σ_u ksi	Elongation in 2" %	Hardness H_B	Melting Point T_m (or Range), °F	Coefficient of Thermal Expansion α 10^{-6}/°F	Thermal Conductivity k, Btu ft / hr ft² °F	Specific Heat c (Btu/lb)/°F or (cal/g)/°C
Ferrous metals												
Cast iron, gray (ASTM class 25)	0.260	13	5.5	0.20	—	T 24 C 120ᵃ	—	180	2150	6.7	27	—
Cast iron, ductile, as cast	.26	25	9.3	.27	68	90	7	235	2100	7.5	19	.107
Steel, 0.2% C, hot-rolled	.283	30	12	.27	40	70	35	125	2760	6.7	30	.107
Steel, 0.2% C, cold-rolled	.283	30	12	.27	65	80	20	160	2760	6.7	30	.107
Steel, 1.0% C, hot-rolled	.283	30	12	.27	84	143	8	293	—	7.3	30	.107
Steel, 1.0% C, hardened and tempered at 800°F	.283	30	12	.27	138	200	12	388	—	—	30	.107
Steel, AISI 4640, hardened and tempered at 800°F	.28	29	11	.30	190	202	15	388	2575 ± 25	—	30	.107
Stainless steel, type 302, cold-rolled	.286	29	10.6	.30	100	140	30	280	—	8.9	9.4	.12
Nonferrous metals												
Aluminum, 1100-O (annealed)	.098	10.0	3.75	.33	3.5	11	25	23	1200 ± 15	13.1	128	.23
Aluminum alloy, 2024-T4	.100	10.6	4.0	.33	44	60	12	—	1075 ± 140	12.9	70	.23
Aluminum alloy, 7075-T6	.101	10.4	3.9	.33	70	80	10	150	1035 ± 145	13.1	75	.23
Brass, yellow, hard	.306	15	5.6	.35	60	74	8	180	1710	10.5	69	.09
Phosphor bronze, grade A, hard	.320	16	6	—	65	80	8	160	1920	9.4	40	.09
Magnesium alloy, ZK51A-T5	.066	6.5	2.4	.35	25	40	8	80	1175	14.5	70	.245
Titanium alloy, 6Al-4V	.161	15.8	6.0	.34	130	140	15	—	2881 ± 95	4.8	3.8	.135
Metallic elements												
Beryllium, extrusions, annealedᵇ	.066	44	—	—	55	90	5	—	2340 ± 70	6.9	92	.52
Cobalt, sinteredᵇ	.32	30	—	—	44	100	13	—	2723 ± 2	6.8	40	.099
Columbium, commercialᵇ	.31	22.7	—	—	24	39	49	—	4380	4.0	—	.065
Copper, annealed	.322	17	6.4	.33	10	32	45	42	1980	9.3	225	.092
Hafniumᵇ	.412	20	—	—	22	59	35	—	3800 ± 200	3.4	—	.035
Lead, chemical, rolled	.410	2	0.7	.43	2	2.5	50	5	621	16.4	20	.030
Molybdenum, as-rolled	.369	42	—	—	75	100	30	250	4760 ± 90	2.67	7.5	.061
Nickel, A, annealed	.321	30	11	—	20	70	40	100	2625 ± 10	6.6	35	.13
Tantalum	.600	27	—	—	100	110	3	123	5425 ± 90	3.6	31	.036
Tungsten, hard (sheet)ᵇ	.697	50	—	—	—	300	0	—	6092	2.4	116	.034
Uranium, annealedᵇ	.676	30	—	—	25	90	13	—	2065	—	15	.028
Vanadium, annealed	.217	21.5	—	—	55	68	34	—	3150 ± 90	4.3	—	.120
Zirconium, annealed	.245	12	—	—	16	36	31	77	3380	2.9	—	.118

518

ᵃ Gray cast iron, a brittle material, has a well-defined compressive ultimate strength.
ᵇ Data courtesy Crucible Steel Co.

Table A.2 Typical Properties of Organic Materials (subject to variations as noted on p. 517)

Material	Specific Gravity	Elastic Constants E[a] ksi	Elastic Constants μ	Tensile Strength σ_{ut} (or σ_y) ksi	Compressive Strength σ_{uc} (or σ_y) ksi	Elongation in 2" %	Hardness H_R	Max Recommended Service Temp °F	Coefficient of Thermal Expansion α 10^{-6}/°F	Thermal Conductivity k_t Btu ft / hr ft² °F	Specific Heat c (Btu/lb)/°F or (cal/g)/°C	Dielectric Constant (60 cps)
Thermoplastics												
Acrylic plastics, cast, type II	1.18	T 400	0.4	8	12(σ_y)	4	M 100	170	50	0.12	0.35	4.0
Cellulose acetate, molded, type I	1.30	B 250	—	5	20	32	R 100	—	70	.15	.36	5.5
Polytetrafluorethylene (Teflon)	2.2	T 50; C 80	.4	2	1(σ_y)	235	J 85	500	30	.15	.25	2.0
Nylon 6ii, general-purpose (polyamide)	1.14	T 410	.4	8	13(σ_y)	60	R 118	250	55	.14	.40	3.9
Polystyrene, general-purpose	1.05	T 500	—	7	14	2	M 80	150	70	—	.32	2.55
Polyethylene, medium-density	0.93	T 60	.45	2	—	350	—	180	125	.20	.55	2.3
Thermosets												
Epoxy, general-purpose, cast	1.12	T 650	—	7	30	4	M 100	176	33	.45	.33	4.3
Phenolic, molded, type 2, general-purpose	1.44	B 1000	—	7.5	30	0.6	M 115	325	21	.13	.38	7.0
Silicone, mineral-filled, molded	1.9	B 1150	—	4	18	—	M 88	550	30	.12	.25	4.3
Rubber, natural, molded	0.92	—	.50	3	—	800	—	150	90	—	—	2.4
Wood												
Douglas fir, air dry (parallel to grain)	0.48	B 1900	—	8.1(σ_y)	7.4	—	—	—	3.0	.77	—	—
White oak, air dry (parallel to grain)	0.67	B 1620	—	7.9(σ_y)	7.0	—	—	—	—	—	—	5.2

[a] Modulus of elasticity measured in tension (T), compression (C), or bending (B).

519

Table A.3 Typical Properties of Ceramics (subject to variations as noted on p. 517)

Material	Specific Gravity	Elastic Constants E, 10^6 psi	Elastic Constants μ	Tensile Strength σ_{ut} ksi	Compressive Strength σ_{uc} ksi	Hardness No.	Melting Point T_m (or Range), °F	Coefficient of Thermal Expansion α 10^{-6}/°F	Thermal Conductivity k, $\dfrac{\text{Btu ft}}{\text{hr ft}^2\,°F}$	Specific Heat c (Btu/lb)/°F or (cal/g)/°C	Dielectric Constant
Polycrystalline glass (Pyroceram)[a]	2.50	12.5	0.25	B 20[b]	—	K 703[c]	2282[d]	1.0	1.13	0.19	6.78[e]
Fused silica glass[a]	2.2	10.5	.17	—	—	—	2885[d]	0.3	0.8	.17	3.8[e]
Tungsten carbide (Carboloy, Grade 999)	15.3	100	.24	—	600	A93[f]	—	2.2	70	—	—
Molded graphite	1.55	0.8	—	0.6	3.4	—	—	1.2	80	.18	—
Alumina ceramics	3.7	45	—	40	350	Mohs 9	3686	4.0	—	.2	10
Concrete											
Low-strength	2.5	2	g	h	2	—	—	6	—	—	—
Medium-strength	2.5	3–4	g	h	3–4	—	—	6	—	—	—
High-strength	2.5	5	g	h	5	—	—	6	—	—	—

a Data courtesy Corning Glass Works.
b Bending modulus of rupture.
c Knoop hardness at 100 g.
d Softening temperature.
e Measured at 10^6 cps.
f Rockwell hardness.
g Poisson's ratio for concrete varies from 0.10 to 0.20.
h Tensile strength of concrete is roughly 10% of the compressive strength (Table 4.1).

520

2.7 Bi: 4.806×10^{-19} coul

2.9 $F(r) = \dfrac{A}{r^M} \left(1 - \dfrac{r_0{}^{N-M}}{r^{N-M}} \right)$; (b) $r_1 = r_0 \left(\dfrac{N}{M} \right)^{\frac{1}{N-M}}$

2.10 (a) $\dfrac{dF}{dr} = \dfrac{1}{16}$; $r_1 = 5.26$ Å; $F_{max} = 0.0240$ units

2.12 (b) $U_b = \frac{9}{10}$ unit; $r_1 = 1.21$ Å

2.18 11°C

3.5 (a) 0.01762 in.; (c) 0.001454 in.^{3}

3.7 (a) 4590 kg/mm^2; (b) 0.0314 kg-mm/mm^3

3.9 (a) 2.04×10^6 kg/cm^2; (c) 2.30 kg-cm/cm^3

3.11 Al: $A = 0.173$ in.^{2}, $U = 156$ in.-lb
Mg: $A = 0.316$ in.^{2}, $U = 132$ in.-lb
Nylon: $A = 1.125$ in.^{2}, $U = 586$ in.-lb

3.13 142.9 psi

3.17 0.527; 0.694

3.19 Range: $\epsilon' = 0.01$ to 0.10; $k = 173{,}300$ psi, $n = 0.171$

3.23 $n = 0.344$, $k = 121{,}700$ psi

3.25 Plastic strain $= (4.55)$(elastic strain)

3.27 (a) 5.97 in.-lb/in.^{3}; (b) 5.3%

4.1 Tension: $\sigma_{pl} = 12{,}500$ psi; $u_r = 6.25$ in.-lb/in.^{3}; % elongation $= 0.35$
Compression: $\sigma_{pl} = 25{,}000$ psi; $u_r = 25$ in.-lb/in.^{3}; % compression $= 6.5$

4.4 $-70{,}000$ psi; -0.0741 in./in.

4.11 (a) 4.2×10^6 psi; (b) 3.4×10^6 psi, 2.6×10^6 psi

5.1 207,000 in.-lb

5.3 9.75 in.-lb/in.^{3}

5.5 $u/u_r = I/Ac^2$; rectangular cross-section, $u/u_r = \frac{1}{3}$

5.7 240,000 psi; residual stress in extreme fibers $\pm 70{,}000$ psi

6.1 (b) 7000 psi, 2000 psi, 5000 psi; (c) 4000 psi

6.3 4.02×10^{-4} in./in., 9.34×10^{-4} in./in., -9.28×10^{-4} in./in.

6.5 Steel: 0.27

6.9   (a) 12,500 psi; (b) 14,430 psi

6.11 (a) 7,250 psi; (b) 7,250 psi

6.13 (a) 18.6×10^6 psi

6.15 70,000 psi

6.17 246,000 psi

7.1   (a) 4.35×10^{-6} (in./in.)/sec; (b) 7.57 lb/min

7.3   Approximately 0.13

7.5   Approximately 0.005

7.7   (a) 800,000 lb-sec/in.²; (b) 32 sec

8.1   86,000 cal/mole

8.3 $v_0 = 0.00166$ (in./in.)/min; $\epsilon_0 = 0.0565$ in./in.

8.5 $E_a/k = 13,120°K$; $A = 8.34 \times 10^{11}$ (in./in.)/hr

8.7 $n = 5.13$; $B = 3.0 \times 10^{-8}$

8.9   0.015%

8.11 (a) 5200 psi; (b) approximately 5300 psi

8.13 (a) 13,800 psi; (b) 1540°F

8.17 $m = 26 \times 10^{-8}$ in.²/lb; $n = 7.5$ days

8.19 (b) 0.022 in.; 0.028 in.; (c) 0.032 in.

8.20 700 psi

9.3 $N_{50} = 5.69 \times 10^6$ cycles; $N_{90} = 2.46 \times 10^6$ cycles

9.4 $\bar{X} = 15.15 \times 10^6$ cycles; $s = 19.57 \times 10^6$ cycles

9.7 $N_{50} = 7.76 \times 10^6$ cycles; $N_{90} = 1.413 \times 10^6$ cycles

9.9   26,400 psi; 24,300 psi

9.11 (b) $\sigma_{ae} = 50 - 0.13 \, \sigma_m$

9.14 1,005,000 cycles

9.15 23.6 ksi

10.3 $H_v = 130$; $P = 175$ g

11.1 (a) 0.451 ohm; (b) 1.174 ohm

11.3 (a) Cu: 6.55×10^{-11} ohm-m/°C
        Mg: 18.19×10^{-11} ohm-m/°C
        Manganin: $<0.48 \times 10^{-11}$ ohm-m/°C
        Nichrome: 17.91×10^{-11} ohm-m/°C

11.5 0.000165 cm/sec

11.8 −11.05; −0.00457

12.2 Approximately 4%

12.5 157°F; 90°F

INDEX